Behavior, Aging, and the Nervous System

Publication Number 600
AMERICAN LECTURE SERIES®

A Monograph in
The BANNERSTONE DIVISION *of*
AMERICAN LECTURES IN GERIATRICS AND GERONTOLOGY

Edited by
JAMES E. BIRREN, Ph.D.
U. S. Department of Health, Education and Welfare
Public Health Service
National Institutes of Health
Bethesda, Maryland

Behavior, Aging, and the Nervous System

Biological Determinants of Speed of Behavior and Its Changes with Age

Edited by

A. T. WELFORD, M.A., Sc.D.

*Fellow of St. John's College
and University Lecturer in Experimental Psychology
University of Cambridge
Cambridge, England*

and

JAMES E. BIRREN, Ph.D.

*Director, Aging Program
National Institute of Child Health
and Human Development
Bethesda, Maryland, U.S.A.*

CHARLES C THOMAS • PUBLISHER
Springfield • Illinois • U. S. A.

Published and Distributed Throughout the World by
CHARLES C THOMAS • PUBLISHER
BANNERSTONE HOUSE
301-327 East Lawrence Avenue, Springfield, Illinois, U.S.A.
NATCHEZ PLANTATION HOUSE
735 North Atlantic Boulevard, Fort Lauderdale, Florida, U.S.A.

*With THOMAS BOOKS careful attention is given to all details of
manufacturing and design. It is the Publisher's desire to present books
that are satisfactory as to their physical qualities and artistic possibilities
and appropriate for their particular use. THOMAS BOOKS will be true
to those laws of quality that assure a good name and good will.*

Printed in the United States of America
Q-1

MEMBERS AND CONTRIBUTORS OF
THE RESEARCH COLLOQUIUM,
CAMBRIDGE, ENGLAND

RICHARD SYDNEY ALLISON, M.D., D.P.M., F.R.C.P.
Senior Physician to the Department of Neurology
Royal Victoria Hospital
Lecturer in Neurology at the Queen's Hospital
Belfast, Ireland

SIR FREDERIC C. BARTLETT, Kt., C.B.E., M.A., F.R.S.
Emeritus Professor of Psychology
University of Cambridge
and Fellow of St. John's College
Cambridge, England

KARL BÄTTIG, M.D.
Privatdozent
Department of Hygiene and Work Physiology
Swiss Federal Institute of Technology
Zurich, Switzerland

JAMES E. BIRREN, Ph.D.
Director, Aging Program
National Institute of Child Health
and Human Development
Bethesda, Maryland, U.S.A.

JACK BOTWINICK, Ph.D.
Associate Professor of Medical Psychology
Department of Psychiatry
Duke University School of Medicine
Durham, North Carolina, U. S. A.

v

JOSEPH F. BRINLEY, Ph.D.
Assistant Professor of Psychology
Department of Psychology
St. Louis University
St. Louis, Missouri, U. S. A.

ENOCH CALLAWAY, III, M.D.
Chief of Research
Langley Porter Institute
Associate Clinical Professor of Psychiatry
University of California
San Francisco, California, U. S. A.

MARCELLO CESA-BIANCHI, M.D.
Professor of Psychology
Medical Faculty of the State University of Milan
Director, Psychological Institute of the Municipality of Milan
Milan, Italy

SANFORD J. COHEN, M.D.
Associate Professor of Psychiatry
Head, Division of Psychophysiologic Research
Department of Psychiatry
Duke University School of Medicine
Durham, North Carolina, U. S. A.

D. R. DAVIES, Ph.D.
Assistant Lecturer
Department of Psychology
University of Leicester
Leicester, England

RICHARD FEINBERG, Ph.D.
Chief, Visual and Auditory Laboratory
Georgetown Clinical Research Institute
Aviation Medical Services
Federal Aviation Agency
Washington, D. C., U. S. A.

JOAN FONTAINE
Psychiatric Institute and Hospital
Ohio State University
Columbus, Ohio, U. S. A.

ERNEST FURCHTGOTT, Ph.D.
Professor of Psychology
Department of Psychology
University of Tennessee
Knoxville, Tennessee, U. S. A.

ETIENNE GRANDJEAN, M.D.
Professor and Director
Department of Hygiene and Work Physiology
Swiss Federal Institute of Technology
Zurich, Switzerland

STEPHEN GRIEW, Ph.D.
Professor of Psychology
University of Otago
Dunedin, New Zealand

WARD CAMPBELL HALSTEAD, Ph.D.
Professor, Departments of Psychology and Medicine
Director of Medical Psychology
University of Chicago, The School of Medicine
Chicago, Illinois, U. S. A.

ROLF HASSLER, Dr. Med.
Professor of Neurology and Psychiatry
Director of the Max Planck Institute for Brain Research
Frankfurt, Germany

L. J. HURWITZ, M.D., F.R.C.P.
Physician to the Department of Neurology
Royal Victoria and Claremont Street Hospitals
Neurologist to the Belfast City Hospital
Belfast, N. Ireland

JAMES INGLIS, Ph.D.
Associate Professor of Psychology
Queen's University
Kingston, Ontario, Canada

EEVA O. JALAVISTO, M.ScD.
Professor of Physiology
University of Helsinki
Director (hon.) of the Research Center
Societas Gerontologica Fennica, Inc.
Institute of Physiology
Helsinki, Finland

HARRY KAY, Ph.D.
Professor of Psychology
University of Sheffield
Shieffield, England

H. E. KING, Ph.D.
Professor of Psychology
University of Pittsburgh School of Medicine
Chief, Psychology Service
Western Psychiatric Institute and Clinic
Pittsburgh, Pennsylvania, U. S. A.

WALTER R. MILES, Ph.D.
Scientific Director
Naval Medical Research Laboratory
New London, Connecticut, U. S. A.

K. F. H. MURRELL, M.A., F.R.P.S.
Reader in Human Aspects of Management
Head, Unit for Research on Human Performance in Industry
Welsh College of Advanced Technology
Cardiff, Wales

WALTER D. OBRIST, Ph.D.
Professor of Medical Psychology
Duke University School of Medicine
Durham, North Carolina, U. S. A.

EDWARD PODOLAK, B.S.
Chief, Biophysics and Electronics Section
Georgetown Clinical Research Institute
Federal Aviation Agency
Washington, D. C., U. S. A.

MAX POLLACK, Ph.D.
Senior Research Associate
Research Department
Hillside Hospital
Glen Oaks, New York, U. S. A.

P. M. RABBITT, Ph.D.
Visiting Scientist
National Institute of Mental Health
Research Psychologist
Medical Research Council
Applied Psychology Research Unit
Cambridge, England

ERNEST RETZLAFF, Ph.D.
Research Neurophysiologist
Psychiatric Institute and Hospital
Ohio State University
Columbus, Ohio, U. S. A.

KLAUS F. RIEGEL, Ph.D.
Associate Professor of Psychology
Department of Psychology
University of Michigan
Ann Arbor, Michigan, U. S. A.

ALFRED H. SHEPHARD, Ph.D.
Professor and Head
Department of Psychology
University of Manitoba
Winnipeg, Manitoba, Canada

BARRY M. SHMAVONIAN, Ph.D.
Associate Professor of Psychiatry
Chief Psychologist
Division of Psychophysiologic Research
Department of Psychiatry
Duke University School of Medicine
Durham, North Carolina, U. S. A.

ERNST SIMONSON, M.D.
Professor of Physiological Hygiene
Laboratory of Physiological Hygiene
University of Minnesota
Minneapolis, Minnesota, U. S. A.

WALTER SPIETH, Ph.D.
Chief, Behavioral Science Section
Georgetown Clinical Research Institute
Federal Aviation Agency
Washington, D. C., U. S. A.

SAMUEL SUTTON, Ph.D.
Senior Research Scientist and Lecturer
Columbia University
Biometrics Research
New York State Department of Mental Hygiene
New York, New York, U. S. A.

JACEK SZAFRAN, Ph.D.
Head, Department of Experimental Psychology
The Lovelace Foundation
Albuquerque, New Mexico, U. S. A.

GEORGE A. TALLAND, Ph.D.
Assistant Professor of Psychology
Harvard Medical School and Massachusetts General Hospital
Boston, Massachusetts, U. S. A.

PETER H. VENABLES, Ph.D.
Member of the Scientific Staff
Medical Research Council
Social Psychiatry Research Unit
Maudsley Hospital
London, *England*

R. A. WEALE, Ph.D., D.Sc.
Head, Department of Physiological Optics
Institute of Ophthalmology
London, England

A. T. WELFORD, M.A., Sc.D.
Fellow of St. John's College
and University Lecturer in Experimental Psychology
University of Cambridge, England

A. J. YARMAT, M.S.
Psychophysiological Laboratory
Department of Psychiatry
Duke University School of Medicine
Durham, North Carolina, U. S. A.

JOSEPH ZUBIN, Ph.D.
Professor of Psychology
Columbia University
Chief of Psychiatric Research (Biometrics)
New York State Department of Mental Hygiene
New York, New York, U. S. A.

PREFACE

T HE PURPOSE of this volume is to bring together a group of papers which review questions and present data related to speed of behavior, directing attention especially to explaining the slowness of behavior associated with advancing age and with certain types of brain damage and psychopathology. The papers were originally presented and discussed at a Colloquium held in Cambridge during August 1963: two papers are included by authors who were originally invited but were unable to attend.

After the colloquium, the authors had the opportunity of revising their papers in the light of the discussions, but no attempt has been made to secure uniformity of view on the many points where the contributions overlap. From the many and varied points of view represented, some striking agreements do emerge, but there are also some point of divergence: in such an active area of research diversity of method and point of view toward common problems is to be expected and can serve as a stimulus to further progress. Nor have we tried to bring together the implications of the various papers in the form of a discussion of "trends in research." Certain issues do, however, recur in the discussions by the various authors and appear to represent leading issues in current research and focal points in the present organization of knowledge. Some of these are: whether the autonomic nervous system has a lower responsivity in old age and what implications change in level of "activation" or "arousal" might have for organized behavior; how much bearing the change in short-term memory with age has on the maintenance of short-term set; how much the changes in sensorimotor capacity which commonly occur in older people are due to processes of identifiable disease, traumatic brain damage, and psychopathology; the extent to which slowness of aging is the result of a single major factor or change in the functioning of the nervous system; and how far the rate of aging can be accelerated or delayed by experimental control of such factors as diet and exercise.

The sequence of the papers in this volume is largely that followed in the colloquium, although some departures have been made from the original order in instances where the papers seemed more logically arranged otherwise. It is hoped that the arrangement will serve a useful role in providing readers with a convenient means of access to published literature in areas of research bordering their own special interests. This is one of the more manifest gains of a multidisciplinary colloquium over and above the professional contacts and stimulating friendships which may be made.

We are pleased to include as an appendix, a paper by Dr. Walter R. Miles. This paper was invited as a special introductory address to the group at its opening session. Dr. Miles was the organizer of what was very likely the first systematic attempt to study the behavioral aspects of aging. His remarks about the origin of the Stanford Studies of Later Maturity are printed since it is thought that they can provide some real information and encouragement to those engaged, or considering becoming engaged, in the fascinating task of unraveling the nature of human aging through experimental studies.

The origin of the Colloquium goes back to the meeting of the European Branch of the Biological Research Committee of the International Association of Gerontology which was held in Paris during April 1962. It was thought by the editors of this volume that research on speed of behavior was sufficiently advanced in fact and theory to warrant a meeting of the more active research workers on the subject.

It seemed clear that such a meeting ought to include representatives of experimental psychology, physiology, anatomy and neurology, and that it should cover both laboratory and clinical approaches. Further, it seemed desirable that it should not be entirely confined to studies of aging but should include for comparison some work in other areas, such as brain damage, schizophrenia and cardiovascular diseases, where slowing of performance is also found. People with such varied interests do not readily speak in a common language, yet the volume does suggest that effective communication can exist when such people address themselves seriously to a common problem.

Following a grant from the National Institute of Mental Health (MH 07295-01) to St. John's College, Cambridge, the Colloquium was arranged for 6-9 August 1963. The particular time was chosen so that the meetings would take place during the week before the Sixth International Congress of Gerontology held in Copenhagen from 11 to 16 August 1963. The editors are grateful for the encouragement given to the Colloquium by the organizers of the Copenhagen Congress and have thought it appropriate to assign any royalties arising from the present volume to the International Association of Gerontology.

Grateful acknowledgement is given to Mr. T. C. Thomas, Senior Bursar of St. John's College, Cambridge who served as the responsible fiscal officer for the colloquium grant. Acknowledgment is also given to Mrs. Dorothy Oest and Mrs. Virginia Marbley of the Section on Aging of the National Institute of Mental Health for their assistance in many of the details of the invitations, manuscripts and publication.

The authors' preferred forms of spelling have been retained in their papers.

JAMES E. BIRREN
A. T. WELFORD

CONTENTS

14. PHYSIOLOGICALLY INDUCED NEUROPSYCHOLOGICAL CHANGES AND
    AGING—*Max Pollack* 272

15. EXTRAPYRAMIDAL CONTROL OF THE SPEED OF BEHAVIOUR AND
    ITS CHANGE BY PRIMARY AGE PROCESSES—*R. Hassler* 284

16. ON THE EYE—*R. A. Weale* 307

17. LATENCY OF PUPILLARY REFLEX TO LIGHT STIMULATION AND
    ITS RELATIONSHIP TO AGING—*Richard Feinberg and Ed-
    ward Podolak* 326

18. FUNCTIONAL AND STRUCTURAL CHANGES IN MOTOR NEURONS
    WITH AGE—*Ernest Retzlaff and Joan Fontaine* 340

19. THE ROLE OF SIMPLE TESTS MEASURING SPEED OF PERFORM-
    ANCE IN THE ASSESSMENT OF BIOLOGICAL VIGOUR: A FAC-
    TORIAL STUDY IN ELDERLY WOMEN—*Eeva Jalavisto* 353

20. SLOWNESS OF TASK PERFORMANCE AND CARDIOVASCULAR
    DISEASES—*Walter Spieth* 366

21. PERFORMANCE AS A FUNCTION OF AGE AND CARDIOVASCULAR
    DISEASE—*Ernst Simonson* 401

22. THE EFFECT OF ORGAN EXTRACTS ON BEHAVIOR OF OLD RATS
    —*Karl Bättig and Etienne Grandjean* 435

23. RADIATION AS A TOOL IN STUDIES OF BEHAVIORAL AGE CHANGES
    —*Ernest Furchtgott* 450

24. FACTORS INFLUENCING PERFORMANCE IN PSYCHOLOGICAL TEST-
    ING OF THE AGED—*L. J. Hurwitz and R. S. Allison* 461

25. PSYCHOMOTOR CHANGES WITH AGE, PSYCHOPATHOLOGY AND
    BRAIN DAMAGE—*H. E. King* 476

26. INITIATION OF RESPONSE, AND REACTION TIME IN AGING, AND
    WITH BRAIN DAMAGE—*George A. Talland* 526

27. EFFECT OF SEQUENCE ON REACTION TIME IN SCHIZOPHRENIA—
    Samuel Sutton and Joseph Zubin 562

28. SLOWNESS IN SCHIZOPHRENIA—*P. H. Venables* 598

    APPENDIX: THE STANFORD UNIVERSITY STUDIES OF MATU-
    RITY—*Walter R. Miles* 613

    INDEX 625

Behavior, Aging, and the
Nervous System

1

PERFORMANCE, BIOLOGICAL MECHANISMS AND AGE: A THEORETICAL SKETCH

A. T. Welford

INTRODUCTION: LEVELS IN THE STUDY OF PERFORMANCE

If we look at the investigations that have been made of human sensory-motor performance during the historical development of experimental psychology, we can identify three levels of study. Firstly there is the straightforward study of *behaviour* of the whole organism. At its simplest, this is the approach of the natural historian, relying wholly on accurate observation of what is done in particular circumstances. Such simple relating of stimulus to response quickly gives way, however, to codifying of relations between environmental events and behaviour in the attempt to find a relatively small number of principles or factors in terms of which performance can be understood, or at least described. Many of these are essentially "pure" psychological concepts, such as "habit," "set," "perseveration," "attitude." Others such as "motivation" or "fatigue," although they do not strictly imply corresponding physiological factors, are almost always thought of as doing so, and have thus served to link the study of behaviour with other branches of human biology.

Traditionally, studies at this level have been of a qualitative nature, concerned to sort out problems of whether particular facets of behaviour are determined by, for example "nature" versus "nurture," or, in the ageing field, whether particular age

3

changes are due to experience or to endogenous biological processes. In the last fifteen years, however, important attempts have been made to achieve quantitative definition and measurement of behavioural *capacity*. Some useful, though not very precise, ideas on the nature of various human capacities have long been with us in the field of psychometrics. Possibilities of quantitative treatment have, however, developed greatly with the application to human performance of "information theory." Whether or not one goes along with all the details of this approach, and whether or not information-theory formulae fit observed data well, it must be admitted that they have provided a metric in many areas where none existed before.

Broadly in these terms, we can distinguish two types of capacity. One is exemplified by the findings summarised by Miller (1956) that if a subject is given a series of stimuli to classify, the number of different stimuli he can identify accurately is limited, and errors occur in predictable quantities if this number is exceeded. Such a finding suggests that the subject possesses a limited number of different "channels" and that there is thus a limited number of discrete states that the brain mechanism concerned can assume. These define the "grain" of the mechanism and thus the limits of discrimination under the conditions of the experiment. It is easy to see analogies in other mechanisms: for example, the number of discrete states that can be taken up in short-term memory "stores" will determine the number of items that can be held at any one time.

The other type of capacity, and the one we are mainly concerned with here, is illustrated in the finding by Hick (1952), and others since, that the lengthening of choice reaction time with increase in the degree of choice can be rather precisely defined by the information-theory formula:

$$\text{Reaction Time} = \text{k Log N}$$

where N is the number of equiprobable choices open to the subject. In other words, the rate of transfer of information from display to control via the subject is constant over time. Capacity in this sense depends not on the number of independent channels available but on the rapidity with which signals can follow each other down a single channel.

The one type of capacity can easily be converted into the other. For example, a scanning device could convert a pattern in several simultaneous channels into a temporal sequence in a single channel, while the rate at which signals can be passed by several parallel channels will obviously rise with the number of channels available. Reducing one type of capacity to the other in this way requires, however, additional postulates about the nature of the neural mechanism involved. The conservative approach is to treat the two types as independent until the evidence requires otherwise.

Whether qualitative or quantitative, studies at the level of the whole organism have tended to look mainly at broad aspects of performance. For example, measurement of capacity in terms of information theory or other formulae is normally concerned only with overall achievement at a task and pays no attention to the details of the manner in which that achievement was attained. Hick's formula for choice-reaction times, for instance, sums up a complex process including identification of signal and selection and initiation of responding action. Studies at this level are, therefore, only a first step towards a full understanding of performance.

A breakthrough from this position occurs when we try to pinpoint particular facets of behaviour, such as changes observed with age, within the chain of bodily and brain mechanisms leading from sensory receptors to effectors. Such attempts lead to *analyses of functional organisation* which may be represented by block diagrams of the type shown in Figure 1. There are "boxes" for, say, perception, choice, control of action, short term and long term memory, and various "feedback loops" which introduce considerations of servo-control and make available an important range of dynamic concepts for the understanding of behaviour. Such functional analyses need not be tied to neuroanatomical knowledge, but they are almost inevitably so to some extent. For example, they customarily distinguish sensory, central and motor functions, and often attempt to relate perception, motor control, memory, etc. to different parts of the brain or to broad neural mechanisms. When such a linking is made, there often occurs a give-and-take between behavioural and neuroanatomical studies

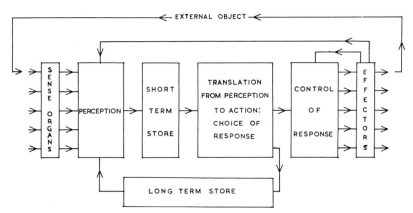

Figure 1. Hypothetical block diagram of the human sensory-motor system, based on various researches on perception, choice, movement and memory. Only a few of the many feedback loops which exist are shown.

in the sense that each provides leads for research in the other.

A further breakthrough occurs when we try to go beyond the block diagram to a detailed consideration of how the various parts of it work. Two kinds of approach have been tried at this level and both seem potentially of great importance. The first is to try to consider very detailed behaviour by looking, for example, at the choice of response in a choice-reaction task as containing a series of sub-choices carried out according to a particular "strategy." These details are seldom observable directly but can often be inferred by comparing performances at subtly different versions of a task.

Such a "microbehavioural" approach has, however, in recent years been overshadowed by the very stimulating consideration of capacity neurologically, in terms of the functioning of neurones, both singly and in large masses to which statistical concepts can be applied.

It must be emphasised that the three levels of study that have been outlined, and the types of theoretical approach they engender, are not mutually exclusive. Many studies, indeed, span more than one level, and the boundaries between them are not always in practice as sharp as they have been drawn here. Insofar as they can be separated, however, it is clear that if work has been well done at, say, the first level, further research at the second or third will serve to refine rather than destroy insights that have been achieved. In the other direction, models built in terms of the assumed statistical properties of neural mechanisms, and functional analyses of the type yielding hypothetical block diagrams, need to be tested against carefully ascertained facts of performance. We do not yet know enough to predict performance reliably from such models used in conjunction with neurological knowledge. Important progress has, however, resulted from a constant to-and-fro between straightforward experimental studies of performance on the one hand and neurological, cybernetic and statistical models on the other, and this seems likely to continue for a long time to come.

CAPACITY AND AGE

The approaches which have been outlined imply a substantial array of questions for research on ageing which are only very partially answered by what is at present known. At first sight the slowing that comes with age, and the reduction of effective capacity that this implies, seem almost too obvious to deserve detailed study. However, researches over the last thirty-five years or so have shown that the extent of this slowing varies widely between different tasks and is by no means uniform in the various mechanisms of the sensory-motor chain from sense-organs to muscles. For example, measurements of reaction and movement times have indicated that changes with age in the times required to execute simple movements tend to be greater than those for simple reaction times, but less than those for more elaborate choices.

No attempt will be made here to survey and appraise the range of evidence available. Instead we shall address ourselves to the possible causes of slowing with age and the types of effect such causes may produce in terms of the conceptual framework which we have attempted to develop.

Peripheral Mechanisms

Before modern research on changes of performance with age gathered momentum, it was customary to assume that slowing with age could be attributed almost entirely to changes in the sense organs and effectors—i.e., at the two ends of the sensory-motor chain. We now know that in many—perhaps most—cases these are not the limiting factors. However, the facts outlined in Dr. Weale's paper on ocular changes with age lead one to wonder whether the pendulum has not perhaps swung too far the other way. For example, narrowing of the pupil, increased opacity of eye media and scattering of light in the eye which occur in older people may not only raise sensory thresholds, but could well affect speed of performance. Reaction times to very dim light signals are longer than to brighter ones (e.g., Piéron, 1920, 1936), and although age changes are unlikely to reduce signal strength to an extent that would lengthen simple reaction time, they might perhaps do so to an extent that would impair performance at more complex visual tasks: although gross outlines may still be clearly seen, finer details, which may be crucial, might cause difficulty. Again, as Weale notes, reduction in the speed of accommodation and limitation of its range in older people may affect performance by either slowing it directly or causing the subject to work with less than optimum focus. Quite apart from strictly ocular defects, one may ask whether troubles such as watering of the eyes increase with age and affect performance by temporarily obscuring vision.

On the motor side, it is clear from a number of researches that the speed of most movements is not determined by the maximum rate at which muscles can act, but by the speed of their central control. However, recent work by the present writer in collaboration with Dr. A. H. Norris and Dr. N. W. Shock suggests that increase of tremor with age may be important in tasks requiring accurate movements: the effect of the tremor is to make the accuracy required greater, and the final stages of the aiming movement therefore slower, than they would otherwise be. Again the increase of body sway with age observed by Sheldon (1963) raises the question of whether deterioration of postural control may not affect the speed of accurate motor performance by older people.

Birren and Botwinick (1955) have shown that slowing in rate of conduction by peripheral nerves cannot directly account for more than a small fraction of the increase of reaction time with age. The nerve conduction speed they measured, using very simple stimuli and responses, was presumably that of spike discharges in large fibres. What, however, might the effect be of a similar *percentage* slowing in smaller fibres? The *absolute* increase with age of time required for an impulse to travel a given distance in small fibres would be much greater than in large so that impulses which started together at one end of a trunk containing fibres of different sizes would arrive at the other end spread over a longer time in old than in young subjects. One might expect a signal to be effectively weaker if diffused over time in this way.

Central Factors

This last point about the relative speeds of conduction in different sizes of nerve fibre applies with even more force to the brain, in which times for conduction along small fibres could account for a very substantial proportion of reaction time. Also the question is raised of the possible importance and change with age of dendritic potentials. These, it may be suspected, play a much more important part in determining performance than has hitherto been recognised.

In the present state of knowledge, however, it is usually easier to step back a pace and consider central processes in terms of *signals* from sense organs to the brain and from one part of the brain to another being disturbed by "*neural noise*" produced by random background neural activity or by irregularities in the action of the cells carrying the signals. The effectiveness of signals will depend on the *signal-to-noise ratio*. This may be impaired by either a reduction in signal strength or an increase in the noise level. Of the several factors which seem likely to affect one or other or both as age advances, four seem especially deserving of mention:

a) *Reduction in the Number of Functional Cells*

The well-known loss of brain cells which occurs with advancing age would obviously tend to reduce signal strength and might also result in some increase of noise in the sense that, if signals are being carried by fewer cells, any irregularity in the operation of these cells will be less "smoothed." Reduction in the effective number of functional cells would also result from restrictions in blood supply to the cells concerned or from physiological barriers to absorption which might prolong recovery times or make cells less sensitive or responsive.

b) Increase of Random Activity

It has been suggested by Crossman and Szafran (1956) and by Gregory (1959) that there may be some actual increase in the level of random activity in the older brain. The latter author suggests as evidence the increase of tinnitus sometimes experienced by older people and some of the phenomena of nerve deafness. Further evidence is perhaps contained in irregularities, large and small, reported in the EEG activity of older people.

c) Longer After-Effects of Neural Activity

An important and far-reaching suggestion with regard to brain activity as revealed by EEG records has been made by Mundy-Castle (1953, 1962) who observed that older subjects showed longer-lasting after-effects of cerebral activity, and that younger subjects who showed similar after-effects displayed temperamental characteristics which in many ways resembled those of old age. Both Mundy-Castle and also Axelrod (1962) have suggested that such after-effects would have a confusing effect on subsequent signals. In our present terms they would act as noise in the sense that although they might not be random they would be unrelated to the patterns of activity produced by subsequent signals. The extent to which they so acted would depend, as Mundy-Castle recognised, on their strength in relation to the strength of the primary cortical activity resulting from signals actually present.

We may consider all these three possible factors together since their effects would all be similar except that the third would show a change with time which the others would not: after-effects would blur signals which immediately followed previous activity in the brain but would have little effect on those which followed after an interval of time; they would thus affect continuous tasks more than discontinuous.

A subject can to some extent compensate for poor signal-to-noise ratio by accumulating the signal over an interval of time. The interval suggested by a number of studies (e.g., Crossman, 1955) is about 0.5 to 0.7 sec. and seems likely to be the factor which normally sets the limits to sensory thresholds: if a sufficient difference between signal and noise has not been built up during the maximum sample time, discrimination cannot be made without the possibility of error. The estimates which have so far been made are for subjects in their twenties and it seems a pertinent question for future research to ask whether the maximum sample time increases or decreases with age.

The results of many studies of choice reactions, aimed movements and other simple tasks relating speed of performance to age can be represented by the equation:

$$\text{Performance time} = a + b\,x$$

where x is a measure of the difficulty of the task concerned. Sometimes a and sometimes b has been found to vary with age, i.e., there is sometimes a *constant* increase with age in the time taken as the task becomes more difficult, and sometimes a *linear* increase (Welford, 1962 a, b). It is not quite clear why there should be this variety of finding. It has been suggested (Botwinick *et al.*, 1958; Welford, 1961) that the former occurs when signals are very brief and the latter when they remain until the subject responds. If so it means that older subjects take a longer sample of the signal before responding *if it is available*. When the signal is only available briefly the constant increase of time with age might be due to the signal having a longer neural aftereffect in older subjects so that its effective duration is a little greater for them than for younger subjects. If so it is understandable that older subjects should (unconsciously) delay their reaction until the full benefit of the after effect had been obtained. A constant increase with age in time taken for different degrees of choice, as found by Crossman and Szafran (1956) in rapid card sorting tasks, might be due to after effects of each response blurring the signal for the response immediately following. A demonstration that after-effects of previous actions can be part of the cause of slowing with age has been given in a serial reaction experiment by Jeeves (*in* Welford, 1958 pp. 96-98).

Reaction times are discussed further by Dr Szafran in his paper and also by Dr. Venables whose paper suggests some interesting parallels and differences, between the effects of age and schizophrenia.

It must be emphasized that linear and constant increases with age of time taken for performance have so far been observed mainly in very simple sensory-motor tasks and have been fairly small—up to about 50 percent from the twenties to the sixties. In certain other tasks the increase of time has been much more pronounced and has accelerated with difficulty. These cases seem so far to fall into two classes:

i) Older people require very much longer exposure times than younger in perceptual tasks. For example, Wallace (1956) found that in order to identify designs and pictures seen in a tachistoscope, subjects in their sixties required an exposure about six times as long as did those in their twenties for very simple designs, and up to twenty times as long for more complex material. The errors made by older subjects were perseverative in the sense that if a subject had identified a picture incorrectly as, say, an animal, he would try several other animals before changing to a different class of object. It was as if the subject had, in his attempts at identification, become fixed within a narrow range of closely related objects. This fixation is obviously similar to some of those reported by Dr. Hurwitz and Dr. Allison in their paper and links closely with the tendency of older people to carry over "sets" from one task to another as is described by Heglin (1956). We may perhaps identify it as a result of persisting after-effects: in order to change from one category of identification to another, the neural activity concerned with the first category must be cancelled and that concerned with the second initiated. We can envisage the after-effects of the first blurring the second and making the change more difficult. Indeed it might well be that the continuing effort to achieve an identification tends to reinforce the patterns of activity already in operation.

ii) Severe slowing with age may occur with problem-solving tasks and other complex activities in which some form of short-term retention is involved, either in carrying data from one point of the task to another or in "holding" the "programme" for a complex sequence of actions. There is some evidence in these cases (Clay, 1957; Bernardelli *in* Welford, 1958 p. 204; Jerome, 1962) that slowing is caused by failure of short-term retention in older people. This results in loss of data and the consequent need to collect it again, in errors which have to be corrected and in confusion which leads to disorganised and inefficient perform- ance. If, following Hebb (1949) we think of short-term retention as being achieved by self-maintaining dynamic traces, changes in the capacity for short-term retention become very much of a piece with slowing of sensory-motor performance. They do so not only as regards effects but as regards cause. Lowering of signal- to-noise ratio in the neural circuits responsible for short-term retention would make them more liable to "run down" and less able to resist interference and disruption from outside. Short- term retention is discussed further by Dr. Inglis in his paper. We may note the clear finding that it is resistance to interference rather than maximum capacity that is the more impaired in older subjects.

The ability to carry a "programme" in the way that has been mentioned here is often taken as another aspect of "set." It would, however, seem to be different from the "set" exemplified by perseverative tendencies. If two separate mechanisms are indeed involved, it is understandable that the one type of set should strengthen and the other weaken with age, as is indicated in the studies reported by Dr. Brinley and Dr. Talland.

d) *Activation and Arousal*

A further possible important source of change with age in both signal and noise levels lies in so-called "activation" or "arousal" effects.

In the late 1920s and early 1930s, Bills (1927), Freeman (1931, 1933) and others found that the performance of many tasks was improved if, during performance, tension was induced in ir- relevant muscles of the body—for instance, rate of learning might be improved by squeezing a hand dynamometer. The work at- tracted relatively little attention until, in the 1940s and 1950s, it became linked with studies of the relationships between arousal and sensory stimulation, and between performance and autonomic activity. The general interpretation of the results obtained in these studies has been that activation, arousal and autonomic activity are related to a stream of impulses impinging on the cortex and that these impulses have a facilitating effect, making the cortical cells more ready to fire. Thus sensory thresholds are lowered and action becomes quicker and more vigorous. It was early found, however, that very high levels of activation had an adverse effect so that, as activation increased, performance rose to an optimum and then declined (Freeman, 1933, 1938).

Probably the simplest model which can account for both trends is to assume that if the stream of impulses impinging on the cortex, or any particular part of it, rises above a certain level, the cells will not only be rendered more liable to be fired by an incoming signal, but will tend to fire spontaneously. Their doing so will make the system noisy, and if this noise rises to a high level there will be so many cells refractory that relatively few will be left to carry signals (Welford, 1963d). In other words, channel-capacity will be reduced in a manner functionally equivalent to a loss of brain cells.

Reduced activation would tend to lower both signal and noise, the former probably more than the latter, rendering the organism less sensitive and less responsive than it would otherwise be. At first sight the changes with age in neural structures make it seem obvious that older people would be likely to suffer from under-activation. Yet both clinical and everyday observations of middle-aged and older people often point rather to *over*-activation resulting in unduly heightened activity, tension and anxiety.

The evidence from two types of measure, commonly regarded as indicators of arousal level in young subjects, is conflicting. Galvanic skin response and skin conductance tend to be lower in older people, although Shmavonian and Busse (1963) have shown that responses among groups of subjects aged sixty to seventy and twenty to twenty-four could be approximately equated, given appropriate stimulation. EEG studies, although showing slower rhythms in older people tend to suggest higher arousal levels in older subjects. The contrasts are well shown and discussed by Dr. Shmavonian in the present volume.

Over-activity might perhaps result from an increase of activation taking place as a compensatory reaction to falling capacity. There is evidence from studies of the effects of loss of sleep that such reactions can occur (Wilkinson, 1964). When they do, experimental results may appear to come from a looking-glass world in which activity rises as cerebral reactivity falls. Such increased activation, while restoring sensitivity and speed of action, cannot of course make good any losses of capacity, and might, indeed, if it rose too high increase the noise in the system and thus further lower the channel-capacity. Compensation of this kind could account for results not hitherto explained by Szafran (1951) and Singleton (1954, 1955) both of whom found that while serial choice-reaction times rose from the twenties to the fifties, movement times fell: even though loss of channel-capacity or increased noise among older subjects might have lengthened reaction times, the facilitatory effects of a compensatory increase in activation could have speeded up the simple motor actions involved in responding.

The possible effects of activation at high levels over long periods, such as would occur with chronic stress or overwork or with prolonged attempts to compensate for age changes, are interesting to consider in the light of modern theories of learning. These, following discussions by Hebb (1949) and Russell (1959) and in the light of neurological work such as that of Eccles and his co-workers (1953), assume that trains of impulses passing through synaptic junctions make these more readily passed on subsequent occasions. If this is true, it follows that continued random neural activity, such as might occur with chronic over-activation, would tend to produce fairly widespread lowering of synaptic resistances. This would have three effects:

a) As Russell has argued, random activity in the brain will tend to be channelled through synapses whose resistances are already low. Moderate random activity will thus tend to strengthen existing memory traces, making them more firmly "ingrained"—a characteristic which, at least in popular observation, is associated with age.

b) More severe activity over a long period would tend to lower synaptic resistances randomly, and thus to blur patterns of activity in the brain. It would, in short, simulate the effects of neural noise by, as it were, destroying the "insulation" of the cells from one another.

c) The resulting increase in the randomness of neural activity would, in effect, lower channel-capacity and thus simulate and add to the effects of the loss of brain cells.

Experiments on the relationships between activation and performance have made it fairly clear that the optimum level of activation varies with different tasks. The model outlined here suggests that the optimum is related to *difficulty* in that easy tasks requiring little channel-capacity benefit from the facilitation produced by high activation, even if this makes the system noisy, whereas more difficult tasks requiring large channel capacity are impaired if activation produces appreciable noise. If loss of cells or other neurological change lowers channel-capacity with age, it follows that the optimum activation level will fall, since the tolerance of the system to noise will be reduced. One might even view a reduction of activation as in this sense *adaptive* for older people.

Whether or not this last is true, a reduction in optimum activation level implies that stimulant drugs or other means of increasing activation are likely to benefit older people only over a rather limited range. In this connection we may note that Kleemeier *et al.* (1956) found that subjects aged sixty-six to eighty-five given small doses of "Meretran" showed significant gains in the simple task of squeezing a hand dynamometer, and also in the *size* of drawings they produced. These changes might be expected if actions became more vigorous under the influence of the drug. Gains in more complex functions were insignificant suggesting, perhaps, that there was great individual variation such as would occur if some subjects were improved but others were taken past their optimum.

DYNAMIC EFFECTS OF SLOWING

Whatever the causes of slowing with age, enough has been said in the foregoing sections to make it clear that the ways in which slowness manifests itself are many and varied. Human age changes take place in a complex dynamic system in which there are many different detailed mechanisms, only one of which may limit performance in any particular task. Further, the system tends to compensate for deficiencies seeking, albeit usually unconsciously, to optimise the use of capacities that remain. Thus older subjects tend to shift from speed to accuracy, and the time they save in correcting errors may substantially offset the slowing of their performance as a whole (Brown *in* Welford, 1958 p. 67). In many cases unconscious attempts seem to be made by older people to simplify tasks by omitting less important details (Kay *in* Welford, 1958 p. 149), or by building up routines and strategies in the course of experience which enable tasks to be performed more efficiently. Such "load shedding" has been surveyed by the present writer elsewhere (1962c, 1963), and the striking role that experience can play is illustrated and discussed by Mr. Murrell and Professor Griew in their paper.

The manifestation of slowing with age is further complicated by the fact that, as Professor Hassler shows in his paper, patterns of neurological change, and thus the incidence of failing capacity in different mechanisms, show wide individual differences. This does not mean that there are not some broad unitary factors, as discussed by Dr. Birren and Dr. Jalavisto in their papers, underlying age changes in many different tasks, but it does mean that at the same time individuals differ greatly in their patterns of slowing with age.

THE DIRECTION OF FUTURE RESEARCH

The overall position of research on changes of performance in relation to age seems to be that a substantial body of well-ascertained fact has been accumulated over the past thirty or forty years. At the present time, patterns of interpretation are emerging, but so far these are not without their anomalies and conflicts of evidence when fitted to the facts. At the same time a very challenging set of ideas and *possible* explanations of age changes is being built up in general experimental and physiological psychology. The immediate task ahead seems to be to exploit these ideas, seeing how far they fit existing facts and using them as leads to further research. Studies of ageing have in the past contributed significantly to the development of some of these ideas, and further research on age changes seems likely to do so still more, especially in view of the close touch which is now traditional in ageing studies between the various human biological disciplines. Modern theories of capacity require a synthesis of behavioural, neuroanatomical, physiological and, perhaps, biochemical studies, and it seems to be of the greatest importance that representatives of these several disciplines should keep closely together. There doing so could well be rewarding for them all.

REFERENCES

Axelrod, S.: (1963) Cognitive tasks in several modalities. In *Processes of Aging*, R. H. Williams, C. Tibbitts and Wilma Donahue, eds., New York, Atherton Press, Vol. I.

Bills, A. G.: (1927) The influence of muscular tension on the efficiency of mental work. *Amer. J. Psychol.*, 38:227-251.

Birren, J. E., and Botwinick, J.: (1955) Age differences in finger, jaw and foot reaction time to auditory stimuli. *J. Geront.*, 10:429-432.

Clay, Hilary M.: (1957) The relationship between time, accuracy and age on similar tasks of varying complexity. *Gerontologia*, 1:41-49.

Crossman, E. R. F. W.: (1955) The measurement of discriminability. *Quart. J. Exp. Psychol.*, 7:176-195.

Crossman, E. R. F. W., and Szafran, J.: (1956) Changes with age in the speed of information intake and discrimination. *Experientia Supplementum*, 4:128-135.

Eccles, J. C.: (1953) *The Neurophysiological Basis of Mind*. Oxford Univ. Press.

Freeman, G. L.: (1931) Mental activity and the muscular processes. *Psychol. Rev.*, 38:428-449.

Freeman, G. L.: (1933) The facilitative and inhibitory effects of muscular tension upon performance. *Amer. J. Psychol.*, 45:17-52.

Freeman, G. L.: (1938) The optimal muscular tensions for various performances. *Amer. J. Psychol.*, 51:146-150.

Gregory, R. L.: (1959) Increase in "neurological noise" as a factor in ageing. In *Proc. IV Cong. Internat. Ass. Geront.* Merano, 1:314-324, 1957.

Heglin, H. J.: (1956) Problem solving set in different age groups. *J. Geront.*, 11:310-317.

Hick, W. E.: (1952) On the rate of gain of information. *Quart. J. Exp. Psychol.*, 4:11-26.

Jerome, E. A.: (1962) Decay of heuristic processes in the aged. In *Aging Around the World: Social and Psychological Aspects of Aging,* C. Tibbitts and Wilma Donahue, Eds., New York, Columbia Univ. Press, Vol. I.

Kleemeier, R. W., Rich, T. A., and Justiss, W. A.: (1956) The effects of Alpha—(2-Piperidyl) Benzhydrol Hydrochloride (Meratran) on psychomotor performance in a group of aged males. *J. Geront., 11:*165-170.

Miller, G. A.: (1956) The magical number seven, plus or minus two: Some limits on our capacity for processing information. *Psychol. Rev., 63:* 81-97.

Mundy-Castle, A. C.: (1953) An analysis of central responses to photic stimulation in normal adults. *EEG Clin. Neurophysiol.,* 5:1-22.

Mundy-Castle, A. C.: (1962) Central excitability in the Aged. In *Aging Around the World: Medical and Clinical Aspects of Aging,* H. T. Blumenthal, ed., New York, Columbia Univ. Press, Vol. 4.

Piéron, H.: (1920) Nouvelles recherches sur l'analyse du temps de latence sensorielle et sur la loi qui relie ce temps à l'intensité de l'excitation. *Année Psychol., 22:*58-142.

Piéron, H.: (1936) Recherches sur la latence de perception des accroissements de luminosité. *Année Psychol.,* 37:1-16.

Russell, W. R.: (1959) *Brain, Memory, Learning.* Oxford Univ. Press.

Sheldon, J. H.: (1963) The effect of age on the control of sway. *Geront. Clin.,* 5:129-138.

Shmavonian, B. M., and Busse, E. W.: (1963) Psychophysiological techniques in the study of the aged. In *Processes of Aging,* R. H. Williams, C. Tibbitts, and Wilma Donahue, Eds., New York, Atherton Press, Vol. I.

Singleton, W. T.: (1954) The change of movement timing with age. *Brit. J. Psychol., 45:*166-172.

Singleton, W. T.: (1955) Age and performance timing on simple skills. In *Old Age in the Modern World.* Edinburgh, Livingstone.

Szafran, J.: (1951) Changes with age and with exclusion of vision in performance at an aiming task. *Quart. J. Exp. Psychol.,* 3:111-118.

Wallace, Jean G.: (1956) Some studies of perception in relation to age. *Brit. J. Psychol., 47:*283-297.

Welford, A. T.: (1958) *Ageing and Human Skill.* Oxford Univ. Press, for the Nuffield Foundation.

Welford, A. T.: (1961) Age changes in the times taken by choice, discrimination and the control of movement. *Gerontologia,* 5:129-145.

Welford, A. T.: (1962a) Changes in the speed of performance with age and their industrial significance. *Ergonomics,* 5:139-145.

Welford, A. T.: (1962b) Changes of performance time with age: a correction and methodological note. *Ergonomics,* 5:581-582.

Welford, A. T.: (1962c) On changes of performance with age. *Lancet,* 335-339, Feb. 17, 1962.

Welford, A. T.: (1962d) Arousal, channel-capacity and decision. *Nature, 194:*365-366.

Welford, A. T.: (1963) Social, psychological and physiological gerontology —an experimental psychologist's approach. In *Processes of Aging,* R. H. Williams, C. Tibbitts and Wilma Donahue, eds., New York, Atherton Press.

Wilkinson, R. T.: (1964) Effects of up to 60 hours' sleep deprivation on different types of work. *Ergonomics,* 7:175-186.

2

DECISION PROCESSES AND AGEING

Jacek Szafran

THIS BRIEF account of a subject on which numerous papers have been written (e.g., Birren, 1955; Birren, Riegel and Morrison, 1962; Miles, 1942; Pacaud, 1960; Szafran, 1951; Welford, 1951, 1958, 1959), is presented from the standpoint of the now familiar assumption that the central decision mechanism has a finite capacity for processing information and that, therefore, it is liable to "break down" when "overloaded." On an a priori basis, this is likely to occur either in the face of a great profusion of signals for action, or when they arrive at a rate faster than the brain can process them. There are a number of important implications of this view for the analysis of decision processes, particularly as they are revealed in sequential performance. Experimental studies suggest that, in general, the time occupied by these cerebral events is a function of the amount of choice to be made, of the relation between signals and responding action, and of the tolerance of errors (Broadbent, 1958; Crossman, 1953; Hick, 1952; Kay and Szafran, 1961; Welford, 1960). Two further, and complicating, constraints on the information intake are "focus of attention" and possibly "level of arrousal" or vigilance (Lindsley, 1958; Long, 1959; Szafran, 1960; Brebner and Szafran, 1961). To the extent that a decision preceding any action is the choice of one from a set of alternatives, certain average properties of choices, such as the increase in response latency with increase in input entropy must, in some sense, reflect the "channel capacity,"

21

that is to say, the rate at which the brain can gain information (Hick, 1952, 1954).

With regard to practical issues, as Sir Frederic Bartlett observed many years ago (Bartlett, 1943, 1947), it should be noted that the human operator of modern control systems, particularly perhaps in aviation, has become progressively less concerned with continuous manual monitoring and more and more concerned with the interpretation of signals for action, which may originate from a variety of sources simultaneously or in rapid succession (Williams and Hopkins, 1958). In so far as control in this sense must involve transfer of information, the emphasis may be said to be on continuous readiness for quite complex judgements and decisions, which have to be made within fairly restricted time limits, if they are not to become antiquated in relation to a rapidly changing display. Moreover, the number of choices facing the operator is increasing with further technological developments, a feature which must add a sense of urgency to the systematic study of decision processes.

Rather than review previous reviews and to avoid a tiresome enumeration of not always relevant facts, the discussion will concentrate upon a single issue which is judged to be of particular theoretical import in studies of ageing. Welford (1961), from whom it will be necessary to borrow heavily and mercilessly, has drawn attention to the conflict of evidence existing in those data on sensory-motor performance in relation to age to which the mathematics of information theory could be reasonably expected to apply in a straightforward manner. Specifically, in the formula for choice reactions: $RT = a + b \log_2 n$ (where n is the number of equivalent choices), the well known slowing of response with age sometimes shows up as an increase in the constant a (Crossman and Szafran, 1956; Botwinick, Brinley and Robbin, 1958; Welford, 1958), and at other times as a rise in b (Goldfarb, 1941; Birren and Botwinick, 1955; Griew, 1959; Suci, Davidoff and Surwillo, 1960). Welford attempts to resolve these contradictory data on choice, discrimination and movement times by suggesting that the effective duration of signals probably determines the outcome, producing an increase with age in the intercept when signals are brief, but an increase of the slope when they are relatively long.

Whereas the latter case leads logically to interpretations in terms of reduced "channel capacity" with age, the former has prompted speculations about the possibility of a change in the level of "neural noise" (Crossman and Szafran, 1956; Gregory, 1957). These ideas, which let it be admitted have never been adequately formulated from the standpoint of neurophysiology, derive from the statistical theory of visual and auditory signal detection as developed by Tanner and Swets (1954) and Swets, Tanner and Birdsall (1961).

As compared with classical psychophysics, the novelty of this approach consists in postulating that the brain is a rather "noisy" communication channel and that a decision about sensory input is based upon information in some way distorted by random neural activity within the central nervous system itself. Hence, the decision mechanism must "test hypotheses," so to speak, to distinguish between the states of "noise alone" and "noise plus signal." The ease or difficulty of deciding between the hypotheses is supposed to depend upon the likelihood ratio of the two probability density functions involved, the problem for the brain being to find the smallest acceptable ratio for signal identification. If one assumes with Bricker (1955) that in the choice reaction time formula the intercept a is likely to be influenced primarily by stimulus factors, whereas the slope b must reflect the response uncertainty, one can see why Crossman and Szafran (1956) have been forced to conclude from their data, showing "easily discriminable" visual and kinaesthetic signals to be relatively more affected than "difficult" ones, that the slowing with age should be attributed to "neural noise" somewhere early in the chain of perceptual mechanisms, probably before discrimination. Yet, apart from emphasizing that the latency of a response must be mainly due to the time necessary to collect a statistically significant sample for a correct decision, it is not clear what properties of the channel are being specified by either type of theory.

Work currently in progress at the Lovelace Foundation (supported by N.I.H. grant RG-7646) may eventually throw some light on this dilemma. Preliminary results, culled from some four dozen commercial, military and test pilots, ranging in age from the twenties to the sixties, reveal one or two interesting trends in performance at a conventional choice reaction task under conditions of what one might call "information overload." The aim is to gauge "spare channel capacity" by the introduction of subsidiary tasks and measurement of their effects on performance of the main task (Poulton, 1958; Brown and Poulton, 1961; Schouten, Kalsbeek and Leopold, 1962). The rationale of this approach lies in assuming that any realistic estimate of the total mental load on the pilot cannot be based solely upon observation of what he is doing at any particular moment during the execution of his skill, but must also take into account all other possible decisions which he might have to make at very short notice (Williams and Hopkins, 1958; Poulton, 1962).

The basic situation is the familiar one in which the subject is presented with a sequence of signals, visual and auditory, is required to identify them one at a time, and then to operate some appropriate control with the maximum of speed and minimum of error. The inter-signal intervals vary randomly between 0.5 sec. and 5 sec., in runs of some 300 in length, each signal having an equal probability of occurrence in emsembles of three, five and eight alternatives, so that at any moment the subject is uncertain which signal is likely to occur and when. A detailed record of response latencies, in milliseconds, and of error rates is obtained on the SETAR (Welford, N. T., 1952), and further quantitative analysis carried out with the aid of a Bendix G-15 computer. The subsidiary tasks employed are of two main types, with certain variations on each theme:

1) A short-term memory sub-task, in which the subject is required to watch a succession of symbols projected onto the centre of the main display, and to recall the symbol presented two stages earlier (Kay, 1953; Welford, 1952, 1958)—or, in other words, to take note of new signals while preparing responses to earlier ones. Single symbols, letters and numbers, or pairs of symbols are used, the presentation lasting in each case some 4 sec. The subject may be asked for recall each time the display changes, or only on certain occasions, on the receipt of a verbal command; also he may be required to carry out both the main and the subsidiary tasks under 4 c/sec. flicker exposure, this extension constituting an attempt to investigate the possible

effects of "flicker-vertigo." It need hardly be explained that the memory "overload" is included because, together with slowing of decision, it could account for a very large proportion of the age changes of performance reported in the literature.

2) The other type of subsidiary task requires the subject, in addition to executing the manual responses in the main task, to "name" each signal by three very simple code words, describing the successive characteristics of display and control. Something approaching a "stress" situation is imposed by arranging for a delay of 0.18 sec. in auditory monitoring of the subject's speech (Lee, 1950; Zangwill, 1960).

In addition, the cardio-vascular system of each individual participating in the study is subjected, by Dr. Robert Proper of the Lovelace Clinic, to a very detailed assessment based on ballisto-cardiogram stroke volume, plethysmograph and pulse wave velocity, recorded before and after exercise (Hamilton, 1962; Schaefer and Haas, 1962).

It will be seen from Table I that, dividing the sample at the age of forty, the average rates of gain of information range from just over five binary decisions per sec. to just over four for the younger group, and from just under five to just under four for the older group. It should be borne in mind that at these rates greater than 95 percent accuracy is maintained in the basic task, after some preliminary practice, and only about 10 percent error is made in the subsidiary tasks. The regression analysis is not as yet fully completed—the computer proved rather temperamental—but it is clear from Tables II and III and Figures 1, 2, and 3 that the principal differences between the two age groups are to be found in the values of the constant a. There is no evidence of any substantial reduction in rate with age until the subjects' maximum capacity is reached under conditions of information overload. It is only then, particularly with the short-term memory sub-task, and less so with delayed auditory feedback in the verbal sub-task, that the slope constants show any increase.* Even so the amount

---

* There is also some evidence in the data, suggestive rather than conclusive, that the central refractory phase may be lengthened when the memory task is added to the main choice reaction. A suitable technique for more detailed recording is being developed.

TABLE I

Regression Analysis of Individual Performance Records
Response Time $= a + b \log_2 n$

Mean values of the intercept and slope constants per subject
($t(b) = $ 't' test on the slope constant)

Younger Group (Range 20-39; Mean Age 31.4)   *Old Group (Range 40-67; Mean Age 48.8)*

N = 25   N = 23

Main Choice Reaction Task Alone:

$RT = .233 + .090 \log_2 n$ $RT = .280 + .085 \log_2 n$
$\quad\quad t(b) = 11.27$ $\quad\quad t(b) = 10.26$
$\quad\quad$ Rate $= 5.15$ bits/sec. $\quad\quad$ Rate $= 4.94$ bits/sec.

With Short-Term Memory Sub-Task:

$RT = .368 + .086 \log_2 n$ $RT = .430 + .099 \log_2 n$
$\quad\quad t(b) = 4.12$ $\quad\quad t(b) = 4.08$
$\quad\quad$ Rate $= 4.17$ bits/sec. $\quad\quad$ Rate $= 3.69$ bits/sec.

With Short-Term Memory Sub-Task and Under Flicker Exposure:

$RT = .356 + .082 \log_2 n$ $RT = .431 + .077 \log_2 n$
$\quad\quad t(b) = 4.81$ $\quad\quad t(b) = 4.01$
$\quad\quad$ Rate $= 4.31$ bits/sec. $\quad\quad$ Rate $= 3.88$ bits/sec.

With Verbal Sub-Task:

$RT = .219 + .117 \log_2 n$ $RT = .252 + .110 \log_2 n$
$\quad\quad t(b) = 11.41$ $\quad\quad t(b) = 9.21$
$\quad\quad$ Rate $= 4.69$ bits/sec $\quad\quad$ Rate $= 4.69$ bits/sec.

With Verbal Sub-Task and Delayed Aural Monitoring of Speech:

$RT = .260 + .105 \log_2 n$ $RT = .299 + .117 \log_2 n$
$\quad\quad t(b) = 7.80$ $\quad\quad t(b) = 7.78$
$\quad\quad$ Rate $= 4.71$ bits/sec. $\quad\quad$ Rate $= 4.18$ bits/sec.

TABLE II

Differences Between Age Groups Within Conditions

	(Older - Younger)	*(Older - Younger)*	*(Older - Younger)*
Main Choice Reaction Task Alone:	$a = +0.47$	$b = -.005$	Rate $= -0.21$ bits/sec.
With Short-Term Memory Sub-Task	$a = +.062$	$b = +.013$	Rate $= -0.48$ bits/sec.
With Short-Term Memory Sub-Task and Under Flicker Exposure:	$a = +.075$	$b = +.005$	Rate $= -0.43$ bits/sec.
With Verbal Sub-Task:	$a = +.033$	$b = -.007$	Rate $= 0.00$ bits/sec.
With Verbal Sub-Task and Delayed Aural Monitoring of Speech:	$a = +.039$	$b = +.012$	Rate $= -0.53$ bits/sec.

TABLE III

DIFFERENCES BETWEEN CONDITIONS WITHIN AGE GROUPS

Younger Group	*Older Group*
(Overload—Basic)	*(Overload—Basic)*

With Short-Term Memory Sub-Task:

a = +.135   b = −.044   a = +.150   b = +.014
              Rate = −0.98 bits/sec.   Rate = −1.25 bits/sec.

With Short-Term Memory Sub-Task and Under Flicker Exposure:

a = +.123   b = −.008   a = +.151   b = −.008
              Rate = −0.84 bits/sec.   Rate = 1.06 bits/sec.

With Verbal Sub-Task:

a = −.014   b = +.027   a = −.028   b = +.025
              Rate = −0.46 bits/sec.   Rate = −0.25 bits/sec.

With Verbal Sub-Task and Delayed Aural Monitoring of Speech:

a = +.027   b = +.015   a = +.019   b = +.032
              Rate = −0.44 bits/sec.   Rate = −0.76 bits/sec.

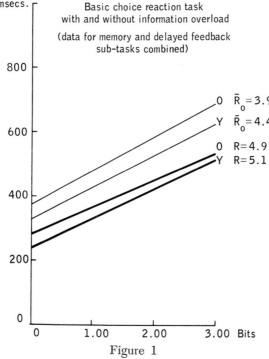

Figure 1

Y = younger group
O = older group
R − rate of gain without overload
$\bar{R}_o$ = rate of gain with overload

of this increase is far from being impressive and basically the curves are displaced upward, changing the intercept *a*. Moreover, exposure to intermittent flashes of light when the memory task is attempted seems to reduce the slope, without however, in the case of older subjects, lowering the intercept (attenuating the "noise" level?). This finding is in line with some of the data on central refractoriness and confirms the earlier speculations that amplification of ambient stimulation tends to improve selective

Memory sub-task with and without flicker exposure

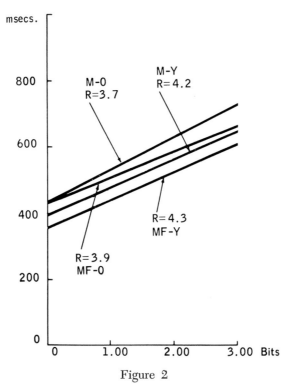

Figure 2

Y = younger group
O = older group
M = memory sub-task without flicker exposure
MF = memory sub-task with flicker exposure
R = rate of gain

responsiveness to high-information signals, presumably by increasing the "gain" of the mechanisms upon which the sensory inflow impinges and thereby enhancing decision processes (Szafran, 1960; Brebner and Szafran, 1961). This particular feature, however, although of considerable import in the field of aerospace medicine (Fitts, 1961), involves many other considerations which are outside the scope of the present paper.

Verbal sub-task with and without delayed feedback

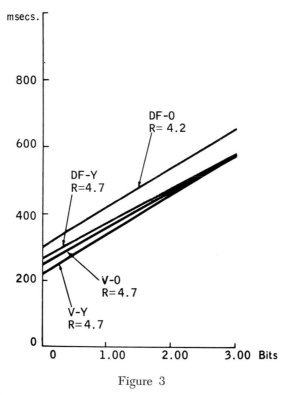

Figure 3

Y = younger group
O = older group
V = verbal sub-task without delayed auditory feedback
DF = verbal sub-task with delayed auditory feedback
R = rate of gain

It is of interest that a trend in the combined cardio-vascular and psychological data can also be discerned. Ranking the efficiency of cardiac output and the magnitude of reduction in the speed of decision under conditions of information overload, a negative correlation Tau = .518 is obtained, and found to be significant at better than p = .001 level, the normal deviate value being 4.08 (Kendall, 1948).

If these essentially preliminary results of a study still in progress can be accepted at their face value, they suggest that:

a) In a sample of individuals representing the profession of piloting aircraft, the practice of which requires making high-speed decisions, age differences in the rate of information transmission are less impressive than might be expected from other data in the field of gerontology.* This raises once again the question of occupational transfer effects in studies of ageing (c.f. Birren, 1959; McFarland and O'Doherty, 1959; Szafran and Welford, 1949)** and suggests that investigators should perhaps be cautioned to test those primary skills which constitute the overlearned repertoire of adult professional life.

b) Pilots over forty years of age are relatively more susceptible than the younger to the effects of information overload, particularly if this involves short-term recall when some other activity intervenes during the period of retention. It is not clear, however, whether the conclusion that, to this extent, they may be said to possess less "spare mental capacity" than the young is really forced upon us by the data. The paramount difficulty is still that of deciding on an appropriate measure of loss. In so far as skill proficiency can be gauged outside the flying situation itself, the routine aspects of their skill are unlikely to be affected by ageing. However, their responses to sudden emergencies under conditions of information overload may conceivably be ex-

---

* It is of interest to note that the highest rates, approaching six binary decisions per second, and remaining so under all conditions of "overload" except the memory task, were achieved by ten experimental test pilots, among whom, over the admittedly restricted age range twenty-nine to forty-five (five under forty and five over forty), no age differences could be discerned.

** The study at the Lovelace Foundation will attempt to circumvent this problem by re-testing at least some of the subjects at periodic intervals over one or two decades.

pected to become less adequate as they grow older. Needless to say, further research is needed to discover the limits within which these assumptions are justifiable.

c) Although the slowing with age, observed in the face of additional information challenge, is equivalent to reducing the rate of transmission of information, it does not unequivocally suggest a reduced capacity for discrimination and choice. It may mean, for instance, that the forms of encoding and decoding operations performed by the brain are adjusted to the characteristics of the available channel according to the nature of prevailing input and the weight assigned to other inputs (Fano, 1961). Until more plausible theoretical conceptions are brought to bear on the problem at issue, the factor limiting decision and short-term storage processes among the older adults appears to be in the nature of an increased "noise-level" in the central nervous system. Moreover, assuming that the agreement between the findings from psychological and cardio-vascular tests is not misleading, it is possible to speculate further that a reduced rate of cerebral blood flow may contribute to the hypothetical random activity in brain cells.

In summing up, it should perhaps be said that these considerations cannot be regarded as wholly inconsequential. They may or may not help to provide a rational basis for adopting a retirement policy for flying personnel, but meanwhile it is gratifying and indeed—given our preferred mode of international travel—very reassuring that they do not inevitably add to an already long catalogue of difficulties in later adult life.

REFERENCES

Bartlett, Sir F. C., Ferrier Lecture: (1943) Fatigue following highly skilled work. *Proc. Roy. Soc. (Biol)*, 131:247-257.

Bartlett, Sir F. C.: (1947) The measurement of human skill. *Brit. Med. J.*, 1:835-838 and 877-880.

Birren, J. E.: (1955) Age changes in speed of single responses and perception, and their significance for complex behaviour. In *Old Age in the Modern World*. Tunbridge, R. E., ed., London, 235-247.

Birren, J. E.: (1959) Principles of research on ageing. In *Handbook of Ageing and the Individual*, Birren, J. E., ed., Chicago, 3-42.

Birren, J. E. and Botwinick, J.: (1955) Age differences in finger, jaw and foot reactions to auditory stimuli. *J. Geront.*, 10:429-32.

Birren, J. E., Riegel, K. F. and Morrison, D. F.: (1962) Age differences in response speed as a function of controlled variations of stimulus conditions: evidence of a general speed factor. *Gerontologia*, 6:1-18.

Brebner, J. and Szafran, J.: (1961) A study of the 'psychological refractory phase' in relation to ageing. *Gerontologia*, 5:241-9.

Bricker, P. D.: (1955) Information measurement and reaction time: a review. In *Information Theory in Psychology*, Quastler, J., ed., Glencoe, 88-116.

Broadbent, D. E.: (1958) *Perception and Communication*. London.

Brown, I. D. and Poulton, E. C.: (1961) Measuring the spare "mental capacity" of car drivers by a subsidiary task. *Ergonomics*, 4:35-40.

Crossman, E. R. F. W. and Szafran, J.: Changes with age in the speed of information intake and discrimination. *Experientia, Supplementum*, 4:128-35.

Crossman, E. R. F. W.: (1953) Entrophy and choice time: the effect of frequency unbalance on choice response. *Quart. J. Exp. Psychol.*, 5:41-51.

Fano, R. M.: (1961) *Transmission of Information*. New York.

Fitts, P. M.: (1961) Skill maintenance under adverse conditions. In *Psychophysiological Aspects of Space Flight*, Flaherty, B. E., ed., New York, 309-22.

Goldfarb, W.: (1941) An investiagtion of reaction time in older adults and its relationship to certain observed mental test patterns. *Columbia Univ. Teach. Coll. Contr. Educ.*, No. 831.

Gregory, R. L.: (1957) 'Neurological noise' as a factor in ageing. *Proc. Fourth Internat. Cong. Geront.*, 1:314-24

Griew, S.: (1959) Complexity of response and time of initiating responses in relation to age. *Am. J. Psychol.*, 72:83-88.

Hamilton, W. F.: (1962) Measurement of cardiac output. In *Handbook of Physiology*, Hamilton, W. F., ed., Washington, D. C., Sec. 2, 1:551-584.

Hick, W. E.: (1952) On the rate of gain of information. *Quart. J. Exp. Psychol.*, 4:11-26.

Hick, W. E.: (1954) The impact of information theory on psychology. In *The Advancement of Science*, 40:397-402.

Kay, J.: (1953) Experimental studies of adult learning. Unpubl. Doctoral thesis, Cambridge Univ.

Kay, J. and Szafran, J.: (1962) Motor performance. In *Psychology Through Experiment*, Humphrey, G., ed., London, 216-240.

Kendell, M. G.: (1948) *Rank Correlation Methods*. London.

Lee, B. S.: (1950) Effects of delayed speech feed-back. *J. Acoust. Soc. Amer.*, 22:824-26.

Lindsley, D. B.: (1958) *International Symposium: Reticular Formation of the Brain.* Jasper, H. H., *et al.*, eds, Boston, Little Brown, 513-534.

Long, R. G.: (1959) Modification of sensory mechanisms by subcortical structures. *J. Neurophysiol.*, 22:412-27.

McFarland, R. A. and O'Doherty: (1959) Work and occupational skills. In *Handbook of Ageing and the Individual*, Birren, J. E., ed., Chicago, 452-96.

Miles, W. R.: (1942) Psychological aspects of ageing. In *Problems of Ageing*, 2nd ed., Cowdry, E. V., ed., Baltimore, 756-84.

Pacaud, S.: (1960) The structure of psychological and psychomotor functions in relation to age, in the light of factor analysis. *Proc. Intern. Sem., 5th Internat. Cong. Geront.*, San Francisco, 836-38.

Poulton, E. C.: (1958) Measuring the order of difficulty of visual-motor tasks. *Ergonomics, 1*:234-39.

Poulton, E. C.: (1962) Some limitations upon ground control systems imposed by the man in the system. In *Human Problems of Supersonic and Hypersonic Flight*, London, 430-42.

Schaefer, H. and Haas, H. C.: (1962) Electrocardiography. In *Handbook of Physiology*, Hamilton, W. F., ed., Washington, D. C., Sec. 2, *1*:323-416.

Schouten, J. F., Kalsbeek, J. W. H. and Leopold, F. F.: (1962) On the evaluation of perceptual and mental load. *Ergonomics, 5*:251-60.

Suci, G. J., Davidoff, M. D. and Surwillo, W. W.: (1960) Reaction time as a function of stimulus information and age. *J. Exp. Psychol., 60*:242-44.

Swets, J., Tanner, W. P. and Birdsall, T. G.: (1961) Decision processes in perception. *Psychol. Rev., 68*:301-40.

Szafran, J.: (1951) Changes with age and with exclusion of vision in performance at an aiming task. *Quart. J. Exp. Psychol., 3*:111-18.

Szafran, J.: (1960) A study of the 'psychological refractory phase' in relation to ageing. *Proc. 5th Intern. Cong. Geront.*, San Francisco, 759-62.

Szafran, J. and Welford, A. T.: (1949) On the problem of generalized occupational transfer effects in relation to studies of ageing. *Quart. J. Exp. Psychol., 1*:160-66.

Tanner, W. P. and Swets, J. A.: (1954) A decision-making theory of visual detection. *Psychol. Rev., 61*:401-09.

Welford, A. T.: (1951) *Skill and Age: An Experimental Approach.* London, Oxford Univ. Press.

Welford, A. T.: (1952) An apparatus for use in studying serial performance. *Amer. J. Psychol., 65*:91-97.

Welford, A. T.: (1958) *Ageing and Human Skill.* London, Oxford Univ. Press.

Welford, A. T.: (1959) Psychomotor performance. In *Handbook of Ageing and the Individual,* Birren, J. E., ed., Chicago, 562-613.

Welford, A. T.: (1960) The measurement of sensory-motor performance: survey and reappraisal of twelve years' progress. *Ergonomics,* 3:189-230.

Welford, A. T.: (1961) Age changes in the times taken by choice discrimination and the control of movement. *Gerontologia,* 5:129-45.

Welford, N. T.: (1952) An electronic digital recording machine—the Setar. *J. Sci. Instrum,* 29:1-4.

Williams, A. C., and Hopkins, C.O.: (1958) Aspects of pilot decision making. *WADS Tech. Rep.,* Ohio, Wright-Patterson AFB, 58-522.

Zangwill, O. L.: (1960) In *Handbook of Physiology,* Field, J., *et al.,* eds., Sec. 1, Washington, D. C., 3:1709-22.

3

AGE AND DISCRIMINATION BETWEEN COMPLEX STIMULI

P. M. A. Rabbitt

Choice-reaction time as measured in the psychological laboratory is something of an academic fiction, since it represents a limiting level of performance under conditions rarely encountered in everyday life. Most of our common responses are not to simple stimuli such as pea-bulbs on a console but to complex stimulus configurations. We must further consider that in everyday life a response is not typically made to a single stimulus which is unique in the universe of percepts. Indeed, it is difficult to imagine what could constitute such a perceptual event. Responses are usually made to any one of a large number of complex stimulus-constellations which may differ considerably in detail. For example, I may sit on any chair and apply the common response "dog" to any one of a variety of quite dissimilar animals. In this sense responses identify objects in the external world as members of classes or categories of things to which the same response is appropriate at a given point in time. The time required to make classifications of this type is thus in many ways a better index of competence in real life than the one-to-one Stimulus-Response situations traditionally investigated.

The identification of a stimulus constellation as a member of a category of items is dependent on the detection of certain critical features. Beginner's handbooks of ornithology are perhaps the best demonstration of this, since their purpose is to emphasise cues which are critical for discriminations between birds, and to teach the student to ignore incidental variations which are not useful for identification. The process of selection between relevant and irrelevant aspects of complex stimuli is closely related to to the problem of responding to categories of stimuli, and is perhaps most interesting when we consider choices between classes of items which are very similar to each other. In everyday life problems of this type are set by the task of scanning a crowd to find members of a group of friends, or in trying to determine whether a certain instrument is used in a complex orchestral passage. In such cases it is logically helpful to consider that we are deciding whether or not certain stimuli belong to a particular class—to the class of acquaintances or of trumpet-notes. In this respect the problem of ignoring irrelevant information becomes a particular case of response to stimuli as members of categories rather than as particulars. We are engaged in discriminating a class of relevant items from a class of irrelevant items.

The experiments which follow are attempts to reach an understanding of the difficulties of discrimination between complex stimuli, and to obtain data which may be integrated in a system quantitative enough to permit of prediction. It was found that the performance of old people in tasks of this type was impaired in interesting ways. As so often, the performance of the aged provides an extra dimension of information which allows the nature of the mechanisms involved to be defined in greater detail. The first experiment described compares the performance of young and old subjects at a task in which responses were made to categories of stimuli rather than to single items. The analogy between tasks of this type and the classification of stimuli or cues as "relevant" or "irrelevant" is further explored in two subsequent experiments. The final experiment described compares the performance of old and young subjects in a situation in which the identification of stimuli is rendered easier by the recognition of an implicit system of classification.

Experiment I. Response Time to Categories of More Than One Stimulus

Subjects. Two groups of subjects were tested: Group 1 consisted of ten young women aged between seventeen and twenty-five years (mean 19.6). Four were students at a teacher's training college and six were junior assistants at a Cambridge department store. Group 2 consisted of ten old people, five men and five women, aged between sixty-eight and eighty-two years (mean 72.4). None of these subjects had any known organic defects or uncompensated visual weaknesses. Their occupational status, and so probably their I.Q.'s, were comparable to those of the young group.

Apparatus. Visiting-card blanks measuring 3-5/8″ x 2-3/8″ were each stencilled with a single letter of the alphabet or a digit in seventy-two point face. These stencilled cards were then made up into eight packs of forty-eight cards each. Subjects were instructed to sort these packs into varying numbers of piles. The number of responses which subjects were required to make was controlled by varying the number of piles into which the cards were sorted. The number of stimuli between which subjects had to select was controlled by varying the number of symbols represented in each pack. Packs were made up to provide eight conditions of stimulus and response entropy as follows:

2-choice Task. Four packs of forty-eight cards were made up to be sorted into two piles: Pack 1 was made up of equal numbers of two symbols, Pack 2 was made up of equal numbers of four symbols, Pack 3 of equal numbers of eight symbols and Pack 4 of equal numbers of sixteen symbols. In all cases subjects thus differentiated between two categories of symbols, there being one, two, four or eight symbols in each category depending on which pack was sorted.

4-choice Task. Four further packs of forty-eight cards each were made up to be sorted into four piles: Pack 1 was made up of equal numbers of four symbols; Pack 2 of equal numbers of eight symbols; Pack 3 of equal numbers of twelve different symbols, and Pack 4 of equal numbers of sixteen different symbols. The packs thus offered four categories of stimuli to be discriminated, each category containing one, two, three or four symbols depending on which pack was sorted.

Procedure. Subjects sorted the packs, holding the cards face down in their non-dominant hands, using their dominant hands to turn and deal each card into the appropriate compartment of a sorting frame. This prevented preview of subsequent symbols during the movement component of the sorting action. The sequence of stimuli in each pack was randomized by shuffling between trials. The time taken to sort each pack was recorded with a stop-watch.

Both old and young groups were first tested on the two-choice task and then on the four-choice task. Both groups were given the four packs in the two-choice task in random order until they had each been sorted six times. The response-latencies given below are calculated from each subject's mean sorting time for the last two trials on each pack.

Results. No significant differences in error scores were observed after practice, the old subjects committing an average of 0.34 errors/subject/pack and the young subjects committing an average of 0.37 errors/subject/ pack. Response times: Mean sorting times/ card for each age-group are given in Table 1 below, where levels of significance are also discussed.

As can be seen, the response times of old and young subjects are differently affected by increases in the number of symbols in each response-category. In both two-choice and four-choice tasks the response times of young subjects rise when the number of stimuli is increased from 1/category to 2/category. Further increases in the number of stimuli in each category have no effect upon response time. The response times of the old subjects are more sensitive to increases in the number of stimuli between which they must discriminate.

To limit consideration to a single aspect of these data, it appears that old subjects are more sensitive to variations in the numbers of complex stimuli (letters of the alphabet) within the arbitrary learned categories between which they were required to discriminate by making appropriate responses. Two further experiments were undertaken to explore this effect in a special case of categorization,—where subjects scanned displays for some stimuli, and ignored others, thus discriminating between "relevant" and "irrelevant" categories of items.

TABLE 1

SORTING TIME/CARD (SEC.) IN SITUATIONS WHERE THE SAME RESPONSE
IS MADE TO ANY ONE OF A GROUP OF STIMULI. THE PERFORMANCE OF
OLD AND YOUNG SUBJECTS IS COMPARED

No. of Stimuli to which each Response is Appropriate		*1*	*2*	*3*	*4*	*8*
2 responses	Young	0.41	0.47		0.48	0.48
	Old	0.51	0.55		0.61	0.68
4 responses	Young	0.45	0.63	0.64	0.63	
	Old	0.79	0.87	0.95	1.21	

Analysis of data: Old group: 2-choice condition: Sorting times for the four packs are significantly different ($p < 0.001$). Comparisons between means for individual packs by t-tests show that the difference between Pack 1 and Pack 2 is significant ($p < 0.05$). The difference between Pack 2 and Pack 3 is not significant ($p > 0.05$), but all other differences between packs are significant ($p < 0.01$). 4-choice condition: the sorting times for the four packs are significantly different ($p < 0.001$). t-tests indicate that all differences between packs are significant ($p < 0.01$).

Young group: 2-choice condition: the sorting time for the four packs are significantly different ($p < 0.01$). t-tests show that this is attributable to the differences between the sorting time for Pack 1 and the other three packs ($p < 0.01$ in each case). The sorting times for packs 2, 3 and 4 are not significantly different ($p < 0.25$). 4-choice condition: As in the 2-choice condition the sorting time for Pack 1 is significantly different to that for Packs 2, 3 and 4, but there is no significant increase in sorting-time with increases in the number of stimuli/category after this point.

Experiment II. Ignoring Irrelevant Information

Subjects. Two groups of subjects were tested; Group 1 consisted of eleven young people aged from seventeen to twenty-four years (mean age 19.0). Group 2 consisted of ten old persons aged from fifty-eight to seventy-four (mean age 63.0) carefully matched with the young group for sex and educational background.

Apparatus. Four packs of white pasteboard blanks measuring 2-1/4" x 3-1/2" were made up to give four conditions of irrelevancy in a two-choice task. Half the cards in each pack were

stencilled with the capital letter "A" and half with the letter "Z."
These letters were 5mm. high, stencilled in India ink so as to
appear equally often at each of nine possible locations on a card
(Cf. Fig. 1).

Subjects sorted cards into two piles, separating cards on which
the letter "A" appeared from cards on which the letter "Z" appeared. The four conditions of irrelevancy were as follows:

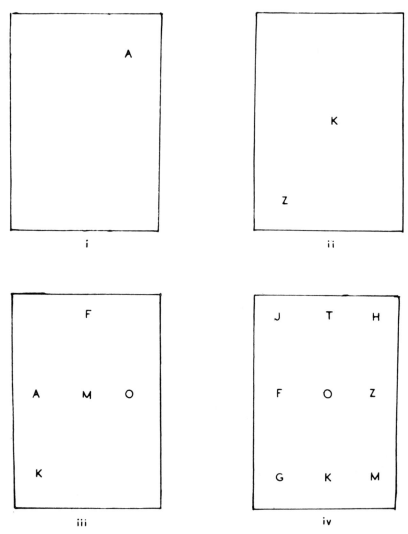

Figure 1. Displays containing irrelevant information used in Experiment II.

Pack 1. No symbol other than A or Z appeared on the cards (Cf. Fig. 1-i).

Pack 2. Besides the letter A or Z one other letter of the alphabet (all letters from B-Y being used equally often for this purpose) was stencilled on each card. The positions of relevant and irrelevant letters were randomized among the nine possible locations on each card (Cf. Fig. 1-ii).

Pack 3. Four irrelevant letters were present on each card (Cf. Fig. 1-iii).

Pack 4. Eight irrelevant letters were present on each card (Cf. Fig. 1-iv).

Procedure. The packs were presented to subjects for sorting in random order, the procedure being essentially that described for Experiment I. Each subject sorted each pack ten times. The means obtained from each subject's last four trials on each pack were used to derive the data shown in Table II below.

The old subjects show a significant increase in sorting-time with every increase in the number of irrelevant symbols. The young subjects, however, do not take longer to sort Pack 4 than to sort Pack 3 ($p > 0.25$). It thus requires to be explained how an increase in the number of irrelevant symbols from 0-1 can result in a significant increase in sorting time for both groups ($p < 0.01$), while an equivalent increase from 4-8 irrelevant symbols affects the sorting time of the old but not of the young.

Studies of the eye-movements of young subjects during reading (e.g., Mackworth and Mackworth, 1958) show that several

TABLE 2
SORTING TIME/CARD AS A FUNCTION OF NUMBER OF
IRRELEVANT ITEMS ON A DISPLAY

	Pack 1 (0 Irrel.)	Pack 2 (1 Irrel.)	Pack 3 (4 Irrel.)	Pack 4 (8 Irrel.)
Young Subjects	0.38 secs.	0.55 secs.	0.64 secs.	0.65 secs.
Old Subjects	0.68 secs.	0.71 secs.	1.03 secs.	1.24 secs.

Analysis of variance shows that sorting times for old and young subjects differ significantly ($p < 0.01$). The interaction-term and Age x Sorting time x Number of irrelevant symbols is also significant ($p < 0.01$). It appears that sorting times of old subjects are more affected than those of young subjects by increases in the number of irrelevant items present in a display.

words or symbols may be processed at a single fixation. It may also be assumed in the present case that young subjects process the letters on the cards in groups of more than one. Such grouping would become more convenient as the density of symbols upon a display increases and the mean distance between them is accordingly reduced. On this hypothesis the transition between Pack 3 and Pack 4 represents a particular case in which the increased density of symbols on a display compensates for their greater number. The fact that no such interaction is observed in the case of the old group suggests that they can only sample symbols one at a time, or at any rate in smaller groups than do the young people.

As in Experiment I, it appears that old subjects have greater difficulty than young people in discriminating between two categories of complex symbols (i.e., relevant and irrelevant items). There are at least two different ways in which such a failure of discrimination might be interpreted:

Firstly, it is well known that old people take longer than young persons to discriminate along some continuum of difference (Birren and Botwinick, 1955; Crossman and Szafran, 1956). The present result may also be interpreted in this way as yet another example of the decline in perceptual function with age, perhaps to be quantified in j.n.d's or some equivalent system; (Cf. also Gregory and Cane, 1955).

A second type of explanation would consider letters of the alphabet as quite complex stimuli. It has been shown by Attneave (1956) and Fitts *et al.* (1956) that optimal performance in discriminations between complex patterns depends on the learning of critical cues and the ability to selectively ignore aspects of stimuli which are misleading or redundant. The slowness of the old people may indicate an inability to learn which cues are critical, and to ignore irrelevant aspects of the stimuli.

Further, if old people fail to ignore the irrelevant symbols in a display this may mean that they are considering a wider range of cues than younger subjects. Old subjects may be said to *use* more information about the symbols to discriminate between them, although such information is not necessary to the discriminations required, and may actually slow them down. It would follow that if old subjects were practised on discriminations involving one set of irrelevant symbols and then transferred to another set, they would be relatively more inconvenienced than young people. Experiment III was done to test this hypothesis, if only for a single level of practice.

Experiment III. Learning of Irrelevant Symbols by Young and Old Subjects

Subjects: Subjects were the same groups who had served in experiment II.

Apparatus: Two packs of cards were made up as for Pack 4 Experiment II above. (Cf. Fig. 1-iv). In Pack 1 the irrelevant letters on each card were always M, Q, H, S, L, R, X and B. In Pack 2 the irrelevant letters were always K, J, F, C, U, Y, G and E.

Procedure: Each subject was first given one of the two packs and told to sort it as quickly as possible so as to separate cards marked with *A* from cards marked with *Z*. The pack was returned to him, after being thoroughly shuffled, until it had been sorted five times. The other pack of the pair was then handed to him without comment to be sorted in the same way. Half the subjects in each age-group first sorted Pack 1 and then transferred to Pack II while the remainder reversed the order of practice. The mean sorting-times before and after transfer from one set of irrelevant symbols to another are shown in Table 3 below:

TABLE 3

TRANSFER FROM DISPLAYS WITH A PRACTISED VOCABULARY OF
IRRELEVANT SYMBOLS TO DISPLAYS WITH AN UNPRACTISED
VOCABULARY OF IRRELEVANT SYMBOLS

Young Subjects

Overall mean sorting time for first pack	51.9 secs.
Overall mean sorting time for second pack	57.1 secs.
Ratio $\dfrac{\text{Overall mean sorting time first pack}}{\text{Overall mean sorting time second pack}}$	0.91

Old Subjects

Overall mean sorting time for first pack	75.4 secs.
Overall mean sorting time for second pack	97.4 secs.
Ratio $\dfrac{\text{Overall mean sorting time first pack}}{\text{Overall mean sorting time second pack}}$	0.77

Results. The older group show a markedly greater increase in sorting time upon transfer to a new set of irrelevant symbols than do the young subjects. The ratios of Last Practice Trial to Transfer Trial were found to be significantly greater for the young group than for the old group ($p<0.01$). It therefore appears that the young subjects are less affected by transfer to a new set of irrelevant stimuli than are old people. A possible inference is that the old subjects improve their performance as a result of learning the set of irrelevant symbols. The fact that old people take longer to discriminate between complex stimuli than do young people thus involves more than the well-described increase in perceptual discrimination time with age. Moreover, since old people take longer to ignore irrelevant symbols upon a display than young people their greater dependance upon learning of irrelevant symbols cannot represent an improvement in strategy. Rather, old people are shown to utilize information which young people do not require, and which must therefore be redundant to the discriminations.

If old subjects employ different, and probably less efficient, systems of cues in discriminating between complex stimuli, this should be more clearly detectable in a task such as pattern learning. Accordingly an age-comparison was made in a pattern —recognition task in which it was possible for subjects to discriminate both between individual patterns and between sub-sets of patterns while learning the identifications required of them.

Experiment IV. Grouping of Stimuli in Pattern-recognition as a Function of Age

Subjects. Fifty-eight postmen, twenty-nine aged from twenty to forty years (mean age 27.4), and twenty-nine aged from forty to sixty (mean age 47.1) learned to recognize and name eight patterns. Each pattern consisted of two groups of rectangles drawn in india ink on white pasteboard. In each pattern two of these were blacked in and two left unfilled. The patterns are symbolically represented in Figure 2 below. The eight patterns divide naturally into two groups of four. In one such sub-set both filled rectangles are either on the right or on the left. In the second sub-set one filled rectangle is in each group of four.

SYMBOLIC REPRESENTATION OF PATTERNS USED IN EXPERIMENT IV

"One Handed" Patterns

1. O O O O　X O O X
2. O O O O　O X O X
3. X O X O　O O O O
4. O X O X　O O O O

"Two Handed" Patterns

5. O O X O　X O O O
6. O O O X　O X O O
7. X O O O　O X O O
8. O O X O　O O X O

Figure 2

Procedure. Subjects were tested in groups, all members of a group being from the same age-range. At first subjects passively observed while the experimenter displayed the patterns in random order and read aloud the responses assigned to them. The eight responses to be used were then copied down by subjects. The experimenter then presented the patterns by holding up the cards one at a time for five seconds. Subjects wrote down their responses and the experimenter again showed the card and called out the correct response. Cards were shown in random order until each had been presented thirteen times.

Results. Rate of learning of correct identifications. Error scores for each successive block of twenty-six trials were obtained for each group (Cf. Table 4 below). No significant differences were found. The groups can thus be equated for rate of learning.

Distributions of Errors. a) Overall randomness of errors: Errors made by each group of subjects were summed in a 7 X 8 error matrix and tested by X^2 to examine the hypothesis that they were randomly distributed. The twenty to forty age-group gave a X^2

TABLE 4

PATTERN LEARNING: ERROR SCORES FOR SUCCESSIVE BLOCKS OF
26 PRESENTATIONS

	1st Quarter	*2nd Quarter*	*3rd Quarter*	*4th Quarter*
Youngs	461	392	337	267
Olds	507	426	341	306

of 259 and the forty to sixty group a X^2 of 125 for 54 degrees of freedom showing that errors were not made at random by either group (p<0.001).

This procedure was repeated for the error matrix obtained for each individual subject and the resulting distributions of X^2 thus obtained were compared: The values obtained for the young group were found to be significantly greater than the values obtained for the old group (Mann-Whitney U, two-tailed equivalent p<0.01). This may be taken to indicate that the younger group is significantly less random in its errors than the older group.

Distribution of Errors within Sub-groups of Patterns. b) Errors can, however, be classified as "correct category" errors or "incorrect category errors." If a stimulus is a one-handed pattern, a wrong response may be that appropriate to another one-handed pattern (correct category error) or appropriate to one of the set of two-handed patterns (incorrect category error). Wrong responses to two-handed patterns can be classified in the same way. On the assumption that the distribution of errors is random between correct and incorrect categories the probability of an error occurring within the correct category by chance is 0.43. It was thus possible to use t-tests to determine whether the means for the ratios of correct to incorrect category errors obtained for each group differ from chance expectation. These results, and the values of t obtained for each group, are given in Table 5 below. While the young subjects made significantly more correct-category errors than would be expected by chance, errors made by the older group are random with respect to this classification.

TABLE 5
PATTERN LEARNING: AGE AND TYPE OF ERROR

Age Group	Total Errors (Max possible =3016)	Correct Category Errors / Total Errors
20-40	1457 (48.3%)	0.56 (t = 3.1; p < .01)
40-50	1580 (52.4%)	0.43 (t = 0.91; p > 0.25)

GENERAL DISCUSSION

The most general implication of all these data is that old subjects have difficulty in ignoring irrelevant or redundant information and are consequently at a disadvantage in searching amongst complex stimuli or learning to discriminate between patterns. It is important to stress that this failure may be interpreted in two rather different ways:

Firstly, old subjects may suffer from a defect in the ability to form or retain sets. They may not know what they are looking for. More exactly, they cannot, unlike young people, improve their anticipation by concentrating upon the most precise and economical set of cues.

Secondly, old people may fail to integrate perceptual information so as to extract general rules which allow critical cues to be discriminated efficiently from incidental or redundant aspects of complex stimuli. Experiment 4 above may be taken to imply a a defect of this type.

The present experiments can be used as a guide for further work only if they are considered in the context of previous work on discrimination. This is most logically done by considering some of the ways in which the problem of discriminability of stimuli has been discussed.

i) Weber's Law. The term "discriminability" has not been used here as in cases to which the Weber-Fechner function and quantification in j.n.d's are applicable. We have been concerned with the *range* of cues necessary to discriminate between complex stimuli, and the selectivity which may be exercised in using some and ignoring others. The *obviousness* of such cues may be estimated in j.n.d's or in some equivalent system of quantification, and is an important consideration not covered by these data. The implications of the present experiments are thus different from those which follow from discussions of discriminability by Welford (1960) and experiments by Birren and Botwinick (1955) and Crossman and Szafran (1956). Two corollaries to work in this area must be borne in mind:

First, work by Crossman (1955) and Rabbitt (1963) implies that there is an interaction between the discriminability of stimuli as measured in j.n.d's and their information load. As far as the present results are concerned it is very probable that variations in the discriminability of stimuli in the Weber-Fechner sense affect the efficiency with which an optimal set of cues may be selected. Such effects will represent the operation of yet another variable in this complex situation. In the terms used above this distinction may be paraphrased as that between the *range* of cues to be considered and the accuracy required in matching any individual cue.

Secondly, discussions of redundancy and of the usefulness of cue-systems have tended to ignore the possibility of relationships between the obviousness of cues and their incorporation into a subject's cue-system. Clearly some trade-off must occur in situations in which the optimal cues for discrimination between members of a set of stimuli are physically less obvious than an alternative set of cues which allow discrimination at the cost of some redundancy.

ii) Information Theory. It has been emphasized that discriminations concern particular aspects of complex stimuli, the points of difference being usually referred to as cues. If the information-theory metric is to be applied to discriminations of this type, it must therefore be applied in terms of the number of *cues* rather than the number of *stimuli*. As Attneave (1956) and Fitts *et al.* (1956) have shown, not all possible cues are used in discriminations of this type, since many cues are unnecessary ("redundant") for this purpose. As a simple example of this, if we are required to discriminate between a Polar bear and an elephant, although there are countless points of difference which might be enumerated it would be sufficient *in this particular case* to know that the bear was white. Difficulty of discrimination is not, therefore, a direct function of stimulus *complexity* per se, but rather a function of the proportion of cues which are critical to the discrimination required, and perhaps also a function of the range of irrelevant or redundant cues which must be ignored. It follows that in applying the information theory metric we must be certain which system of cues subjects choose to employ. This will be the more necessary where familiarity with material similar to that discriminated may lead to habits of coding, with the result that subjects may find it easier to employ a sub-optimal coding-system with which they are familiar than to work out a new system more appropriate to the particular situation they encounter. One may well inquire whether old people experience particuilar difficulty with complex discriminations because it is easier for them to attempt to use learned coding systems, which may be clumsy, than to develop systems more appropriate to novel material.

A more serious difficulty in applying the information metric is the absence of sufficient data for a quantitative description of the difficulty in choosing between relevant and irrelevant cues. The performance of young subjects in Experiment II above suggests that choice between relevant and irrelevant items in a display, and hence probably also between relevant and redundant aspects of complex stimuli, is not a function of information load in any simple sense. Variations in the vocabulary of irrelevant items (from 24 in the 2-relevant situation to 18 in the 8-relevant situation) are clearly less critical in their effects upon discrimination time than equivalent variations in the number of relevant items (from 2-8). Earlier results obtained on categorization tasks by Pollack (1963) and Rabbitt (1959) do not resolve this question. While it is clear that the time taken to choose between categories of stimuli varies as some multiplicative function of the number of categories into which the stimulus population is divided by the subject's responses and of the number of stimuli in each category, both Pollack and Rabbitt only investigated situations in which all classes or categories always contained the same number of stimuli. Experiment II, and similar cases of choice between "relevant" and "irrelevant" categories may, however, best be described as situations in which subjects respond to classes of stimuli of unequal sizes: viz. two or eight classes with one relevant stimulus in each class and a single class of eighteen or twenty-four irrelevant items. The relationship between functions obtained under these conditions and the expressions derived from information—theory formula so far applied to choice-response situations remains to be determined.

Span of Absolute Judgment. When a subject is required to identify a stimulus presented to him in the absence of other members of a set to which the stimulus belongs he is said to make an absolute judgment. Experiments concerned with discriminations of this type have typically been conducted with stimuli representing points along a single continuum of operation of a sense-organ. That is to say, subjects have been required to discriminate between tones differing in loudness but not in frequency, or to make identifying responses to a series of positions of a point along a single spatial continuum. Miller (1956) reviewing the literature in this area argues that human beings do not appear to be able to learn to discriminate between more than a few points along any such continuum of operation of a sense-organ. Miller remarks that the number of such absolutely discriminable points (7 ± 2) is curiously similar for all sensory continuua for which such data are available. Pollack (1953) has further shown that such limitations are not necessarily related to the size of intervals along the sensory continuua between these points—in other words, to their mutual separation in j.n.d's. Such a distinction precisely parallels that made above between the discriminability of stimuli and their information load.

Complex stimuli, with which the present discussion is concerned, differ from each other in terms of more than one sensory continuum. As Miller (1956) points out, little is known of the span of absolute judgment for multidimensional stimuli. Experiments by Klemmer and Frick (1953) on the span of apprehension for positions of a dot on two spatial dimensions, and by Pollack and Ficks (1954) on absolute judgment for tones differing along as many as six perceptual dimensions indicate that the span of absolute judgment increases with the number of dimensions of difference between stimuli, but is not a simple multiplicative function of the number of dimensions of difference and the number of steps discriminable along each dimension in isolation. However, caution is necessary before these findings are generalized, since although there are about seven discriminable points along a single spatial continuum (Hake and Garner, 1951) and about twenty-four discriminable points within a square (Klemmer and Frick, 1953), it does not follow that there would be a similar reduction of the number of discriminable points along combined continuua of difference if subjects were required to identify points by their *colour* and *position*. This is a further difficulty in the application of the information theory metric to these situations, since it is probable that there are interactions between the numbers of discriminable steps along some pairs of continuua and not others. The further investigation of this problem appears to offer a first approach to the understanding of perceptual coding, which is not only of great intrinsic interest, but, as Welford (1958) has shown, vital to an understanding of age-decrements in perception and storage.

Learning of Systems of Classification and Perceptual Set

It is not self-evident which aspects of a given set of stimuli are optimal cues for discriminations between them. The structure of other stimuli in a set will determine whether any particular feature of a given stimulus is a critical or a redundant cue. The addition or subtraction of other stimuli may radically change the information value of all cues within such a set.

It is difficult to imagine that an adult human ever encounters a stimulus configuration which is so novel in his experience that he has no preconceptions as to how it may be broken down into parts which are familiar in other contexts. With experience, a repertory of techniques of classification is built up. For example, one of the commonest linguistic techniques for reducing redundancy in description is the "like" statement. It would be very difficult to describe a griffin if it were not possible to trigger information available to the listener from his past experience by saying "it has an head like an eagle, a body and tail like a lion and it is as big as two elephants." It is not impossible for the speaker to now draw a recognizable picture of a griffin by assembling his recollections of other fauna, without having any clear picture in his mind as to what the griffin he actually saw looked like. Arguments of this type derive from Bartlett's classical work on memory (1932) and have been expanded by Oldfield (1954) and Vernon (1937). Their implications for age investigations were first pointed out by Welford (1958). The results of Experiment IV suggest that old subjects either do not recognize the presence of a simple scheme of classification, or cannot use it though they are aware of it.

The experiments discussed offer no footholds for those concerned with building bridges between the biological phenomena of aging and performance data. If they have any place in such a volume as this it must be as a reminder that, in the common behavior of everyday life, adequate criteria for the quantification of performance-data have not been established. If there is another moral, it is that in tasks of this type the human being must be regarded as choosing between a repertory of possible strategies. It is probable that with increasing age this repertory diminishes; but the choice between strategies will still be determined to a great degree by the subject's personal experience. One may compare the aging organism to a disabled analog computer, whose capacity for carrying out programs is increasingly limited as components fail. The range of the computer's performance will be determined by both the total and the specific loss of components, but these losses can be circumvented to some degree by alternative programming, allowing the best use of existing potential. It is frequently the case that both a simple and a complex computer can carry out parallel sequences of operations leading to the same output. Here the task of programming the simple computer may be much more laborious, since it may be necessary to break up the task into a long series of separate and elementary operations while the capacity of the larger machine permits of more direct solutions, and a variety of "short-cuts" to the same end. While the logical structure of a program is related to events in the computer's circuitry, and the circuitry determines the choice of operations available to the programmer, this correspondence is not complete. To behave as though the translation from neurology to performance were unmodified by the life experience of an organism would repeat the error of confusing a computer's program with its hardware. This might well cost more time in the end than the development of separate, but adequate, terminologies for both areas.

REFERENCES

Attneave, F.: (1956) Symmetry, information and memory for patterns. *Amer. J. Psychol.*, 68:209-222.

Bartlett, Sir F. C.: (1932) *Remembering*. Cambridge, Cambridge Univ. Press.

Birren, J. E. and Botwinick, J.: (1955) Speed of response as a function of perceptual difficulty and age. *J. Geront.*, 10:433-436.

Crossman, E. R. F. W.: (1955) The measurement of discriminability. *Quart. J. Exp. Psychol.*, 7:176-195.

Crossman, E. R. F. W. and Szafran, J.: (1956) Changes with age in the speed of information intake and discrimination. *Experientia, Supplimentum* 4:128.

Fitts, P. M., Weinstein, M., Rappaport, M., Anderson, N. and Leonard, J. A.: (1956) Stimulus correlates of visual pattern recognition; A probability approach. *J. Exp. Psychol.*, 51:1-11.

Gregory, R. L. and Cane, Violet: (1955) A statistical information theory of visual thresholds. *Nature*, 176:1272.

Hake, H. W. and Garner, W. R.: (1951) The effect of presenting various numbers of discrete steps on scale-reading accuracy. *J. Exp. Psychol.*, 42:358-366.

Klemmer, E. T. and Frick, F. C.: (1953) Assimilation of information from dot and matrix patterns. *J. Exp. Psychol.*, 45:15-19.

Mackworth, N. H. and Mackworth, J. F.: (1958) Eye-fixations recorded on changing visual scenes by the television eye-marker. *J. Optic. Soc. Amer.*, 7:439-445.

Miller, G. A.: (1956) The magical number seven, plus or minus two. Some limits on our capacity for processing information. *Psychol. Rev.*, 63:81-97.

Oldfield, C.: (1954) Memory mechanisms and the theory of schemata. *Brit. J. Psychol.*, XIV:14-23.

Pollack, I.: (1953) The assimilation of elementary auditory displays, II. *J. Acous. Soc. Amer.*, 24:765-769.

Pollack, I. and Ficks, L.: (1954) Information of elementary multi-dimensional auditory displays. *J. Acous. Soc. Amer.*, 26:155-158.

Pollack, I.: (1963) Speed of classification of words into superordinate categories. *J. Verb. Learn. Verb. Behaviour*, 2:159-165.

Rabbitt, P. M. A.: (1959) Effects of independent variations in stimulus and response probability. *Nature*, 183:1212.

Rabbitt, P. M. A.: (1963) Information load and discriminability. *Nature*, 197:4868:726.

Vernon, M. D.: (1937) *Visual Perception*. New York, Macmillan & Co.

Welford, A. T.: (1958) *Ageing and Human Skill*. London, Oxford University Press, (for the Nuffield Foundation).

Welford, A. T.: (1960) The measurement of sensory-motor performance: study and reappraisal of twelve years progress. *Ergonomics*, 3:189-230.

4

AGE AND VIGILANCE

D. R. Davies and S. Griew

INTRODUCTION

THE RESULTS of the few available studies comparing the performances of older and younger subjects at vigilance tasks have generally indicated that there is no significant difference with age either in the number of signals correctly detected or in the number of occasions on which a signal is reported when none was in fact present. York (1962) found no age difference in the performance of a visual vigilance task where subjects were required to detect single flashes of a light from a background of double flashes, and Obrist (personal communication) reports no age difference with an auditory vigilance situation. Similarly Griew and Davies (1962) using an auditory task in which subjects were presented with a series of digits and required to detect and respond to sequences of three consecutive odd digits while ignoring all others, found no significant differences between the performances of groups with ages from the mid fortys to the mid sixtys and from the late teens to the early thirtys. This was true whether the frequency of signals was relatively high (66 per hour) or relatively low (24 per hour) (Davies and Griew, 1963). In a subsequent experiment, previously unreported, Davies and Griew found no significant difference in the detection rates of older and younger subjects performing an auditory vigilance task under conditions of isolation, darkness and a constant background of low intensity noise—in other words of reduced sensory stimulation. Again in a cancellation task in which subjects listened to a tape-recording of digits and were required to check the digits they heard against a printed list and to record discrepancies, Griew and Davies (1962) found no difference in the number of discrepancies reported by older and younger subjects although both groups performed at a much higher level than in the auditory vigilance task.

Griew and Davies (1962) did find significant differences between their two age-groups when two methods of recording signals were compared. Although there was no significant difference between the number of correct detections when subjects responded to a sequence of three consecutive odd digits by pressing a key, a difference was found when subjects were required to respond to such a sequence by writing it down. In the latter situation, the number of correct detections made by older subjects was significantly fewer than both the number made by younger subjects in the same situation and the number made by older subjects in the key-pressing condition. It is thought that writing the signals down imposed a load on short-term memory of the type that has previously been shown to affect older subjects more severely than young (Welford, 1958). It appears, then, that in vigilance situations as such no age differences of performance occur although they have been shown to occur in other continuous work situations such as self-paced addition (Botwinick and Shock, 1952).

AROUSAL AS A FACTOR IN VIGILANCE SITUATIONS

The notion that arousing properties of vigilance tasks largely determine the quality of performance is receiving much theoretical attention (Frankmann and Adams, 1962; Broadbent, 1963). Studies by McGrath (1960) and by McGrath and Hatcher (1961) suggest that varied environmental stimulation such as music can enhance visual vigilance performance and similarly that auditory vigilance is improved when subjects are allowed to look at pictures. Adams, Stenson and Humes (1961) found that subjects who had both to detect and also to evaluate visual signals performed better than those who had merely to detect them. They interpreted their results in terms of the variety of response-produced stimulation. Thus although the variety of stimulation (or lack of it) in a vigilance situation appears to be a major factor in determining the level of performance, it is uncertain whether environmental or response-produced stimulation is the more important. The mere amount of environmental stimulation does not appear to influence performance very much: McGrath (1960) for example, found that performance of a visual vigilance task was not enhanced by white noise; similarly, on the response side, Whittenburg, Ross and Andrews (1956) found that increasing the number of times subjects were required to press a key in performing a visual vigilance task made no difference to the number of signals detected.

If, as is reasonable, we can think of Griew and Davies' cancellation task as more arousing than their conditions of reduced sensory stimulation, we can argue that the performance of older and younger subjects in vigilance situations seems to be susceptible to the effects of arousing properties, in that the level of performance for both groups improves when the situation is made more arousing, as in the cancellation task, and deteriorates under conditions of reduced sensory stimulation. However the performance of the two groups does not appear to be differentially affected by age either in respect of the average level of performance throughout the task or the rate of decline in performance with time. It remains nevertheless to be seen whether their performance of such tasks is differentially affected by other arousal factors such as sleep deprivation and time of day.

POSSIBLE REASONS FOR THE FAILURE TO OBTAIN AN AGE DIFFERENCE

The first possible interpretation of the lack of an age difference in the experiments described is a fairly simple one, and is that the older subjects were not old enough. The oldest subject who took part in our experiments was sixty-six years of age and the mean age of the seventy-six older subjects was fifty-four years. The mean age of the younger subjects was twenty-three years. It is possible therefore that if all the older subjects used had been over sixty, or over sixty-five, then an age difference would have appeared. There are two reasons that make us doubtful of this explanation. The first is that of the nine subjects we used over the age of sixty none showed any marked difference in the level of signal detection from the average of younger subjects with which they were compared. The second reason is that in the condition where subjects performed a vigilance task with an additional immediate memory load an age difference was found.

For a second possible interpretation we are indebted to Obrist (personal communication) who has suggested that age differences in the performance of vigilance tasks might perhaps be found only when older subjects show definite signs of slowing in the EEG rhythms. In his experiment, quoted above, older subjects showed neither significantly slower EEG nor poorer vigilance than younger. If slowing of the EEG frequently should prove to be a critical factor in determining whether or not deterioration of performance occurs in older subjects, the establishment of some criterion of the term "older subjects" other than simply chronological age appears to be necessary. Meanwhile the hypothesis regarding EEG slowing, age, and vigilance remains to be tested.

A third interpretation which is the one that we are inclined to favor can be made in terms of motivation. Birren (1960) has pointed out that anecdotal accounts of experimenters give the impression that older subjects are more motivated to achieve a high level of output and are concerned with avoiding errors to a greater extent than are younger subjects. Differences in motivational level have been related to age by Botwinick, Brinley and Robbin (1958) and Welford (1956) but, Birren observes, there is as yet no appreciable body of experimental evidence. It is our impression also that when older subjects are aware that they are performing a similar task to younger subjects in a laboratory setting they are more concerned about how well they perform than are younger subjects, but we too have no formal evidence to offer.

Vigilance tasks seem to provide examples of situations where motivation is much more important than in the majority of perceptual-motor tasks. The amount of skill required appears to be minimal and little or no practice is required for the subject to achieve a high level of performance. Thus the deterioration of skilled performance with age seems to have little application here. The only aspects of skill which may be applicable in such situations are the ability to form expectancies and the ability to estimate time intervals. An experiment by Griew (1962) indicates that it is at least possible that older subjects form expectancies more rather than less quickly than younger, but an experiment by Feifel (1957) has demonstrated that the estimation of time intervals by older subjects is significantly less accurate than that of younger ones.

If the lack of an age difference is to be explained in terms of motivation, some statement should be made of how such a hypothesis can be tested. Ryan, Cottrell and Bitterman (1950) and Ryan (1953) have successfully used muscle tension as an indicator of effort, and Wilkinson (1960) has shown that the level and variability of muscle tension was higher than normal in subjects who maintained their level of performance in spite of lack of sleep. If older subjects are putting more effort into their performance then this should presumably be reflected in a relative increase in muscle tension during their performance of a task.

It is to be expected in such a situation that older subjects would show greater differences between working and resting levels of muscle tension than would younger ones. It is also possible that such measures of states of alertness as skin resistance would show differences between younger and older subjects during performance of vigilance tasks.

The differential effects of stimulating drugs such as benzedrine sulphate and ephedrine hydrochloride, and of depressant drugs such as atropine would be of interest in this connection. On the behavioral side, the relative effects of rest pauses and knowledge of results would provide useful information.

ACKNOWLEDGMENTS

This work was supported in part by a grant from The Medical Research Council. The authors are grateful to Mr. R. Brown, Mr. M. J. Krakauer and Mr. K. F. H. Murrell for their comments on a draft of this paper.

REFERENCES

Adams, J. A., Stenson, H. H. and Humes, J. W.: (1961) Monitoring of complex visual displays: II. Effects of visual load and response complexity on human vigilance. *Human Factors,* 3:213-221.

Birren, J. E.: (1960) Psychological aspects of aging. *Ann. Rev. Psychol.*, *11*:161-198.

Botwinick, J., Brinley, J. F. and Robbin, J. S.: (1958) The effect of motivation by electrical shocks on reaction-time in relation to age. *Amer. J. Psychol.*, *71*:408-411.

Botwinick, J. and Shock, N. W.: (1952) Age differences in performance decrement with continuous work. *J. Geront.*, *7*:41-46.

Broadbent, D. E.: (1963) Possibilities and difficulties in the concept of arousal. In *Vigilance: A Symposium*, D. A. Buckner and J. J. McGrath, eds., New York, McGraw-Hill, pp. 184-198.

Davies, D. R. and Griew, S.: (1963) A further note on the effect of aging on auditory vigilance performance. *J. Geront.*, *18*:370-371.

Feifel, H.: (1957) Judgment of time in older and younger subjects. *J. Geront.*, *12*:71-74.

Frankmann, J. and Adams, J. A.: (1962) Theories of vigilance. *Psychol. Bull.*, *59*:257-272.

Griew, S.: (1962) The learning of statistical structure: a preliminary study in relation to age. In *Social and Psychological Aspects of Aging*, C. Tibbitts and Wilma Donahue, eds., New York, Columbia University Press.

Griew, S., and Davies, D. R.: (1962) The effect of aging on auditory vigilance performance. *J. Geront.*, *17*:88-90.

McGrath, J. J.: (1960) The effect of irrelevant environmental stimulation on vigilance performance. *Human Factor Problems in ASW. Tech. Rep. No. 6*, Los Angeles, Human Factors Research, Inc.

McGrath, J. J. and Hatcher, J. F.: (1961) Irrelevant stimulation and vigilance under fast and slow stimulus rates. *Human Factor Problems in ASW. Tech. Rep. No. 7.*, Los Angeles, Human Factors Research, Inc.

Ryan, T. A.: (1953) Muscular potentials as indicators of effort in visual tasks. In, *Fatigue*, W. F. Floyd and A. T. Welford, eds., London, H. K. Lewis and Co., (for the Ergonomics Research Society).

Ryan, T. A., Cottrell, C. L. and Bitterman, M. E.: (1950) Muscular tension as an index of effort: the effect of glare and other disturbances in visual work. *Amer. J. Psychol.*, *63*:317-341.

Welford, A. T.: (1956) Age and learning: theory and needed research. *Experientia, Supplementum 4:* 136-143.

Welford, A. T.: (1958) *Ageing and Human Skill.* Oxford University Press, (for the Nuffield Foundation).

Wilkinson, R. T.: (1960) Effects of sleep deprivation on performance and muscle tension. In *The Nature of Sleep*, G. E. W. Wolstenhome and M. O'Connor, eds., Boston, Little, Brown & Co., (for the Ciba Foundation).

York, C. M.: (1962) Behavioral efficiency in a visual monitoring task as a function of signal rate and observer age. *Percept. Mot. Skills, 15*:404.

5

AGE, EXPERIENCE AND SPEED OF RESPONSE

K. F. H. MURRELL and S. GRIEW

T HE OBJECT of this paper is to resurrect, and if possible to clarify, the concept of experience which, when used in conjunction with the notion of a decrease of capacity with age, accounts well for the typical rise and subsequent fall during life of the level of performance (e.g., Murrell, 1962; Welford, 1958). The paper is based on work which has been concerned mainly with complex skilled performance, and which had as its ultimate object the amelioration of work for older employees in industry.

PRELIMINARY INDUSTRIAL STUDIES

We started with preliminary industrial studies which were concerned with the fundamental question: are older workers in more difficulty in some jobs than in others? Previous studies had provided somewhat equivocal evidence, and it was thought that this was likely to be due almost entirely to most previous workers having failed to consider in sufficient detail differences between one job and another, dealing rather with broad classes of job (Griew, 1959). We accordingly examined the relations between age, occupation and accidents, and between age, occupation and labour turnover for a number of individual jobs, and found that in certain jobs older workers were liable to substantially higher rates of accidents and labour turnover than in others (Griew, 1958a, 1958b). In studies of the age distribution of occupants of various jobs we found that the hierarchy of jobs in terms of the median ages of workers employed in them was reproduceable in different firms, different areas of the country, and at different times (Murrell, Griew and Tucker, 1957; Murrell and Griew, 1958). We were unable directly to study output, as such, but we were confident that our results support the suggestion that the success of an older worker will depend very largely on the nature of his work, since satisfactory output is known to be very closely related to less direct measures of satisfactoriness.

Two job analyses were conducted in order to specify the actual features of jobs which might be associated with the difficulties met by older workers. In one, the work of a young and an old group, each consisting of about forty individuals and employed on very similar jobs, was compared. The results indicated that young workers tended to be engaged on jobs which demanded less natural postures and a greater amount of perceptual activity, and that they made greater use of complex controls on machine tools than older workers (Griew and Tucker, 1958). In the second, a greater proportion of young workers were found on jobs where instructions were complex, measuring instruments required accurate reading, components being made contained fine details, and the tolerances to which the machinist was required to work were close (Murrell and and Tucker, 1960). These age trends were probably due more to the older workers moving to work suitable to their capabilities than to any conscious reallocation of older workers by labour officers or workshop supervisors —in short the trends probably reflected a kind of "natural selection."

EXPERIMENTAL STUDIES OF PSYCHO-MOTOR PERFORMANCE

In an effort to clarify some of the issues raised by these industrial findings, particularly when taken in conjunction with the results of previous experimental studies of ageing, a series of laboratory tasks was designed and the performance of young and older subjects on them was studied (see Griew, 1963). The tasks were designed to help elucidate the question of whether advancing age is associated with reduction in an operator's capacity to process information. The answer which most studies supported was affirmative, and the results were very much in line with those reported previously by Welford (1958) and others, in that the perceptual-motor performance of older subjects was found to be substantially worse than that of younger.

In so far as the experiments allowed the isolation of specific factors contributing to the overall decrement in performance, the actual times taken to make *movements* did not seem to differ much between young and old: rather the difference was in the times required for *decision-making* and *discrimination*. It seemed that both young and old were, however, able to overlap some part of a decision into the movement phase of a simple response (Murrell and Entwisle, 1960).

One study particularly produced a somewhat unexpected result which we now believe to be germaine to the argument which we intend to present shortly. This result was that older subjects appeared, in a task extending for about 120 responses, to learn the statistical structure of a series of signals significantly *more* quickly than their young colleagues (Griew, 1962).

LATER STUDIES OF INDUSTRIAL TASKS AND OF A TASK RESEMBLING THOSE FOUND IN INDUSTRY

From the slowing with age of the various functions which we and others before us have found to occur, we expected that the performance of older people would be easily distinguished from that of younger ones on industrial tasks. Much of the evidence from our early industrial studies added weight to this expectation. We accordingly undertook several investigation in an attempt to test its validity. Our earlier work had suggested that it was in the perceptually demanding (skilled) jobs that older workers were found least. It was these jobs, therefore, that received our attention.

Age trends in the expected direction were obtained in a study of micrometer reading. The subjects were divided into three groups (aet. 20-34, 35-49, 50-64 yrs.) who were progressively slower at 8.4, 9.0 and 10.0 secs, respectively ($p < 0.005$). The young subjects seemed to have achieved speed as well as accuracy, the error scores being 0.8 percent, 4.2 percent and 3.5 percent respectively. It is possible that these speed differences were due to increasing difficulty in reading the micrometer scales but this does not seem to have been so; with a digital micrometer all the subjects improved by the same amount, there being no significant difference between the age trends on the two micrometers. This, perhaps surprising, finding is confirmed by the results of a tool room study referred to later: the replacement of the graduated scale on the cross slide of a centre lathe produced about 12.5 percent improvement in cutting time for both younger and older subjects.

On the other hand, studies of actual industrial work showed no clear trends with age. We obtained from a large engineering firm element times obtained by stop-watch for setting synthetic time values in the machine shop. We found that there were no significant differences between the times generatd by the young (aet 22-29 years.) and the older (aet 40-46 years.) machinists (Murrell and Forsaith, 1960). Again in a recent thirty week study (Murrell and Edwards, 1963) of four turners of ages twenty and one-half, twenty-one and one-half, fifty-eight and sixty-one years on production work in the tool room, the cutting time of the older men was fractionally *less* than that of the younger although they took longer in comprehending the instructions and preparing the work.

These latter results suggest that there may be a conflict between the results of traditional studies of psychomotor performance in relation to age and those of performance at the actual tasks which people have to do in real life. There are doubtless many possible reasons for this conflict, but four seemed to us to deserve serious consideration:

a) It is conceivable that progressive "natural selection" resulting from men moving away from work when it becomes a strain may mean that only those who are especially able remain to a late age (Welford 1957). This explanation is clearly true in part, but in some cases where labour turnover is small it seems not to be sufficient.

b) One obvious factor which requires consideration is that in real life people are very rarely stressed to the extent they are in the laboratory, so that older workers are not required to use their capacities to the full. However, some of the studies we made which failed to generate age differences purposely pushed subjects towards the limits of their capacity, and so thais factor must be ruled out as a primary contributor.

c) It is just possible that changes with age in the motivation of subjects may play a part in determining their performance in the "real life" tasks. This is a topic which is discussed further in the paper by Davies and Griew in this symposium (Ch. IV).

d) A fourth possibility is the one which at present we favour most, and this is that "experience" does an increasing amount to compensate for changes in biological capacity. On this view, it could be argued that those individuals who are eliminated by "natural selection" during later years are those in whom biological changes outrun the compensating effects of experience. Evidence favouring such a view of the compensatory role of experience is contained in a study by us of pillar drilling. This operation can take two forms, jig drilling, and "free drilling" in which the operative must aim the drill at a punch mark with zero error. It was this latter process of aim which was studied. Four groups of subjects were used, younger and older experienced drillers obtained through the help of the Amalgamated Engineering Union, and younger and older men without previous experience of drilling. It was found that the experienced subjects took about the same time to aim (younger = 3.22 sec.; older = 3.08 secs.) but that the younger inexperienced subjects were significantly faster at 1.02 secs. and the older inexperienced subjects significantly slower at 5.28 secs. (Murrell, Powesland and Forsaith, 1962). In addition both groups of older subjects were more accurate than were the younger; the young inexperienced subjects being rather "slap-dash" and significantly less accurate than the rest, which no doubt was why they were so fast.

There are several ways in which one can conceive of "experience" as facilitating performance at this kind of task, of which two seem especially important:

First, it could be that a worker tends, albeit unconsciously, in the course of time to replace uneconomical responses with less demanding and more economical ones (Crossman 1959). One could conceive of this as a form of what Welford (1963) has termed "load shedding," and it may well be that some of the differences we found in our job analyses were due to the action of long term adaptive processes of this type. It would be comparatively easy to test the hypothesis, but it would take a long time to do so since any test would inevitably involve the longitudinal study of workers.

Secondly, it may be that the older a man grows the better is he able to rely on expectancies which are built up as a result of long association with specific tasks. We had already found in the laboratory task described earlier that older subjects may learn the statistical structure of a series of signals more quickly than young subjects even though the process of learning extends over a comparatively limited number of trials. It seems likely, therefore, that they would benefit even more from a learning process extending over many months or years. Perhaps the adaptive value of reliance on expectancies encourages older subjects unwittingly to adopt the strategy of mastering the statistical properties of sequences of events as quickly as possible.

CONCLUSION

The difficulties we have found in extrapolating from laboratory findings to the industrial situation suggest that there is an important additional factor in the latter which laboratory experiments have so far failed to measure. We suggest that this factor is *experience* gained over months or years of work and that it can, in many instances, fully compensate for decrease of biological capacity with age. It seems to us that the nature of the changes of performance which result from such long-term experience and their relation to age from a topic in urgent need of research.

ACKNOWLEDGMENT

The major part of the research reported here was done while the authors were members of the Unit for Research on Employment of Older Workers which was financed by the Nuffield Foundation. Later parts were conducted under the auspices of the Unit for Research on Human Performance in Industry supported by the Department of Scientific and Industrial Research.

REFERENCES

Crossman, E. R. F. W.: (1959) A theory of the acquisition of speed-skill. *Ergonomics*, 2:153-166.

Griew, S.: (1958a) A study of accidents in relation to occupation and age. *Ergonomics, 2*:17-23.

Griew, S.: (1958b) Some experimental and industrial studies of ageing. Unpublished Ph.D. Thesis, University of Bristol.

Griew, S.: (1959) Methodological problems in industrial ageing research. *Occup. Psychol., 33*:36-45.

Griew, S.: (1962) Learning of statistical structure. A preliminary study in relation to age. In *Social and Psychological Aspects of Ageing*, Tibbits, C., and Donahue, W., eds., New York, Columbia University Press.

Griew, S.: (1963) The relationship between age and information transmission and its significance for the interpretation of age changes in perceptual motor performance. In *Processes of Aging: Social and Psychological Perspectives*, R. H. Williams, C. Tibbitts and Wilma Donahue, eds., New York, Atherton Press, Vol. I.

Griew, S. and Tucker, W. A.: (1958) The identification of job activities associated with age differences in the engineering industry. *J. Appl. Psychol., 42*:278-282.

Murrell, K. F. H.: (1962) Industrial aspects of ageing. *Ergonomics, 5*: 147-153.

Murrell, K. F. H. and Edwards, E.: (1963) Field studies of an Indicator of Machine Tool travel with special reference to the ageing worker. *Occup. Psychol., 37*:267-275.

Murrell, K. F. H. and Entwisle, D. G.: (1960) Age difference in movement pattern. *Nature, 185*:948-949.

Murrell, K. F. H. and Forsaith, Bel: (1960) Age and the timing of movement. *Occup. Psychol., 34*:275-279.

Murrell, K. F. H. and Griew, S.: (1958) Age structure in the Engineering Industry. A study of regional effects. *Occup. Psychol., 32*:86-88.

Murrell, K. F. H., Griew, S. and Tucker, W. A.: (1957) Age structure in the Engineering Indutry. A preliminary study. *Occup. Psychol., 31*: 150-169.

Murrell, K. F. H., Powesland, P. F. and Forsaith, Bel: (1962) A study of pillar drilling in relation to age. *Occup. Psychol., 36*:45-52.

Murrell, K. F. H. and Tucker, W. A.: (1960) A pilot job-study of age-related causes of difficulty in light engineering. *Ergonomics, 3*:74-79.

Welford, A. T.: (1957) Methodological problems in the study of changes in human performance with age. In *Colloquia on Ageing 3. Methodology of the Study of Ageing*, Wolstenholme, G. E. W. and O'Connor, C. M., eds., London, Churchill.

Welford, A. T.: (1958) *Ageing and Human Skill*. London, Oxford University Press, (for the Nuffield Foundation).

Welford, A. T.: (1963) Social, psychological and physiological gerontology —an experimental psychologists approach. In *Processes of Aging: Social and Psychological Perspectives*, R. H. Williams, C. Tibbitts and Wilma Donahue, eds., New York, Atherton Press, Vol. I.

6

THEORIES OF ANTECEDENT CONDITIONS
OF SPEED OF RESPONSE*

JACK BOTWINICK

INTRODUCTION

LET US BEGIN with the assumption that the state
of the central nervous stystem (c. n. s.) is vitally important in
how quickly one can respond. To many, this assumption is so
much a part of accepted fact that it may appear as an unnecessary and obvious platitude. It is well to bear in mind, however,
that what data relate to such an assumption are most often indirect, and sometimes, as will be seen, interpreted from negative
results.

If the state of the c.n.s. is an antecedent condition of reaction
time (RT), then this would suggest that differing states within
the c.n.s. result in differing RT's, and that individual differences
in a state of the c.n.s. contribute to individual differences in RT.
The corollary of this is that inferences about the state of the
c.n.s. are possible with knowledge of RT's. More correctly, inferences about states of the c.n.s within an individual and differences between individuals are presumed feasible with information of RT's appropriate to the situation.

* This paper was supported in part by a Public Health Service research career
program award (5153) from the Mental Health and from the Child Health and
Human Development Institutes, and in part by a supplemental research grant
(08244) from the Mental Health Institute.

THREE THEORIES OF C.N.S. CONTRIBUTION TO RT

Nerve Conduction Theory

RT as a measure of voluntary behavior is considered analyzable into component parts, including neural conduction sequences. Thus, the total time from the environmental event to the behavior itself is segmented and associated with physiological function. The research goal is to determine the portion of total RT that is associated with functions of the receptor organs, the portion associated with the afferent pathways, with the central pathways, the efferent pathways, and finally the portion of RT associated with the effector muscles. An example of this may be seen in the statement of Davis (1957, p. 126), "For an auditory stimulus activity reaches the cerebral cortex 8-9 milliseconds after stimulation . . . a visual stimulus 20-40 milliseconds may elapse before activity reaches the cortex. . . . On the motor side nerve conduction may account for 10-15 milliseconds and the time elapsing before action current is translated into movement of a reaction key has been estimated as 30-40 milliseconds. . . . Thus, for a response to a visual signal, at least 60 milliseconds or so is spent in the periphery, whereas for an auditory signal . . . about 30 milliseconds . . . the central mechanisms may be dealing with the signal for a time equal to (Normal RT-total peripheral conduction time) say 90-100 milliseconds . . . "

This statement by Davis was made in the context of the problem of "psychological refractory period" which has been explicated in detail by Welford (1952). The "psychological refractory period" is that brief interval of time during which the organism cannot efficiently carry out response sequences due to involvements of prior response to prior stimulation. The "psychological refractory period" occurs within the time between two stimuli presented in temporal sequence. If the time between stimuli is brief enough, RT to the second stimulus is slower than the RT to the first. If the duration between stimuli is long enough, it is greater than the "refractory period" and RT's to both simuli are of similar latency. If all neural pathways of RT are conceptualized as part of a single channel, "the psychological refractory period" may be viewed as that period of time during which transmission of new impuses via or through the "single channel" is blocked or delayed.

Davis' data and speculations (1957) gave rise to a postulation of a "refractory period" due to central mechanisms of the order of 100 milliseconds.

Studies of the "psychological refractory period" typically involve simple stimuli and simple responses, as in RT situations. The concept of "psychological refractory period" may be related to the concept of "neural noise" which has been put forth by Gregory and Cane (1955) and Gregory (1956) to account for increases in threshold with decreases in stimulus intensity, and applied to the more complex problem of perceptual discrimination (Crossman, 1955; Crossman and Szafran, 1956, p. 133; Welford, 1959). Neural noise, "In physiological terms . . . might be an increased rate of spontaneous firing of neurones, or an increased likelihood of neighboring neurones to excite one another by non-synaptic pathways" (Welford, 1959, p. 574). Low signal strength (low stimulus intensity) makes for slow RT's. It may be hypothesized that high "neural noise" in the nervous system also makes for slow RT's. Thus, the signal-to-noise ratio, within the single channel nervous system, in affecting RT level, may also affect "psychological refractory period." An indicated experiment would be one wherein measurements of refractoriness are made in relation to stimuli varied in intensity. The prediction is of increased refractoriness with decreased stimulus intensity.

Aging Studies

There have been several efforts to investigate the well-documented loss of speed with age by analysis of neural conduction velocities of components sequences. Many of these efforts have been reviewed very ably by Magladery (1959) as the focus of a chapter on the neurophysiology of aging. In general, conduction speeds of peripheral neural components have been measured, and then, comparisons made between or among age groups. Typically, age differences in conduction speed of peripheral mechanisms have been found too small to account for age differences in total behavioral RT, or have not been found at all. The reader is then left with the inference, only sometimes clearly made by the investigator, that central mechanisms change with age, and these changes in central mechanisms account for the age differences in RT. Only examples of research of this kind will be presented here since, as indicated, Magladery (1959) has provided a thorough review.

Norris, Shock and Wagman (1953) measured speed of impulse conduction in the peripheral motor nerve component of reflex and voluntary behavior of twenty-five men in each decade from the third through the ninth. They found that conduction velocity of ulnar nerve motor fibers decreased with increased age. It was suggested that neither nerve fiber degeneration nor temperature differences in the arm were likely explanations for the peripheral nerve slowing; vascular changes were more likely, perhaps, but age alterations in nerve metabolism "is the most suitable explanation for the observed changes in conduction velocity." In any case, this reduction of peripheral nerve conduction time with age was estimated to account for only about 4 per cent of the age difference in total RT. It was suggested that the age difference in total RT may be accounted for more importantly in "other nerve tissue."

Birren and Wall (1956) examined the conduction velocity and other aspects of the sciatic nerve of albino Norwegian rats of a wide age range. While conduction velocity was found to increase during development up to about 300 days, velocity changes were not found with increasing age beyond 300 days. It was concluded that "Changes in peripheral nerve do not appear to be important in the changes in simple reaction time which occur during development and later life" (p. 14).

A more recent study in which it was concluded that peripheral neural mechanisms could not account for age differences in RT, Hugen, Norris, and Shock (1960) measured plantar reflex latencies of eighty-one subjects aged three to ninety-eight years, abdominal reflex latencies of forty-six subjects of corresponding age, and RT to touch in 111 subjects aged seven to ninety-two years. Reflex latencies were not found to vary significantly with age but RT was found to be increased significantly in young children and elderly subjects. It was concluded that "age differences become most apparent in latencies of voluntary responses involving participation of higher levels of the central nervous system." The slowing of RT with age "is due primarily to functional alterations in the central nervous system" (p. 391).

An effort to investigate age changes in conductivity within the central nervous system more directly, as distinguished from other investigations of age changes at clearly peripheral levels, was seen in the study of Wayner and Emmers (1958). Evidence of increasing delay with age of transmission time across single synapse within the spinal cord was impressive in that statistically significant differences were found between contiguous age groups of hooded rats. Spinal synaptic delay time was again obtained indirectly, however, this time by the subtraction of the conduction time to and from the spinal cord from the total reflex delay of afferent input via the dorsal root below lumbar region 5 and efferent output via the ventral root of the same lumbar region. Wayner and Emmers suggested in the introduction of their study that, "It seems reasonable that because of aging there might be a general slowing of integrative processes in the central nervous system due to prolonged excitation at synapses" (p. 403). In addition to increased synaptic delay with age, they found a significant age difference of mean ventral root conduction velocity, but not significant age difference in mean afferent conduction velocity. They concluded that these results were difficult to assess in relation to increased RT of rat subjects with age. "Additional information on the delay at the neuromuscular junction, muscular contraction, and the actual pathways and number of synapses involved in mediating the response are required" (p. 405).

Set Theory

Underlying some of the analyses of RT into component sequences in the previous section, was the implicit assumption that conduction velocities were measured under conditions of optimum RT. That is, if specific components of RT are measured in relation to one another (or, if groups are compared with respect to the different components and relations among them), and inferences about time courses of neural transmission of central mechanisms are made, it is assumed that RT is the quickest possible, or, at least, the quickest possible for the conditions of measurement. If an RT component, for example, one that is thought to be associated with a central mechanism, reflects a long RT segment, or reflects a large group difference in the RT segment, then the particular central mechanisms may be indicted or implicated in such a way as to suggest "capacity" or biological limitation in the speed of transmission impulses. It may be, however, that the conditions of measurement were such as to not be an adequate test of the capacity of the central mechanism in speed of neural transmission. The case may be that the conditions of measurement provided for inattention, low motivation, or other states of the responder, which while reflecting states of central mechanisms, did not necessarily reflect capacity of speed of impulse transmission. The conclusion, therefore, of limitation in the speed of neural transmission would be a questionable one.

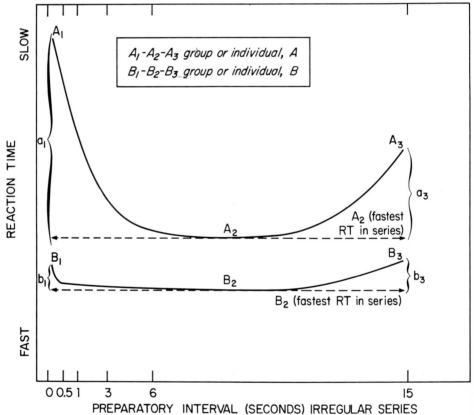

Figure 1. Hypothetical curves of reaction time as functions of the preparatory intervals of irregular series. A_2 and B_2 are points of optimum reaction time of two groups or two individuals. A_1 and B_1, and A_3 and B_3, points of slow reaction time, reflect relatively poor states of set of the responders.

The notion of quickest possible RT may be an unrealistic one in the practical sense, although not in the theoretical sense. We never will know whether with more training, different conditions, etc., RT of a particular subject may be reduced further. We do know, however, what can be done to make for *optimum RT*, which may be defined as the quickest RT's measured under varied preparatory conditions [PI] of the experiment. Thus, in Figures 1 and 2, optimum RT was represented by A_2 and B_2, and is most meaningful when considered in relation to values a_1 and a_3, or b_1 and b_3 respectively.

Figures 1 and 2 are of hypothetical curves drawn to reflect what much of the data appear to indicate. When RT is measured in relation to the foreperiods or preparatory intervals (PI) of an irregular series (Fig. 1), the particular PI is often related

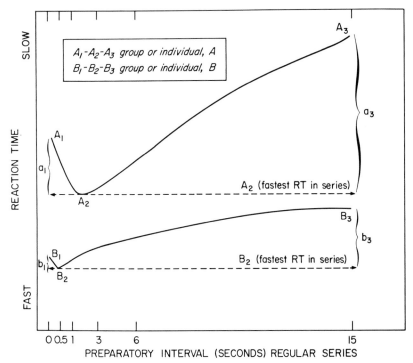

Figure 2. Hypothetical curves of reaction time as functions of the preparatory intervals of regular series. A_2 and B_2 are points of optimum reaction time of two groups or two individuals. A_1 and B_1, and A_3 and B_3, points of slow reaction time, reflect relatively poor states of set of the responders.

to quite a different RT than when the same PI is in regular series (Fig. 2). Not reflected in these Figs. is the frequent finding that if the PI's are of relatively short duration, then RT's associated with these PI's are quicker with regular series than with irregular series. If the PI's are relatively long, then RT's of regular series are similar to or longer than RT's of an irregular one. The exact PI-length in which this is the case is related to the type of sample of subjects tested. While the type of subject is a factor, the sense modality does not appear to be one. In Figure 3, it

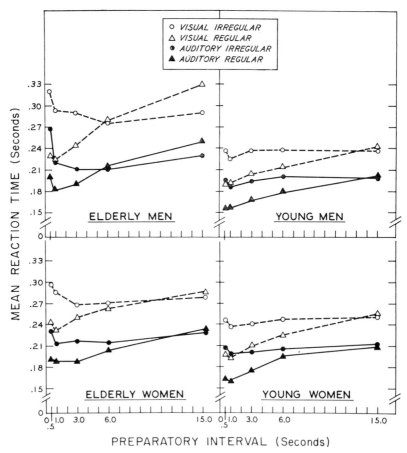

Figure 3. Reaction time as a function of the preparatory interval. For each sample population, the abscissa value at which the function of regular series crosses the function of irregular series, is approximately the same for visual reaction time as for auditory reaction time.

may be seen that the PI point of cross-over of regular and irregular curves is fairly constant for the particular subject group. What appears to be more and more clear with recent studies (e.g., Klemmer, 1956; Botwinick, Brinley, Birren, 1957; Karlin, 1959; Zahn, Rosenthal and Shakow, 1961; Drazin, 1961; Botwinick and Brinley, 1962 a, b) is that RT is not only a function of PI, but it is a function of PI *and* its context within a series, particularly within an irregular series.

The data of Figures 1 and 2, reflect some of the ideas of set which have been advanced throughout the years. Reviews of the literature have indicated the long history of this problem (Gibson, 1941; Botwinick, 1959) and it is not, therefore, necessary to review all the literature here. It is important for the present purpose, however, to indicate that the variation in RT due to PI and its context, has been attributed to variation in states of the responder, which have been referred to as set, expectancy, attentiveness, alertness, anticipation, and so on. In Figure 1, for example, RT at point A_1 would represent a poor state of set, while A_2 would represent an optimum set (for this series). Thus, what statements about neural conduction velocities of central mechanisms might be made in comparing A_2 with B_2, would be modified in comparing A_1 with B_1. Points A_2 and B_2 represent the optimum RT's often implicit in studies of neural conduction velocities. This is not to say that studies of neural conduction velocities may not appropriately be carried out with RT's of A_1 and B_1, but inferences need to be adjusted accordingly. The fact is, RT as a sum of neural transmission events, cannot be measured without also measuring transmission events as it is reflected in momentary states of set, arousal, etc.

As indicated, much of the literature has been reviewed elsewhere. In addition some interesting work is currently being carried out by T. Zahn (personal communication) and is not yet published. Thus, this is not the place for a comprehensive review, although some published studies not included in the reviews are reported here. Lacey and Lacey (1959) measured RT's of two samples of subjects differentiated on the basis of the extent of spontaneous fluctuations of the resting level of the EKG. The RT's were measured in relation to PI's of 3, 4 and 5 sec. The group with fewer spontaneous fluctuations was not only found to have slower RT's, but in terms of set, their responses to the PI of 5 sec. were especially slow—reflecting a difficulty in maintaining a set or an attentive state of alertness.

Drazin (1961) measured RT's to PI's which were varied with respect to the minimum PI in the series, the range of PI's in the series, and the probability of stimulus occurrence. The minimum PI that Darzin used was 0.125 sec. This value is probably as short, or shorter than has been reported up to date. In general, Drazin found that not only was RT a function of the PI, but it was a function of the previous PI in the series, and to a lesser extent, the second preceding PI. These findings are similar to those of Klemmer (1956). Drazin reported that when PI's were between 0.125 and 0.25 sec., the preceding PI did not appear related to RT. RT was found to vary inversely with the probability of stimulus occurrence. "The experimental finds are interpreted as evidence in favor of the view that RT reflects S's state of readiness for the stimulus" (p. 50).

Set has been described in terms of a variety of aspects—reaching, maintaining, developing, organizing, mobilizing, and others, and "the hypothesis that the various aspects of set are distinguishable, different in meaning, and independent was tested by principal component analyses" (Botwinick and Brinley, 1962 a, p. 568). RT's in relation to PI's in 6 different series were intercorrelated and subjected to the principal component analyses. Components of general RT level or RT set were found on which all PI's were substantially represented. Also, short-interval components were found which were independent of the general components. Although relatively small in the amount of overall variance accounted for, these short interval components suggested "ability to become set for quick response within short time durations . . . was independent of the one for quick response where the interval indexing set was longer" (p. 573). Analyses based on RT's of two sense modalities, suggested that set, as inferred from the relation between RT and PI, was independent of the sense modality.

Aging Studies

A previous review of the literature on set in relation to age (Botwinick, 1959, p. 748-752) included most of the published work. At least two studies, however, were published subsequent to the review, and these will be briefly described. Effort was directed toward testing four hypotheses. These hypotheses were that "with advanced age, more time is required to: 1) develop a state of optimum set, or to program response; 2) overcome the effects of inaccurate, overestimation of the time available to organize response; 3) respond in general, and that aspects of set are not independent of the over-all slowing processes, and 4) disengage attention from prior involvement with the signal . . ." (Botwinick and Brinley, 1962b, p. 300). For men, the second hypothesis was found tenable, the other hypotheses were not supported. For women, the data were quite different, introducing an unexpected element, and perhaps a worthy one for future test.

Another study was concerned with the concept of maintaining RT set, but the concept was defined as the point of cross-over for an RT curve of regular PI's and of irregular PI's. Set was said to be the better maintained, the longer the PI duration for which RT was faster in regular series than irregular series. It was concluded that set was maintained better by a younger group than an elderly one, and that while shock motivation lowered RT's, it had no effect on the set-phenomenon (Botwinick, Brinley, and Robbin, 1959).

Bio-Potential Wave Theory

In the previous section, the primary experimental manipulation was the duration of the PI which, although it is presumed to contribute to variations in states of arousal or set, does not presuppose any one physiological mechanism as antecedent (although it does not rule out any one either). In the present section, aspects or phases of different types of biopotential measures, principally EEG, have been investigated in relation to RT, and theory often directed to a particular part of the nervous system. As will be seen, the experimental manipulation of PI is crucial in these studies too (as it has to be due to the role of PI in RT), and thus the studies in this section are not necessarily best separated or dichotomized from those studies of the previous section. The distinguishing feature between them, however, is the clear effort in the present section to implicate a particular part of the c.n.s.

Taking the lead of Moruzzi and Magoun (1949), and others, Lansing, Schwartz and Lindsley (1959) discussed the EEG alpha blockade which occurs with sensory stimulation as a reflection of alerted states due to activation of the ascending projections of the reticular formation of the brain stem. They also discussed level of RT as a reflection of alerted states. With this background, they sought "to relate RT as a psychological or behavioral performance measure to EEG activation (alpha blockade), both measures reflecting a "neurophysiological index of alertness or attention" (p. 3). The method of their study included the measurement of RT under two general conditions which they labelled *alerted* and *non-alerted*. Operationally, the former condition involved an auditory warning signal preceding the visual reaction stimulus, and in the latter condition, no such warning signal was available to the responding subject. EEG's were recorded during the RT measurements.

Within the non-alerted condition, RT was not related to the state of alpha blockade. Within the alerted condition, the state of alpha blockade was related to level of RT, but it was also related to the duration of the PI. That is, Lansing, Schwartz and Lindsley (1959) found that the percent of alpha blocking was a function of the duration of the PI. Lansing, Schwartz and Lindsley wrote that "Since alpha blockade or EEG activation typically occurs within the same interval, both reduced RT and activation are believed to be identified with an alerted or attentive state produced through action of the ascending reticular activating system (ARAS) resulting from sensory stimulation and instructional set" (p. 6). Evidence for this belief would have been more convincing had RT been related to spontaneous blocking during the non-alerted RT condition. In addition, it is possible that although alpha blockade and reduced RT are both related to PI, they are not related to each other.

In an earlier paper, Lansing (1957) made an effort to determine whether the alpha cycle and RT are related. He measured visual RT's while recording the EEG of visual and motor cortex. Here, no warning signals appeared to be used (i.e., RT's were measured in a way comparable to the non-alerted RT condition of the later, 1959 paper). Lansing reported that "individual subject means for reaction time showed a definite correlation with individual subject means for blocking time. This suggests that the two measures may be dependent upon a common factor yet undetermined" (p. 504). Even here, however, RT showed "no clear phase to phase differences" when the six phases of the alpha cycle were considered. Mean RT was shortest with phase 1 of the occipital alpha cycle and longest with phase 5. The RT difference between these two phases was statistically significant.

A very similar result was found in relating RT to phases of the cardiac cycle of the EKG. Birren, Cardon and Phillips (1963) measured auditory RT of men and of women aged twenty to thirty years while EKG was recorded simultaneously. RT differences were not found across the four phases of the cycle, but RT differences were statistically significant in both sex samples between the quickest RT (associated with the P-phase) and the slowest RT (associated with the QRS-phase). Birren, Cardon and Phillips suggest that "cyclical changes in alerting are associated with both EEG and EKG."

Aspects of relations between RT and alpha EEG activity were also examined by Callaway (1961, 1962) and Callaway and Yeager (1960). In these studies, data were collected by a method of much technological sophistication. Rather than record the stimulus for RT and alpha activity simultaneously, as was done previously, reaction stimuli were automatically triggered by predetermined phases of the alpha rhythms. In a series of studies, it was seen that RT did appear to be related to the phase of the alpha cycle, but there was significant inter and intra-individual variability. These data suggest a common alerting mechanism for RT and for EEG patterns, but two items of information seem to mitigate such a conclusion. First, Callaway (1961) reported that, "We find a parallel between reaction time and alpha phase only when we use visual stimuli. Thus far we have been unable to demonstrate any variation in reaction time when auditory signals are presented at various phases of the alpha cycle" (p. 1184-1185). Second, stimulus intensity, while related to RT was not found to shift the alpha phase associated with slowest RT (Callaway, 1962). The information is mitigating of a conclusion of a mechanism common to both RT and reticular system arousal because it would suggest two mechanisms of RT —one for auditory stimulation and one for visual stimulation— perhaps a possible situation, but an unlikely one. Second, since RT is a function of stimulus intensity, the RT-alpha phase relation would be expected to shift with variations in stimulus intensity.

An interesting study of normal and schizophrenic subjects with somewhat puzzling results, was carried out by Fedio, Mirsky, Smith and Parry (1961). Using an auditory stimulus, not a visual one, they measured RT's with the same two conditions of Lansing, Schwartz and Lindsley (1959), i.e., with no warning signal (non-alerted condition) and with a warning signal (alerted condition). In addition, in the alerted condition Fedio *et al.* used two sub-conditions of PI duration (2 and 4 sec.). The alerted condition is the one where alpha of the EEG was experimentally blocked. In the non-alerted condition, Fedio *et al.* measured RT when alpha was present and when it was blocked spontaneously. Normal and schizophrenic subjects were matched for age, I.Q., level of education, and for RT ability without a warning signal.

With the non-alerted condition (no warning signal), mean *RT of the normal subjects was reliably quicker while alpha was present than while alpha was temporarily absent or spontaneously blocked.* This result, it would seem, is counter expectation on the basis of reticular activation theory if it is used to suggest that arousal or alert states underlie both quick RT and alpha block-ade. It is well to note here that although Lansing, Schwartz and Lindsley (1959) in the comparable experimental condition did not show statisticaly significant slowing with alpha present, they failed to show quicker RT's with spontaneous alpha blocking. Fedio *et al.* concluded that "spontaneous blockade is not as-sociated with *improved* performance. Apparently alpha activity may be spontaneously blocked for a variety of reasons which do not necessarily reflect increased readiness to respond to the task at hand." They also raised "some question about the validity of considering either spontaneous *or* evoked alpha blockade as evidence of behavioral arousal" (p. 925).

If their data of the schizophrenic subjects are disregarded, or considered as representing different relationships among the variables due to the very nature of the subject population, then the best RT's (of the normals) were found with the evoked alpha blockades. If the data of Fedio *et al.* were viewed in this way, then there would tend to be a corroboration of the findings and position of Lansing, Schwartz, and Lindsley (1959). However, it would still be necessary to regard the spontaneous alpha blocking as reflecting states of drowsiness or similar non-alert states, and it would still be important to evaluate the effect, if any, of variations in PI on extent of alpha blocking.

There have been efforts to relate RT to other measures of psycho-physiological response, without necessarily bringing to bear upon the data, theory in the formal sense. In the report by Miller, Pfaffmann, and Schlosberg (1962) of research in the U.S.S.R., there is this statement. "Reaction time varies from time to time. The cause of this variation has been unknown, but Roitbak thinks he has found one cause. Reaction time is associated with phases of breathing. During the inspiration phase, reaction time is shortened by as much as 100 milliseconds (visual or auditory RT), using a key pressure as a response. There seems to be no relation between RT and EEG" (p. 238).

Aging Studies

There have been two aging studies of this problem, both similar in content, and both by Surwillo (1961, 1963). Rather than the phase of the alpha cycle, Surwillo chose to measure the alpha period as a correlate of RT. The alpha period is an inverse function of the frequency of alpha cycles occurring between stimulus and response. In both studies the stimulus was auditory. The response was a verbalized "pow" in the earlier study (1961), and a key press in the more recent study (1963). No warning signal was provided (non-alert condition), but two types of conditions were used. Two sessions of RT involved irregular time intervals between successive stimulus presentations, each stimulus being presented for 3 seconds. The third session also included stimuli of 3 seconds duration, but the last series of stimuli were of only 0.3 sec. The subject was told about this condition which was used to maintain a "high-vigilance, high-motivation" level.

It was reported that for the data of the third session considered alone, mean RT's and mean alpha periods were computed for each subject. The Pearson product-moment correlation of these mean values was .72. Age was not highly correlated with RT ($r = .19$), and when age was partialled out from the RT-alpha period correlation, it remained substantially unchanged. When the RT-alpha period correlation was computed for each subject, the mean of this within-individual correlation was found to be only .41. With the data of all three sessions combined, the respective within-individual correlation dropped to .30. Surwillo (1963, p. 113) concluded that, taken as a whole, "the data support the hypothesis that the brain-wave cycle is the basic unit of time in terms of which a response is programmed by the central nervous system." "It appears, therefore, that frequency of the EEG is the central nervous system factor behind age-associated slowing in response time" (p. 112).

SUMMARY AND EVALUATION

Three theories explaining variations in RT, each referring to central nervous system contribution, were presented along with related literature. The literature was not meant to be comprehensive as a reiew, but illustrative of the theories that were represented. It should be made clear that some of the studies that were rviewed were carried out without regard to theory, and perhaps, the respective investigators would not agree that their studies might best be included in a theoretical context. Nevertheless, there is the clear expectation, even if only implicit, in all the studies, that functioning levels of central factors are antecedent or even causally responsible for levels of RT—and not the other way around.

The first theory presented was referred to as *nerve conduction theory*. Total, or behavioral RT is considered analyzable into component parts, and emphasis is directed to impulse transmission within the nervous system subsequent to input, and prior to response. There appears to be major difficulty with research representing this theory. Because it is so difficult to measure RT sequences of central nervous mechanisms, particularly of the brain itself, measurements most frequently tend to be of peripheral mechanisms. These measurements tend to account for a relatively small portion of total RT, and speed of neural transmission within central mechanisms is then implicated. Not only is the concept "central mechanism," or "central factor" vague, but in terms of speed of neural transmission, it is every far removed from the data. For example, we know that states of set, motivation, factors such as understanding instruction, learning, and so on affect RT. To refer to these as central factors is one thing— to discuss speed of neural transmission of these factors is another. What needs to be done by way of research in this area, is to vary states of set, and other central apects, to determine the optimum RT, and to measure component sequences during the varying conditions of the experiment. Subjects must be extremely well-trained and very practiced, and then inferences might be more tenable. The same holds for sub-human subjects, although here the experimental techniques are more difficult.

These criticisms are even more appropriate when populations, such as age groups, are compared. Typically, groups are compared on speed of conduction of peripheral neural sequences, and found either to not differ, or differ insufficiently to account for the group difference in total RT. Then, by default, from negative results, one group—an old one—is implicated with respect to loss of speed of neural transmission of central factors.

The studies involving nerve conduction theory are, in general, well thought out, and well carried out. What is lacking are the techniques to provide the data of more direct tests of central nervous system functioning. Newer techniques are becoming available, and at least one study, reported here, measured a central RT sequence. The conclusions of some of the studies on peripheral mechanisms and the theorizing related to them were compatible with the results of this study and it is not unlikely that this will be the case with future studies. A positive aspect of the theory and related studies is that the data are rooted very directly to the biology of the organism. Also, the data can be integrated with concepts and data of other related behavioral phenomena.

Set theory is the second theory that was presented. The major experimental manipulation of RT studies of set is the PI and its context. Studies of this group can contribute to those of nerve conduction. As indicated, better controls of states of set can provide the investigator with a variety of conditions, including one of optimum RT for each subject. RT's for each condition of set may then be analyzable into component sequences, giving a clearer understanding of speed of nerve conduction of central mechanisms.

Set theory suffers from a major problem which almost amounts to a tautology—good set becomes almost synonomous with fast RT, and poor set with slow RT. In operational terms, the state of set is defined as the relation between RT and the PI, including its context. Thus, it is possible to discard concepts pertaining to states of the organism, and describe RT in purely non-theoretical, experimental, manipulative terms. In so doing, however, we negate, or at least overlook, the fact that the responding organism is faster or slower because of something occurring within—something related to the PI condition. While it may be questionable that this something within is best described as "set," it is clear that in describing it in terms of organism, rather than apparatus, we may hope to find physiological correlates. And, even on a purely behavioral level, in describing RT changes in terms of set, even when related to PI and context, we may make effort to manipulate set, as for example, by instruction, keeping constant the operations of PI and context.

Biopotential wave theory, the third theory that was discussed, may not really be conceptually different from set theory, but it is distinguishable by the fact that experimental measurements include physiological recordings, principaly the EEG, and that a particular c.n.s. mechanism is thought to underlie arousal, alertness, set, etc. Alpha blockade, in response to sensory stimulation, is believed to be a reflection of alerted states of the organism due to activation of the ascending projections of the reticular formation of the brain stem. By hypothesis, alerted states of the organism are expected to be related to fast RT, and non-alerted states to slow RT. The data are, in general, supporting of the hypothesis, but also mitigating of it. Alpha is blocked experimentally by providing the subject with a warning signal of the PI. Per cent alpha is related to duration of PI. Thus, when RT is found to be a function of per cent alpha blockade, it is confounded with PI. That is, the operation of PI variation both leads to alpha blockade and to RT reduction. Investigators have concluded that both these aspects are related to a common mechanism. This may be, but it may also be that they are independent aspects of the organism, each related to PI, but not co-related to reticular formation activation, or any other mechanism. Supporting this conclusion are the data of RT measurements with spontaneous alpha blocking. Here, RT is not at all related to the state of alpha.

The common mechanism hypothesis does receive support from those studies that successfully indicate relation between RT and phases of the alpha cycle. The relationship as reported, however, appears variable, and not necessarily of great extent. This would suggest that even if a common alerting mechanism were involved, other mechanisms, common or otherwise, play an important role in RT.

The three theories are complementary, and perhaps, may even be regarded as three aspects of one comprehensive theory. Total RT is analyzable into component sequences—the central mechanism sequences are further analyzable into subparts—one subpart involves set—and set is an arousal mechanism which is activated by reticular formation, due to sensory stimulation, and reflected in alpha blockade. This, perhaps, is overly simple and neat, but it does provide a unitary framework.

REFERENCES

Birren, J. E., Cardon, P. V., Jr. and Phillips, Shirley L.: (1963) Reaction time as a function of cardiac cycle in young adults. *Science, 140:*195-196.

Birren, J. E. and Wall, P. D.: (1956) Age changes in conduction velocity, refractory period, number of fibers, connective tissue space and blood vessels in sciatic nerve of rats. *J. Comp. Neurol., 104:*1-16.

Botwinick, J.: (1959) Drives, expectancies and emotions. In J. E. Birren, ed., *Handbook of Aging and the Individual,* Chicago, U. of Chicago Press, 739-768.

Botwinick, J. and Brinley, J. F.: (1962a) Analysis of set in relation to reaction time. *J. Exp. Psychol., 63:*568-574.

Botwinick, J. and Brinley, J. F.: (1962b) Aspects of RT set during brief intervals in relation to age and sex. *J. Geront., 17:*295-301.

Botwinick, J., Brinley, J. F. and Birren, J. E.: (1957) Set in relation to age. *J. Geront., 12:*300-305.

Botwinick, J., Brinley, J. F. and Robbin, J. S.: (1959) Maintaining set in relation to motivation and age. *Amer. J. Psychol., 72:*585-588.

Callaway, E.: (1961) Day-to-Day variability in relationship between electroencephalographic alpha phase and reaction time to visual stimuli. *Ann. N. Y. Acad. Sci., 92:*1183-1186.

Callaway, E.: (1962) Factors influencing the relationship between alpha activity and visual reaction time. *Electroenceph. Clin. Neurophysiol., 14:*674-682.

Callaway, E. and Yeager, C. L.: (1960) Relationship between reaction time and electroencephalographic alpha phase. *Science, 132:*1765-1766.

Crossman, E. R. F. W.: (1955) The measurement of discriminability. *Quart. J. Exp. Psychol., 7:*176-195.

Crossman, E. R. F. W. and Szafran, J.: (1956) Changes with age in the speed of information intake and discrimination. *Experientia, Supplementum IV.,* Symposium on Experimental Gerontology, Basel Berkhausen, pp. 128-135.

Davis, R.: (1957) The human operator as a single channel information system. *Quart. J. Exp. Psychol., 9:*119-129.

Drazin, D. H.: (1961) Effects of foreperiod, foreperiod variability, and probability of stimulus occurrence on simple reaction time. *J. Exp. Psychol., 62:1,* 43-50.

Fedio, P., Mirsky, A. F., Smith, W. J. and Parry, D.: (1961) Reaction time and EEG activation in normal and schizophrenic subjects. *Electroenceph. Clin. Neurophysiol., 13:*923-926.

Gibson, J. J.: (1941) A critical review of the concept of set in contemporary experimental psychology. *Psychol. Bull., 38:*781-817.

Gregory, R. L.: (1956) An experimental treatment of vision as an information source and noisy channel. In C. Cherry, ed., *Information Theory: 3d London Symposium 1955,* London, Methuen & Co.

Gregory, R. L. and Cane, Violet: (1955) A statistical information theory of visual thresholds. *Nature, 176:*1272.

Hügin, F., Norris, A. H. and Shock, N. W.: (1960) Skin reflex and voluntary reaction times in young and old males. *J. Geront., 15:*388-391.

Karlin, L.: (1959) Reaction time as a function of foreperiod duration and variability. *J. Exp. Psychol., 58:*185-191.

Klemmer, E. T.: (1956) Time uncertainty in simple reaction time. *J. Exp. Psychol., 51:*179-84.

Lacey, J. T. and Lacey, B. C.: (1958) The relationship of resting autonomic activity to motor impulsivity. *The Brain and Human Behavior,* Baltimore, Williams and Wilkins, pp. 144-207.

Lansing, R. W.: (1957) Relation of brain and tremor rhythms to visual reaction time. *Electroenceph. Clin. Neurophysiol., 9:*497-504.

Lansing, R. W., Schwartz, E. and Lindsley, D. B.: (1959) Reaction time and EEG activation under alerted and nonalerted conditions. *J. Exp. Psychol.*, 58:1-7.

Magladery, J. W.: (1959) Neurophysiology of aging. In J. E. Birren, ed. *Handbook of aging and the individual.* Chicago, U. Chicago Press, pp. 173-186.

Miller, N., Pfaffmann, C. and Schlosberg, H.: (1962) Aspects of psychology and psychophysiology in the U.S.S.R. In *Some views on Soviet Psychology.* Washington, D. C., Amer. Psychol. Ass., Inc., pp. 189-252.

Moruzzi, G. and Magoun, H. W.: (1949) Brain stem reticular formation and activation of the EEG. *Electroenceph. Clin. Neurophysiol.*, 1:455-473.

Norris, A. H., Shock, N. W. and Wagman, G. H.: (1953) Age changes in the maximum conduction velocity of motor fibers of human ulnar nerves. *J. Appl. Physiol.*, 5:589-593.

Surwillo, W.: (1961) Frequency of the alpha rhythm, reaction time, and age. *Nature, 191:*823-824.

Surwillo, W.: (1963) The relation of simple response time to brain-wave frequency and the effects of age. *Electroenceph. Clin. Neurophysiol.*, 15:105-114.

Wayner, M. J. and Emmers, R.: (1958) Spinal synaptic delay in young and aged rats. *Amer. J. Physiol.*, 194:2:403-405.

Welford, A. T.: (1952) The "psychological refractory period" and the timing of high-speed performance—a review and a theory. *Brit. J. Psychol.*, 43:2-19.

Welford, A. T.: (1959) Psychomotor performance. In J. E. Birren, ed.: *Handbook of aging and the individual.* Chicago, U. Chicago Press, pp. 562-613.

Zahn, T. P., Rosenthal, D. and Shakow, D.: (1961) Reaction time in normal and schizophrenic subjects in relation to the sequence of series of regular preparatory intervals. *J. Abnorm. Soc. Psychol.*, 63:161-168.

7

IMMEDIATE MEMORY, AGE AND BRAIN FUNCTION*

James Inglis

T his paper, unlike most of the other contributions to this volume, will not be directly concerned with age changes in the speed of behaviour. Studies of the role of immediate memory may not even prove to be indirect relevance to the main topic: there does not, in fact, seem to be any crucial evidence which would rule out the notion that speed and storage capacity may vary quite independently as age advances. Nevertheless, there is now sufficient information at hand to suggest that immediate memory processes play quite a central part in many of the behavioral changes that take place with age. Consideration of these processes, therefore, at least seems worthy of being placed side by side with the discussion of speed if only to prepare the way for the evaluation of any significant relations which may now, or may eventually, be traced between them.

By way of illustration one might compare human behaviour to a rather complex tapestry which, it is acknowledged, becomes worn and frayed with the passage of time. We can, it would seem, at present disentangle only some of the more obvious threads which go to composing the total picture. We may find that each

* The studies by the author and his associates described in this paper were, for the most part, carried out with the assistance of Canadian National Health Grants Administration Mental Health Grants (Projects 605-5-285 and 605-5-340). This aid is most gratefully acknowledged.

of these is woven into many different parts of the whole pattern. In some cases we can discern common elements if only because certain areas appear to show a similar susceptibility to the effects of age. It remains to be seen if we can trace more minutely the contribution of particular elements to the overall design and even tease out the subtler composition of the more important strands.

Speed of function, to which this volume is mainly devoted, is, of course, one such element. One other strand which it seems possible to trace in various parts of the design is learning ability. This paper will simply try to point to some areas of wear in the fabric of behaviour where this second element seems to figure and then try to discern some of its component parts.

In anticipation it may be stated, firstly, that the areas of behaviour change with age where some parts of the learning process seem to have an important influence probably range wider than is commonly emphasized. Secondly, the functional properties of the learning process which seem to be principally affected by age involve an increased rate of "trace-decay" and an increased susceptibility to "interference," both being aspects of short-term storage or immediate memory function.

Support for these contentions may be secured both from studies of normal ageing and from investigations of pathological ageing or senility. Since the evidence from these two sources has seldom been brought together it seems worth while to cite some of the relevant data, as follows:

DIVERSE PERFORMANCES WHICH MAY BE RELATED TO CHANGES IN LEARNING ABILITY

No attempt will be made here at a complete review of all the studies in any particular field, the material cited is intended to be representative rather than comprehensive.

Intelligence

The effect of ageing upon intelligence scores is well illustrated by the data gathered by Doppelt and Wallace (1955) from their Kansas City sample of 475 persons aged sixty and over. When these are considered together with the results obtained from the younger standardization groups, different kinds of "intellectual trajectory" may be plotted. These phenomena are familiar enough. Verbal ability proves to be relatively stable, but decreasing Performance Scale ability is associated with increasing years. Even greater differences between results on the same two scales have been reported for another elderly sample by Eisdorfer and Cohen (1961).

Inferences about some of the functions underlying decreasing Performance Scale scores may be drawn from various kinds of evidence. At first sight it might seem that because Performance Scale items are timed, speed could be the important factor in this age decrement. Doppelt and Wallace (1955), however, found little difference in their elderly subjects' accomplishments within the standard time limits and with unlimited time.

One might speculate, however, as others including Cattell (1943) have already done, that in responding to the Verbal Scale the subject is engaged in running off sequences of old learning whose initiation does not require him to hold in mind any very complex instructions. In the case of the Performance Scale, on the other hand, a fairly long set of instructions typically precedes each test and, in addition, more novel response patterns are required for the successful solution of the items themselves. It seems possible, therefore, that one important function underlying decline with age on these items is a progressive decrease in some aspect of learning capacity.

Evidence in support of this notion may be taken, in the first instance, from some of the correlational studies which have been carried out on the WAIS data. Cohen (1957), for example, found that factor analysis of the correlations between the subtests produced five factors (these he labelled: A for Verbal Comprehension; B Perceptual Organization; C Memory; D and E were left unlabelled). A fair amount of factorial invariance was shown for groups between the ages of eighteen and fifty-four. For the group aged sixty and over, however, a change seemed to occur in intellectual organization, with an increase in the amount of variance accounted for by the memory factor. Perhaps an analogy from visual acuity might be used to elucidate this kind of change in factorial structure. Thus, in the case of normally sighted persons simple visual capacity probably does not account for any of the variance on a performance test of intelligence since, beyond a certain threshold value, increase in acuity would not create any advantage. In the case of the partially sighted, however, vision might come to play an important role in the differential perception of cues which would aid performance; with the blind, of course, being unable to perform at all. This point has previously been made in general terms by Welford (1958) who has suggested that, in some skills, "Achievement is independent of potential capacity until this falls to a point at which it becomes the limiting factor. Beyond this point achievement shows a functional dependence upon the capacity concerned" (Welford, 1958, p. 5).

Unfortunately for the content, if not the form, of the present argument it must be noted that Riegel and Riegel (1962) have failed to confirm the kind of changes in factorial structure reported by Cohen (1957).

However this may be, it is the case that in another factorial study of the WAIS standardization data, in which age and education were also included as variables, Birren and Morrison (1961) showed that, in addition to a general factor, not associated with age, there was extracted a second component which proved to be intimately related to age, even when the influence of education was held constant. It is of especial interest that these investigators found that many of the Verbal Scale items were positively related to the age component and that all the Performance Scale items were negatively related to it. The largest positive relation was with the Vocabulary subtest, the greatest negative association was with the Digit Symbol item. If it were the case that a learning component was involved, then it could be argued that this apparent bipolarity might reflect the age-related increasing actualization of an age-related decreasing potential. In other words, while what has been already learned and stored continues to increase with age, what is capable of being further learned and stored at the same time diminishes with advancing years.

It is certainly the case that when memory-disordered elderly psychiatric patients are compared with non-memory disordered controls (Inglis, 1957; Inglis, 1959a; Inglis and Sanderson, 1961; Caird and Inglis, 1961) it can be shown that, even when these groups are matched for Verbal Scale scores, there is a consistent and significant deficit in the Performance Scale Scores of the memory-disordered. In one study (Inglis, 1957) it appeared that the actual size of the discrepancy between the Verbal and Performance Scales in the memory-disordered group was related to the amount of impairment they showed on a learning test. It did not, however, prove possible to repeat this result (Inglis, 1959a).

It seems, then, that alterations in learning ability may have some part to play in the changes in quite general intellectual functions which are associated with age and with senile pathology. This relation can probably be even more clearly traced in studies of more restricted cognitive activity.

Conceptual Ability

In his studies of changes of aspects of cognitive ability with age Bromley (1956) has, among other measures, used the Shaw test (Bromley, 1955) of creative thinking. This is essentially a test of conceptual function, employing four wooden blocks so constructed as to be capable of being arranged in a number of different series, some "abstract," and hence satisfactory, others less so. Bromley (1956) has shown that, according to his criteria, both the quantity and quality of the responses to this test fall off from the age decade twenty to thirty. The effect of holding intelligence constant was to lower the apparent association between age and reduced quantity and quality of output. Bromley has related these results to a diminution in the ability to develop new skills and concepts with age.

Talland (1961) has also examined the relation between age and concept attainment. He divided the kinds of concepts to be attained in one experiment into a sequential and a spatial type and showed that the former kind of problem was more seriously affected by age than the latter. He states that, "It is proposed that ability to attain the two types of concept changed with age at different rates because one task did and the other did not require the storage of strings of items in an ordered sequence, and that aging gradually reduces man's capacity for the short-term retention of this kind of information" (Talland, 1961, p. 210).

Evidence of a relation between even more extreme conceptual

dysfunction and memory disorder in elderly patients was first produced by Cameron (1939). He showed that of a group of six senile patients who gave clinical evidence of severe memory disorder, none was able to perform adequately on the Hanfmann-Kasanin (1937) sorting test of conceptual ability.

A further connection between memory disorder, ability on such conceptual tasks and also performance on the Wechsler scale, was demonstrated by Cleveland and Dysinger (1944) who found that the disability shown by memory disordered elderly patients in their handling of the Goldstein-Scheerer (1941) sorting test was associated with low scores on the Performance Scale relative to scores on the Verbal Scale of the intelligence test.

The present author (Inglis, 1959a) has shown that poor ability on the Shaw test may also be associated with Wechsler Verbal-Performance discrepancies and with learning defect in elderly psychiatric patients.

There is thus evidence connecting the kind of Verbal-Performanc differences previously discussed, with data on impairment of conceptual ability. There is also evidence to connect both of these, in turn, with that diminution in learning ability which seems to take place with increasing age and which reaches pathological proportions in cases of senile memory disorder.

The evidence for a decrease in learning ability with age can, of course, be adduced from studies directly involving the learning process itself.

Learning

It would seem quite unnecessary to labour the points which may be made under this heading. A growing body of evidence shows that, for example, performance on rote learning tasks becomes less adequate as age advances and this deficit becomes enormous in cases of so-called "senile dementia."

Bromley (1958) gave, among other items, a rote learning test involving the serial anticipation of nonsense syllables to 256 normal men and women between the ages of seventeen and eighty-two years. He concluded from his results that ageing impairs rote learning, especially in the later years.

A number of studies by the present author and his associates (summarized by Inglis, 1959b, and Caird, Sanderson and Inglis, 1961) have shown that an important component of senile disorder lies in the breakdown of learning ability. A very simple paired-associate learning test can discriminate between memory-disordered and non memory-disordered elderly psychiatric patients. The memory disordered perform so poorly in this kind of task, even when they are matched on Verbal Scale intelligence with control subjects, that the learning scores of the two groups barely overlap.

Having tried to trace the element of learning which seems to show as a common thread in various parts of the changing pattern of human behaviour, the question remains as to what may be the likely functional aspects of learning ability which seem principally to be affected by age and senility.

FUNCTIONAL PROPERTIES OF LEARNING ABILITY WHICH MAY BE PRINCIPALLY AFFECTED BY AGE AND SENILITY

In his dissection of the essential aspects of learning and memory function Welford (1958) has described seven crucial phases. These comprise, perception, short-term storage, evolution of a durable trace, the endurance of such a trace, recognition, recall or retrieval and, finally, the use of recalled material. Many of these stages overlap. Welford has pointed out, for example, that the second stage of short-term retention may often encroach upon, and, indeed, often be essential for completion of, comprehension at the first, perceptual, stage. Welford (1956) has also stressed the likely importance of short-term retention and has argued that the key to understanding many of the performance decrements associated with age may lie in a better knowledge of the processes underlying this stage. Quite evidently, if we may regard the several phases which he has described as being sequential then any breakdown in the system at this point could disrupt the whole later succession of the learning process.

There is, in fact, a good deal of evidence which indicates that the stage of short-term retention has characteristics which are affected by age and pathology, these include trace decay, and susceptibility to interference.

Trace Decay

The decay of the immediate memory trace with time in young, normal subjects has been demonstrated by a number of investigators. Conrad (1957), for example, has shown that when such subjects were required to listen to tape-recorded 8-digit number series at a speed of either 30 or 90 digits per minute, and their recall was also paced at one or other of these speeds, then the longer the delay the worse the recall.

When the influence of age was taken into account in the same kind of experimental situation Fraser (1958) showed that while there was no difference between a younger (18-29) group and an older (30-55) group in their recall performance at fast rates of digit presentation and reproduction, there was a difference between them at slow rates. The performance of the younger group was itself affected by the slow rates relative to the fast, but the performance of the older group was even more impaired at the slow speeds. It can therefore be concluded that the rate of decay of immediate memory tends to increase with age.

Results of an investigation by Inglis and Caird (1963b) suggest that memory-disordered patients are, in turn, even more affected than elderly patients without memory disorder when delays are introduced in the presentation or reproduction of such digit series.

Taken together, then, these results suggest that the storage process underlying immediate memory is subject to decay with time; that as age advances such decay becomes more rapid and that in the pathological conditions of senility characterized by memory-disorder, such trace decay takes place at an even faster rate.

Interference

Again in the case of young normal subjects, Conrad (1959), for example, has shown that the interpolation of a task *between* the presentation and recall of digits impairs performance. Broadbent and Heron (1962) have shown that older people are more susceptible to the effects of distraction on short-term memory than are younger subjects.

Cameron (1943) had previously shown that patients suffering from senile memory disorder are probably even worse affected by a distracting task inserted between the presentation and recall of digit series.

These results, then, suggest that the short-term storage process underlying immediate memory is susceptible to interference when distracting material is intruded between the presentation and the recall of the data to be reproduced. As age advances this storage system becomes increasingly sensitive to interference and this susceptibility is even more exaggerated in those pathological conditions of the aged characterized by memory disorder.

The technique of simultaneous stimulation developed by Broadbent (1957) appears to engage short-term storage and to involve both the trace decay and interference phenomena together. Broadbent's method has been used by the present author and his associates to examine the effects both of age and senility on immediate memory with apparently quite consistent results.

The method of dichotic stimulation is probably now so familiar as not to require extended description. Briefly, spoken digits are recorded on separate channels of a single magnetic tape in such a way that different digits may be played back simultaneously to both ears. Given the appropriate temporal relationships, subjects commonly recall all the digits which were read into one ear before going on to recall the numbers heard in the other ear. It has therefore been suggested by Broadbent (1958) that the material recalled second in series may be regarded as having been held in some short-term storage process while the material first recalled has only passed through some kind of perceptual system.

It may be, however, that a slightly simpler model can account for the data at least as well. On this view *both* half-spans have entered (different) storage systems, but the half-span recalled second has been held in storage for a much longer period of time.

Suppose, for the sake of illustration, three digits have been read into each ear and these have both been delivered *and* recalled at the rate of one per second. Suppose further that the time required for the actual enunciation of each digit is negligible. Reflection will show that, under these circumstances, each item of the half-span recalled first will have been retained for an *equal* length of time and be recalled without the interpolation of material *between* presentation and reproduction. The digits recalled second, however, will have been held *longer*. Furthermore the reproduction of the first half-set will have intervened between the administration and recall of the second half-set, thus creating some degree of interference.

Let us suppose that the digits 1_R, 2_R, and 3_R were presented to the right ear and recalled first while, at the same time, the digit 1_L, 2_L, and 3_L were presented to the left ear and recalled second. The digit 1_R will, under the conditions specified, have been in the storage system associated with the right ear for the time taken for its own delivery (negligible), plus the time taken between its own delivery and the presentation of 2_R (one second), plus the time between 2_R and 3_R (one second), plus the time between the presentation of 3_R and the recall of 1_R (one second), this amounts to some three seconds in all. The digit 2_R will have been in the same storage system for as long as its own delivery (negligible), plus the time between its own delivery and the presentation of 3_R (one second), plus the time between the presentation of 3_R and the recall of 1_R (one second), plus the time between the recall of 1_R and 2_R (one second), again making three seconds in all. By analogy, the digit labelled 3_R will also have been in the storage system for the same length of time.

The first digit of the set recalled second (1_L) will, however, have been in storage for slightly longer than the length of time it has taken to complete *all* of the previous cycle. Counting from just after the negligible time for the delivery of 1_R, this comprises the time between the delivery of 1_R and 2_R (one second), between 2_R and 3_R (one second), between 3_R and the reproduction of 1_R (one second), between the reproduction of 1_R and 2_R (one second), between 2_R and 3_R (one second), and between 3_R and 1_L (one second), making six seconds in all. The digit labelled 2_L will have been in storage for the same length of time as will digit 3_L.

Broadbent's (1958) view is that the material recalled second has passed through a storage process subject to decay, whereas the material recalled first has merely gone through a "perceptual system." It seems equally plausible to suggest, on the above reasoning, that the greater number of errors noted, even in the performance of young normal subjects, in the recall of the second half-spans is due to the fact that this material has, in each case, spent at least twice as much time in a holding system as has the material recalled first. The material recalled second has also been subject to the interference caused by the reproduction of the first half-span while the second was itself being held.

It would thus be expected that if the trace decay is speeded up with age and even more accelerated in cases of memory disorder, and if age causes increased sensitivity to the interference effect, this also being even greater in cases of memory disorder, then there should be quite characteristic and predictable effects of age and senility on responses to simultaneous stimulation. In terms of the notions discussed, it would be anticipated that as age advances the greatest impairment should be shown in the half-spans recalled second. This defect should also be exaggerated in the case of memory-disordered elderly patients.

An experimental test conducted by this technique has an advantage over many other means for the investigation of learning, in that a *differential* decline is predicted in the performance elicited by two aspects of a single kind of material delivered at precisely the same point in time. It would therefore be difficult to explain any differences found between age groups or diagnostic groups as being due, say, to differences in motivation, or the like (Jerome, 1959).

The data to be presented here have been secured from four separate studies. The first of these (Inglis and Caird, 1963a) was designed to examine, by the means already discussed, any changes that might be shown by normal subjects as age advances. The second study (Inglis and Mackay, 1963) is simply a replication of the first. The third study (Inglis and Sanderson, 1961) was concerned with differences between memory-disordered and non memory-disordered elderly psychiatric patients. The fourth study (Caird and Inglis, 1961) mainly involved a replication of the third.

The subjects in the first study comprised 120 people between the ages of eleven and seventy. There were twenty subjects in each decade group, ten male and ten femal. In the second study there were 160 persons between the ages of eleven and ninety, and the decade groups were similarly composed. It should be admitted at the outset that these subjects were drawn from the community haphazardly rather than systematically or even randomly. All these groups, however, were matched in terms of mean orthodox digit span forward score. They were then given the dichotic digits to reproduce, there being from one to six digits per half-span.

The differences between the groups on the first and second half-spans were assessed by means of trend analysis (Edwards, 1960). The findings for the two studies may be shown in the form of graphs, as in Figures 1 and 2.

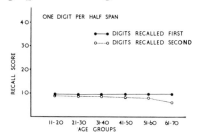
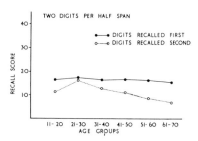
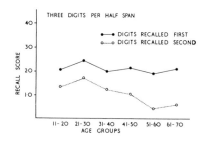
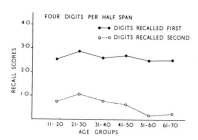
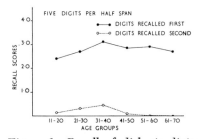
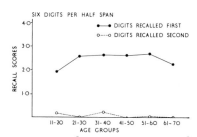

Figure 1. Recall of dichotic digits by age groups eleven to seventy with from one to six digits per half-set. (After Inglis and Caird, 1963.)

The results of these two experiments, conducted upon different subjects by different experimenters can be seen to be in remarkably close accord. The plots very clearly show the effects of increasing age on the dichotic digit half-spans of different lengths. As age increases there is no significant impairment in the ability to recall the half-spans reproduced first. Progressively and significantly greater difficulty is, on the other hand, shown in the reproduction of the second half-spans. Furthermore the longer the

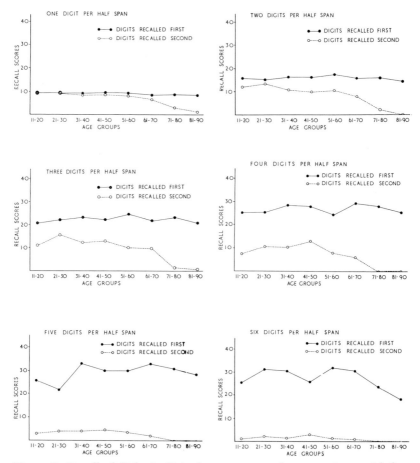

Figure 2. Recall of dichotic digits by age groups eleven to ninety with from one to six digits per half-set. (After Inglis and MacKay, 1963.)

span to be recalled the greater the difference, overall, between the first and second half-spans.

These results confirm in quite striking fashion Welford's (1956) suggestion that short-term memory storage deteriorates with age.

The effect of memory-disorder in elderly patients on the same kind of performance has also been examined in two studies, again carried out by different investigators on different subjects. In each case fifteen elderly patients with memory disorder were matched with fifteen without memory disorder on such variables as age and Wechsler Verbal Scale intelligence. The recall of the two types of patient on the first and second half-spans of different lengths can be seen in Figures 3 and 4.

Once more there emerges a close agreement between the two sets of results and expectation. In both studies the memory-disordered patients show impaired ability in the second half-spans recalled, which have, by hypothesis, been most subject to time decay and interference. It is also worth noting that significant

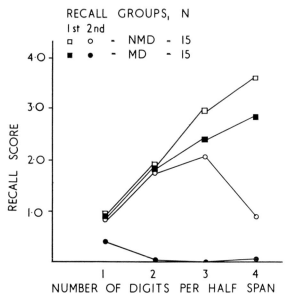

Figure 3. Recall of dichotic digits by memory-disordered and non-memory-disordered elderly patients. (After Inglis and Sanderson, 1961.)

differences also appear between these groups on the first half-spans recalled as these get longer (e.g., 3 and 4 digits). This fact might be interpreted as support for the notion that both half-sets go into storage under rather different circumstances.

Such findings do not, of course, exclude the possibility that other, concurrent but independent, functions may become progressively less efficient, or even break down altogether, as a result of age or disease; nevertheless, the implication of these findings seems to be that the process shown is probably one of some importance for ongoing adjustment. If a link in the learning process is broken at this point then the whole subsequent chain or sequence of learning may be disrupted. It may not be too much of an exaggeration to suppose that the diminished efficiency of this kind of short-term store might underly some of the intellectual impairment associated with ageing, and its complete breakdown may contribute largely to the severe memory disorder and disorientation seen in the psychoses of senility.

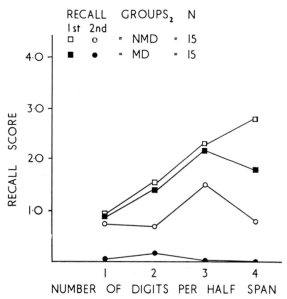

Figure 4. Recall of dichotic digits by memory-disordered and non-memory-disordered elderly patients. (After Caird and Inglis, 1961.)

STORAGE PROCESSES, BRAIN FUNCTION AND AGE

At the neurophysiological level, too, there seems to be a growing body of agreement (Delafresnaye, 1961; Deutsch, 1962; Schmitt, 1963) that the substrate of learning involves, as two important stages, a pre-consolidation phase and a consolidated phase. These would seem to be the equivalent of two of the seven phases described by Welford (1958), namely the stages of short-term retention and the evolution of an enduring trace.

Evidence that various kinds of extrinsically induced disturbances of the pre-consolidation phase can interfere with more permanent learning comes from a number of sources. Glickman (1961) and Caird (1963) have summarized much of the relevant literature, part of which may be briefly reviewed under the following heads.

Head Injury

In their survey of 1,029 cases of head injury Russell and Nathan (1946) found that in only about 13 percent was there no report of retrograde amnesia, or failure of memory for events preceding trauma. In about 67 percent of cases amnesia was reported for events occurring from a few seconds to thirty minutes before injury. In another 13 percent there was retrograde amnesia for a longer duration than thirty minutes. Records were not available for the remainder. Russell (1959) has argued that since recent memory is more affected by brain injury than is remote memory, this phenomenon must be closely linked with the physiology of remembering. Memories, he suggests, become more strongly established with time; the more recent they are the more liable to traumatic extinction.

These findings might be interpreted in the light of Hebb's (1949) hypothesis that short-term memory may be maintained by electrical activity in complex reverberatory neuronal circuits. Repeated excitation of these circuits leads to permanent, structural changes in the interconnection of neuronal pathways, thus constituting long-term retention. It may be supposed that generalized head-injury has its principal effect upon the preconsolidation phase, resulting in the clinical state of retrograde traumatic amnesia. The electrophysiological disturbances which follow upon cortical insult could presumably swamp the activity of the discrete circuits carrying the impulses of the short-term storage phase, and hence disrupt later recall.

Electro-convulsive Treatment (ECT)

It has been pointed out by Campbell (1961) in his review of the psychological effects of electroshock that, despite the very frequent psychiatric use of ECT, very few good systematic studies of its effects on learning ability have been reported.

One of these few studies, by Zubin and Barrera (1940), showed that shock diminishes recall of previously learned paired associates. In their study the original learning took place either in the morning or the evening of the day before ECT was given. Shock was given the next morning and then relearning took place the following afternoon. It appeared that the more recent learning of the treated group was the more affected when their relearning was compared with the performance of a control group who had not had ECT.

Cronholm and Molander (1961) have also studied the effects of ECT on the retention of material learned one hour before shock was administered. Their subjects were then retested six hours after ECT. The learning performance of this group was significantly worse than that of a matched, non-shocked control group.

It is Hebb's (1949) view that ECT also creates a kind of hypersynchrony which might "pick up" any neuronal activity which is not structurally embedded in cell-assemblies, and so lower intellectual competence, presumably by interfering with the functional activities of the stage of short-term storage.

The probability seems to be, therefore, that ECT like head injury, if it intervenes between learning and later recall, disturbs the preconsolidation phase and so interferes with long-term retention.

Anaesthesia

It has been reported in a study by Steinberg and Summerfield (1957) that the acquisition of new learning by male students was affected by the inhalation of 3 percent nitrous oxide in oxygen during the learning phase. Summerfield and Steinberg (1957), on the other hand, also found that nitrous oxide administered twelve and one-half minutes *after* learning actually reduced forgetting. It could be argued that when anesthesia is given during learning it affects the pre-consolidation phase but that when it is administered after learning has been consolidated it then serves to prevent the further acquisition of new, interfering responses.

Pauling (1961) has put forward the view, analogous in many ways to Hebb's (1949) notions, that more permanent learning takes place by an alteration in the material brain brought about through the action of electrical patterns which constitute what he calls "ephemeral memory." Such ephemeral memory, he maintains, consists of shifting electrical impulses in the brain carried by ions and groups of proteins. Some anaesthetics, Pauling suggests, cause the formation of hydrate microcrystals which both trap these electrically charged particles and block off synaptic transmission.

Again it might be claimed that the effects of anaesthesia on learning may depend, in part at least, upon influencing the pre-consolidation stage, or phase of ephemeral memory.

A study carried out by Caird, Laverty and Inglis (1963) attempted to conjoin Pauling's view of the role of electrical conduction in ephemeral memory with Hebb's notions concerning reverberatory neural circuits. If anaesthetics can produce a reduction in the adequacy of these basic electrical processes and if an already existing inadequacy underlies the learning disability of memory-disordered patients, then these patients, it was argued, should show a greater susceptibility to the effects of anaesthetics and thus also show lower sedation and sleep thresholds than should matched controls. This expectation was, in fact, upheld when these latter thresholds were estimated by administering sodium amytal intravenously to ten elderly psychiatric patients with memory-disorder and their performance compared with that of ten elderly patients without memory disorder.

There is, then, evidence that a number of extrinsic factors, including trauma, electroshock and anaesthesia, can disturb the short-term storage phase of the learning process and so lead to

what is evinced clinically as disorder of memory. What the intrinsic effects of age and senile pathology may be that produce
learning disturbances analogous to, and often even more severe
than, these means is still unknown. To talk of increased rate of
trace decay and increased susceptibility to interference is to be
rather more descriptive than explanatory.

There are investigators, like Katz and Halstead (1950) and
Cameron (1963) who believe that the answer to this latter problem may best be sought at the macromolecular level, in protein
systems and nucleic acids, respectively. Cameron and Solyom
(1961) have claimed some success in an attempt to improve
memory deficit in elderly patients by the oral and intravenous administration of ribonucleic acid. As yet, however, there seems to
be no precisely, or testably, formulated hypothesis concerning
the actual effect of age upon such molecular substrates. Cameron
(1963) has noted that one of his associates, S. Sved, has found
evidence of elevated levels of ribonuclease (the enzyme which
breaks down ribonucleic acid) in memory disordered individuals.
This, Cameron says, suggests the hypothesis that one factor in
memory disturbances may be the over-activity of ribonuclease.
If accurate, quantitative estimates of this substance can be made
it would certainly be of interest to see if it also varies in amount
as normal age advances.

At a more molar level it is interesting to note that some specific
brain areas which show a relatively high incidence of pathology
in the aged are also those whose abnormal functioning or removal
is associated with learning defects in younger individuals. These
areas are in the region of the temporal lobes.

Both Meyer (1959) in London and Milner (1958) in Montreal
have produced evidence to show that a significant impairment of
auditorily mediated learning follows surgical removal of the dominant temporal lobe in patients so operated upon for the relief of
psychomotor epilepsy. Milner (1958) has reported that such a
learning deficit may be shown to exist even in the presence of
pre-operative, electrical disturbances of the dominant lobe.
Meyer and Falconer (1960) have shown that space occupying
lesions in this area are certainly related to a defect in auditory
learning.

Milner (1958) has also found that an electrical disturbance in, or removal of the non-dominant temporal lobe results in a defect of some visual organizational ability. Kimura (1963) has even suggested that this latter defect may be due to an impairment of short-term visual memory.

Certainly it has been shown that when *both* temporal lobes have been surgically removed, or when one has been removed and the other is electrically abnormal, then a more or less complete loss of recent memory usually appears. Evidence to this effect has been cited by Milner and Penfield (1955), Scoville and Milner (1957), Penfield and Milner (1958) and Serafetinides and Falconer (1962).

One might therefore infer that when the dominant lobe alone, for example, is removed some degree of learning ability is retained, partly by some transfer of function to the opposite lobe partly by the difference in modality specialization between the lobes, which may permit some degree of learning to proceed via other sensory channels. When both lobes are removed, however, neither transfer nor modality substitution is possible and hence learning is more or less completely impaired.

Among the electroencephalographic studies of aging it is perhaps significant that there are a fair number which have reported a relatively high incidence of electrical disturbances in the area of the temporal lobes in elderly persons. For example, Busse *et al.* (1956) found fifty-four cases of temporal lobe EEG disturbances in a study of 223 "functioning community volunteers" of mean age 72.2. Of these fifty-four, forty-two or 78 percent of the foci were in the left (dominant) temporal lobe and 74 percent were in the anterior region. Busse (1962) has since noted that there is a tendency for such temporal lobe abnormalities to occur in people with deficient learning ability.

Also as part of the Duke University study Barnes *et al.* (1956) examined the records of 198 hospital patients with a mean age of 72.4. There were 126 of these patients who showed clinical symptoms of memory impairment, confusion and disorientation. Of the EEG abnormalities shown by these patients, 43 percent had either focal or focal and mixed recordings mainly in the dominant posterior temporal lobe.

So far as learning is concerned, then, in young, old or senile, it seems that the integrity of the temporal lobe area is a rather necessary condition for successful memory storage. This view is further supported by the neuro-pathological study of the lesions correlated with amnestic disorders. Brierley (1961) in his review concludes as follows, "The failure of memory in the ageing subject is relatively greater for recent than for past events. This type of amnesia is also a feature of Korsakoff's psychosis where the minimal pathological lesion is damage to the mamillary bodies. The amnesia resulting from surgery of the temporal lobes and in certain cases of temporal lobe encephalitis, Alzheimer's and Pick's disease, indicates that the hippocampus and the hippocampal gyrus are essential to the process of memorizing" (Brierley, 1961, p. 107).

It may be worth pointing out here that Kimura (1961) has found that patients after dominant temporal lobectomy are also deficient in the recall of dichotic digits. The present author (Inglis, 1962) has interpreted her results as being related to the defect of auditory learning shown by these same patients after surgery. It may even be the case that the memory defect shown by patients after ECT is not entirely unrelated to the positioning of the electrodes over the temporal regions.

From studies of brain function then, both molar and molecular, come hints and clues regarding the essential bases of learning. As yet, it must be admitted, these constitute merely parts of the problem rather than part of the answer. Like the bits of a jigsaw puzzle, however, we may hope that they will eventually come together within the larger solution.

What dare one now say about the connection between diminished speed of function and the impairment of immediate memory? There are undoubtedly many empirical relations that may be traced. It seems likely, as Welford (1963) has suggested, that decision time and short-term memory must even be conceptually regarded as mutually dependent. As he has pointed out, "On the one hand the build-up of activity required for decision implies the cumulation, and therefore the storage, of data over brief periods. On the other hand, accurate short-term memory implies the giving of clear and unambiguous signals by the memory traces, and the process of achieving signals is probably akin to that of making decisions" (Welford, 1963, p. 125).

Moreover, it might be suggested that there could be an increasingly pathological, positive feed-back effect brought about by interaction between psychomotor slowness and rapid trace decay. If, for example, the production of a certain series of activities were very much slowed down then this might cause some essential self-created sequences of stimuli to enter their relevant storage systems at a rate which would, in any case, expose them to the greater possibility of trace decay. The earlier items in any sequence might then be expunged by the faster trace decay before the later impulses had been delivered to store. The end result would be the same as one would find in trying slowly to fill a vessel with a very fast leak; the material would, so to speak, drain away quicker than it was being poured in. Under these circumstances much less would be retained than in either one or other of the pathological conditions alone.

SUMMARY

In summary it may be said that learning ability can at least be strongly suspected of having an important part to play in the changes that take place with age in a number of apparently different areas of behaviour. The nature of the processes which mediate alterations in such ability relate principally to short-term storage and comprise at least an increase in the rate of trace decay and an increased susceptibility to interference in immediate memory. Age and senility, in other words, have an effect on the pre-consolidation phase of learning which is in some ways not unlike the effects of trauma, electroshock, anaestheia and the like. At present we can only speculate upon the nature of the neuro-physiological bases of such impairment; any adequate hypothesis must eventually take into account what are at present some rather discrete data relating to both molar and molecular levels of brain function. Finally, storage and speed are likely to show some important interactions in their influence upon performance as age advances.

REFERENCES

Barnes, R. H., Busse, E. W. and Friedman, E. L.: (1956) Psychological functioning of aged individuals with normal and abnormal electro-encephalograms. II. A study of hospitalized individuals. *J. Nerv. Ment. Dis.*, 124:585-593.

Birren, J. E. and Morrison, D. F.: (1961) Analysis of the WAIS subtests in relation to age and education. *J. Geront.*, 16:363-369.

Brierley, J. B.: (1961) Clinico-pathological correlations in amnesia. *Geront. Clin.*, 3:97-109.

Broadbent, D. E.: (1957) Immediate memory and simultaneous stimuli. *Quart. J. Exp. Psychol.*, 9:1-11.

Broadbent, D. E.: (1958) *Perception and Communication.* London, Pergamon Press.

Broadbent, D. E. and Heron, A.: (1962) Effects of a subsidiary task on performance involving immediate memory by younger and older men. *Brit. J. Psychol.*, 53:189-198.

Bromley, D. B.: (1955) Notes on the Shaw Test. *Brit. J. Psychol.*, 46:310-311.

Bromley, D. B.: (1956) Some experimental tests of the effects of age on creative intellectual output. *J. Geront.*, 11:74-82.

Bromley, D. B.: (1958) Some effects of age on short term learning and remembering. *J. Geront.*, 13:398-406.

Busse, E. W.: (1962) Findings from the Duke geriatrics research project on the effects of aging upon the nervous system. In H. T. Blumenthal, ed.: *Medical and Clinical Aspects of Aging*, New York, Columbia Univ. Press.

Busse, E. W., Barnes, R. H., Friedman, E. L. and Kelty, E. J.: (1956) Psychological functioning of aged individuals with normal and abnormal electroencephalograms. I. A study of non-hospitalized community volunteers. *J. Nerv. Ment. Dis.*, 124:135-141.

Caird, W. K.: (1963) Short term storage in the senium. Unpublished Ph.D. dissertation, Queens Univ.

Caird, W. K. and Inglis, J.: (1961) The short-term storage of auditory and visual two-channel digits by elderly patients with memory disorder. *J. Ment. Sci.*, 107:1062-1069.

Caird, W. K., Laverty, S. G. and Inglis, J.: (1963) Sedation and sleep thresholds in elderly patients with memory disorder. *Geront. Clin.*, 5: 55-62.

Caird, W. K., Sanderson, R. E. and Inglis, J.: (1962) Cross-validation of a learning test for use with elderly psychiatric patients. *J. Ment. Sci.*, 108:368-370.

Cameron, D. E.: (1943) Impairment of the retention phase of remembering. *Psychiat. Quart.*, 17:395-404.

Cameron, D. E.: (1963) The process of remembering. *Brit. J. Psychiat.*, 109:325-340.

Cameron, D. E. and Solyom, L.: (1961) Effects of ribonucleic acid on memory. *Geriatrics, 16:*74-81.

Cameron, N.: (1939) Deterioration and regression in schizophrenic thinking. *J. Abnorm. Soc. Psychol., 34:*265-270.

Campbell, D.: (1961) The psychological effects of cerebral electroshock. In H. J. Eysenck, ed.: *Handbook of Abnormal Psychology,* New York, Basic Books.

Cattell, R. B.: (1943) The measurement of adult intelligence. *Psychol. Bull., 40:*159-193.

Cleveland, S. and Dysinger, D.: (1944) Mental deterioration in senile psychosis. *J. Abnorm. Soc. Psychol., 39:*368-372.

Cohen, J.: (1957) The factorial structure of the WAIS between early adulthood and old age. *J. Consult. Psychol., 21:*283-290.

Conrad, R.: (1957) Decay theory of immediate memory. *Nature, 179:* 831-832.

Conrad, R.: (1959) Errors of immediate memory. *Brit. J. Psychol., 50:*349-359.

Cronholm, B. and Molander, L.: (1961) Memory disturbances after electroconvulsive therapy. *Acta Psychiat. Scand., 36:*83-90.

Delafresnaye, J. F., ed.: (1961) *Brain Mechanisms and Learning.* Oxford, Blackwell.

Deutsch, J. A.: (1962) Higher nervous function: the physiological bases of memory. *Ann. Rev. Physiol., 24:*259-286.

Doppelt, J. E. and Wallace, W. L.: (1955) Standardization of the Wechsler Adult Intelligence Scale for older persons. *J. Abnorm. Soc. Psychol., 51:*312-330.

Edwards, A. L.: (1960) *Experimental Design in Psychological Research.* New York, Holt, Rinehart and Winston.

Eisdorfer, C. and Cohen, L. D.: (1961) The generality of the WAIS standardization for the aged: a regional comparison. *J. Abnorm. Soc. Psychol., 62:*520-527.

Fraser, D. C.: (1958) Decay of immediate memory with age. *Nature, 182:*1163.

Glickman, S. E.: (1961) Perseverative neural processes and consolidation of the memory trace. *Psychol. Bull., 58:*218-233.

Goldstein, K. and Scheerer, M.: (1941) Abstract and concrete behavior; an experimental study with special tests. *Psychol. Monogr., 53:*2.

Hanfmann, Eugenia and Kasanin, J.: (1937) A method for the study of concept formation. *J. Psychol., 3:*521-540.

Hebb, D. O.: (1949) *The Organization of Behaviour: A Neuropsychological Theory.* New York, Wiley.

Inglis, J.: (1957) An experimental study of learning and "memory function" in elderly psychiatric patients. *J. Ment. Sci., 103:*796-803.

Inglis, J.: (1959a) Learning, retention and conceptual usage in elderly patients with memory disorder. *J. Abnorm. Soc. Psychol., 59:*210-215.

Inglis, J.: (1959b) A paired-associate learning test for use with elderly psychiatric patients. *J. Ment. Sci., 105*:440-443.

Inglis, J.: (1962) Dichotic stimulation, temporal-lobe damage, and the perception and storage of auditory stimuli—a note on Kimura's findings. *Canad. J. Psychol., 16*:11-17.

Inglis, J. and Caird, W. K.: (1963a) Age differences in successive responses to simultaneous stimulation. *Canad. J. Psychol., 17*:98-105.

Inglis, J. and Caird W. K.: (1963b) Modified digit spans and memory disorder. *Dis. Nerv. Syst., 24*:46-50.

Inglis, J. and Mackay, H. A.: (August 1963) The effects of age on a short-term auditory storage process. Paper read at the *Sixth International Congress of Gerontology*, Copenhagen.

Inglis, J. and Sanderson, R. E.: (1961) Successive responses to simultaneous stimulation in elderly patients with memory disorder. *J. Abnorm. Soc. Psychol., 62*:709-712.

Jerome, E. A.: (1959) Age and learning—experimental studies. In J. E. Birren, ed.: *Handbook of Aging and the Individual*, Chicago, Univ. Chicago Press.

Katz, J. J. and Halstead, W. C.: (1950) Protein organization and mental function. *Comp. Psychol. Monogr., 20*:1-33.

Kimura, Doreen: (1961) Some effects of temporal-lobe damage on auditory perception. *Canad. J. Psychol., 15*:156-165.

Kimura, Doreen: (1963) Right temporal-lobe damage: perception of unfamiliar stimuli after damage. *Arch. Neurol., 8*:264-271.

Meyer, V.: (1959) Cognitive changes following temporal lobectomy for relief of temporal lobe epilepsy. *Arch. Neurol. Psychiat., 81*:299-309.

Meyer, V. and Falconer, M. A.: (1960) Defects of learning ability with massive lesions of the temporal lobe. *J. Ment. Sci., 106*:472-477.

Milner, Brenda: (1958) Psychological defects produced by temporal lobe excision. *Proc. Ass. Res. Nerv. Ment. Dis., 36*:244-257.

Milner, Brenda and Penfield, W.: (1955) The effect of hippocampal lesions on recent memory. *Trans. Amer. Neurol. Ass., 80*:42-48.

Pauling, L.: (1961) A molecular theory of general anaesthesia. *Science, 134*:15-21.

Penfield, W. and Milner, Brenda: (1958) Memory deficit produced by bilateral lesions in the hippocampal zone. *Arch. Neurol. Psychiat., 79*:475-497.

Riegel, Ruth M. and Riegel, K. F.: (1962) A comparison and reinterpretation of factor structures of the W-B, the WAIS and the HAWIE on aged persons. *J. Consult. Psychol., 26*:31-37.

Russell, W. R.: (1959) *Brain, Memory, Learning: A Neurologist's View.* London, Oxford Univ. Press.

Russell, W. R. and Nathan, P. W.: (1946) Traumatic amnesia. *Brain, 69*:280-300.

Schmitt, F. O., ed.: (1962) *Macromolecular Specificity and Biological Memory.* Cambridge, Mass., M.I.T. Press.

Scoville, W. B. and Milner, Brenda: (1957) Loss of recent memory after bilateral hippocampal lesions. *J. Neurol. Neurosurg. Psychiat.,20:*11-21

Serafetinides, E. A. and Falconer, M. A.: (1962) Some observations on memory impairment after temporal lobectomy for epilepsy. *J. Neurol. Neurosurg. Psychiat., 25:*251-255.

Steinberg, Hanna and Summerfield, A.: (1957) Influence of a depressant drug on acquisition in rote learning. *Quart. J. Exp. Psychol., 9:*138-145.

Summerfield, A. and Steinberg, Hanna: (1957) Reducing interference in forgetting. *Quart. J. Exp. Psychol., 9:*146-157.

Talland, G. A.: (1961) Effect of aging on the formation of sequential and spatial concepts. *Percept. Motor Skills, 13:*210.

Welford, A. T.: (1956) Age and learning: theory and needed research. In *Symposium on Experimental Gerontology,* Basel, Birkhauser.

Welford, A. T.: (1958) *Ageing and Human Skill.* London, Oxford Univ. Press.

Welford, A. T.: (1963) Social, psychological and physiological gerontology: an experimental psychologist's approach. In W. Donahue, C. Tibbitts and R. H. Williams, eds.: *Processes of Aging: Social and Psychological Perspectives,* New York, Atherton Press.

Zubin, J. and Barrera, S. E.: (1941) Effect of electroconvulsive therapy on memory. *Proc. Soc. Exp. Biol. Med., 48:*596-597.

8

COGNITIVE SETS, SPEED AND ACCURACY OF PERFORMANCE IN THE ELDERLY

Joseph F. Brinley[1]

T HE PURPOSE of this paper is twofold. First, it attempts to focus attention on the utility of set constructs in interpreting age differences in speed and accuracy of performance. Second, it presents the results of a relevant study. In order to better accomplish these main objectives, the preliminary section presents a brief discussion concerned with the problems involved in defining and using set constructs.

Issues related to set constructs have been discussed in detail by Gibson (1941). Allport (1955) has been particularly concerned with cognitive sets, and Broadbent (1958) has dealt with the related problem of attention. Another recent source on general issues is Solley and Murphy (1961). The notion that set constructs may have relevance to the interpretation of age differences in speed of cognitive function is not novel (see Birren, 1955). Botwinick (1959) has reviewed much of the literature and discussed the relevance of set constructs to the interpretation of performance deficits in the elderly and much of Botwinick's work has been involved with set constructs.

[1] The study which takes up the main portion of this paper was done while the author was employed by the Section on Aging of the National Institutes of Mental Health and a student at the Catholic University of America. A debt owed several individuals in both institutions is gratefully acknowledged.

SET CONSTRUCTS AND SPEEDED PERFORMANCE

Sets are typically conceived of as inferred states of anticipation, readiness or predisposition which *facilitate* the response or responses toward which the subject is predisposed and *inhibit* irrelevant or competing response tendencies (Woodworth and Schlosberg, 1958, p. 830). However, if this definition is taken literally, the term set can be broadened to refer to the subject's inferred predispositions toward the entire task.[2] For example, it is possible to speak of *speed set* as opposed to *accuracy set.* In such cases set constructs may become indistinguishable from attitudinal or motivational constructs. Attitudinal or motivational influences are not the main concern of this paper. The term set as it is employed here refers specifically to inferred anticipations and predispositions with respect to the concrete details of performance. For example, the subject may be set to add rather than substract at some particular instant during arithmetic calculation. Set constructs of this type are of the class Tolman has referred to as "means-end readinesses" (Tolman, 1932, p. 450).

Set constructs appear to be particularly useful in analyzing performance in self-paced, speeded tasks for at least two reasons. First of all, *self-paced* tasks do not pressure subjects to respond at speeds beyond the limits of their capacities. Furthermore, tasks are conventionally characterized as *speeded* only to the extent that they involve operations which the subject can perform if given sufficient time to do so. Consequently, these tasks are primarily intended to assess the efficiency rather than the power aspects of performance. In such tasks, it appears likely that factors which influence readiness and predisposition for response can provide a main source of variability in performance. To the extent that subjects can anticipate exactly what types of operations will be required of them and when they will be required, performance becomes routine.

A second advantage of the use of set constructs is that it can bring accuracy as well as speed of performance into the same conceptual framework. Sets are conceived as inhibiting inappropriate responses as well as facilitating appropriate ones. When an ap-

---

[2] Thanks are due Dr. M. K. Rigby for pointing out the need for this distinction.

propriate set is present as indicated by performance at better than
the chance level of accuracy and where there is no question as to
the subject's actual capacity to produce a correct response under
better circumstances, an error can be interpreted as set failure or
set lapse. This notion of set lapse is, of course, similar to the idea
of memory fault. However, if the subject is responding at better
than chance levels of accuracy, it cannot be maintained that he
has forgotten the set itself. In other words, retention of set and
set failure are operationally distinguishable. Furthermore, memory capacity is usually defined operationally either in relation to
time lapsed or to the quantity of material to be retained. Subjects
frequently make errors in tasks in which there is little reason to
suspect that either the time intervals involved or the quantity to
be retained places any burden on their actual powers of retention
as it would be measured by conventional memory procedures.

Analysis of behavior in relation to set constructs focuses attention first of all on those factors which can predispose the subject
to respond in one way rather than another. Such factors can be
roughly categorized as those associated with task instructions and
those introduced by task features themselves. Instructions can be
either appropriate or inappropriate and they can also vary in the
extent to which they specify the exact details of performance.
Task features may influence the subject's set for response in at
least two ways. First, they may involve either positive or negative transfer effects from previously established habits. A classic
example of negative transfer effect of this type is found in tasks
which reverse the conventional significance of arithmetic signs so
that the subject is required to substract whenever he encounters a
plus sign. Second, when tasks involve more than a single response, the set at any particular instant may vary depending on
the sequence of events in the preceding performance. An example
of this type of influence is the effect of set-inducing sequences in
the so-called water jar experiments (Luchins, 1959).

Analysis of behavior in relation to set constructs also focuses
attention on the fact that tasks vary in the extent to which the
sets induced by instructions and task features can actually be
expected to control the subject's activity during performance.
The power of set constructs in this regard goes beyond pointing
to the obvious fact that some tasks involve greater uncertainty or

a greater number of possible alternative responses than others, and that consequently sets can be more specific in some tasks than in others. Of further interest is the fact that the processes involved in selection of alternative responses appears to be under more direct control in some situations than in others. In a conventional choice reaction time task, for example, the subject can anticipate that the signal for response will be one of several specific lights. He merely needs to determine which of these anticipated signals does occur in order to respond correctly. In a multiple choice vocabulary test on the other hand, the subject may anticipate that one of the alternative signals presented will be a synonym. However, in the vocabulary test he needs to actually analyze the alternative signals present in order to determine which of them falls into the set appropriate category. The set in the choice reaction time task consequently exercises more direct control of the subject's choice activity than the set in the vocabulary test. In certain cases, these variations in the amount of task control of sets may conceivably constitute the essential differences between two tasks. For example, both an information test and an analogies test require the utilization of stored information. However, task control of this search for stored information is much more direct in the information test than in the analogies test. Variations in the extent of task control of the subject's sets may also relate to very simple features of tasks. For example, two tasks might involve sorting red and black cards into separate bins. However, one task might provide visible cues indicating which bin should contain red cards and versus while the other task might not.

In summary then, set constructs may be particularly useful in analyzing performance in self-paced, speeded tasks. Analysis in relation to set constructs points up factors which predispose the subject to respond in one way rather than another. It also emphasizes the fact that tasks vary in the extent to which these predispositions can be expected to control the subject's performance.

Unfortunately, analysis of behavior in relation to set constructs is not simple. Factors influencing sets and the extent to which they control the subject's activity cannot be expected to function independently of one another. However, the complexity of the issue does not preclude scientific treatment. Set constructs can be operationally defined. Antecedent variables include manipulations of instructions and task features and consequent variables are the observed facilitating or impeding effects on either speed or accuracy of performance.

There has been considerable looseness in the use of sets as explanatory constructs. At least part of this can be attributed to failure to employ consistently a framework of sufficient breadth in considering the possible sources of predisposition for response. Discussion frequently focusses on the appropriateness or inappropriateness of sets. Confusion may result when discussions of set phenomena fail to consider the source of influence as a relevant variable. In the case of the aged, for example, it is possible that instructional sources have less influence, relatively speaking, than task sources and that some task sources may have greater influence than others. Such possibilities are, of course, obscured unless an adequate conceptual framework is consistently employed.

AGE, SETS AND EFFICIENCY OF PERFORMANCE

The question now turns to the value of set constructs in the analysis of the self-paced, speeded performances of the elderly. Older individuals are expected to be slower than younger adults in performing any speeded task. More recent interpretations of this fact agree that a major part of this slowing is associated with age changes in speed of cognitive function (Birren, 1955, 1956; Jones, 1959; Welford, 1958, 1959). There is further agreement that the cognitive deficit involved is not merely a matter of changes in receptor acuity. However, theoretical interpretations available at present do not lead to very specific predictions concerning the types of manipulations of the cognitive dimensions of tasks which can be expected to produce disproportional slowing of responses or to increase error proneness in the elderly. An analysis of experimental results from the viewpoint of set constructs may clarify some issues involved in making such predictions.

Sets and Disproportional Slowing of Responses

The results of several studies indicate that disproportional slowing of responses in the elderly is not a simple function of the amount of uncertainty or degree of choice involved in performance. For example, Goldfarb (1941) found that age difference in speed of choice reaction time varied little depending on whether subjects were required to choose from five rather than two alternatives. Similarly, both Crossman and Szafran (1956) and Botwinick, Robbin and Brinley (1960) found that merely increasing the numbers of categories into which playing cards had to be sorted failed to increase response times in older groups any more than in younger groups. Griew (1959) found that the response times of older individuals did, in fact, slow disproportionately as a function of an increase in the number of possible sources from which the signal could come in a reaction time task. However, he also found that it was possible to eliminate the disproportional slowing by reducing the exposure time of the light signals. Griew's results were similar to those obtained by Botwinick, Robbin and Brinley (1958), with a task requiring simple perceptual discriminations involving two alternatives. In discussing the results of this latter experiment, Botwinick suggested that older individuals might tend to take more time than they actually needed for accurate discrimination in order to achieve greater confidence. Welford (1960) has generalized this type of interpretation by showing that the functional relationship between age and "choice" time may have a steeper slope than that between age and time actually needed to discriminate for several types of tasks. However, the point made here is that the evidence suggests that, within a considerable range, variations in the extent to which sets permit subjects to anticipate which signals will occur do not necessarily effect disproportional changes in response speeds in the elderly. Furthermore, Griew's results suggest that in cases where there is such disproportional slowing, it may be possible to eliminate it or reduce it by forcing subjects to choose more rapidly.

From the viewpoint of set constructs, instructions and task conditions in the experiments cited in the preceding paragraph induce sets which confine the subject's uncertainty to where, when or whether *anticipated* signals arrive. However, other experimental procedures employing roughly the same types of perceptual-motor features have introduced uncertainty of another type which has tended to slow the responses of older individuals disproportionately. Studies reported by Kay (1954, 1955) and another facet of the study reported by Botwinick, Robbin and Brinley (1960) illustrate this fact. In his experiments, Kay employed a serial, choice reaction time task. This involved pressing a key which extinguished the one of twelve alternative lights which was lit and at the same time lit up another of the lights which provided the cue for the next response. The procedures are described in detail by Kay (1955) and by Welford (1958). One of these tasks (Key, 1955, p. 260, Condition B), permitted the subject to directly anticipate the signals which could occur and the responses which were to be made. In this task the subject was required to press a key directly in front of the light which happened to come on. However, in another task (Kay, 1954, Condition 1) the subject had to first determine the number of the light which came on by counting from the left in the visual display and then find that number printed on a card directly in front of the appropriate key. In other words, in order to respond appropriately to the third light from the left in the visual display in this task, he had to find the key labeled 3 which occurred in the seventh position from the left in the row of twelve keys. Comparison of response times in seconds per operation for the two tasks shows that age differences in time taken to respond were much greater in the second task than in the first one. Similarly, the study reported by Botwinick *et al.* (1960) varied the conditions under which subjects of different ages were required to sort playing cards into bins. In one condition subjects had merely to sort cards by number; in the second they had to sort by number but only if the card was an appropriate color; in the third condition, they had to evaluate the card with respect to both number, color, and also with respect to oddness or evenness of the number in order or to sort appropriately. Here again, age differences in response speed were greater in the second and particularly in the third condition than in the first.

The results of both the Kay and Botwinick experiments suggest that when sets no longer confine the subject's uncertainty to where, when or whether anticipated signals arrive, older persons tend to slow disproportionately. Consequently, comparison of the results of experiments employing simpler choice tasks with the results of the Kay and Botwinick studies suggests that disproportional slowing of responses in the elderly is not merely a function of the extent to which sets fail to provide anticipations concerning the exact response to be made. It further suggests that disproportional slowing of response may be a function of the extent to which sets fail to provide anticipations concerning which signal calls for which response. In other words, disproportional slowing of response in the elderly may be specifically associated with increased difficulty in maintaining effective control of sets for the cognitive activity involved in selecting responses when sets no longer permit subjects to directly anticipate which signal calls for which response.

The more complicated choice reaction time and card sorting tasks employed by Kay and by Botwinick require activities similar to those involved in performing other multiple-choice type tasks. In a multiple-choice vocabulary test, for example, the subject searches for a synonym or an antonym without being aware of the exact perceptual properties of the stimulus he is seeking. If disproportional slowing of responses in the elderly reflects increased difficulty in maintaining effective control of sets which direct cognitive activity involved in selecting responses, then age differences in speed of response should be greater for vocabulary performances than for simpler choice reaction time tasks. Birren, Riegel and Morrison (1962) report such a finding. It would also be expected that age differences in speed of response would increase as a function of increased complexity of the cognitive activity involved in selecting an appropriate response. Jones' report that age differences in response speed were greater in an analogies test than in an information test fits this prediction (Jones, 1955, p. 273). A similar interpretation can be placed on Riegel's findings concerning the differential decline of efficiency in various types of verbal performance with age (Riegel, 1959).

Kay (1954) notes that performance in more complicated psychomotor tasks shares something in common with even more complicated reasoning and problem solving activities. From the viewpoint of set constructs, this relates to the fact that both types of tasks require subjects to maintain effective control of cognitive activity with respect to sets which fail to specify the details of performance completely. However, true problem solving activities also require subjects to generate their own sets about which operations are necessary to solve the problem. Consequently, speedy solutions of problems may depend as much upon the subject's skill in generating sets for activities relevant to task solution as on his capacity to maintain effective control of his cognitive activity in relation to these sets. Furthermore, as Welford (1958, p. 223) emphasizes, more complex problem sloving tasks place greater demands on the subject's capacity to hold in mind the data necessary for solution. In view of these complexities, it is not clear that difficulty in maintaining effective control of cognitive activities in relation to sets would necessarily predict systematic increases in problem solving time with age. Clay (Welford, 1958, pp. 205-219; Clay, 1956) has in fact failed to find systematic trends. However, studies of reasoning and problem solving do provide evidence that difficulty in maintaining sets impedes the performance of the elderly in more complicated reasoning and problem solving activities. Allan's study reported by Welford (Welford, 1958, pp. 193-198) found that older subjects were less successful in assessing the logical compatability of a series of propositions because of an increased difficulty in confining their critique to the formal rather than the material truth value of the propositions involved. Furthermore, Jerome (1962) has reported that older subjects had "extreme difficulty" in maintaining order in their search procedures during attempts to find solutions for complex problems. Jerome writes that "as a result of this lack of order in the search plan, information concerning any given conceptually unified sequence was temporally distributed in a haphazard fashion" (Jerome, 1962, p. 819). Consequently, the results of studies related to age differences in reasoning and problem solving activities contribute to the impression that older subjects have difficulty in maintaining cognitive sets even though they do not necessarily find that older individuals take more time at complex problem solving.

Sets and Error Pronesness
Some studies have found slow performances of the elderly associated with greater accuracy (e.g., Brown's studies reported

by Welford, 1958, pp. 66-74). However, others have found slowness accompanied by increased error proneness (e.g., Birren and Botwinick, 1951; Kay, 1954). From the viewpoint of set constructs, it seems possible that error proneness, like disproportional slowing, may be associated with the extent to which tasks require subjects to maintain effective control of cognitive activity in selecting responses. There is, in fact, little evidence that older individuals are more error prone in speeded, self-paced performances, when sets permit direct anticipation of which response should be matched with which signal. This accuracy may be associated with a tendency to be more careful (Welford, 1958). However, in certain cases it may even be possible to pace older subjects to respond more rapidly in these tasks without observing increased error proneness (Botwinick, Robbin and Brinley, 1958).

Where older subjects have displayed increased error proneness in self-paced, speeded performance, tasks often appear to involve selecting appropriate responses on the basis of sets intended to direct cognitive activities more complex than perceptual identifications and discriminations of anticipated signals. For example, Cherns (Welford, 1958, pp. 162-166) found that when subjects were required to employ multiple perceptual criteria in deciding whether to accept or reject aluminum blocks in an experiment designed to simulate an industrial inspection operation, older subjects proved more error prone. Birren and Botwinick (1951) report increased error proneness in the elderly as a function of an increase in the number of digits to be added in arithmetic calculation. Significantly, Jones (1955) reports that age affected error proneness in an analogies task to a much greater extent than in a task requiring direct recall of stored information. Jones indicates that for the same subjects accuracy of performance actually increased with age in the information task while it declined abruptly in the analogies task. Consequently, it seems implausible that such a contrast would be associated with an age difference in the information necessary to performance in the analogies task.

Older individuals may be particularly error prone when tasks not only require maintaining sets for relatively complex cognitive activities but where task features tend to generate sets which compete or interfere with sets induced by the instructions. The

Kay experiment (Kay, 1954) illustrates this point dramatically. In each condition of the serial, choice reaction time procedure, the subject had to determine the number of the light which came on by counting from the left in a visual display and then find that number printed on a card placed in front of the appropriate key. However, in one condition the card was placed immediately in front of the key while in another the card was placed in close proximity to the visual display. Older subjects made more errors in both conditions. Subjects in both age groups made more errors when the card was placed near the visual display. However, the increase in error proneness associated with age was much greater in the second condition. In this condition, as Kay's analysis of errors shows, it was more difficult to maintain the set that the card number referred to this key rather than the light.

Kay's results illustrate an increased susceptibility to influence of interfering sets generated by task conditions. This susceptibility may also account for the age differences in reasoning and problem solving behavior observed in the Allan and Jerome studies cited previously. However, another factor may also be involved. Birren (1955) has noted a tendency among victims of senile deterioration to generate their own interfering sets. According to Birren senile subjects when asked to write down words beginning with the letter "S" might list a sequence like *swim, water, cloud, rain,* etc. in which the appropriate set for "S" words was lost and another "set" for associative meaning seemed to emerge. Botwinick (1959) has suggested that this susceptibility to interference effects is similar to that observed in the brain-damaged.

AGE DIFFERENCES IN THE CAPACITY TO EMPLOY SETS WHICH INVOLVE SHIFTING[3]

Hypotheses, Procedure and Subjects

The study under consideration was designed to test several hypotheses concerning the manner in which speed of cognitive functioning in the elderly might be related to the type of "rigidity" inferred from performance in shift or alternation tasks. Previous studies by Botwinick, Brinley and Robbin (1958) and

---

[3] A more complete account of this study is available in Brinley (1963).

by Schaie (1958) had suggested that when sets in speeded tasks involved shifting from one type of activity to another, the elderly were relatively slower than would have been anticipated on the basis of age differences in response speeds observed when tasks did not involve shifting. In general, the questions which the study was designed to answer were the following: 1) whether older individuals would behave more rigidly in shift tasks despite variations in task content; 2) whether factor analysis would reveal that some relatively independent "rigidity" factor or factors were more important in determining response rates in an older population than in a younger one, and 3) whether the greater slowing which older individuals exhibited in shift tasks would be associated with shifting *per se*, what Catell and Tiner (1949) termed "process rigidity," or whether it might be associated with other aspects of shift tasks.

In order to answer these questions three sets of highly speeded shift and nonshift tasks were constructed, one employing verbal materials, another involving arithmetic items and the third, perceptual items. In this respect the design was similar to that of Kleemeier and Dudek (1950). Table 1 presents examples of the verbal and arithmetic items employed. A parallel set of items was constructed with materials similar to those of Thurstone's Faces test (Thurstone, 1944). An example of these perceptual items is presented in Figure 1; in each item, one face was different from the other two on the basis of its "hair" or "eyebrows" or "mouth." All tests were a series of multiple-choice items in which subjects were required to check the correct one of three alternative answers.

In each of the nine nonshift tasks subjects had simply to perform one type of operation repetitively. For example, one task was to check synonyms, another to check sums, another to check the "face" with the different "hair."

Each of the nine shift tasks involved all three of the operations employed in its own content category. Three different types of shift tasks were employed, parallel tasks being constructed with each type of task content. In the three *Selections* tasks subjects had to discover which of three categories of responses was appropriate for each item. For example, in the verbal selection task

TABLE 1
EXAMPLES OF VERBAL AND ARITHMETIC MATERIALS

NONSHIFT TASKS

Verbal

Synonyms Test	*Wild*	Tame ( )	Tiled ( )	Savage (✓)
Antonyms Test	*Right*	Correct ( )	Wrong (✓)	Bite ( )
Rhyming Test	*Near*	Far ( )	Close ( )	Beer (✓)

Arithmetic

Addition Test	8+3	13 ( )	11 (✓)	12 ( )
Subtraction Test	9−4	5 (✓)	4 ( )	6 ( )
Multiplication Test	8×7	54 ( )	55 ( )	56 (✓)

SHIFT TASKS

Verbal Shift Tasks

Selection Test	*Hard*	First ( )	Beat ( )	Soft (✓)
	Quiet	Better ( )	Find ( )	Silent (✓)
	Wide	Lied (✓)	Bitter ( )	Careful ( )
Directions Test	*Sweat* (opposite)	Beat ( )	Sugary ( )	Sour (✓)
	Bare (same)	Covered ( )	Naked (✓)	Wear ( )
	Bad (rhyme)	Wicked ( )	Add (✓)	Good ( )
Memory Test	*Over*	Above (✓)	Under ( )	Clever ( )
	Tiny	Small ( )	Huge (✓)	Shiny ( )
	Kind	Dined (✓)	Friendly ( )	Cruel ( )

Arithmetic Shift Tasks

Selection Test	*6*	*2*	11 ( )	5 ( )	8 (✓)
	9	*2*	12 ( )	18 (✓)	6 ( )
	9	*7*	2 (✓)	62 ( )	17 ( )
Directions Test	*4−2*		8 ( )	2 (✓)	6 ( )
	8+3		11 (✓)	5 ( )	24 ( )
	4×3		1 ( )	12 (✓)	7 ( )
Memory Test	*6*	*4*	24 ( )	2 ( )	10 (✓)
	7	*4*	11 ( )	3 (✓)	28 ( )
	8	*3*	11 ( )	24 (✓)	5 ( )

Figure 1. An example of the type of perceptual materials employed.

the subject was "set" to check either a synonym, an antonym or a rhyme depending on which one of these was present among the possible alternatives. In *Directions* tasks, subjects were provided with step by step directions for each successive item in the sequence. For example, if "same" was printed after the key word, he was required to check a synonym, and "opposite" printed after the key word required him to check an antonym. In *Memory* tasks the subject was required to hold in mind the appropriate sequence. For example, in the verbal memory task, he was required to check successive items in a fixed sequence: a synonym and then an antonym and then a rhyme and then a synonym, etc.

In order to make a correct response in either the Directions or Memory tasks, the subject had to avoid making either of the other responses involved in the given content category. For example, in order to correctly check a synonym, he had to avoid checking both an antonym and a rhyme. This problem of inhibiting task relevant but incorrect responses was not, of course, involved in the Selection tasks.

An attempt was made to make the parallel tests in the three content categories similar. The perceptual-motor features were similar. All materials were very easy. As many of the words as possible were selected from the high frequency categories of the Thorndike-Lorge lists (Thorndike and Lorge, 1944). The arithmetic tests involved only single digit numbers. Cues in the perceptual tasks were made obvious. There were, however, from the viewpoint of set constructs, two differences between the arithmetic tests and the other tests in the battery. First, in every arithmetic test, the subject knew the exact answer he was looking for providing he had the correct set; in the word and perceptual tasks he could only anticipate the correct category of the response. Secondly, in the non-shift arithmetic tests, alternatives to correct responses were simply wrong whereas in the other nonshift tasks alternatives to a correct response were relevant to the other sets employed in the content category. For example, the alternatives to a correct response in the synonyms test were always an antonym and a rhyme.

Subjects were individually tested with two sixty-second forms of each test in the main battery. Tests, with some exceptions, were presented in a balanced order. Three tests, one involving checking identical words and another, identical numbers and the copy digits test of Birren and Botwinick (1951) were included as psychomotor speed reference variables. The checking tasks involved finding the word or a number among three alternatives which was identical with a word or number printed in the left hand margin. The psychomotor features of these tasks were thus nearly identical with the psychomotor features of tasks in the main battery.

The older sample comprised thirty men and twenty-one women, age range fifty-nine to eighty-two years; $\overline{X}$ = 71.4 years; S.D. = 6.1 years. The younger sample comprised thirty men and thirty women, age range eighteen to thirty-five years; $\overline{X}$ = 24.0 years; S. D. = 5.2 years. Analysis revealed sex had no systematic influence on rate scores in either group and the data of men and women subjects were combined in each age group.

Education in the elderly ranged four to nineteen years; $\overline{X}$ = 11.4 years; S.D = 3.6 years. Education in the young ranged ten to twenty years; $\overline{X}$ = 13.6 years; S.D. = 1.7 years. The older sample was thus a superior one by educational criteria since the median years schooling of twelve years was about four years above that which would have been expected for that age group on the basis of census figures.

The vocabulary scale of the S.R.A. Primary Mental Abilities test (intermediate level) was given *without time limits.* In both populations the mean raw score was 45.5 with S.D. = 4.5 words. This did not necessarily indicate that populations were matched with respect to vocabulary level since the test is an easy one (maximum score = 50). However, it did give some assurance that vocabulary level of the less competent individuals in the older population did not fall below that of the less competent in the younger group.

Sixteen of the thirty older men reported that they were or had been involved in professional or managerial occupations. The rest had been clerks or skilled workers with one unskilled worker in the lot. Most of the older women were housewives. Among the younger group, about half were students, four were professionals, the others had technical, clerical or housewife occupations.

Results

Speed of Performance

Table 2 presents information concerning rate scores (operations per second) for the two groups. Mean rates were significantly lower for the older group in every test (t tests, P < 01). The reliability of measures was uniformly high. S.D.'s are about equal for the two groups. However, had rate scores been transformed to time scores, the typically greater variability of time measures in older populations would appear.

TABLE 2
MEANS, S.D.'s AND RELIABILITIES OF RATE SCORES

Test		Elderly, N = 51			Young, N = 60		
		Mean	*S.D.*	r_{12}	*Mean*	*S.D.*	r_{12}
Word	Same	29	08	85	46	08	78
"	Opposite	32	09	76	50	08	68
"	Rhyme	37	10	90	54	10	85
"	Selection	22	08	83	38	08	74
"	Directions	23	07	84	36	06	80
"	Memory	23	07	90	38	08	82
Number	Add	59	14	94	80	15	92
"	Subtract	55	13	92	76	15	94
"	Multiply	56	11	91	78	19	94
"	Selection	24	07	87	34	08	77
"	Directions	40	10	92	61	14	87
"	Memory	38	12	89	60	14	92
Faces	Hair	53	12	88	77	12	88
"	Eyebrows	44	11	88	67	09	83
"	Mouth	53	11	86	74	10	87
"	Selection	26	07	88	42	08	85
"	Directions	34	07	84	51	08	78
"	Memory	38	09	82	60	10	79
Copy Digits		1.16	24	85	1.65	29	85
Check Numbers		50	12	88	79	11	80
Check Words		54	12	88	80	11	80

NOTE: Scores are in operations per second.

A comparison of shift and nonshift performance times is presented in Table 3. The values are the mean ratios of time (seconds/operation) spent in shift tasks to average time spent in nonshift tasks in the same content category. Analyses by one-tailed t tests indicated that mean ratios were significantly higher in the older group for 8 of the 9 comparisons. Age differences in these mean ratios are consistently least for the *Directions* tasks. On the other hand, *Selections* tasks measured the more consistently impressive age differences. Age differences in *Selections* ratios were significantly greater than age differences in *Directions* ratios for both Word and Faces materials (t tests of the average difference between differences, $p < 01$). Older individuals thus tended to spend relatively more time in shifting than younger persons. This was true despite variations both in task content and in the type of shift tasks employed. Step by step directions tended to minimize this slowing in shift tasks, whereas uncertainity with respect to which operation to perform as in the *Selection* tasks, tended to increase it.

Despite the fact that older persons took relatively more time in shifting and were thus observed to behave more rigidly, the average trends revealed a high degree of functional interdependence for age differences in shift and nonshift speed scores. Speed of performance was related not only to the shift-nonshift dimensions of tasks but also to variations in task content, the verbal

TABLE 3
RATIOS OF PERFORMANCE TIMES ON SHIFT AND NONSHIFT TASKS
(SHIFT TIME/NONSHIFT TIME)

| | Elderly | | Young | | | |
	Mean	S.D.	Mean	S.D.	t	p
Word Selection	1.53	.40	1.32	.21	3.5	<01
Directions	1.43	.24	1.39	.14	.9	ns
Memory	1.38	.19	1.32	.19	1.7	.05
Number Selection	2.49	.40	2.28	.32	3.1	<01
Directions	1.42	.20	1.28	.14	4.2	<01
Memory	1.53	.32	1.30	.16	5.1	<01
Face Selection	1.95	.32	1.74	.23	4.0	<01
Directions	1.48	.20	1.41	.14	2.0	<05
Memory	1.35	.24	1.20	.21	3.4	<01

tasks, in particular, being performed more slowly than the others. This permitted a comparison of task difficulty defined in relation to the shift-nonshift dimensions of tasks with task difficulty defined in relations to task content. Figure 2 presents the regression of mean time scores for the elderly on those for the young. Time of response in the old is simply and accurately described as a linear function of performance time in the young group. The slope of the regression line for shift tasks appears identical with the one for nonshift tasks. Consequently response times for both groups and for each type of task variation may be conceived as varying along a single dimension which might be termed "task difficulty."

Correlation matrices for the twenty-one rate scores were computed for each of the two age groups. These matrices were then subjected to Hotelling principal component analyses (Hotelling,

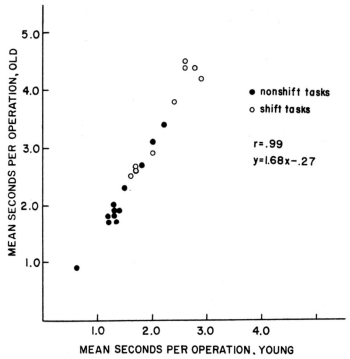

Figure 2. Response times of the elderly as a function of response times of the younger group for twenty-one tests.

1933).[4] Table 4 presents the first five principal components for
each group. Five components accounted for 90.4 per cent and
87.1 per cent of task variance for the old and young matrices respectively. The first component for each matrix is general with
high loadings for every variable. Second and third components
in each case are bipolars dividing the variance of the word, number and faces tasks. The first three components are thus determined by task content; they account for 83 per cent and 79 per
cent of test variance in the old and young matrices respectively.

TABLE 4

PRINCIPAL COMPONENTS BEFORE ROTATION

				Elderly					Young		
	Test	I	II	III	IV	V	I	II	III	IV	V
Word	Same	86	−10	−40	13	−09	81	−02	43	04	05
"	Opposite	84	−10	−38	21	−16	84	−08	45	16	−17
"	Rhyme	78	−29	−35	07	04	80	−04	44	15	−12
"	Selection	85	−08	−32	02	−02	69	−07	54	06	−10
"	Directions	93	00	−27	−04	17	87	−04	38	−12	08
"	Memory	91	−15	−31	−02	04	75	10	42	−19	25
Number	Add	78	−40	32	−08	−08	74	−53	−24	−05	−06
"	Subtract	83	−35	23	−06	−04	75	−48	−31	−10	−05
"	Multiply	78	−38	36	−15	−01	78	−47	−26	08	00
"	Selection	80	−14	12	−34	−27	84	−36	−05	−15	−07
"	Directions	82	−31	14	−26	18	82	−41	−17	−08	04
"	Memory	87	−15	01	−26	05	78	−46	−21	−21	09
Faces	Hair	77	52	14	−04	−25	68	56	−29	−08	−06
"	Eyebrows	82	47	10	02	−09	81	31	−29	−15	03
"	Mouth	81	48	15	05	−12	78	45	−21	−09	−07
"	Selection	85	45	04	−12	01	72	43	−01	−10	−03
"	Directions	87	40	−03	−06	14	80	40	−14	−24	09
"	Memory	80	37	−02	−18	34	76	50	−04	−14	09
Copy Digits		66	01	42	49	20	50	00	−14	55	64
Check Numbers		83	−12	22	36	02	70	19	−34	40	−22
Check Words		88	−15	06	36	−07	73	16	−12	53	−24
Latent Roots		14.38	1.96	1.07	.90	.45	12.19	2.54	1.87	1.06	.69
Percent Variance		68	9	6	4	2	58	12	9	5	3

NOTE: Involves rate scores only.

---

[4] These principal component analyses were done under the direction of Dr. Donald
Morrison, National Institutes of Mental Health, whose help is gratefully acknowledged.

The fourth and fifth components in both matrices make some differentiation between shift and non-shift tasks.

Rotations, the results of which are not presented here, were made graphically by the radial method described in Guilford (1950). These were made in an attempt to obtain clearer definition of shift rigidity factors. Good simple structure was obtained for oblique verbal, number and perceptual vectors. These factors were, of course, more highly correlated in the old matrix. However, the amount of variance associated with rotated rigidity factors remained small in both matrices and there was little to suggest that relatively independent rigidity traits were either more or less important in determining response rates in the older sample. Consequently, the main change in the correlational structure associated with age was the increased importance of a general component or higher order factor for the older sample.

There is evidence that the cognitive rather than psychomotor components of tasks were of primary importance in limiting rate of performance for elderly subjects. Age differences in performance times were in fact least for the tasks which were performed most rapidly (see Figure 2). Furthermore, loadings of psychomotor reference variables in the component analyses suggest the same interpretation. In Table 3 it will be seen that the checking tasks load with the faces and number tasks in components II and III for the young matrix. In the old matrix, the checking tasks load more with the word tests and number tests. The number and faces tasks were performed more rapidly than the word tasks. Slow psychomotor function would be expected to be relatively more important in limiting response rates in the tasks which were performed most rapidly. Consequently, limitations imposed by slow psychomotor function would be more likely to produce the pattern of loadings present in the young matrix.

In summary, then, analysis of the speed scores revealed several things. First, while older individuals reliably spent more time in shifting, there was a high degree of functional interdependence for age differences in shift and nonshift speed scores. This was apparent both from the analysis of average trends and from the component analyses and in the latter case there was no evidence for the increased importance of rigidity traits in determining response rates in the elderly. Second, the main difference in the correlation structure of the battery for old and young samples was the increased importance of the general component or higher order factor for the elderly. Finally, cognitive slowness rather than slow psychomotor function appeared to be the main factor in limiting response rates in the elderly.

Accuracy of Performance

Subjects in both groups made relatively few errors. The median probability of a wrong response on any single test did not exceed .024 for the young group and .062 for the old group. However, as Table 5 indicates, older subjects made errors more frequently. Mann-Whitney U tests found significant age differences in the average probability of a wrong response when scores were total errors per operation for the combined six tests in each content category.

Older individuals were not more error prone in all tasks. They did not make significantly more errors in the nonshift arithmetic tasks nor in the rhyming tasks nor in the arithmetic, Selection and Directions tasks.

In some instances, shifting increased age differences in error proneness. Age differences in the probability of a wrong response were significantly greater in word Directions and Memory tasks and in the arithmetic Memory task than for the corresponding nonshift tasks (U tests of the age difference in difference scores, $P < 01$). There is evidence that the same task features contributed proportionately to age differences in error frequency in the two populations. Figure 3 plots the regression of mean scores of the old on those for the young. This regression was quite steep. It will be noted that the same distance on the ordinate in Figure 3 represents an interval which is four times larger than that on the abscissa.

Speed in Relation to Accuracy

Pearson r's between rate scores for every test in the battery and errors per operation for the combined tests in each content category were computed for each age group. Table 6 gives a summary of the results of these tests. A value outside parenthesis in

TABLE 5
MEDIAN PROBABILITY OF AN ERROR

	Word			Number			Faces		
	Old	Young	P	Old	Young	P	Old	Young	P
Nonshift	.024	.010	<.01a	.005	.004	ns	.041	.015	<.01a
Selection	.037	0	<.01a	0	0	ns	.044	.023	<.01a
Directions	.062	0	<.01a	.020	.014	ns	.046	.023	<.01a
Memory	.057	.020	<.01a	.024	.005	<.05a	.029	.023	<.01a
Total	.048	.012	<.01b	.012	.008	<.01b	.042	.015	<.01b

a. Median Test.
b. Mann-Whitney U Test.

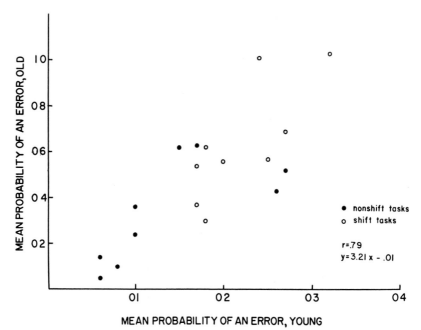

Figure 3. Error proneness in the elderly as a function of error proneness in the younger group for eighteen tests.

TABLE 6

AGE DIFFERENCES IN AVERAGE CORRELATIONS OF SPEED WITH
ERROR SCORES

	Elderly		Young		
WORD ERRORS	$\overline{X}r$	range	$\overline{X}r$	range	t
Word Rates (n = 6)	−56	(−42, −61)	−36	(−29, −42)	5.66
N and P Rates (n = 12)	−38	(−28, −48)	−11	(−01, −21)	9.54
Copy Digits	−44		−17		
NUMBER ERRORS					
Number Rates (n = 6)	−51	(−45, −59)	−32	(−26, −39)	6.07
V and P Rates (n = 12)	−44	(−33, −55)	−12	(03, −28)	9.38
Copy Digits	−49		17		
PERCEPTUAL ERRORS					
Perceptual Rates (n = 6)	−50	(−46, −55)	−06	(06, −18)	10.33
V and N Rates (n = 12)	−29	(−15, −45)	03	(14, −17)	9.06
Copy Digits	−27		26		

NOTE: For the older group an r of .28 is significant, P less than .05; and r of .37 is significant, P less than .01. Corresponding values for the young are .26 and .35.

Table 6 represents the mean value of the correlations between error scores for the specified task content and the rate scores indicated. For the older group, scores in all instances correlate negatively indicating a positive relation between slowness and inaccuracy. Correlations between speed and accuracy increased with age. The mean age difference in correlations is highly significant for each comparison made. It will also be noted that correlations of rate and error scores are significantly negative in nearly every instance for the older group. The correlations for the young group reach significance only in instances in which the rates of performance in word and number tasks are correlated with error scores for their respective content categories. The fact that error scores are more generally correlated with speed of performance in the elderly seems to indicate that slowness was a more general index of error proneness in the older population.

AN INTERPRETATION OF THE EXPERIMENTAL RESULTS

This section is mainly concerned with an attempt to give a consistent interpretation of the results of the preceding experiment. The section which follows is concerned with the further utility of set constructs.

Interrelationships among Speed Scores

With respect to the analysis of average trends in rate and time scores, the results of the study are in good agreement with the findings of Botwinick *et al.* (1958) Schaie (1958) and Chown (1961). As in these other studies, age related slowing of response speeds was relatively greater in tasks which required shifting than in tasks which did not. In addition, the results of this study provide some evidence that slowing in shift performances associated with age may be reduced when tasks provide step by step directions for the sequence of operations to be performed (Directions tasks) and exaggerated when tasks fail to provide information concerning the required sequence (selection tasks). In other words, the extent to which older individuals behaved more "rigidly" in shift tasks seemed to depend on the extent to which the tasks required them to direct and control their own shifting.

Another point to be made with respect to average trends is that the shift dimensions of tasks may be viewed as elements of task difficulty or task complexity. If this view is taken, the results are in agreement with those studies which report an increase in age related slowing of responses when tasks involve increased difficulty or complexity (e.g., Botwinick, Robbin and Brinley, 1960) but disagree with those which do not (e.g., Crossman and Szafran, 1956). However, despite the fact that older individuals, on the average, had more difficulty in shifting, the results as analyzed in Figure 2, do not suggest that increased difficulty defined in relation to the shift-nonshift dimensions of tasks was disproportional to "difficulty" associated with variations in task content. Consequently, it might be possible to conclude from these data *alone* that more "rigid" behavior of older individuals reflected nothing more than the fact that shift tasks were more difficult.

With respect to the correlational analyses of speed scores, the results of the principal component analyses suggested that a general component or, after rotations, a higher order factor was relatively more important in determining response rates in the older group. This appeared to be the main difference between correlational structures for the battery in the two groups. The increased importance of the general component in the older sample was not due to limitations imposed by the psychomotor features of tasks. In these respects, the results of the study agree with findings of Birren, Riegel and Morrison (1963). The fact that rigidity components or factors were not more important in accounting for individual differences in response rates in the older sample despite the fact that older individuals tended to behave more rigidly in shift tasks appears to be in general agreement with Chown's findings (Chown, 1961).

The main point to be made with regard to the outcome of the analyses of interrelationships among speed scores is that in themselves they reveal little concerning the nature of the functional changes which underlie the slower performances of the elderly. Had the regression of mean time scores, as plotted in Figure 2, been steeper for shift tasks than for nonshift tasks, it would have been possible to conclude that some sort of group rigidity trait contributed to slower responses in the elderly. Had the component analyses obtained evidence for larger shift rigidity factors in the older sample, it would have been possible to conclude that rigidity conceived as a source of individual variation in response speeds was relatively more important in determining response rates in the older population. However, neither of these conclusions can be drawn. The analysis of average trends reveals only that slowing of responses in the elderly increased as a function of increased task "difficulty." The correlational analyses suggest that slowing was associated with the increased importance of a general speed factor in the older population and that this was due to something other than psychomotor deficits in the elderly.

Speed and Accuracy

From a theoretical viewpoint, the experimental results relating accuracy, speed and age are of much greater interest than those involving speed scores alone. Correlations between speed and accuracy or, conversely, between slowness and error proneness were consistently higher in the older group. They were also less related to specific task content: in the old group, error scores for each type of task content were significantly correlated with rate scores for nearly every test in the battery. In the young sample, on the other hand, significant correlations were obtained only between arithmetic rates and arithmetic accuracy and between verbal rates and verbal accuracy. These age differences in the correlations between speed and accuracy thus suggest that the slowing of responses in older individuals may be interpreted as a general index of increased error proneness in these same individuals.

At first glance the notion that slowing of responses in older individuals is an index of increased error proneness seems to run contrary to the notion that slowness in the elderly reflects increased carefulness. Increased carefulness or caution in the elderly has been hypothesized in certain contexts by Welford, (1958, 1959), by Korchin and Basowitz (1956) and Basowitz and Korchin (1957) and by Botwinick, Brinley and Robbin (1958). In the latter study, Botwinick employed the notion of "increased responses reviewing tendency," pointing up the fact that older individuals may engage more or less automatically in such activity without conscious intent. However, increase in carefulness is not incompatible with increased error proneness since it may reflect a more or less conscious attempt on the part of the individual to compensate for error proneness. Consequently, the point here seems to be that if slowness in older individuals was to any extent the result of increased carefulness, this carefulness did not effectively compensate for increased error proneness despite the fact that tasks were self paced.

Birren (1955) proposed a possible interpretation of positive relationships between age related slowness and error proneness in self-paced tasks, hypothesizing that loss of speed associated with age might lead to inaccuracies when slowing began to affect the individual's capacity to integrate necessary items of information over time. In such a view, slowing in the primary change which places a greater burden on immediate memory capacity. A somewhat different notion might place the primary deficit in immediate memory capacity and view slowness as the effect. However, the relations between accuracy, speed and age obtained in the preceding experiment seem better rationalized by *set* rather than by immediate memory *constructs*.

Cognitive Sets and Error Proneness in the Elderly

Although subjects in both groups made relatively few errors, the average probability of a wrong response was higher for the older group with each type of task content. These age differences in error proneness could hardly have been due to the intrinsic difficulty of task elements. The materials were easy and the older subjects competent to handle them. Consequently, if any error in a *speeded* task may be interpreted as a set lapse, one might at the outset interpret age differences in error proneness in relation to set constructs. However, the case for set lapse does not end here.

There was definite evidence that age related error proneness in the nonshift word tasks was associated with failure to maintain sets. In these tests the subject was required to check one of three alternatives, two of which were appropriate to the other sets in the word category. Consequently, when the correct response was a synonym it was necessary to avoid checking an antonym and a rhyme. An error could thus occur as the result of an intrusion of what was an appropriate response for a previous task or as the result of some tendency to confuse synonyms with antonyms. Although the number of errors was too few to permit separation of these sources, it was apparent that subjects did tend to confuse synonyms with antonyms. In both the synonym and antonym tests about 90 per cent of errors made by both groups involved checking an antonym for a synonym or the reverse error. Only 50 per cent would have been expected on a chance basis. Since error proneness was significantly greater for the elderly in these tasks, older individuals tended to confuse synonyms and antonyms more frequently. This is in line with reports by Welford (1958), Kay (1955) and Birren (1955) that older individuals failed to inhibit response tendencies which were somehow task relevant but inappropriate.

Consideration of the regression of mean error scores for the elderly on those for the young (see Figure 2) finds the nonshift arithmetic tasks in which older persons were not significantly more error prone at the lower left. The verbal directions and memory tasks in which age differences in error proneness were greatest are at the upper right. Roughly arranged in between are the arithmetic shift tasks, the perceptual tasks and the nonshift verbal tasks. The fact that older individuals did not make errors more frequently in the nonshift arithmetic tasks compared with the fact that age differences in error proneness were greatest in the verbal Directions and Memory tasks points up the probable source of age differences in error proneness observed in this study. With the arithmetic materials, if the subject knew what operation he was to perform, he simply had to look for the correct answer among three possible alternatives. Given a pair of digits, 2 and 3, and the set to add, he could search for the exact answer, 5. With both verbal and perceptual materials on the other hand, he could be set only for the *category* of response. Consequently, both verbal and perceptual materials required the subject to actively consider and to accept or reject possible alternatives to an extent which was not the case in the arithmetic tasks.

It was also the case that alternatives to correct responses in the nonshift arithmetic tests were not relevant to the other sets employed with arithmetic materials. With both verbal and perceptual materials, on the other hand, wrong responses were always appropriate responses for other tasks in the given content category. There was thus a greater possibility that what were appropriate response tendencies for previous tasks would interfere with verbal and perceptual performances. In the verbal tasks there was the additional possibility of confusion between synonyms and antonyms on the basis of strong associational ties.

The conditions in shift tasks offered the possibility of further uncertainty concerning the response to be made. In addition, shift tasks provided more possibilities of interference from sets relevant to performance in previous tasks and to prior operations within the same task.

These considerations suggest the following interpretation of the increased error proneness associated with age. If, as in the nonshift arithmetic tests, the task provided the subject with a direct set for the exact answer, older individuals were not significantly more error prone. Age differences in error proneness increased as tasks required subjects to consider actively possible alternative responses, to inhibit inappropriate response tendencies and to shift from one type of operation to another. Age differences in error proneness were greatest in the verbal Directions and Memory tasks in which each of these factors might be expected to have maximal influence. Each of the factors operating along this complex dimension can be related to variation in the extent to which task conditions exercised control over the subject's activity by either directing the search for the correct answer or reducing the opportunity for set inappropriate responses. Consequently, both the existence and magnitude of age differences in error proneness may be interpreted as evidence that the elderly have difficulty in maintaining effective control of cognitive sets.

Conclusion

If error proneness in older individuals was primarily a function of set failure, the slow performances may be interpreted in the same way. The results of the experiment thus suggest that slow cognitive function associated with aging may be an index of increased difficulty in maintaining effective control of cognitive activity. Under circumstances in which the task itself provided direct control of the subject's search activity or where it failed to provide task relevant alternatives to the set appropriate response, this deficit was reflected primarily in slowing. However, when tasks placed an increased burden on the subject to control the direction of his own activity and particularly on his capacity to inhibit set inappropriate responses, this increased difficulty in maintaining set resulted in errors. This interpretation fits well with the outcome of the analysis of rate scores. To the extent that speed loss in older individuals reflects increased difficulty in maintaining cognitive sets, it would not be expected to vary independently in the shift and nonshift tasks employed in this experiment. On the other hand, slow individuals within an older population would be expected to have greater difficulty in shift tasks. Consequently, the results of this study, although not specifically designed to test the hypotheses suggested in the preceding section of the paper, are in agreement with them.

THE UTILITY OF SET CONSTRUCTS

The interpretation imposed on the results of the study presented in the preceding section agrees with hypotheses generated from the after-the-fact analysis of other studies reviewed in the second section of the paper. This interpretation was also imposed, after the fact, on the results of an experiment which was not explicitly designed to test hypotheses within the framework required for analysis of performance in relation to set constructs presented in the first section. Consequently, the main point to be made at present is that future analyses of age differences in speed and accuracy of performance in relation to set constructs can prove fruitful in generating specific hypotheses and in pointing out sources of variability which need to be controlled in testing other hypotheses.

One problem in the use of set constructs is that they are difficult to distinguish from immediate memory constructs. In order to employ sets effectively the subject must be able to hold them in mind. It is possible to make operational distinctions between set lapse and immediate memory lapse? First of all, as mentioned previously, it seems possible to distinguish between holding a set in mind and effectively employing it. If individuals give evidence of performing at above chance level of accuracy with respect to the set in question, it seems possible to conclude that they have "held" or retained the set. However, they may still vary in the effectiveness with which they employ the set, some individuals making more errors than others. The question arises as to whether a deficiency of this type is related to memory impairment as it is more conventionally defined in relation to holding time or quantity to be retained. For example, it may be possible to show that older persons can maintain complicated cognitive sets which place an increased burden on immediate memory more effectively than simpler sets if task features tend to generate more interference with the simpler sets. Such an experiment would not prove the difference between set lapse and brief memory lapse due to interference effects. It would, however, refine notions as to the exact nature of the cognitive impairment involved.

Another question arises concerning the interpretations of the higher correlations between slowness and error proneness reported in the previous section. These were interpreted as evidence for the notion that both slowness and error proneness reflect difficulty in maintaining sets for cognitive activity. This interpretation is somewhat more parsimonious than the notion that slowness reflects the operation of compensatory mechanisms. However, even if these results were repeated, the latter type of interpretation might still hold in certain cases. It might be argued that as older individuals perceived themselves operating more and more slowly, as a function of altered task conditions, they may have tended to hurry more and thus failed to take sufficient time for compensation. Such an explanation may have some attraction in view of the fact that errors measured in this task were errors of commission. Both Korchin and Basowitz (1957) and Talland (1959) have reported that older individuals tend to make errors of omission rather than of commission. Their tasks seem more likely to focus the subject's attention on responding to discrete cues rather than to completing a series of responses. Series tasks may place an increased emphasis on speed at the expense of accuracy which is not apparent when tasks focus more on responses to discrete signals (see (Welford, 1960). Consequently, the question of whether older individuals can effectively employ time to compensate for set lapse provides an interesting issue.

Finally, other testable hypotheses which may be generated by analysis of speeded performance in relation to set constructs relate to questions concerning rigidity factors and higher order speed factors in the elderly. The study presented in the preceding section was designed to test the hypothesis that "shift rigidity," considered in the factor analytic sense as an independent trait, would be a more important determinant of response rates in the elderly. Although older individuals did tend to behave more rigidly in shift tasks, this specific hypothesis had to be rejected. Instead it was suggested that the increased importance of a general component or higher order speed factor in the elderly might be associated with difficulty in maintaining effective control of cognitive sets in the absence of specific anticipations concerning what was to be done. This notion differs from the typical conceptualization of shift or process rigidity (see Cattell and Tiner, 1949) since it does not emphasize the importance of shifting *per se*. Instead it suggests that shifting is merely one of several factors which contribute to task uncertainty and thus place an additional burden on the subject's capacity to select appropriate and inhibit inappropriate responses. Birren has consistently emphasized the possible importance of a general, higher order speed factor in accounting for speed loss in the elderly (Birren and Botwinick, 1951; Birren, 1955; Birren, Riegel and Morrison, 1962). If such a factor exists, it seems likely that it is in some way associated with reduced efficiency of cognitive function. It is conceivable that it is associated with the capacity to maintain effective control of sets. In order to perform any task efficiently it is necessary to maintain effective control of the direction of activity. However, other factors might be more basic. For example, the deterioration of existing habit patterns might make cognitive control more necessary in the elderly or there may be some basic deterioration in capacity for activation and arousal.

Even if other alternatives prove correct, it seems unlikely that much progress can be made in isolating the relevant factor without employing a framework which explicitly emphasizes the analysis of the factors which condition and control the subject's predispositions for response.

SUMMARY

This paper first attempts to provide a conceptual framework for the systematic analysis of sppeeded performance in relation to set constructs. Detailed treatment was confined to the type of set which is conceived as an inferred state of predisposition for some specific goal related activity, a means-end readiness. These set constructs can be operationally defined in relation to variations in the subject's pre-task experience, by variations in task instructions and by variations in the sequence of events actually occurring during the performance. The subject's set at any particular instant during performance can be conceptualized as an effect of the interaction of these various types of influences. Sets, so defined, can be either appropriate or inappropriate and they can also vary in the extent to which they permit the subject to anticipate the exact details of performance. They are conceived as facilitating set appropriate responses and as inhibiting irrelevant or competing response tendencies. They appear to be particularly useful in the analysis of self-paced, speeded performances. One particularly useful feature is that errors in tasks which subjects perform at better than chance levels of accuracy can be interpreted as due to set lapse. Speed and accuracy can thus be rationalized within the same framework.

In the second section, there is an attempt to show how set constructs of this type may be used to clarify certain issues concerning slowness and error proneness in the elderly. At the present time we expect that older individuals will, on the average, perform more slowly in any task. In certain cases, the elderly may also be more error prone. Slowing appears to be linked, at least in part, with a cognitive deficit. However, theoretical formulations at present do not provide very specific predictions concerning which types of task manipulations can be expected to lead to either disproportional slowing or increased error proneness. After the fact analysis of different studies suggests that both disproportional slowing and increased error proneness may be related to difficulty in maintaining effective control of *cognitive sets*.

The third part of the paper presents the results of a study designed to test the hypothesis that slowness in the elderly can be attributed in part to rigidity of the type inferred from performance on shift or alternation tasks. This hypothesis was rejected. While older subjects did perform disproportionately slower in shift than in nonshift tasks, there was evidence for a high degree of correlation between speed loss in shift tasks and speed loss in nonshift tasks. However, here, too, the data support the notion that older individuals were disproportionately slower and more error prone in tasks which placed an increased burden on capacity to maintain effective control of cognitive sets. More specifically, the tasks employed varied in the extent to which the subject's previous experience, task instructions and the actual dimensions of the task itself could be expected to "set" the subject to respond accurately. Older subjects appeared at a disadvantage to the extent that these conditions failed to induce sets for the exact response. Of particular interest in this study was the fact that slowness and error proneness were more highly correlated in the older sample than in the younger one.

In the fourth section there is some consideration of how set constructs may prove of further use in the analysis of certain specific issues related to age differences in speed of performance. For example, set constructs may be of considerable use in the refinement of notions concerning how immediate memory deficit affects speed and accuracy of performance in the elderly.

REFERENCES

Allport, F. H.: (1955) Theories of Perception and the Concept of Structure. New York, John Wiley and Sons, Inc.

Basowitz, H. and Korchin, S. J.: (1957) Age differences in the perception of closure. *J. Abnorm. Soc. Psychol.,* 54:93-97.

Birren, J. E.: (1955) Age changes in speed of simple responses and perception and their significance for complex behavior. In *Old Age in the Modern World,* London, E. and S. Livingstone.

Birren, J. E.: (1956) The significance of age changes in speed of perception and psychomotor skills. In J. E. Anderson, ed.: *Psychological Aspects of Aging,* Washington, D. C., American Psychological Association, pp. 97-104.

Birren, J. E. and Botwinick, J.: (1951a) The relation of writing speed to age and to the senile psychoses. *J. Consult. Psychol.,* 15:243-249.

Birren, J. E. and Botwinick, J.: (1951b) Rate of addition as a function of difficulty and age. *Psychometrika,* 2:219-32.

Birren, J. E., Riegel, K. F. and Morrison, D. F.: (1962) Age differences in response speed as a function of controlled variations of stimulus conditions. *Gerontologia,* 6:1-18.

Botwinick, J.: (1959) Drives, expectancies and emotions. In J. E. Birren, ed.: *Handbook of Aging and the Individual: Psychological and Biological Aspects,* Chicago, University of Chicago Press, pp. 739-768.

Botwinick, J., Brinley, J. F. and Robbin, J. S.: (1958a) Task alteration time in relation to problem difficulty and age. *J. Geront.,* 13:414-417.

Botwinick, J., Brinley, J. F. and Robin, J. S.: (1958a) Task alternation effects of perceptual difficulty and stimulus exposure time on age differences in speed and accuracy of response. *Gerontologia,* 1:1-10.

Botwinick, J., Robbin, J. S. and Brinley, J. F.: (1960) Age differences in card-sorting performance in relation to task difficulty, task set and task practice. *J. Exp. Psychol.,* 59:10-18.

Brinley, J. F.: (1963) Unpublished doctoral dissertation. The Catholic University of America.

Broadbent, D. E.: (1958) *Perception and Communication.* London, Pergamon.

Cattell, R. B. and Tiner, L. G.: (1949) The varieties of structural rigidity. *J. Personality,* 17:321-341.

Chown, Sheila M.: (1961) Age and the rigidities. *J. Geront.,* 16:353-362.

Crossman, E. R. F. W. and Szafran, J.: (1956) Changes with age in the speed of information intake and discrimination. *Experientia, Supplementum IV.,* Symposium on Experimental Gerontology, Basel, Birkhauser, pp. 128-135.

Gibson, J. J.: (1941) A critical review of the concept of set in contemporary experimental psychology. *Psychol. Bull.,* 38:781-817.

Griew, S.: (1959) A further note on uncertainty in relation to age. *Gerontologia,* 3:335-339.

Guilford, J. P.: (1954) *Psychometric Methods.* 2nd ed., New York, McGraw-Hill.

Hotelling, H.: (1933) Analysis of a complex of statistical variables into principal components. *J. Educ. Psychol.,* 24:417-441, 498-520.

Jones, H. E.: (955) Age changes in adult mental abilities. In *Old Age in the Modern World,* London, E. and S. Livingstone.

Jones, H. E.: (1959) Intelligence and problem-solving. In J. E. Birren, ed.: *Handbook of Aging and the Individual: Psychological and Biological Aspects,* Chicago, University of Chicago Press, pp. 700-738.

Kay, H.: (1955) Some experiments on adult learning. In *Old Age in the Modern World,* London, E. and S. Livingstone, pp. 259-267.

Kay, H.: (1954) The effects of position in a display upon problem solving. *Quart. J. Exp. Psychol.*, 6:155-69.

Kleemeier, R. W. and Dudek, F.: (1950) A factorial investigation of flexibility. *Educ. Psychol. Measmt.*, 10:107-118.

Korchin, S. J. and Basowitz, H.: The judgment of ambiguous stimuli as an index of cognitive functioning in aging. *J. Personality*, 25:81-95.

Korchin, S. J. and Basowitz, H.: (1957) Age differences in verbal learning. *J. Abnorm. Soc. Psychol.*, 54:64-69.

Riegel, K. F.: (1959) A study of verbal achievements of older persons. *J. Geront.*, 14:453-456.

Schaie, K. W.: (1958) Rigidity—flexibility and intelligence: a cross-sectional study of the adult life span from 20 to 70 years. *Psychol. Monogr.*, 72:9, No. 462.

Solley, C. M. and Murphy, G.: (1960) *Development of the Perceptual World*. New York, Basic Books.

Talland, G. A.: (1959) Facilitation of accurate perception by anticipatory sets: the progressive effects of aging. *Gerontologia*, 3:339-350.

Thorndike, E. L. and Lorge, I.: (1944) *The Teacher's Word Book of 30,000 Words*. New York, Teachers College, Columbia University.

Thurstone, L. L.: (1944) *A Factorial Study of Perception*. Chicago, Univ. Chicago Press., pp. 148.

Tolman, E. C. *Purposive, Behavior in Animals and Men*. Berkeley, University of California Press, 1932.

Welford, A. T.: (1958) *Aging and Human Skill*. London, Oxford University Press.

Welford, A. T.: (1959) Psychomotor performance. In J. E. Birren, ed.: *Handbook of Aging and the Individual: Psychological and Biological Aspects*, Chicago, University of Chicago Press, pp. 562-613.

Welford, A. T.: (1960) Age changes in the time taken by choice, discrimination and the control of movement. *Gerontologia*, 5:129-145.

Wordworth, R. S. and Schlosberg, H. E.: (1954) *Experimental Psychology*. Rev. Ed., New York, Henry Holt and Co.

9

SPEED OF VERBAL PERFORMANCE AS A FUNCTION OF AGE AND SET: A REVIEW OF ISSUES AND DATA[1]

Klaus F. Riegel

THE ANALYSIS of verbal behavior is important for psychology as well as for other sciences because verbal behavior mediates observations, recording, processing, and analysis, but most important all our interpretations of scientific data. In comparison to simple sensory-motor performances, verbal behavior is more complex and thus its execution is more time consuming. However, the greater complexity and duration allow to analyze intervening components and to estimate their relative contribution to the overall results. Such an analysis has been facilitated by recent developments in linguistics and quantitative methods in the study of language.

In contrast to other skills, there exists a distinct repertoire of linguistic forms which an individual acquires slowly. The individual is—so to say—born into an environment of linguistic forms which are more or less systematically related to one another. For no other skill does a comparable structure of symbolic elements exist. If we take the attempts of a child to climb a staircase as an example, there is nothing except the physical conditions of the

[1] The studies by the present author included in this report have been supported by grants from the Foundations' Fund for Research in Psychiatry, New Haven, Connecticut, U. S. A.

environment that guide externally the performance of the child. But such physical conditions are merely comparable to the desk on which words are written or to the room in which they are spoken. Whereas at least psychologists do not thoroughly disagree about the components of verbal performances, namely the phonemes, letters, morphemes, syllables, words, and sentences, as well as sentence-parts, word types, pauses, etc., no ready made system is available by which the various movements of the child could be categorized. Consequently, it is extremely difficult and arbitrary to break the child's performance into component parts and to estimate their relative significance.

The case of describing distinct parts of verbal behavior facilitates the analysis of factors that intervene between stimulation and responding. Intervening variables can be studied in two ways. The first places greater emphasis on formal aspects, the other on the content of the components. On the basis of external response restrictions imposed in a task of verbal fluency and on the basis of the observed reaction times, for instance, we might postulate two intervening speed factors: the speed with which appropriate associations occur and the speed of selecting among these associations. In this case we emphasize the formal aspects and do not know the precise nature of the intervening components. However, we might also observe that old Ss shift in their approach to the task during continued performance or exhibit a different attitude from its beginning by emitting selected responses such as class names, function words, emotionally loaded words, etc. In this case we emphasize the content and the type of the intervening variables.

THE DISTINCTION OF INTERVENING VARIABLES IN THE STUDY OF VERBAL BEHAVIOR

The intervening components have been conventionally classified in a number of ways. The best known division is the classification into receptor, translation, and effector components of which the last term, because the motor action represents already a directly observable event, stretches the concept of intervening variables farthest beyond its limits. As mentioned before, psycholinguistic investigations allow more clearly than the study of any other form of behavior for an analysis of intervening events. In measuring, for example, the reaction time to a light stimulus, it is difficult to ascertain whether the delay is mainly caused by the slowness of the perception of the stimulus, the channelisation of the incoming information, or the execution of the movements. In the study of verbal behavior, however, we might measure separately the time taken for the *identification* or *recognition* of verbal stimuli which constitutes a small portion of the total time which Ss need to respond, for instance, by associating a word to a given stimulus. Of course, all we can observe under appropriately modified experimental conditions, namely in determining thresholds for visual identification, are again the reactions of the Ss, but the time of naming the stimuli becomes of little importance and all that is investigated is the exposure level at which Ss are able to name the stimulus correctly. The farther we delay Ss' responses by instructions or by other additional tasks, the more his accuracy as well as speed of performance will be obstructed by other intervening, namely memory, factors.

In order to obtain a relatively pure measure of verbal *motor* speed we might ask Ss to write or to read a paragraph aloud as fast as possible. The result will depend on Ss' perceptual speed but since we are able to obtain independent estimates of this variable, corrections of the data can be made. Moreover, we might ask Ss to name or write any word that comes into their minds. Thus, we obtain a measure of S's personal response speed which is not only independent of the complexity of the stimulation but also eliminates completely S's recognition or identification time.

The speed of fluency with which Ss emit words is, of course, dependent on other factors, such as the type of the tasks and the degree of response restrictions. Thus, it makes a difference whether we ask an S to name all words or only those beginning with a certain letter. More important, S's verbal fluency depends on the size of his own repertoire of words and subsequently on the degree of interference between competing words and the speed of their availability. All these factors and numerous other characterize the translation rather than the motor phase of a response sequence. While, thus, the verbal fluency test does not yield as pure a measure of motor speed as a copying or reading task does, it leads us into the analysis of the translation phase which seems of greatest significance for the study of verbal behavior and aging.

The processes of *transmission* or *translation* that intervene between stimulus perception and response emission are dependent on long-term habits as well as on short-term sets of an individual. In addition, we will distinguish between cognitive and non-cognitive components. On one hand cognitive components represent long established verbal habits such as sentence and word familiarities and on the other are dependent on particular task conditions such as the probabilities of the possible responses, or of response classes. Non-cognitive components are either long-term interests and attitudes or the motivational or emotional conditions which an individual faces during the particular testing situation and which might be imposed upon him by the experimentors instruction.

Since the two classifications are not mutually exclusive, we have: 1) long-term, cognitive habits such as word or sentence familiarity; 2) long-term, non-cognitive interests and attitudes. Note that the effectiveness of both these long-term conditions is implicit and not necessarily known to Ss. In contrast, the short-term conditions of 3) a cognitive, or 4) a non-cognitive set are usually explicitly induced by the task instructions. They either characterize the restrictions imposed upon the class of responses or the incentives and motives, as in the case of the need for achievement instructions.

While, thus, the translation process seems complex from the beginning, its close relationship to thinking and reasoning increases the difficulties. Thinking and reasoning involve internal processes which are not directly dependent on the experimenter's stimuli and instructions and intervene in addition to the other factors before a performance is completed. In spite of these difficulties, and keeping the above distinctions in mind, we begin the following review with a discussion of the most complex and general findings and proceed to explicate the results and to analyse their components.

SPEED AND ACCURACY OF VERBAL PERFORMANCE

In discussing changes in verbal behavior over the life span it seems reasonable to assume that an individual's vocabulary and his repertoire of grammatical forms undergo a continuous, even if slight, expansion. Stated differently, the ensemble of words that a person has heard, read, said or written increases with age. Although, as it follows from Lehman's (1953) data of figure 1A, this relation between age and total number of words will be S-shaped rather than linear, the curve will not reach a

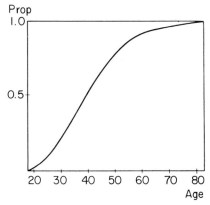

Figure 1A. Accumulative record of 843 works by 330 American authors plotted against age at which written (after Lehman 1953, p. 80)

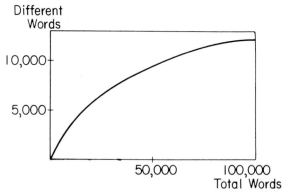

Figure 1B. Theoretical curve of the number of different words plotted against total number of words, derived by Carroll (1938) for James Joyce's Ulysses.

maximum as long as the individual continues to engage in some form of verbal communication. As the ensemble of words becomes larger the likelihood increases that some very rare words appear that have not occurred before to the S. These words might have been only recently introduced into the language, i.e., the universe of words is not necessarily regarded as fixed or static —or might be so rare that they require such a large ensemble of words for their occurrence.

Our assumption implies also that the number of different words increases with the size of the total ensemble of words perceived or used which in turn is positively related to the age of an individual. This statement reveals a close similarity of our analysis with those of word variability and text length in literary statistics as proposed by Carroll (1938), Yule (1944), Zipf (1949), and recently discussed by Herdan (1960) as well as the present author (1964a) (See Figure 1B, 9A and 9B).

Instead of the formal analyses suggested by these and other authors it is of greater importance in the present context to search for empirical support for the assertion that the vocabulary size increases even if slightly during the whole age span. Here, ample evidence has been accumulated. A high stability during middle and late adulthood or even a slight increase in the passive vocabulary has been observed for open-ended or multiple choice recognition tests (see Riegel, 1958). Madorah Smith (1955, 1957a, b) found similar evidence for the active vocabulary by analyzing the letters, journals and diaries written by two ladies during periods of about fifty years of their lives. Some additional results have been obtained in the following vocabulary study.

Study 1. 120 Ss between the ages of seventeen and nineteen years and seventy-six Ss each of the age groups fifty-five to fifty-nine, sixty to sixty-four, sixty-five to sixty-nine, seventy to seventy-four, and seventy-five years and over were individually tested. Five verbal achievement tests consisting of twenty items each were administered. Among these only the vocabulary or Synonym test is presently of interest. Here, Ss had to identify one response among five alternative words which means the same or almost the same as the test or stimulus word. Although the test was given without any limitation the total time of performance was recorded. According to the results the performance time increases markedly with age whereas the vocabulary scores change only slightly during the later years of life (Riegel and Riegel, 1964b).

In order to explain the increase in performance time with age in the simplest possible manner we could expand our previous assumption, and postulate that the larger the vocabulary of a person, the longer it will take him to check it completely. Such a search is afforded for detecting the correct response of the vocabulary items and thus the increase in performance time with age might simply depend on the increase in the number of different words known and stored by a person.

However, the results of study 1 do not support this interpretation since the performance time increases over and above that amount which is predictable on the basis of the vocabulary changes. Further negative evidence is obtained by a correlation analysis of the power and time scores of the test. For such an analysis we pooled the old Ss into the two larger age groups of fifty-five to sixty-four and sixty-five years and older. For most of the five tests mentioned and for the Synonym test in particular, the correlations for the young and the Ss above sixty-five years were positive and significant. Most correlations for the age group fifty-five to sixty-four years, however, were negative and significant.

The age differences in the correlations between power and time scores suggest again that the performance time increases over and above that amount which can be accounted for by the increase in the size of the verbal repertoire. Consequently, we have to take age differences in the speed of functioning or association into account. Such speed of functioning which is the first of at least two components determining the observed speed of performance will be highest for the young Ss, and decreases slightly toward our first elderly group. For the oldest Ss, however, the decline is considerable. The size of the repertoire represents a second component which is higher for both elderly groups than for the young Ss.

Stated differently, young Ss have a relatively small vocabulary. Since they also function very fast, time and power scores are

positively correlated. The overall time of performance which is
dependent on both these factors is low and it is to an advantage
for the young Ss to take much time for the completion of the
multiple choice items. For the first elderly group the vocabulary
is larger but the association time is still low. Thus, the overall
time of performance is higher than for the young, but time and
power scores are negatively correlated and it does not necessarily
pay off for these Ss to spend too much time for the solution of the
items. For the very old Ss the vocabulary is large but the association time has also increased to a considerable extent. Therefore,
power and time scores are positively correlated and the overall
performance time is very high.

Our interpretations have to be regarded as tentative only and
should be compared with those reported by Brinley in the present
book as well as with the general interpretations advanced by
Lorge (1936, 1940). In our discussion of a formal analysis of
processes intervening in verbal performance to be presented below, related evidence will be cited. The following study lends
more direct support to our assumption on age changes in association time and implies that a free word association task represents
a relative pure measure of the speed of functioning, i.e., is relatively unaffected by the size of the vocabulary.

> *Study 2.* The same 500 young and old Ss of study 1 gave re-
> sponses to 120 stimuli of a word association test. These 120
> words were identical with the stimuli of the five verbal achieve-
> ment tests. S was asked to respond with the first word that
> came to his mind after perceiving the stimulus. The responses
> were recorded and the associative reaction time was measured
> in units of half seconds. The reaction times of the first elderly
> group were found to be slightly but insignificantly lower than
> those of young Ss. The reaction time increases significantly be-
> yond the age level of sixty-five years. The results are presented
> in greater detail in Figure 4 (Riegel and Riegel 1964b).

The high stability of the association reaction times up to an age
of about sixty-four years and the marked increase thereafter support our interpretation of the relationship between the time and
power scores of the achievement tests. Over and above the
changes in performance time that were due to an increase in the

size of their vocabularies, our oldest Ss are indeed less efficient than both the younger age groups. Similar findings have been reported in the Stanford Later Maturity Study (Miles, 1931), where the reaction time was found to be relatively stable throughout most parts of the adulthood and to increase only late in life. Changes in performance speed had to be primarily attributed to the decline in other components such as in movement speed or motility.

THE DEVELOPMENT OF LONG-TERM VERBAL HABITS

According to our previous assumption, S's continuous participation in verbal communication leads to a progressive enlargement of his verbal repertoire. Certainly, the acquisition of language does not merely imply the learning of isolated elements of such a repertoire but at the very moment a person is exposed to a linguistic environment he is also confronted with its structural characteristics. Thus, a child that hears the explanation: "A zebra is an animal with stripes" does not only become familiarized with words (particularly with the word ZEBRA) but also with the syntactical organization and the semantic or logical relations of class concepts and attributes (Riegel and Riegel 1963).

In the following discussion we are emphasizing these semantic and logical relations which represent the linguistic counterparts of the individual's conceptualizations and thinking.

> *Study 1 (continued).* In a pilot investigation to the main study 56 Ss between sixteen and nineteen years and seventy-four Ss above sixty-five years of age were tested individually. Aside from the Synonym test mentioned before the following multiple choice tests were applied: Antonym test, Selection test (an essential part or attribute has to be identified, like leg to table), Classification test (two coordinates had to be identified, like chair and bed to table), and Analogy test. The scales consist of twenty items each (Riegel 1959).

In order to derive testable hypotheses the association model of Figure 2 has been developed. It contains all test and response words which are of interest for our demonstration while all other words, even those which might be much closer associated have been excluded. In particular, it was reasoned that associations between words which are related in meaning to one another (e.g., synonyms, antonyms, attributes or parts, coordinates, superordinates, etc.) should become strengthened during life by continuous accumulation of information. Therefore, old persons who had more linguistic experience should have an advantage in the use of such associations. These associations play an exceptional role for the solutions of the Synonym test, because there exists only a very limited number of synonyms to any given word.

Excluding all but the Selection test from our present discussion, a greater number of possible responses exist. Some of these responses are shown in Figure 2. Even if all possible connections become strengthened during the life span, the great number of associations requires some specific discriminations, and the recognition of the relationship particularly demanded by the test item. Thus, the strengthening of the associations and the ad-

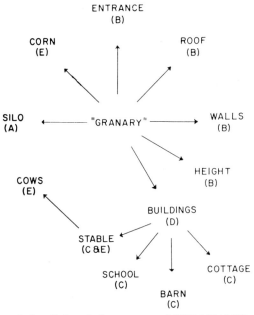

Figure 2.   Associative links of the test word "GRANARY" to possible response words of four verbal tests: (A) response word of the Synonym Test; (B) possible response words of the Selection Test; (C) possible response words of the Classification Test; (D) supraordinate for the response words of the Classification Test; (E) test words and response word of the Analogy Test.

vantage to older persons are less significant for the solutions of the Selection items than for the solutions of the Synonym items.

Stated in terms of information theory, all words shown in Figure 2 have a certain probability of being evoked by the test word. These probabilities differ between the tests. While for the items of the Synonym Test one can think of very few alternatives or correct answers only, there exist many more possible responses for the Selection as well as for the Classification test. The probabilities for selecting any particular reponse decrease in the order of the tests just mentioned. Since the association structure becomes increasingly strengthened by the accumulation of experiences during the life span, older persons are particularly favored in their performance the more the tests require the use of redundant knowledge, i.e., the less information is provided by the response term.

As shown in figure 3B, old Ss were indeed more handicapped when the redundancy between test and response words was

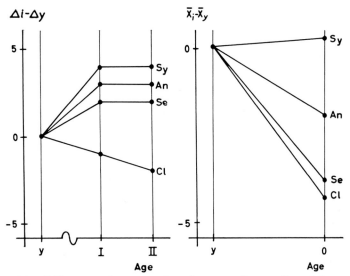

Figure 3A. Differences in proportions between "correct" and "incorrect" associations by tests.*

Figure 3B. Average scores on four verbal tests.*

————

* (Sy = Synonym Test, An = Antonym Test, Se = Selection Test, Cl = Classification Test).

small. The degree of decline was zero for the Synonym Test and increased in the order: Antonyms, Selections, Classifications, Analogies. Thus, the results support the model. Since the degree of association between test and response words has been inferred only, more direct evidence was required. In particular it had to be shown whether the differential changes in verbal achievement with age might be at least in part explained by changes in associative verbal habits.

For this purpose we enumerated for each item all associations given in study 2 that were either identical with the "correct" or any of the four "incorrect" responses of the multiple choice tests. For further simplifications, we computed the differences in the proportions of "correct" and "incorrect" associations and held the level of the young Ss constant for all tests. In this way, we can evaluate age changes in associative habits in reference to our standard group of young Ss. As shown in Figure 3A, the trends of the difference scores in associations are clearly proportional to the trends of the achievement tests. The associative differences of the Synonym items show the greatest increase with age and are followed first by the Antonym, and second by the Selection items. The scores of the Classification items decline slightly with age.

Although we succeeded in supporting our interpretation, we did not expect that changes in associative habits would explain all the age differences in achievement scores. In particular, the unadjusted results of the association test suggest that most achievement tests would become progressively easier to aging Ss. Since the data of Figure 3B certainly do not support such an interpretation, other factors than associative habits influence the performance of Ss. For instance, a decline in short-term retention as suggested by Welford (1956) and tested by Fraser (1958) and Inglis and Caird (1963), might hinder elderly Ss to scan the alternatives of the achievement items as efficiently as young Ss. Moreover, they might not be equally susceptible to the particular test instructions. While the methods of studies 1 and 2 do not allow for a precise analysis of these factors, our data supports very clearly a general correlation between differential changes in associative habits and verbal achievements.

THE EFFECT OF LONG-TERM HABITS
ON VERBAL PERFORMANCE

Thus far, our concern has been with complex psychological functions as measured by our achievement tests. Also the associative reaction times are gross indices of psychological processes only since they embrace receptor, translation, and effector components. Certainly, separate estimates of the relative importance of these components are desirable. In order to derive such estimates the responses of the word association test have been subdivided into various classes. Figure 4A shows such a classification. Here responses are separated that occur only once to a given stimulus within each of the three age levels from those that are most commonly given. The proportions of the most common, or primary responses decrease slightly, although not significantly. The proportions of single responses increase rather markedly. The

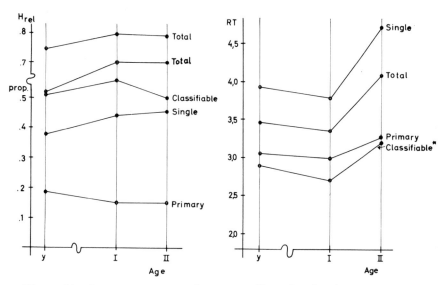

Figure 4A. Average measures of response dispersion for three age groups.
Figure 4B. Average latencies (sec.) for four response classes for three age groups.

---

* Since single responses were excluded from the classification the figures represent the proportions of classifiable responses out of all but the single responses. Primary responses might be part of the classifiable responses.

average reaction times of single responses are higher than the total averages of all responses, which in turn are higher than the averages of all primary responses. It should be noted that these results are not in full agreement with those of Doerken (1956). However, in his as well as in the few other relevant investigations (Kent and Rosanoff, 1910; O'Connor, 1934) relatively young adults have been employed.

The observed changes in response commonality and uniqueness support indirectly our previous assumption on the increase in word variability with age. The proportions of different responses and the relative uncertainty of the responses lend more direct support to this assumption. As shown in the upper part of Figure 4A, both measures increases from age level to age level. Quite to the contrary, the proportions of responses called classifiable are significantly higher for the first elderly group than for both the young and the very old Ss. This result does not follow from our assumption and some other factors seem effective, factors which might represent the task orientation or differences in the set of Ss. For a detailed analysis of this question more has to be said about the classification of the response.

> *Study 2 (continued)*. Classifiable responses are words that have a certain abstract, linguistic relation to the stimuli. For this classification nine judges gave two restricted associations to each of the same 120 stimuli used in the main study of free word associations. The retrictions are in terms of the following word relations: superordinates (Su), coordinates (Co), synonyms (Sy) antonyms (An), and parts or attributes (Pa). The criterion lists derived were applied to all but the single responses of the free word association test (Riegel and Riegel, 1963, 1964b).

As shown in Figure 5, the high proportion of classifiable responses in the first elderly group is particularly due to their preference for synonyms, coordinates and parts or attributes as responses. The proportions of antonyms show a slight decline which is comparable to the decline in primary responses and is indeed linked with this change as a more detailed analysis has revealed (Riegel and Riegel, 1964b). The low reaction times of the first elderly group, on the other hand, are particularly due to the fast emission of antonyms and to a lesser extent to the emission of the other types of responses mentioned above.

Further insight into the age differences can be obtained by pooling all classifiable responses and subdividing them according to the frequencies of the stimulus words. In particular, three frequency classes were used, namely of stimuli occurring more than 1000 times (ho) according to Kaeding's count (1898), between ten and 1000 times (mi), and less than ten times (ni). As shown in Figure 6A, the differences between the three age levels have to be attributed primarily to the preference of the first elderly group to give classifiable responses to very rare stimuli (ni), i.e., in situations where they find a challenge and opportunity to exhibit their knowledge and experience. Their low re-

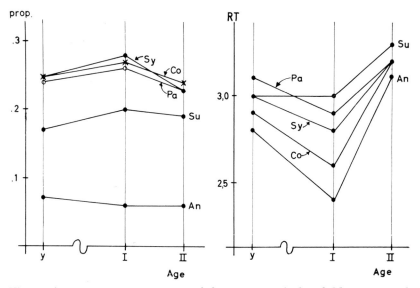

Figure 5A. Average proportions of five groups of classifiable responses*
for three age groups.**

Figure 5B. Average latencies of five groups of classifiable responses for
three age groups.**

---

* Because of the overlap between the response classes, responses might be repeatedly listed and thus the sum of the proportions exceeds 1.00.

** (Sy = Synonyms, Co = Coordinates, Pa = Parts or Attributes, Su = Superordinates, An = Antonyms).

action times, on the other hand, have to be least attributed to their fast response to common stimuli. In this case the reaction times of the classifiable responses do not differ between the young and the first elderly group (see Figure 6B). Giving such a high proportion of meaningful responses, seems to indicate that S's of the first elderly group regard the test as an achievement rather than an association task. However, this interpretation raises the question as to why very old Ss regress from classifiable to less meaningful responses.

An answer is not readily available but some observations during the testing sessions are helpful for an interpretation. In general, the association test was extremely difficult to administer to both elderly age groups. To respond with any word that occurs to him does not seem to make enough sense to an elderly S and thus he tries particularly hard to structure the testing situation according to his own thoughts. At first, this leads to a preference for classifiable and meaningful responses. But very old Ss are often unable

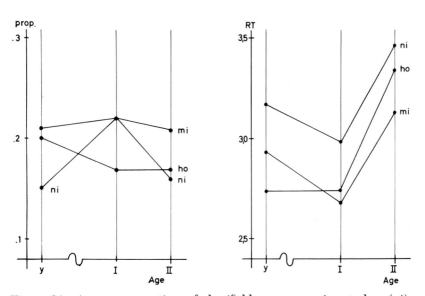

Figure 6A. Average proportions of classifiable responses given to low (ni), medium (mi), and high-frequent stimuli (ho) by three age groups.

Figure 6B. Average latencies (sec.) of classifiable responses given to low (ni), medium (mi), and high-frequent stimuli (ho) by three age groups.

to respond in proper time and regress to subjective evaluations of the stimulus or even of the testing situation. This leads to a significant increase in stereotyped, emotional and evaluative statements usually given in the first person singular. At the same time a marked increase in response time does occur.

It should be realized that nothing in the instructions could have encouraged the first elderly group in their preference for meaningful responses and the second elderly group in their regression toward subjective responses. The decision for a particular approach to the task was completely left to the Ss. Thus, the most remarkable result of the reported study is the systematic preference of elderly Ss for such a cognitive orientation. Because of the importance of learning, achievement, and success in our western cultures such a strategy is of no surprise. It also indicates an interdependency between the non-cognitive need for achievement and the cognitive test orientation. Because of their self-restriction to such a subset of responses, or more generally, because of their non-cognitive need for achievement old Ss succeed in keeping their response speed at a low level. Still later in life, however, Ss do not always succeed in applying such a strategy in a proper manner and in proper time, and regress to an unspecific and unstructured way of responding. At the same time their response time increases markedly.

AN ANALYSIS OF TRANSLATION PROCESSES IN VERBAL PERFORMANCES

As a second possibility, the effect of long-term habits on verbal performances can be studied by applying grammatical classifications such as form classes. Excluding the single responses from our analysis, it becomes technically feasable to use this classification for both stimuli and responses.

Classifying both the stimuli and the responses into form-classes moves our study quite close to an analysis of information exchange, in which a message quantified into four classes is received, transmitted, and sent off by the Ss. Accordingly, we will regard the dependency of the responses on the stimuli as more or less random and thus, the success of predicting the responses will vary. If all Ss in a group give unique responses, our prediction attains its lowest value; if all Ss emit the same response our prediction is perfect. The more the responses approach the second condition, the greater will be our inclination to derive specific interpretations and to detect systematic features of the intervening transmission or translation processes.

As shown in Figure 7, Ss use quite frequently the form class of the stimuli for their responses. This is particularly true for concrete nouns and is least true for abstract nouns. There are also some age differences. Old Ss are less inclined to use the same form class and thus the degree of distortion is again greater for the old than for the young Ss. In particular, old Ss shift toward a greater use of verbs in response to concrete-noun-stimuli; toward

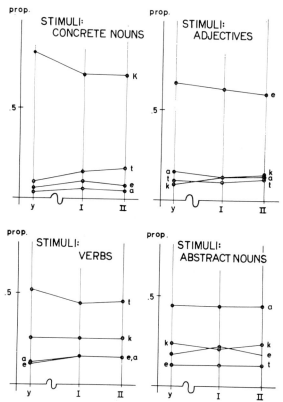

Figure 7. Average proportions of responses falling into four form classes given to stimuli grouped into the same four form classes (k = concrete nouns, a = abstract nouns, t = verbs, e = adjectives).

concrete nouns in case of adjective-stimuli; and toward either adjectives or abstract nouns in case of verb-stimuli.

For the interpretation of these results, we follow Jenkins (1954) and Susan Ervin's (1961) distinction between paradigmatic and syntagmatic verbal associations. In the first case, Ss use the form class of the stimuli in their responding. They are scanning their repertoire for responses that are possible substitutes for the stimuli. The response RUN to WALK would be an example and all synonyms and most coordinates fall into that class. Giving syntagmatic responses, Ss are following more closely grammatical pattern, as in TOWN to WALK. The response might be a word next or near to the stimulus when used in a phrase. In this case greater deviations from the form classes of the stimuli are to be expected and the responding is not in terms of a set of alternatives which might be substitutes to one another.

According to our data, all Ss prefer paradigmatic over syntagmatic responses, but older Ss rely relatively more on grammatical habits than the young. Because verb-responses to concrete nouns are most likely to indicate the usage of the stimulus-object, the differences between the age groups indicate also a greater preference for functional responses on the part of old Ss. On the other hand, concrete nouns given to adjective-stimuli seem to denote the objects which have the qualities indicated by the stimulus. The same might be true when adverbial responses qualify verb-stimuli and thus, there is another way of interpreting the differences in long-term verbal habits between young and old Ss.

SHIFTS IN THE UTILIZATION OF LONG-TERM HABITS DURING CONTINUED VERBAL PERFORMANCE

The tendency of our first elderly group to search for meaningful responses can be regarded as a learned set which is not necessarily explicitly known to Ss. While we will not attempt to analyse differences in verbal learning and memory between young and old Ss as studied by Ruch (1933, 1934), Gilbert (1941), Korchin and Basowitz (1957), Bromley (1958) and reviewed by Jerome (1959), of particular interest for the present discussion is the question of whether old Ss are able to change their set and, thus, are incidentally learning during continued performance. In the following study, we are dealing again with a cognitive set, but while previously Ss were allowed to follow any tendency in their responding which they felt inclined to choose, in this study the approach to the task is more distinctly determined by the stimuli and the instructions. Shifts between cognitive and non-cognitive tendencies are hardly possible.

Study 3. A group of twenty-three elderly and thirty young volunteers at the Clinical Center of the National Institute of Mental Health participated in the experiment. They were requested to complete forty syllables into words by adding other syllables or letters. In the first task (discrete word completions) they gave one response orally. The reaction time was recorded. In the second task (continuous word completions) they wrote as many words as they could find within the time

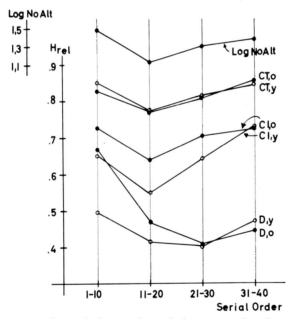

Figure 8A. Logarithms of the number of alternatives listed in the Thorndike-Lorge Count (log NoAlt) and relative entropy of responses (H rel) by old (O) and young subjects (Y) plotted against serial order of stimuli.*

---

* D = responses of discrete task; Cl = first responses of the continuous task; CT = all responses of the continuous task.

limit of forty-five seconds. Identical stimuli were used in both tasks. Stimuli were first syllables of words in the Thorndike-Lorge Count (1944). The response variability within the age groups was determined for each item by computing the relative uncertainty of the distribution. In Figure 8 this measure as well as the reaction time are plotted against the serial order of the items (Riegel and Birren, 1964).

The results of Figure 8A indicate differences in the response variability of young and old Ss for the four consecutive blocks of ten items. Apparently, we did not completely succeed in randomizing the stimuli and in eliminating differences in the response availability. The response variability is lower for the second and third than for the fourth and particularly the first set of items. Supportive evidence for this interpretation is obtained from the logarithms of the average number of different words that begin with the same syllables and are listed in the Thorndike Lorge

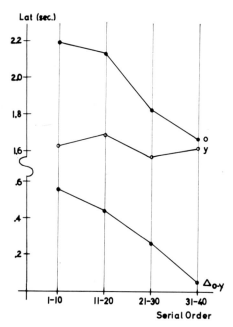

Figure 8B. Responses latencies (Lat) of old (O) and young subjects (Y) plotted against serial order of stimuli.

Count. These figures follow a trend closely parallel to that of the response variability and are lower for the second and third than for the fourth and the first block of stimuli.

The number of different words listed in the word count could be used to correct the data, i.e., to level out the differences in response availability between the four consecutive blocks of items. If such corrections are made differences between the age groups on the discrete task will not disappear, however. As shown in Figure 8A the response dispersion of the old Ss on the discrete task begins at a much higher level but is considerably reduced during continued performance until it drops below the level of young Ss. In other words, the commonality of their responses increases the longer the task lasts and at the same time (shown in Figure 8B) the speed of their reactions increases until it reaches almost the level which young Ss attain right at the onset of their performance. Our results indicate that old Ss are able to change their approach to the task during performance by shifting between different verbal habits and thus become increasingly efficient. Our results do not indicate that young Ss are unable to do so. They rather attain a most efficient set at the very beginning and do not need to change thereafter. Again, old Ss do not need to be clearly aware of their change in the approach to the task. However, appropriate inquiries on this question were not included in the present study.

THE EFFECTS OF SHORT-TERM, COGNITIVE SETS ON VERBAL PERCEPTION

The word completion task is similar to the word association test mentioned above in that no explicit instructions are given that might induce Ss to change their approach in the manner observed. The analysis of the utilization of such explicit information is, however, as important as the study of the adaptation of the most efficient approach without explicit cues. Unfortunately, no investigations are available that are applying comparable association techniques and thus are dealing with psychological processes that embrace receptor, translation, and effector aspects. The two studies available give particular emphasis to perceptual processes of young and old Ss.

Study 4. A group of twenty-four young and sixteen old Ss participated in an experiment in which tachistoscopic recognition thresholds for words were measured. The stimuli were taken from the verbal achievement tests mentioned in study 1 and thus are also identical with some of the stimuli of the word association test of study 2. They were exposed under the following conditions: 1) The test words were administered in order to determine a base level of perceptual functioning. 2) The correct response words of the multiple choice tests were exposed to a subgroup of Ss with no further instructions. (NI-treatment). 3) The results were compared with those of another subgroup of Ss to which the same words as under 2) were administered with the additional instructions of the tests (WI-treatment), i.e., the test words were shown printed on cards and Ss were informed that the words to be tachistoscopically exposed would mean the same or almost the same as the word on the card (synonym item); or that it would mean the opposite (antonym item) etc. 4) A third subgroup of Ss were treated as under 3) but the correct response word of the multiple choice tests were shown together with their four wrong alternatives (WIA-treatment). Thus, the stimulus uncertainty was increased and the experimental situation simulated almost perfectly the conditions of the achievement testing (Riegel, Riegel, and Wendt 1962).

As expected from previous reviews of the evidence (see Weiss, 1959; and Braun, 1959), the perceptual thresholds of old Ss were much higher than those of the young. Indeed, there was hardly any overlap in the threshold distributions. More important, old Ss failed completely to make use of the additional instructions provided under the WI-treatment which led to a significant decrease in thresholds for the young Ss. Since old Ss perform well above chance level in the multiple choice tests, it seems quite unlikely that they failed to comprehend the experimental instructions in general. Nevertheless, they did not limit their search to words that are related to the printed key words in the instructed manner but seemed to have continued to search over the whole range of possible perceptual hypotheses that were appropriate under the NI-treatment.

The results are even more dramatic when the uncertainty of

the stimuli was increased by presenting simultaneously the wrong alternatives together with the correct response word (WIA-treatment). Under such condition a highly significant increase in thresholds was observed for the old Ss in comparison to their performance under both the NI- and the WI-treatments, and in comparison to the young Ss. This result is the more remarkable because the thresholds under the WIA-treatment are but a fifth of the scores actually observed. In other words, we rely on an estimated threshold for the detection of one out of the five words only. Since a S was not requested to identify all the remaining words after he had recognized that one which he regarded as the correct response, lower thresholds were expected under the WIA- than the WI- or even the NI-treatments.

This prediction was confirmed for the young Ss, who frequently recognized the correct response word after only one or even after none of the wrong alternatives were identified. Old Ss, however, seemed markedly confused by the simultaneous presentation of five words. In their attempt to avoid any risk, they frequently proceeded to identify all the five words before they reached a decision. Also quite often, and possibly because of lack in short-term retention, they had to go through the blocks of five words more than once since they had already forgotten the words that they had identified before.

Thus, old Ss lack the ability to utilize instructions given to them explicitly by the experimenter, and fail to relate the perceived information to their stock of prior knowledge. However, they seem to be well able to apply their own implicit set as well as to change such a set during their performance and to their own advantage as the results of study 3 and 4 have shown. Indeed, one might venture to say that their own implicit set overshadows the set induced by the experimenter and thus interferes with their performance. Their failure is, however, only revealed under the more difficult conditions of our perceptual tasks. Old Ss are well able to comprehend and utilize the task instructions for their performance on the multiple choice test which was not administered under any time stress.

Some additional evidence on the inability of old Ss to utilize explicitly induced sets has been obtained from the multiple choice tests of study 1. One list including ten items each of three of these tests were administered in a random order. This made replications of the test instructions for each item necessary. Under a second condition, ten items from each of the same three tests were presented as blocks. Here the instructions were given only once at the beginning of each test.

The repeated shifts between the items of the three tests under the random condition were expected to hinder the performance of the old who are known to be less flexible in their thoughts and judgements than young Ss (see Heglin, 1956; Schaie, 1958; Riegel and Riegel, 1960). This expectation was not confirmed. Since old Ss performed even slightly better under the random than under the ordered conditions, our result seems to indicate again some difficulties of old Ss in utilizing the task instruction. Their performance is improved if they are repeatedly made aware of the task.

THE EFFECT OF A SHORT-TERM, NON-COGNITIVE SET ON VERBAL PERCEPTION

In the preceding study the emphasis was on the application of cognitive sets in perceptual recognition tasks. In the following discussion we turn our attention to the question whether a non-cognitive instructional set influences recognition thresholds for words and whether age differences can be detected. The growing interest in the influence of social and personality variables on psychological behavior, which originated during the early forties, has produced a great number of studies in which particularly motivational variables and perceptual thresholds have been analysed. The following study is devoted to the analysis of age differences in the effect of achievement motivation on visual recognition thresholds.

> *Study 5.* A group of twenty-four old and twenty-four young Ss participated in the experiment. At the beginning of the first session Ss were matched into three subgroups according to their need for achievement (long-term motivational habit) as measured by McClelland's test (1953) and according to their tachistoscopic recognition thresholds as measured in some preliminary trials. Subsequently, in the first group (control group) young and old Ss had to read a pack of cards on which nonsense

words of the form CVCVC (paralogs) were typed at varying frequencies, namely one, two, five, ten, and twenty-five times respectively. One week later tachistoscopic recognition thresholds were measured. In the first experimental group of young and old Ss a need for achievement arousing instruction was given prior to the reading of the cards and thus the acquisition of the word frequencies was motivated. The particular instruction included some remarks on the significance of the tasks and on the possibility of evaluating the intelligence of Ss on the basis of their performance. Thus, they were encouraged to do the best they could. Again, one week later the tachistoscopic recognition thresholds were determined. The second experimental group of young and old Ss was treated in almost the same manner except that the need for achievement arousing instruction was given during the second session, just prior to the recognition measurements. Thus the perceptual process rather than the acquisition of the word frequencies was influenced by the motivation arousing instructions (unpublished study by the present author).

Previous interpretations of the effect of personality variables on perception such as Dember's (1958) have emphasized that the influence of word frequencies on thresholds can be considered as an influence of an implicit, cognitive set. During their acquisition of the language, Ss became more familiar with some words than with others and thus gain some notions of their relative frequencies. Subsequently, they will find it easier to recognize common, instead of unfamiliar, words.

In our present investigation we confirmed these findings for old Ss. They were found to be about as able as young persons to gain a notion about the relative frequencies of our paralogs merely by reading the deck of cards presented to them. The correlations between the logarithms of the frequencies and the recognition thresholds are —.87 for the young and —.76 for the old control group. This result is the more remarkable since in previous studies of young Ss intermission periods of only twenty minutes instead of one week were used. It also confirms the findings of the studies 1 and 2 that old Ss are well able to acquire and to utilize a set unless it is explicitly imposed upon them by the experimenter.

In regard to the second manipulation, i.e., the induced motivational set, we failed again to detect a positive effect upon the performance of our old Ss. Whereas the threshold of young Ss were significantly lowered when the motivation arousing instructions were given prior to the learning of the paralogs, the thresholds of old Ss were significantly higher than those of the control group when the motivation arousing instruction was given prior to either the learning or the perceptual task.

The failure to influence the performance of the old by an explicit, non-cognitive set is similar to the results of our previous attempt to improve their performance through the induction of an additional cognitive set. This result is also similar to findings by Engler and Freeman (1956) who noted an inability in highly anxious Ss to utilize set inducing instructions in a profitable manner. In general, old Ss are well able to apply implicit cognitive and non-cognitive sets, particularly when these are acquired over long periods of time, such as verbal habits, interests or attitudes. Old Ss are also able to change their orientation during the task and thus might improve their performance considerably. They fail, however, when a cognitive or non-cognitive set is explicitly given to them. Instead of improving their performance, they seem to become irritated and fail to relate the perceived information to their previously acquired knowledge.

THE EFFECT OF A SHORT-TERM, COGNITIVE SET
ON VERBAL PRODUCTION

Beginning with a discussion of complex psycholinguistic performance we tried to analyse the translation phase of such processes as well as some of its perceptual aspects. In both cases emphasis was given to the concept of set or task attitude as a link that joins closely and overlaps with the separated components. Next, we will give attention to the motor aspects of psycholinguistic performance. Unfortunately, few relevant studies are available and thus our report will consist even more than the previous discussion of an outline of suggestions for research and of some methodological considerations.

In particular we rely on Bousfield's method of verbal fluency which provides data that are not directly dependent on stimuli previously presented but merely on a more or less restricted instructional set. Thus, by asking Ss to produce as fast as possible all words that come into their minds, data are obtained which are quite similar to those on instrumental conditioning, namely accumulated records of Ss' reactions. The verbal fluency tasks differ in the degree of restriction imposed on the responses and thus they differ in cognitive set. One might ask his Ss, for instance, to produce words beginning with a particular letter of the alphabet, one might ask for nouns only, or one might restrict the content of the output to such classes as names of vegetables, authors, countries, US-States, etc. The degree of restriction has, of course, an impact on the performance. Through comparisons between tasks special inferences can be drawn. Previous studies of verbal fluency of old Ss like those by Birren and Botwinick (1951 a,b), Birren (1955), Birren, Riegel, and Morrison (1962), and Birren, Riegel, and Robbin (1962), have not emphasized task differences, however.

> *Study 6.* A group of thirty-one college students and twenty-three old Ss, most of whom were above sixty-five years old, wrote as many words beginning with the letter S and, in another task, beginning with the letter Q as they could think of during ten minute intervals. Ss marked the end of two-minute periods on their papers. The accumulated number of responses were plotted against time and the data analysed by a method suggested by Bousfield and Sedgewick (1944). In such an analysis, two parameters are determined. One is a theoretical value for the size of the repertoire of available words. This parameter is dependent on the restrictions imposed by the instructions and thus characterizes the cognitive set to be applied. It also varies between individuals, as for instance between high and low intelligence persons. The second parameter characterizes the depletion rate of the repertoire and, although not completely independent from the first, seems particularly influenced by non-cognitive components, such as the activity and motivational level of Ss. Short-cut methods allow us to estimate both parameters which are substituted into a negatively accelerated growth function of the form: $D = L (1-e^{-mt})$. Here L denotes the size of the repertoire and m the depletion factor. The equation is derived on the assumption that the increase in D is proportional to the words that have *not yet* been used by S (unpublished study by the present author).

According to the assumption which was stated in our introduction, we expect old Ss to have a larger response repertoire than young persons. Subsequently they should excel the latter in their amount of output in the verbal fluency test. As shown in Figure 9 this expectation could not be confirmed. In both tasks, L is much smaller for old than for young Ss, namely 110 as compared to 230 for the S-words and twenty-two as compared to forty for the Q-words. However, the m-values of old Ss exceed those of the young and thus old Ss seem to invest more energy and motivation in their performance. While we do not venture to endorse such an interpretation at this stage of knowledge with great certainty, some detailed remarks need to be made on our failure to confirm the assumption about the larger response repertoire of old Ss. Apparently other factors than vocabulary size interfere with the verbal output and do not allow old Ss to make full and efficient use of their large vocabularies. First, we have to realize that the verbal fluency test is a speed task, whereas time limitations are not necessarily imposed upon a writer of a book or of letters who provides the data on which our as-

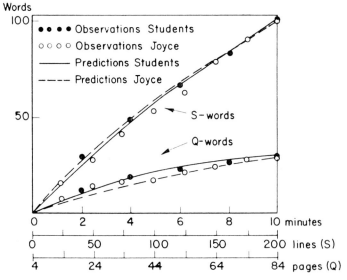

Figure 9A. Number of different Q and S-words written by students and by James Joyce plotted against time or text length.

sumption is based (see Figure 1). Since we know from the previous studies (see studies 1 and 2) that Ss above sixty-five years of age require greater reaction and association time than the young, we should expect that they do not necessarily reach the output level of the latter unless greater time allowance is made. Second, in verbal fluency tasks, Ss are prevented from using the same response twice, whereas a writer will avoid undue repetitions but is not as rigidly restricted in his output. Thus, Ss have to check any response they are intending to give against all the others previously emitted. This causes interference and might again differentially affect the output of old Ss as it has been indeed observed by Broadbent and Heron (1962). Third, and closely related to the second point, deficiencies in short-term retention might be a particular handicap for old Ss (see Welford, 1956; Fraser, 1958; and Inglis and Caird, 1963). The prediction of a larger response repertoire of old Ss has been based on the notion of slowly acquired variety in long-term verbal habits. The counter-checking of words mentioned above requires, however, a good short-term retention span, which old Ss are likely

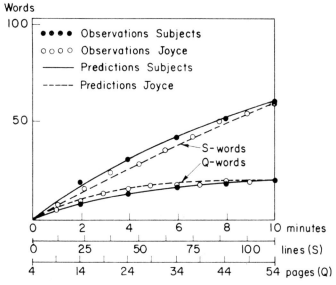

Figure 9B. Number of different Q and S-words written by old Ss and by James Joyce plotted against time or text length.

to be lacking. Fourth, although both groups of Ss had about an equally high educational level, differences in the results might merely reflect failures in the sampling procedures or differences in the degrees of individualization. Thus, old Ss might differ more markedly in their vocabularies between themselves than do young Ss. In other words, the increase in the size of the verbal repertoire with age might reflect an increase in inter- rather than intra-individual variations.

THE EFFECT OF LONG-TERM, NON-COGNITIVE SETS ON VERBAL PRODUCTION

The above list of factors that might possibly hinder old Ss to make full and efficient use of their large vocabularies has to be regarded as tentative. Further research might substantiate the validity of such explanations. At this moment we will discuss only one of these possibilities. The fourth of the above inter-pretations implies that the large vocabulary of old Ss might re-flect an increase of the inter-individual variation in word knowl-edge rather than a genuine enlargement of the single individuals' vocabularies. In other words, the increase in the vocabulary might merely indicate an increased degree of vocabulary spe-cialization. The analysis of this question leads us into the in-vestigation of the interaction between long-term non-cognitive and short-term cognitive sets and their effect on verbal produc-tion. Some preliminary results on this problem have been ob-tained in an extension of study 6.

> *Study 6 (continued).* The same Ss mentioned above completed ten items of an inventory on their interests in gardening and reading which allowed us to classify the Ss according to both these variables. They also completed two additional verbal fluency tasks in which they had to name all the flowers and authors of books which they could think of in periods of ten minutes each.

As a first result, the interest in reading was found to correlate with verbal abilities and possibly with intelligence as well. Ss who scored high in reading interest produced not only more names of authors in the verbal fluency task, but also more names of flowers, S-words, and Q-words than the less interested Ss.

Second, age differences in both the flower and the author tasks disappear almost completely when the expressed interests for the two areas of activities are taken into account. Particularly, old Ss with high interest in reading do not only excel the total group of young Ss in the respective fluency task but seem to be slightly superior on the other three tasks as well. They do not quite reach the performance level of those young Ss that are highly interested in reading although the interest scores of the young Ss do not allow for as clear a discrimination in performance as among old Ss. The results of Ss that express high interest in gardening are similar but not as pronounced as those on the reading scores.

According to our findings, the larger vocabulary of old Ss might be in part attributed to an increase of vocabulary specialization with age. They also support the common-sense notion that long-term, non-cognitive factors such as specialized interests or attitudes will direct Ss' cognitive orientation and acquisition of verbal habits. Presumably, the earlier such tendencies develop, the stronger will be the effects they produce. However, here, as well as in most of the other areas of inquiry insufficient information is available only.

A FORMAL ANALYSIS OF PROCESSES INTERVENING IN VERBAL PERFORMANCES

Using a more formal analysis than in the investigations of cognitive and non-cognitive conditions, we return to the third study previously mentioned, and to the second explanation of our failure to observe a higher degree of verbal fluency among old than young Ss. In this explanation it was claimed that Ss have to check any intended response against all those previously emitted, a process which might cause interference and might differentially affect the performance of old Ss in verbal fluency tasks.

Our following discussion deals with the tasks in which Ss had to search for words that begin with given syllables (study 3). This task can be regarded as an association test, and in particular, can be compared with those verbal fluency tests in which Ss have to find words that begin with a certain letter of the alphabet. Since our forty syllables varied in length between two

and four letters, we applied this classification of syllable length
for our further analysis.

Intuitively it is apparent that the greater the number of letters
which make up a stimulus syllable the fewer words will be
available as responses, i.e., the greater is the degree of response
restriction. In order to analyse more precisely the amount of restriction imposed, the number of alternatives listed in the Thorndike-Lorge Count (1944) was determined by enumerating all the
words that begin with each of the particular syllables used. The
mean logarithms of the number of alternatives shown in Figure
10A decrease in precisely the same manner as the mean number

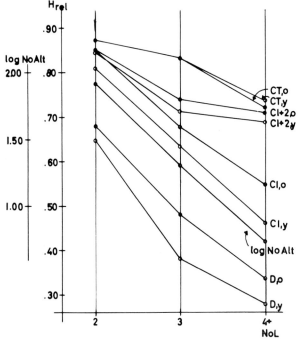

Figure 10A. Logarithms of the number of alternatives listed in the Thorndike-Lorge Count (log NoAlt) and relative entropy of responses (H rel) by
old (O) and young subjects (Y), plotted against number of letters per
stimuli (NoL).*

----

* D = responses of the discrete task; Cl = first responses of the continuous task;
Cl + 2 = first two responses of the continuous task; CT = all responses of the
continuous task.

of responses emitted by both the young and old Ss in the continuous task of word completion, i.e., within forty-five seconds per
item. The correlation between the two variables equals .94 for
the young as well as for the old Ss.

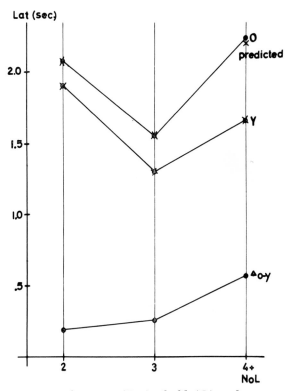

Figure 10B. Response latencies (Lat) of old (O) and young subjects (Y)
plotted against number of letters per stimuli (NoL).

The response latencies of the discrete test shown in Figure 10B
are more difficult to interpret. Relying on commonsense, these
data indicate that *too many* responses are available in case of the
two-letter syllables. Accordingly, the response latencies are relatively high as compared with those to the three-letter stimuli,
for which the degree of restriction seems to be optimal and the
number of responses available seems to be *just right*. The latencies increase again with further restrictions under which *too few*

alternative responses are available to Ss. While such an interpretation holds up well for both age groups, a differential effect can also be observed. The increasing degree of restriction delays in particular the responses of old Ss.

For a more comprehensive interpretation of the results we regard the observed latencies as composed of two intervening speed factors that counteract each other. We shall call these factors emergence time (ET) and selection time (ST), but do not attach at this moment any definite psychological or physiological meaning to these terms. In particular, emergence time (ET) should be inversely related to the logarithm of the number of alternative responses. In other words, the more responses available, the shorter the time for the emergence of any one of them:

$$ET = \frac{1}{\log \text{NoAlt}}$$

Selection time (ST) should be directly related to the number of alternative responses. Imposing the most severe condition, we maintain that selection time is directly proportional to the squared logarithm of the number of alternatives. Thus, we imply that every possible response might conflict with or inhibit any other before it is selected for emission:

$$ST = (\log \text{NoAlt})^2.$$

Adding both components and determining multiplicative constants, we obtain the following two equations for the mean response latencies (Lat) of young and old Ss:

$$\text{Lat}_y = .35 \, (\log \text{NoAlt})^2 + 1.08 \, \frac{1}{\log \text{NoAlt}}$$

$$\text{Lat}_o = .34 \, (\log \text{NoAlt})^2 + 1.50 \, \frac{1}{\log \text{NoAlt}}$$

As shown in Figure 10B our equations predict almost perfectly the observed response latencies but are remarkable only because no additive constants are used. The multiplicative constants are averages of figures which have been determined by solving the three equations for the two-, three-, and four-letter stimuli in all possible pair combinations. The differential increase in latencies with age has to be explained in terms of an increase in emergence rather than selection time. The weights of the latter are almost identical, while the weight assigned to the emergence time is larger for the old than for the young Ss.

At this point of our analysis we might ask ourselves whether the present interpretation is compatible with our discussion of the speed and power scores in the verbal achievement tests (study 1). In this study the total performance time was regarded as being dependent on two factors, the size of the repertoire and the speed of functioning or association. The speed factor was directly measured in a task in which the size of the repertoire had presumably no impact on the performance, namely in a free word association test (study 2). Association time was stable up to an age of about sixty-five years and increased markedly thereafter. This result in connection with our observation of a slight increase in the size of the repertoire with age allowed to explain age differences in the correlations between the time and power scores as well as the marked increase in total performance time with age.

In our present experiment on sylable associations or word completions (study 3) we subdivided association time into an emergence and selection factor. Although no age differences in the size of the vocabulary were taken into account, the association time was predicted very accurately on the basis of the number of alternatives listed in the Thorndike-Lorge Count. Our procedure might not only be excused by its apparent success but also by the lack of appropriate frequency counts. Moreover, differences in the number of common words used by adults or by old adults are likely to be negligible and thus we might generalize the results of study 3. With the necessary reservations and realizing that the speed of associating words to given stimuli cannot be directly equated with the speed of a cognitively more restricted task in which syllables are to be completed into words, we conclude that not only the age differences in the speed of syllable associations have to be attributed to differences in emergence speed but that the age differences in the speed of word associa-

tions and in the speed of test performance as well are primarily
due to the influence of this factor.

CONCLUSION

In the last part of our discussion we investigated whether the
overall speed of performance could be broken into component
parts. This idea is certainly not new in psychology but has
dominated the thinking of many psychologists at least since
Donders' experiments at the turn of the last century. In the field
of psychological gerontology similar attempts have been made in
recent years and discussed by Welford (1960). However, little
attention has been given so far to the analysis of age differences
in the speed of verbal functioning.

The investigation which we have touched upon in the last
section of our report covers the receptor, translation as well as
effector phases of a psychological performance. Thus, this discussion overlaps with our earlier interpretations. The differences
between the two parts lies in the emphasis on formal aspects of
the analysis. Formal aspects have received greater weight in the
second part, whereas in the first part the content as well as the
structure of the psychological events was of greater significance
for our discussion. Following traditional distinctions, we subdivided this part in a number of ways but, at the same time, applied the concept of psychological set or task attitude as a unify-
ing principle which in the present terminology embraces purely
situational components as well as long developed habits on one
hand and cognitive as well as emotional, motivational or attitudinal tendencies on the other.

It has not been an intention of the present paper to provide a
particular system by which different sets or task attitudes might
be classified. We are rather inclined to regard this as an
arbitrary and conventional matter for which any decision should
be primarily based on the possibility to operationalize the suggested components. The emphasis which we gave to the concept of set or task attitude was, however, quite intentional. Thus,
it should not be surprising that probably the most interesting
findings discussed in the present report were related to age differences in the utilization of set.

First, we noted a tendency among elderly Ss to utilize implicit, organized sets in their reactions in relatively unstructured situations, such as in a word association test. Elderly Ss have a distinct tendency to give meaningful and logical responses and to follow grammatical patterns although they are not requested to do so. Because of their inability to react in such a manner in proper time Ss in their late adulthood (above 65 years) might fail, however, and are likely to regress to an emotional and subjective type of responding. Their verbal performances are well maintained only if they can rely on overlearned and redundant stimulus-response patterns. In extension, old Ss were found well able to change their implicit set during continued performance and thus to improve their efficiency until they reacted almost as fast as young Ss. If, however, explicit, set-inducing instructions were provided in a visual recognition thresholds of words they failed completely. Both in the case of a cognitive set as well as in the case of motivation-arousing instructions old Ss either showed no change in their performance or a marked decrease in efficiency.

Many of our interpretations were based on the assumption that the size of the vocabulary necessarily increases with age. Support for such an assumption has been obtained in studies in which the passive vocabulary has been estimated by means of psychometric tests and the active vocabulary by means of statistical word counts of written material. In measuring the verbal fluency of young and old Ss, however, we failed to confirm such a prediction. The young group produced many more words than the old in fixed periods of time. The time stress imposed in this task as compared to the measures cited above seems to be the main reason for the failure of our prediction. Furthermore, the increase in the size of the vocabulary with age might indicate an increasing degree of vocabulary specialization rather than genuine intra-individual changes. Finally, a certain degree of response interference will arise in verbal fluency tests since each intended response has to be checked against all the others that have been used previously. This might differentially affect the performance of old Ss.

Proceeding in a more formal manner, we explored this last problem by relying again on the study of word completions. In particular, the reactions were fastest at a medium level of response restriction, namely when 3-letter syllables were used as stimuli. When there was more interference between possible responses, as in the case of two-letter stimuli, the reaction time increased markedly as well as for the four-letter stimuli for which there was less interference. Apparently, here too much time is afforded for the detection of appropriate responses.

BIBLIOGRAPHY

Birren, J. E.: (1955) Age changes in speed of simple responses and perception and their significance for complex behaviour. In *Old Age in the Modern World*, Edinburgh, Scotland, Livingstone, pp. 235-247.

Birren, J. E. and Botwinick, J.: (1951a) Age changes in verbal fluency. *J. Geront.*, 6:62.

Birren, J. E. and Botwinick, J.: (1951b) The relation of writing speed to age and to the senile psychoses. *J. Consult. Psychol.*, 15:243-249.

Birren, J. E., Riegel, K. F. and Morrison, D. F.: (1962) Age differences in response speed as a function of controlled variations of stimulus conditions: evidence of a general speed factor. *Gerontologica*, 6:1-18.

Birren, J. E., Riegel, K. F. and Robbin, J. S.: (1962) Age differences in continuous word associations measured by speech recordings. *J. Geront.*, 17:95-96.

Bousfield, W. A. and Sedgewick, C. H. W.: (1944) An analysis of sequences of restricted associative responses. *J. Gen. Psychol.*, 30:149-165.

Braun, H. W.: (1959) Perceptual processes. In J. E. Birren, ed.: *Handbook of Aging and the Individual*, Chicago, Ill., Chicago University Press, pp. 543-561.

Broadbent, D. E. and Heron, A.: (1962) Effects of a subsidiary task on performance involving immediate memory by younger and older men. *Brit. J. Psychol.*, 53:189-198.

Bromley, D. B.: (1958) Some effects of age on short term learning and remembering. *J. Geront.*, 13:398-406.

Carroll, J. B.: (1938) Diversity of vocabulary and the harmonic series law of word-frequency distribution. *Psychol. Rec.*, 2:379-386.

Dember, W. N.: (1960) *Psychology of Perception.* New York, Holt.

Doerken, J. J.: (1956) Frequency of common associations. *Psychol. Rep.*, 2:407-408.

Engler, J. and Freeman, J. T.: (1956) Perceptual behavior as related to factors of associative and drive strength. *J. Exp. Psychol.*, 51:399-404.

Ervin, Susan M.: (1961) Changes with age in the verbal determinants of word-association. *Amer. J. Psychol.*, 74:361-372.

Fraser, D. C.: (1958) Decay of immediate memory with age. *Nature,* *182*:1163.

Gilbert, Jeanne G.: (1941) Memory loss in senescence. *J. Abnorm. Soc. Psychol., 36*:73-86.

Heglin, H. J.: (1956) Problem solving set in different age groups. *J. Geront., 11*:310-317.

Herdan, G.: (1960) Type-Token Mathematics: A Textbook of Mathematical Linguistics. The Hague, Mouton.

Inglis, J. and Caird, W. K.: (1963) Age differences in successive responses to simultaneous stimulation. *Canad. J. Psychol., 24*:46-50.

Jenkins, J. J.: (1954) Transitional organization: association technique. In C. E. Osgood and T. A. Sebeok, eds.: *Psycholinguistics, Supplement, J. Abnorm. Soc. Psychol., 52*:112-118.

Jerome, E. S.: (1959) Age and learning—experimental studies. In J. E. Birren, ed.: *Handbook of Aging and the Individual,* Chicago, Ill., Chicago University Press, pp. 655-699.

Kaeding, F. W.: (1898) *Häufigkeitswörterbuch der deutschen Sprache.* Berlin, Selbstverlag.

Kent, G. H. and Rosanoff, A. J.: (1910) A study of association in insanity. *Amer. J. Insanity, 67*:37-96, 317-390.

Korchin, S. J. and Basowitz, H.: (1957) Age differences in verbal learning. *J. Abnorm. Soc. Psychol., 54*:64-69.

Lehman, H. C.: (1953) *Age and Achievement.* Princeton, Princeton University Press.

Lorge, I.: (1936) The influence of the test upon the nature of mental decline as a function of age. *J. Educ. Psychol., 27*:100-110.

Lorge, I.: (1940) Psychometric; evaluation of mental status as function of mental test. *Amer. J. Orthopsychiat., 10*:56-59.

McClelland, D. C., Atkinson, J. W., Clark, R. A. and Lowell, E. G.: (1958) *The Achievement Motive.* New York, Appleton-Century-Crofts.

Miles, W. R.: (1931) Measurement of certain human abilities throughout life span. *Proc. Nat. Acad. Sci. U. S. A., 17*:627-633.

O'Connor, J.: (1934) *Psychometrics.* Cambridge, Harvard University Press.

Riegel, K. F.: (1958) Ergebnisse und Probleme der psychologischen Alternsforschung, Teil II. *Vita Hum., 1*:204-243.

Riegel, K. F.: (1959) A study of verbal achievements of older persons. *J. Geront., 14*:453-456.

Riegel, K. F. and Riegel, Ruth M.: (1960) A study on changes of attitudes and interests during later years of life. *Vita Hum., 3*:177-206.

Riegel, K. F., Riegel, Ruth M. and Wendt, D.: (1962) Perception and set: a review of the literature and a study on the effects of instructions and verbal habits on word recognition thresholds of young and old subjects. *Acta Psychol., 12*:224-251.

Riegel, K. F. and Riegel, Ruth M.: (1963) An investigation into denotative aspects of word meaning. *Language Speech, 61*:5-21.

Riegel, K. F. and Riegel, Ruth M.: (1964a) Vorschläge zu einer statistischen Interpretation von Alternsveränderungen sprachlicher Leistungen. In Hardesty, F. P. and Eyferth, K., eds.: *Herausforderungen an die Psychologie: Festschrift für Professor C. Bondy*, Bern, Huber.

Riegel, K. F. and Riegel, Ruth M.: (1964b) Changes in associative behavior during later years of life: a cross-sectional analysis. *Vita Hum., 7*:1-32.

Riegel, K. F. and Birren, J. E.: (1964). Age differences in verbal associations. *J. Genet. Psychol., 104:*

Ruch, F. L.: (1933) Adult learning. *Psychol. Bull., 30*:387-414.

Ruch, F. L.: (1934) The differentiative effects of age upon human learning. *J. Genet. Psychol., 11*:261-286.

Schaie, K. W.: (1958) Rigidity-flexibility and intelligence: a cross-sectional study of the adult life span from 20 to 70 years. *Psychol. Monogr., 72:* 9.

Smith, Madorah E.: (1955) Linguistic constancy in individuals when long periods of time are covered and different types of material are sampled. *J. Gen. Psychol., 53*:109-143.

Smith, Madorah E.: (1957a) Relation between word variety and mean letter length of words with chronological and mental ages. *J. Gen. Psychol., 56*:27-43.

Smith, Madorah E.: (1957b) The application of some measures of language behavior and tension to the letters written by a woman at each decade of her life from 49 to 89 years of age. *J. Gen. Psychol., 57*:289-295.

Thorndike, E. L. and Lorge, I.: (1944) *The Teachers' Word Book of 30,000 Words.* New York, Teachers Coll., Columbia University.

Weiss, A. D.: (1959) Sensory functions. In J. E. Birren, ed.: *Handbook of Aging and the Individual*, Chicago, Ill., University of Chicago Press, pp. 503-542.

Welford, A. T.: (1956) Psychological aspects of ageing. In W. Hobson, ed.: *Modern Trends in Geriatrics*, London, Butterworth.

Welford, A. T.: (1960) The measurement of sensory-motor performance: a survey and reappraisal of twelve years' progress. *Ergonomics, 3:*189-230.

Yule, G. U.: (1944) *The Statistical Study of Literary Vocabulary.* London, Cambridge University Press.

Zipf, G. K.: (1949) *Human Behavior and the Principle of Least Effort.* Cambridge, Mass., Addison-Wesley.

10

AGE CHANGES IN SPEED OF BEHAVIOR: ITS CENTRAL NATURE AND PHYSIOLOGICAL CORRELATES

James E. Birren

THE SLOWING of behavior with age in man and other animals was for a long time not considered as an important or systematic problem in psychology or physiology. This may have resulted from the fact that the slowness of the older organism was overly obvious. Whatever the reason it is clear that more restricted features of behavior pre-empted attention of the researcher and theorist. In the present discussion slowness of behavior is made the central point of consideration accepting the fact that this raises some conceptual as well as factual issues. Welford has considered these in some detail in Chapter 1. Certain assumptions are made here about the implications of published research on this topic which should be made explicit to avoid misunderstandings.

It is taken as fact that slowness of behavior with age has been reliably observed in man and other mammals in a wide variety of contexts. It is also taken as fact that most of the slowness of behavior associated with advancing age can be attributed to the time taken or required by the central nervous system in mediating the input and output relations in behavior. Generally, not much of the slowness with age can properly be attributed to motility of joints or muscular contraction. Also, limitations of sensory input or the primary sensations are not usually the major contributor.

Since there have been comprehensive discussions of the evidence prior to 1960 there is little reason to attempt a new review (Birren, 1954; Welford, 1959). The earlier literature will be cited only in those instances where a reinterpretation or different emphasis is perhaps indicated.

AN INITIAL VIEW OF THE NATURE OF SLOWNESS OF BEHAVIOR

Observation suggests that the older individual can do most if not all of the things he did at a younger age but not do them as quickly. Early research indicated that the diminuition of sensorimotor speed with age was not limited to one sense modality or to a particular motor response (Birren and Botwinick, 1955; Koga and Morant, 1923; Miles, 1931). Mostly, however, the speed of performance of a variety of types of behavior was not measured on the same individuals and inter-correlated. Hence, while the evidence was circumstantial that the slowing was general or diffuse in nature within individuals, proof was needed that aging individuals were or were not independently quick or slow depending upon the particular task. With this issue in mind, Birren, Riegel, and Morrison (1962) carried out an experiment in which the form of the response (quickness of button pressing) was held constant while systematically varying the complexity of stimuli. Under all stimulus conditions used, elderly subjects were found to be slower than young adult subjects. This would have been predicted from previous work, however the additional point was established that response speed to the various type of stimuli was more highly intercorrelated among older subjects. Thus in a group of thirty young subjects (18-30 years) the "speed factor" accounted for 29 per cent of the variance compared with 43 per cent of the variance in twenty-three older subjects (60-80 years). Since the experimental stimuli were varied, e.g., verbal associations as well as numbers and colors, there is reason to believe there is a rather broad or general factor which emerges with age that imposes a common limitation on the speed of all behavior mediated by the central nervous system. Restating the results, young subjects appear to be task specific in their response speed, i.e., they are quick or slow depending upon the nature of the task. With increasing age individuals tend to show a characteristic slowness of response regardless of the nature of the task.

That this general quality of slowness is not limited to effector or motor response processes is also shown in the work of Chown (1961). She gave a wide range of intelligence, speed, and "rigidity" tests to 200 men who ranged in age from twenty to eighty-two years. Of considerable present importance is her conclusion "The most marked change in the interrelationships between factors with age was in the role of speed. The speed tests formed their own unique factor in the young group, maintained this to a lesser extent in the middle group, and were loaded most highly on the nonverbal Intelligence factor in the old group. Thus among old people, but not among the young, these speed tests became a measure of intellectual capability and of the extent of the preservation of this function" (Chown, 1961, p. 361). Such evidence suggests that the limitation on speed with age does not to a major degree involve the most remote elements of the input-output processes, but more importantly involves association time and the time to select appropriate response elements.

SLOWNESS OF BEHAVIOR AND A PRIMARY PROCESS OF AGING

The slowness of behavior with advancing age is less suggestive of punctate neurological damage, as might be associated with disease, than of a primary change in the nervous system. The implications of the expression "primary age change in the nervous system" are not always clear. Here it is taken to mean a progressive change which will eventually appear in every individual who lives long enough. To be regarded as a primary manifestation of aging the constellation of functional and structural changes should appear independently of any particular disease or environmental condition. A primary age change would eventually be shown by all individuals despite optimum health, education, good personal habits, and advantageous social and physical environments. This does not imply that environmental differences and disease could not interact with a primary process and modify the appearance and the rate of change. Conceptually one is distinguishing the contribution of environmental differences and disease from an invariant biological transformation of members of a species, recognizing that in real life these factors are interacting. Defining aging as an invariant biological transformation with the passage of time leading to lowered functional capacity and probability of survival does not preclude individual differences or environmental modifications of the rate of aging.

From the concept of a primary age change in the nervous system one excludes damage due to age related diseases and those syndromes which are age related and hereditary, such as the presenile dementia. The timing of the appearance of such mid or late life diseases may have some relevance to aging although the link is not presently obvious. One would similarly exclude from the concept of a primary age change such alterations in behavior and structure of the nervous system as those which may be brought about in aged persons because of cerebrovascular disease. The distinction is between changes which have a pathogenetic basis and those which are physiologic or inherent in the nature of the species and thereby constitute senescence. There is of course an uncertain or grey conceptual area for future resolution since the appearance and rate of development of a disease itself can often be found to be a function of age.

If there is a pattern of behavioral changes shown by all older persons then one would have reason to expect in advance of any physiological or anatomical evidence that the nervous system was undergoing a primary change with age. It seems appropriate for the development of the subject matter that the hypothesis should be posted for substantiation or refutation that slowness of behavior is a primary change of aging.

The logical point may be raised as to whether the change in speed could ever be validly regarded as an independent or primary change in behavior. With qualifications it would appear to be so since the brain is not essentially an organ for the production or storage of energy. Because its dominant characteristic is that of an integrator or mediator of processes, changes in speed of operation of the nervous system could be an independent variable. One is tempted to elaborate here by using an analogy to computers in which reading time, access time to storage, transfer time, or the output time are variables among computers. Time of operations can be reduced to other variables of physical-chemical nature yet at the functional level operation time can be used as a primary descriptive characteristic or variable in comparing one system with another. The length of unit operation has general implications for comparing complex input-output systems. In accord with the hypothesis the position is taken here that the time constants in the operation of the nervous system are likely independent variables in the age changes in behavior. Whether one or a group of elementary time constants are in fact changing with age is an empirical question for research to answer. For the experimental psychologist there has been the problem of determining if there are one or several changes in the time constants of the operation of the nervous system involved in the slowness of behavior with advancing age. A search for the physiological correlates of age changes in speed of behavior would be less compelling if there were many, rather than one or a few, time constants involved in the slowness of behavior.

The experimental biologist's interest in age changes in speed of behavior rises in proportion to the evidence provided by the psychologist that the alteration in speed has some general properties not specific to a particular sensory modality, kind of association, or type of response. If the speed of response were dependent upon the type of information, e.g., visual, auditory, verbal, numerical, or spatial, then the operations-time would be suspected of varying with the nature of the input or information in storage or memory than with a change in access time to what is stored.

A useful digression may be made at this point by the citation of another previous study which points to the general nature of the change in speed. In a study of speed of arithmetic addition it was found that older persons completed fewer addition problems in a fixed time. Conceivably this could be due to slowness in recording answers rather than to slowness of the mental operation of addition. However, a separate test of speed of writing was found to correlate with speed of addition in long problems where the length of time taken to record the answer was a trivial part of the total process (Birren and Botwinick, 1951).

The fact that the correlation between writing speed and addition speed is higher in older adults than in young, implies that the importance of the speed factor grows with age. That is, performance was not limited because of the inability to write quickly enough but because a common process was responsible to a considerable degree for slowness of writing and slowness in mental addition. Young people tend to add and write at independent speeds whereas older adults are jointly slow in both tasks. This data which pointed to a common link between speed of association and speed of response, also implied a change with age in speed in completing problems of minimum difficulty. If one adds series of digits of variable length, a curve is generated showing the change in time as a function of problem length. If one extrapolates the curve to the axis one presumably has approximated the time required to do a problem of zero difficulty. At this hypothetical level of zero difficulty there is a residual difference between young and old subjects, suggestive of an age difference in the minimum operations time. These results and those reviewed by Welford in Chapter 1, point to the desirability of broadening our concepts and terminology to recognize that time changes are manifest in a broad field of behavior including information input, storage access, storage search, association, and motor output and to be alert to the fact that common processes may be involved.

The correlation between writing and addition speed indicates that one may not assume independence of the output time (writing) and association time (addition) in the aging as in the young. These times grow interdependent with the age of the subject and apparently with senile mental disease as well, although the latter should not be regarded as part of the pattern of senescence. It should also be pointed out that the registration strength of an item or stimulus may affect the length of time it will remain in memory, and in turn may reflect a common operations speed. For example, it has been noted that auditory acuity tends to be correlated with auditory reaction time even in instances wherein attention has been paid to variations in input intensity (Weiss, 1963). Thus quickness and acuity and perhaps ultimately memory as well may covary in older persons as a consequence of a common process.

HEALTH AND SPEED OF BEHAVIOR IN THE AGED

A highly relevant question is whether older persons judged to be healthy, in the sense of freedom from disease, show a slowness of behavior characteristic of their age group.

A group of forty-seven men above the age of sixty-five were studied at the National Institute of Mental Health with regard to a broad range of physiological, medical, psychological, and social characteristics. Among the measurements was that of simple reaction time (Birren, *et al.*, 1963). Simple auditory reaction times in these subjects were not significantly different from previous subjects less well selected for good health (Botwinick, *et al.*, 1963). In addition, the group of forty-seven men when divided into two groups, one of optimum health and the other with subclinical or symptomatic disease, no difference in reaction time was found. This would suggest that slowness of response occurs with advancing age even in individuals relatively free from disease.

The above facts would initially seem to contradict some previous data which indicated that senile dementia patients were particularly slow in doing a rather simple task, speed of writing (Birren and Botwinick, 1951). Upon review, both sets of data appear to be valid representations of the changes which occur with age and, in the one instance, exacerbated by disease. In the healthy group of forty-seven elderly men, previously cited, writing speed was faster than a previous less well selected sample for health. Also, the men differed in writing speed between the two groups divided on the basis of health. What seems to characterize the speed tasks which show health differences as well as age difference is their greater information content.

Benton and Joynt (1958) have reported a slowing of reaction time in relatively young patients with brain damage thus it is appropriate to consider that a factor of cortical integrity may be involved in the slowness of some older individuals as well. The healthy older men previously mentioned showed significantly

TABLE 1

TEST SCORES OF A SAMPLE OF ELDERLY MEN COMPARED WITH SCORES OF OTHER SAMPLES
(FROM BOTWINICK AND BIRREN, 1963)

	Present Sample						Elderly Samples			Young Samples		
	Group I			Group II								
	Mean	S.D.	No.	Mean	S.D.	No.	Mean	S.D.	No.	Mean	S.D.	No.
Raven	25.59	9.32	27	24.00	9.19	20	Median = 24			48	8.2	44
WCST	3.81	3.37	26	2.25	2.29	20						
Card Sorting	116.50	25.54	24	122.05	34.29	20				88.03	11.22	34
Learning	43.35	16.25	20	34.53	19.82	17				.70	.33	58
Addition Rate	.94	.30	24	.83	.38	20	0.60 (approx.)			.78 (approx.)		
Alternation Rate	.36	.13	24	.29	.12	20				.32	.14	58
Copy Digits	1.11	.25	27	.96	.32	20	.82	.32	66	1.62	.26	57
Word Fluency	17.22	8.28	27	16.33	9.21	18	9.7	4.6	43	24.9	7.0	31
Line Difference	1.09	.20	27	1.26	.26	19				1.42	.37	41
Reaction Time	.22	.03	23	.24	.06	19	.23	.05	32	.18	.03	32

higher scores on verbal information tests than did young populations, leading to the inference of relative cortical integrity. Their
concomitantly lower performance on simple reaction time and on
the Digit Symbol test of the WAIS may thus be indicative of a
subcortical process of aging. This leads to the suspicion of at
least two speed factors: a primary age factor of subcortical basis
reflected in all or most processes mediated by the central nervous
system, and a factor of cortical integrity influenced by disease,
particularly those resulting in local cell loss and interference with
circulation and ischemia.

The fact that speed changes may result from two markedly different but often concomitant processes a normal physiological
change of age and brain pathology, lessens the expectations for
parsimony of explanation previously generated. Perhaps further
questions should be raised, e.g.: 1) what psychological measurements seems most related to differential survival of older adults,
and 2) can measurements be devised which will separate the
cortical and subcortical contributions to slowness of behavior.

SURVIVAL RELATIONSHIPS

A follow-up study was made of the forty-seven elderly men
originally measured. Thirteen men failed to survive over a
period of approximately five years. If one divides the initial data
in terms of survivors and non-survivors some interesting differences among the measurements appear.

In the following table it can be seen that the measurements
most differentiating of the survivors and non-survivors were not
those dealing with speed but in one instance, verbal information,
it was the same measurement which differentiated best according
to level of health.

In Table 2 it can be seen that the two intelligence tests, the
WAIS and the Raven discriminated survivors and non-survivors.
The fact that these tests did discriminate survivors and non-survivors from among a group typified as rather well-functioning
suggests that even greater differentiation might be obtained in
samples of great initial differences in health. Also the fact that
measures of speed did not significantly discriminate survivors and
non-survivors suggests that the slowing of behavior in these men

TABLE 2

DIFFERENCES BETWEEN SURVIVORS AND NON-SURVIVORS ON ORIGINAL TESTING

PRINCIPAL COMPONENTS (STANDARD SCORES)

		I Information Achievement	*II* Enumeration Speed	*III* Set Flexibility	*IV* Speed Association	*V* Concept & Stimulus Orientation	*Total WAIS Score*	*Raven Matrices*
Group I Survivors N = 34	M	.190	-.012	.062	.040	.018	100.85	27.7
	σ	.98	1.10	.99	.84	1.00	25.84	12.2
Group II Non-survivors N = 13	M	-.442	.036	-.090	-.085	.117	82.85	17.5
	σ	.81	.59	.89	1.29	.70	17.22	6.9
$M_1 - M_2$	t =	2.18	.19	.49	.31	3.66	2.68	3.51
	p =	<.05	N.S.	N.S.	N.S.	<.01	<.05	<.01

was not the result of disease. This point reinforces the implication of the previous results showing that the subjects did not differ by response speed according to gradations of health judged from the medical examinations.

To some extent the disease-intelligence test relationship is also seen in the character of the distribution of changes in WAIS test scores over the five-year interval. Table 3 shows that a significant mean decrement in tests scores occurred over the five-year interval. The distribution of these changes appears to be independent of the initial level and to be non-normally distributed.

If the changes in intelligence scores were part of a process of primary aging every individual would have been expected to show some moderate amount of change over the interval. The change was not uniform and some individuals showed large decrements and some no change or an increment. Tentatively it would seem that these intellectual changes are best viewed as resulting from disease processes experienced in variable amounts by some members, but not all, of the population studied. The measures being discussed were not of course designed to discriminate between likely survivors and non-survivors of an aging population. While all were not statistically significant, *all* differences in mean initial performance between survivors and non-survivors were in the direction of poorer performance on the part of the subsequent non-survivors. Thus a trend appears toward lower mean performance by non-survivors in all measures including the speed measures. If larger samples are studied, cause of death might be found to be related to initial performance as well as change on the various measurements.

ISSUES IN THE RELATIONS OF MEMORY, SPEED AND AGE

Many of the terms used to describe behavior in relation to age lack specificity including those of memory and speed. From one point of view a *definition vocabulary test* is a measure of memory in an older person since it measures how well the individual has retained the words he has learned. The fact that vocabulary scores are higher with age for healthy subjects suggests that both the input of new words to memory storage and storage itself are efficient. Since concurrent speed measures show decrements one

TABLE 3
STUDY OF HUMAN AGING
ORIGINAL AND RETEST WAIS TOTAL SCALED SCORES

Group	Subject	Age	Follow-up in Months	1956 Total Scaled Score	1961 Total Scaled Score	Diff.	Difference
I	6	72	57	72	56	-16	Total Subjects
	12	70	56	97	92	-5	$\bar{X} = -9.59$
	1	80	60	82	82	0	$\sigma = 7.78$
	47	65	46	147	149	+2	$\sigma m = 1.47$
	15	75	58	98	99	+1	$t = 6.52$
	20	73	57	106	92	-14	
	14	68	59	82	80	-2	
	5	69	61	126	114	-12	Group I
	16	71	61	101	79	-22	$\bar{X} = -8.32$
	9	67	64	87	79	-8	$\sigma = -7.63$
	36	69	54	82	69	-13	$\sigma d = 1.80$
	19	70	62	103	84	-19	$t = 4.62$
	51	71	53	105	90	-15	
	58	71	52	112	97	-15	
	59	74	52	126	115	-11	Group II
	54	73	54	137	138	+1	$\bar{X} = -12.0$
	55	65	54	153	147	-6	$\sigma = 7.48$
	53	81	54	115	120	+5	$\sigma d = 2.49$
	56	69	58	113	104	-9	$t = 4.81$
II	28	74	49	79	72	-7	
	35	74	47	89	76	-13	
	10	92	57	45	37	-8	
	18	66	55	104	93	-11	
	39	69	47	91	88	-3	
	32	77	50	70	38	-32	
	27	66	55	128	112	-16	
	23	74	57	94	84	-10	
	42	68	51	104	92	-12	
	8	71	64	83	75	-8	

suspects that long-term memory and speed are largely independent in adults. An exception to this might be the fact that reduced speed could result in a reduced number of words entering into long-term storage; thus speed might be related to the learning component but not to the memory component.

As part of a study of cognitive functioning in young and old subjects the Wechsler Memory Scale and several measures of cognition and speed were made. Of particular relevance here are the correlations among the vocabulary measure, the memory score and the measure of speed of writing digits. The next table shows these correlations for thirty young (18-32 years) and forty-seven elderly subjects (over age 60 years).

TABLE 4

CORRELATIONS BETWEEN PSYCHOMOTOR SPEED, VOCABULARY, AND MEMORY IN YOUNG AND ELDERLY SUBJECTS

	Vocabulary (WAIS)	*Wechsler Memory Scale*
Speed of Copying Digits		
Young, N = 29	.40	−.01
Elderly, N = 47	.37	.52
Wechsler Memory Scale		
Young, N = 29	.36	
Elderly, N = 47	.77	

TABLE 5

MEAN PERFORMANCE LEVELS OF YOUNG AND ELDERLY SUBJECTS ON THE PSYCHOMOTOR SPEED, VOCABULARY, AND MEMORY MEASUREMENTS

	Young *N = 29*	*Elderly* *N = 47*
Vocabulary (WAIS)		
Mean	55.6	49.6
S.D.	11.2	15.7
Wechsler Memory Scale		
Mean	67.2	50.4
S.D.	7.3	13.5
Speed of Copying Digits		
Mean	1.50	1.05
S.D.	0.27	0.27

The changes in the correlations with age are of interest. One notes that in young subjects the vocabulary and memory scores are less closely correlated than they are in the elderly subjects. This perhaps corroborates to some extent the notion that a vocabulary test is a measure of the learning process in young persons and a measure of the efficiency of memory in the aged. In a similar way the speed of writing digits test was more closely related to the memory measure in the old than in the young subjects. It would be reasonable at this point to mention that the Wechsler Memory Scale is not a specific test of memory containing as it does measures of long-term information retention and short-term as well. While suggestive, in view of the non-specificity of the measures the results cannot be readily used to substantiate any particular interpretation of aging of cognition. They do however underscore the important point that what in youths may be primarily a measure of learning efficiency may in old adults be a measure of the efficiency of long-term memory. This leads to the caution that one may not impress interpretations of cognitive organization gained from studies of young adults and children upon mental test performance of older adults. Particularly with regard to the emergence of a limiting speed process with age there may not be a homology of function between young and old adults.

OBSERVATIONS OF AGE AND FINGER TREMOR[1]

An exploratory study was carried out on finger tremor in the expectation that it might bear a relation to speed of movement in the aged. It has long been observed that man has a normal resting oscillating motion of body parts. In the psychological literature this is often described as steadiness and in the physiological literature as tremor. The fine oscillatory movements found in normal persons should be distinguished from gross tremor observed in patients with neurological disease. Some persons find it difficult to maintain an upright posture with eyes closed because of the amplitude of some of the body movements. A considerable increase in body sway is noted with eyes closed, i.e.,

──────────
[1] The assistance of Mr. Carl Ravin in these observations and in the analysis of the data is gratefully acknowledged.

from a total of 28.5 cm./two minutes with eyes open to 41.6 cm/ two minutes with eyes closed (Fisher, Birren and Leggett, 1945). This suggests that vision can be used to dampen the normal or physiological oscillation of the body or body parts. Because of the commonness of falls in older persons some exploratory studies might be undertaken of body sway with eyes open and closed; falls perhaps being influenced by the rapidity of corrective movements as well as by the frequency and amplitude of the oscillating movements. In the present pilot study of finger tremor it was desired to study frequency in relation to age and to visual control. The purpose was to see if the frequency of tremor was less influenced by vision in older persons.

A previous report described the use of an accelerometer to measure tremor in the outstretched arm (Marshall, 1961). The modal frequency was found to be about 10 cycles/sec. in young adults (20-30 years) and about 6 cycles/sec. for adults over the age of seventy, indicating a decline with age in the frequency of tremor.

In the present study, finger tremor was recorded from the output of Ballistocardiograph which was adapted for the purpose (Arbeit d-v-a- Ballistocardiograph, Model 2A, Industrial Development Laboratory). The output was amplified and recorded by means of a Sanborn D.C. amplifier and polygraph. The subject rested his arm and the side of his hand on a table; his extended forefinger was placed against the button end of the solenoid. Finger movements were thus not *free* oscillatory movement but were to some extent damped by the small resistance of the device.

The number of oscillatory displacements over half minute periods was measured from the records (expressed as frequency/sec.) for the following conditions: eyes open; eyes closed; eyes open; eyes fixed on wall; eyes open immediately after two minutes of hyperventilation; eyes open after five minutes rest. Only the young subjects were tested under the conditions of hyperventilation. In the present study the older subjects were competent independently living individuals who for the most part are retired Civil Service employees. As a group they would be of better than average health and educational background.

It is of interest that the mean frequency observed for finger tremor although slightly lower was not grossly different (ten percent) from that observed for the extended arm by Marshall (1961). The difference in mean frequency of finger tremor between the young and old subjects was not as large as that reported for the arm. The next table shows the mean values for the young and old subjects under the various experimental conditions. The fact that the frequency of tremor did not increase significantly as a result of hyperventilation is in contrast to its marked effect on amplitude which was in fact so great that the experimenters were quite unprepared to measure it. Suffice it to say that hyperventilation of two minutes duration is of sufficient influence as to result in an increased amplitude of finger tremor of tenfold or more.

In the process of the analysis of the data it was noted that the secretaries as a group showed a lower frequency than non-secretaries of the same age. Furthermore, in the eyes closed position the secretaries increased their frequency of tremor compared with eyes open. With eyes closed, five of six secretaries increased their frequency of finger tremor and ten of ten non-secretaries decreased their finger tremor. These data suggest that occupation may influnce the characteristic frequency and control over finger tremor. They also caution against enthusiasm for linking the tremor with such central electro-physiological phenomena as the alpha frequency which is inviting since they both appear to be in the same frequency range and tend to decrease in frequency with age.

REACTION TIME AND THE CARDIAC CYCLE

Generally with advancing age there is a trend toward elevated blood pressures and several sets of data gathered in the Section on Aging have indicated that reaction time and blood pressure in the high normal range are negatively related, i.e., slower reaction times are associated with high systolic and diastolic blood pressure. It might be assumed that the slower reaction times of older persons were a result of damage to the central nervous system secondary to the elevated blood pressure or to the primary conditions leading to an elevated blood pressure; however it

TABLE 6
FREQUENCY OF FINGER TREMOR IN YOUNG AND ELDERLY SUBJECTS

		Eyes Open	Eyes Closed	Eyes Open	Eyes Fixed on Wall	After Hyper-ventilation Eyes Open	After Rest Eyes Open
Young (Age 23.6) 18-36	Mean	8.8	8.5	9.0	8.4	8.5	9.0
	σ	1.31	1.32	1.42	1.32	1.32	1.45
	N	42	42	41	39	42	42
Old (Age 70.5) 61-82	Mean	7.8	8.1	8.2	7.6		
	σ	0.80	0.87	0.89	0.86		
	N	13	13	13	13		
Young Males	Mean	9.0	8.4	9.2	8.2	8.4	8.9
	σ	1.45	1.64	1.70	1.52	1.56	1.71
	N	22	22	22	19	22	22
Females	Mean	8.7	8.6	8.7	8.7	8.6	9.2
	σ	1.14	0.84	1.02	1.10	1.00	1.09
	N	20	20	19	20	20	20
Female Secretaries	Mean	8.2	8.7	8.9	8.6	8.3	9.6
	σ	1.43	1.00	0.97	1.46	1.29	1.58
	N	6	6	6	6	6	6
Young-Old	t	3.33	1.25	2.28	2.50		
	p	<.01	>.20	<.05	<.02		

should be pointed out that even subjects with blood pressures in the normal ranges show the tendency to slowing with age. Lacey and Lacey have noted (1958) that variability in heart rate is associated with fast reaction time. One implication was that sympathetic nervous system activity was related to lower cerebral cortical excitability. By analogy a rise in systolic blood pressure presumably could lead to an increase in inhibitory impulses from the carotid sinus. These implications led to the decision to study variations of reaction time occurring during the cardiac cycle since blood pressure varies significantly during each cycle.

A preliminary report has been made of this work on young subjects (Birren, Cardon, and Phillips, 1963). The same method was applied to an older population. In this study, concurrent with measurements of simple auditory reaction time, an electrocardiogram was recorded. At the onset of a light signal, the subject depressed a telegraph key until a 1000 cycle tone was presented whereupon he raised his finger as quickly as possible. There was a two second delay between each reaction and the light signal to replace the finger, and one second to the next auditory signal to react. Within the series there were ten per cent long delays (11 seconds) as a catch series to reduce false anticipatory responses. The reactions to the delayed catch stimuli and the ones immediately following were not included in the analysis.

Each auditory signal presentation was marked on the EKG record. The reaction times were recorded from a 1/100 second electric time clock. Subsequent analysis of the records related each reaction time to the phase of the cardiac cycle in which the signal was presented. Each session consisted of 100 reaction times after an introductory practice period. Between blocks of fifty trials, the subjects were given a rest period.

From the method it will be noted that no attempt was made to synchronize the stimuli with the cardiac cycle; stimuli were presented randomly over the cycle. For purposes of classifying the data, the cardiac cycle was divided into four intervals as seen in the next figure. For each subject median values were obtained in the four phases of the cardiac cycle.

The subjects for these measurements were thirty-one young men and twenty-five women (20-30 years) and fifteen older men

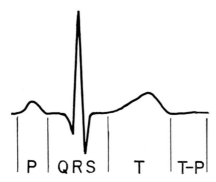

Figure 1. Representation of the cardiac cycle by a normal electrocardiogram. Vertical lines arbitrarily divide the cycle into the four intervals used for the analysis of the reaction time data as shown in Table 1. Letters are those conventionally used to designate the principal deflections of the EKG.

TABLE 7

MEAN RT FOR CARDIAC CYCLE PHASES

Young Age Range 20-30 years	P	QRS	T	T-P
Men N =31				
Mean	.141	.150	.144	.143
S.D.	.023	.028	.035	.028
Women N =25				
Mean	.1432	.157	.157	.155
S.D.	.020	.028	.029	.030
Old Age Range 60-90 years				
Men N =15				
Mean	.248	.222	.247	.232
S.D.	.107	.092	.124	.104
Women N =26				
Mean	.273	.281	.272	.277
S.D.	.173	.207	.171	.205

and twenty-six women (65-90 years). All were judged normotensive by the collaborating physician. The data for the young men showed a significant difference between the P phase and the QRS interval; the former showing faster reaction times. In contrast the older men showed slower reaction times than the young men but they did not vary significantly with the cardiac cycle.

One might hold that associated with reduced cardiac variability with age, the correlation between reaction time and the cardiac cycle disappears. Also, the "normal" increase in blood pressure in older subjects may remove the correlation. As a partial experimental attempt to answer this question, twenty-nine of the thirty-one subjects were given a cold pressor test several weeks after the previous described routine. After a control series of measurements the subject was required to submerge his left hand in ice-water while continuing to perform the reaction time test with his right hand. During the cold pressor test, the reaction time slowed slightly but most clearly for the P phase which had previously been the fastest. Thus raising the blood pressure experimentally removed the reaction-time cardiac cycle correlation. After the cold pressor test, reaction times became faster, more notably so for the reactions to signals presented during the P phase.

There may be a subjective element in that some distraction may be produced by the cold pressor test, but it seems most unlikely that this distraction could have produced a differential effect for the phases of the cardiac cycle. The results hardly explain the relation between blood pressure and reaction time but they do point to a physiological relationship between variations in the cardiac cycle and reaction time. Apparently the cerebral cortex is not uniformly excitable one moment to the next.

PRELIMINARY FINDINGS OF THE RELATION BETWEEN RESPONSE SPEED AND CHARACTERISTICS OF THE ELECTROENCEPHALOGRAM[2]

Reaction time has been studied in relation to characteristics of the electroencephalogram (EEG) in young adult subjects and more recently work has been reported relating the EEG to

---

[2] These data were gathered through the collaboration of James E. Birren, Kirstoff Abraham, P. M. Rabbitt, Shirley L. Phillips and Maureen B. De Lemos.

slowing of response time with advancing age (Surwillo, 1963). Obrist (1963) and others have commented about the tendency for the mean alpha frequency to decline with age. It is to be noted that the changes in the EEG are more commonly observed in older subject populations in which the presence of disease, particularly cerebrovascular, has not been excluded. By contrast, healthy elderly subjects show the characteristic psychomotor slowing of advancing age (Botwinick *et al.*, 1963).

The present study was an initial attempt to relate characteristics of the EEG to simple auditory reaction time in young and old subjects. The purpose was to determine to what extent characteristics of the EEG and slowing of reaction time might be changing jointly as a function of age. This work bears directly on the discussions of Obrist and of Callaway, presented separately in this volume.

METHODS

After a clinical EEG recording, subjects had a continuous recording from two occipital leads, two temporal leads and one central lead; one EKG lead, one EMG from the extensor digitalis, and one signal marker which recorded the onset of a 1000 cycle tone to which the subject had to react by raising his forefinger. The signal marker indicated the response, which also turned off the auditory signal; the closest interval between stimuli was 10 secs. and the longest 12 secs. The paper-speed during recording was 6 cm/sec.

Each response speed was measured from the paper and related to the characteristics of the EEG at the time of the signal presentation. Only waves greater in amplitude than 20 microvolts, and between 8 and 15 cycles per second were counted as alpha. Reaction times were classified as occurring to stimuli presented during alpha and no alpha. Reactions to signals during alpha were further classified according to the frequency of the wave at the time of the signal and its voltage. Reactions were further classified according to the phase of the EKG as previously described (P, QRS, T, T-P).

Each subject was given 100 auditory signals to which his response time was measured. Following this, the subject was asked to hyperventilate for two-three minutes after which he was given 25 more signals, and after five-minutes rest twenty-five more signals. The order of hyperventilation and rest was varied from subject to subject to counterbalance the effects of practice.

Subjects for this study were twenty-one young men aged twenty to thirty years, and thirteen elderly subjects.

It should be mentioned that simple reaction times during this procedure tend to be slower than those recorded using warning signals. Also the subjects for these observations were lying down with their eyes closed. It may be questioned whether the data are comparable with reaction times in the sitting subject, with eyes open, and employing warning signals. The reaction times of the younger subject would seem to be about 30-40 per cent longer in the present method than under the more conventional experimental arrangements. Simple auditory reaction times are usually found to be about .15 secs. in young subjects whereas the means in the present study were about .21 secs.

RESULTS

No correlation was found between either mean alpha frequency or mean voltage and mean reaction time in the young subjects. Furthermore, when the reaction times of each subject were divided into two groups according to whether the signal occurred at alpha frequencies greater or lesser than the mean for the individual or at voltages greater or lesser than the mean of the individual, no significant difference was found. In young male subjects therefore, no relationship was found between response speed and alpha frequency or voltage either within or between subjects.

Differences in mean response times were found between response to signals in alpha or no alpha phases. These and other data are presented in Table 8.

DISCUSSION

Faced with the evidence of a pervasive change in psychomotor speed with advancing age the researcher may well consider whether the changes of speed are not highly specific to aging. It is plausible that some part of the slowing is the result of the accumulation of irreversible effects of sensory diminution or depre-

TABLE 8

AGE DIFFERENCES IN MEAN SIMPLE AUDITORY REACTION TIME IN RELATION TO CHARACTERISTICS OF THE ELECTROENCEPHALOGRAM, ELECTROCARDIOGRAM, AND TO HYPERVENTILATION

Characteristics of the EEG at the Time of Signal Presentation

	No Alpha	Alpha	Freq. > Mean	Freq. < Mean	Volt. > Mean	Volt. < Mean	Mean μV Volt.	Mean Freq.
Young Mean reaction time	.226	.214	.215	.212	.210	.214	34.25	10.70
	t = 3.33; P < .01		t = 1.50; P > .05		t = 1.08; P > .05			
Elderly Mean reaction time	.255	.245	.244	.246	.243	.248	34.76	10.79
	t = 1.43; P > .05		t = .306; P > .05		t = .229; P > .05			

	Control	Hyperventilation	Rest	
Young Mean reaction time	.214	.223	.221	No sign. dif. between conditions
Mean frequency	10.7	10.6	10.6	No sign. dif. between conditions
Elderly Mean reaction time	.245	.253	.242	No sign. dif. between conditions
Mean frequency	10.79	10.43	10.98	No sign. dif. between conditions

Phase of the cardiac cycle

		P	QRS	T	T-P
Young	Alpha				
	Mean reaction time	.210	.214	.216	.213
	S.D.	.046	.042	.042	.040
	No Alpha				
	Mean reaction time	.230	.222	.234	.231
	S.D.	.048	.051	.063	.050
Elderly	Alpha				
	Mean reaction time	.263	.231	.241	.244
	S.D.	.053	.046	.070	.044
	No Alpha				
	Mean reaction time	.241*	.255*	.248	.241
	S.D.	.051	.056	.047	.036

*dif., P < .01

ciation; other contributors are also conceivable at this juncture in our knowledge, e.g., disuse, disease, fatigue, and physiological loss of cells. Perhaps many of these express themselves through a common locus that has special vulnerability with age. If this were the case then the generality of the phenomenon of slowing would be due more to the change in the common pathway rather than in a commonality of remote causes.

Since the work of Brody (1955) it seems reasonable to proceed on the assumption that the adult nervous system loses neurons with advancing age. In addition to cell loss, which seems to occur for other species as well as for man, the viable cells show a tendency to diminution of chromidial substance and an accumulation of pigment granules, lipofuscin (Bondareff, 1959; Birren, Imus, and Windle, 1959). The latter accumulation remains without a functional explanation either in terms of origin or consequences for cellular function. Hyden (1961) has more recently pointed out that motor neurons tend to lose RNA with age. In young cells, RNA content is increased by normal stimulation and decreased by exhaustion (see chapter 18 by Retzlaff and Fontaine.) By analogy to aging there is the question of whether aging cells lose RNA through exhaustion, fail to produce it because of stimulation lack, or whether there is a reduction in synthesizing capacity. Reduced sensory stimulation may play a role but it should not be assumed that if the loss of RNA is associated with reduced sensory stimulation that increasing the level of stimulation would reverse the process for the old cells.

The issue facing us at this point is what to do experimentally to what portion of the nervous system by stimulation through electrodes, by drugs, induction of fatigue, or other conditions. Experimental manipulation of the reticular formation of the midbrain and the basal ganglia would be such a possible locus because of the implications of this system for arousal or alerting.

There is a tendency to compartmentalize speed components according to one's background. That is, one seeks anatomical, neurophysiological, or behavioral localization in processes of perception, association, and response depending upon one's interest. The slowness being emphasized is primarily a neural and not a muscular phenomenon. While changes have been observed in the speed of relatively simple reflexes, the slowness is much more obvious in complex behavior mediated at some point by the cerebral cortex. Although present in simple skills, the slowing appears larger as one ascends a hierarchical ladder of complexity of process. Speed of perception seems to some extent related to speed of association and in turn both are related to simple reaction time. This has not been found to be so in young subjects. With advancing age it seems that there is a growing general limiting influence on the rapidity of mediation by the central nervous system. Were the central nervous system a system of pipes one would think partly in terms of diminution in output of some central pump and in terms of diminution of flow in particular pipes in selected areas. I have heard the terms viscous and noise used to describe the functioning of the older nervous system and these metaphors seem apt. We seem to be entering a new phase, however, in which through experimentation of the type reported in this volume we will know the nature of aging of the nervous system and behavior in operational rather than in metaphorical terms.

REFERENCES

Benton, A. L. and Joynt, R. J.: (1958) Reaction time in unilateral cerebral disease. *Confin. Neurol., 19:*247-256.

Birren, J. E.: (1955) Age changes in speed of simple responses and perception and their significance for complex behavior. In *Old Age in the Modern World*, London, E. and S. Livingstone, Ltd., pp. 235-247.

Birren, J. E. and Botwinick, J.: (1951) The relation of writing speed to age and to the senile psychoses. *J. Consult. Psychol., 15:*243-249.

Birren, J. E., Cardon, P. V., Jr. and Phillips, Shirley L. (1963) Reaction time as a function of the cardiac cycle in young adults. *Science, 140:* 195-196.

Birren, J. E., Imus, H. and Windle, W., eds.: (1959) *The Process of Aging in the Nervous System*. Springfield, Ill., Charles C Thomas.

Birren, J. E. and Morrison, D. F.: (1961) Analysis of the WAIS subtests in relation to age and education. *J. Geront., 16:*363-369.

Bondareff, W.: (1959) Morphology of the aging nervous system. In J. E. Birren, ed.: *Handbook of Aging and the Individual*, Chicago, University of Chicago Press, pp. 136-172.

Botwinick, J. and Birren, J. E. (1963) Mental abilities and psychomotor responses in healthy aged men. In J. E. Birren, R. N. Butler, S. W. Greenhouse, L. Sokoloff and Marian R. Yarrow, eds.: *Human Aging,*

Washington, D. C., Public Health Service, Publication No. 986, pp. 97-108.

Brody, H.: (1955) Organization of the cerebral cortex. III. A study of aging in the human cerebral cortex. *J. Comp. Neurol., 102*:511-556.

Chown, Sheila M.: (1961) Age and the rigidities. *J. Geront., 16*:353-362.

Fisher, M. B., Birren, J. E. and Leggett, A. L.: (1945) Standardization of two tests of equilibrium: the railwalking test and the ataxigraph. *J. Exp. Psychol., 35*:321-329.

Hyden, H.: (Dec. 1961) Satellite cell in the nervous system. *Scientific American, 205*:62-70.

Koga, T. and Morant, G. M.: (1923) On the degree of association between reaction times in the case of different senses. *Biometrika, 14:* 346-372.

Lacey, J. I. and Lacey, Beatrice C.: (1958) The relationship of resting autonomic activity to motor impulsivity. In *The Brain and Human Behavior*, Baltimore, Williams and Wilkins; *Proc. Ass. Res. Nerv. Ment. Dis., 36*:144-209.

Marshall, J.: (1961) The effect of ageing upon physiological tremor. *J. Neurol. Neurosurg. Psychiat., 24*:14-17.

Miles, W. R.: (1931) Correlation of reaction and co-ordination speed with age in adults. *Am. J. Psychol., 43*:377-391.

Obrist, W. D.: (1963) The electroencephalogram of healthy aged males. In J. E. Birren, R. N. Butler, S. W. Greenhouse, L. Sokoloff and Marian R. Yarrow, eds.: *Human Aging*, Washington, D. C., Public Health Service Publication No. 986, pp. 79-93.

Raven, J. C.: (1954) *Guide to Using Progressive Matrices*. Beverly Hills, California, Western Psychological Services.

Surwillo, W. A.: (1963) The relation of simple response time to brainwave frequency and the effects of age. *Electroenceph. Clin. Neurophysiol., 15*:105-114.

Wechsler, D.: (1955) *Manual for the Wechsler Adult Intelligence Scale*. New York, Psychological Corporation.

Weiss, A. D.: (1963) Auditory perception in relation to age. In J. E. Birren, R. N. Butler, S. W. Greenhouse, L. Sokoloff and Marian R. Yarrow, eds.: *Human Aging*, Washington, D. C., Public Health Service Publication No. 986, pp. 111-140.

Welford, A. T.: (1959) Psychomotor performance. In J. E. Birren, ed.: *Handbook of Aging and the Individual*, Chicago, University of Chicago Press, 1959, pp. 562-613.

11

RESPONSE SPEED, THE EEG ALPHA CYCLE, AND THE AUTONOMIC CARDIOVASCULAR CYCLE[1]

Enoch Callaway III

T HE PURPOSE of this paper is to describe and contrast ways in which the EEG alpha cycle and the autonomic cardiovascular cycle influence the speed of motor response. Although both cycles influence simple reaction time, they do so by very different mechanisms. The autonomic cardiovascular cycle acts independently of stimulus modality and at the motor end of things. In addition to its theoretical significance as a factor in speed of performance, it can be put to practical use by reducing the variance of simple reaction time. By contrast, the EEG alpha cycle acts early in the course of visual responses and is of little apparent practical significance.

I. THE INFLUENCE OF ALPHA ON REACTION TIME EARLY IN THE COURSE OF NEURAL EVENTS

Simple visual reaction times to stimuli presented at different phases of the alpha cycle differ significantly (Callaway and

[1] This work was supported by Project 61-1-24 from the California Department of Mental Hygiene; and by Office of Naval Research Contract NONR 2931(00). Reproduction in whole or in part is permitted for any purposes of the United States Government. The author is indebted to Mrs. August, Mr. Buchsbaum and Miss Elder for assistance in conducting the experiments and preparing the manuscript. Computer services were supported by Grant FR-00122, from the Division of Research Facilities and Resources, National Institutes of Health.

217

Yeager, 1960). The differences are small and there is significant variability of alpha phase-reaction time relationships within a single subject (Callaway, 1961). However, there is usually enough short-term consistency so that data from several consecutive days on a single subject can be pooled.

Bernhard (1940) has shown that changes in latency of response due to changes in stimulus intensity probably occur early in the course of neural events. If alpha cycles influence reaction time late in the course of neural events, then stimuli being processed with differences in latencies on the order of 50 msec. should interact with the same alpha cycle phase if presented 50 msec. apart with respect to the alpha waves (i.e., if phases at stimulus presentation differed by half a cycle). In other words, phase at stimulation associated with fast reaction time should be changed by changing stimulus intensity.

We studied two different light intensities that yielded mean reaction times differing by about 50 msec. No such phase change was observed (Callaway, 1962). On this basis we inferred that alpha influences reaction time early in the course of neural events. Some preliminary work with averaged evoked responses also suggested that alpha phase dependent changes in the visual evoked response could be detected earlier than 70 msec. after stimulation (Callaway, 1963).

II. ALPHA AND BRIGHTNESS JUDGMENT

One might suspect that since alpha cycle appears to act early in the course of neural events, it might influence brightness judgment as well as reaction time. In other words, we postulated an excitability cycle and during a crest of high excitability reactions should be faster and the stimulus should appear brighter.

In the experiments to be reported we used a device (Callaway, 1962-a) that presented a flash of light at 10 pre-set time intervals following the occiput most positive phase of a well formed alpha wave. These 10 time intervals, called phases, covered 90 msec. in 10 msec. increments from the starting phase. They were written down on cards and during an experiment the cards were shuffled and stimuli were presented at the ten phases according to the order of the cards. Then the cards were reshuffled and the procedure was repeated. We called a set of responses, consisting of one response for each phase, a row. Responses were collected one row at a time for completion of the experimental sitting.

The subject sat in a darkened room with his eyes closed. The stimulus was a flash of a Strobe light placed about a meter away from the subject's face. First the subject was required to press a switch as rapidly as possible in response to each light flash. Several rows of reaction times were collected. After a brief rest period the subject, still reclining with his eyes closed, was asked to judge the brightness of the flashes. He was shown a flash at phase 5 and told that it was a flash of intensity 10. Then he was asked to judge all the other flashes he would see in relationship to the standard one. He was allowed to see the standard flash whenever he wished, and except for standard flashes the collection of brightness judgments proceeded in the same way as for reaction times. After a few rows of brightness judgments, the subject was again returned to the reaction time task. This cycle was repeated over and over until the subject was tired.

First we studied brightness judgments and reaction times as functions of alpha phase and ignored the cardiac cycle. Figure 1 shows data from one subject. Both reaction time and brightness judgment tend to show a parallel relationship to alpha phase. High brightness judgments correspond with slow or long reaction times; and when mean brightness judgments are correlated with mean reaction times across alpha phase, a rank order correlation of .9 is obtained. This correspondence between brightness judgment and reaction time is not particularly typical. It is emphasized because it so completely contradicts the expected relationship between fast reaction times and high brightness judgments which had been predicted from the usual excitability cycle theory.

The relationship can be viewed somewhat better in terms of harmonic dials (Callaway, 1962-b). In the figures the angle of the vectors indicate phase like hands on a clock indicate time; vector length indicates amplitude. The vector terminating in a circle represents brightness judgment, and the triangle represents reaction time. Phase advances clock-wise with O corresponding

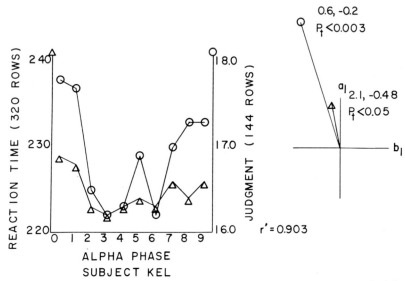

Figure 1. Reaction times and brightness judgments as functions of alpha phase.

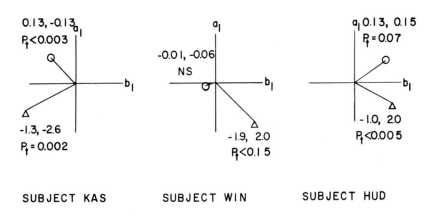

REACTION TIME = △   JUDGMENT = O

Figure 2. Harmonic dials of reaction times and brightness judgments for three subjects.

to 12:00. If pure sine waves were fit to the two sets of data, the highest brightness judgments and the longest reaction times would both fall between phases 9 and 0. The significance of each vector is indicated at P_t. The reaction time—alpha phase relationship is significant at better than the .05 level of confidence, the brightness judgment relationship at better than the .003 level of confidence. The coordinates for each vector are given in the order A, B. Note that the brightness judgment vector is drawn to 10 x the scale of reaction time.

Three other subjects were studied on similar tasks. The resulting harmonic dials are shown in Figure 2. The alpha phase—brightness judgment relationship was confirmed. As with reaction time, among subjects no particular phase seemed related to high brightness judgments, nor were the phases associated with high brightness judgments in any regular relationship to the phases associated with fast reaction times.

III. THE INDEPENDENCE OF ALPHA EFFECTS AND THE CARDIAC CYCLE

The brightness judgment effect made us wonder if time-locking between alpha and the cardiac cycle could be influencing our results. By using a Computer of Average Transients to determine time-locking of alpha to the cardiac cycle (Callaway, 1963), we found that Subject KEL's occiput went positive in a well formed alpha wave most often 110 msec. after the Q wave of his EKG. Since alpha and cardiac cycle are synchronized, we needed to determine if there were also relationships between reaction times, brightness judgments and time of stimulation measured from the Q wave of his EKG. To make comparison with alpha easier, phase intervals were 10 msec. as for alpha, and two sets of experiments were run; one with phase 0 being set 50 msec. from the Q wave, the second with phase 0 being set 100 msec. from the Q wave.

The results are shown in Figure 3. Reaction times as a function of time from Q are plotted on the graph and harmonic dials are shown at the right. The correspondence between the two sets of curves is striking. The shift in harmonic dials is 5 phase units or 50 msec. as it should be. None of the brightness judgments are significant under this condition. Failure to demonstrate a relationship may reflect technical inadequacies rather than a true absence of the sought-for phenomenon. Nevertheless, it is interesting that several attempts to demonstrate autonomic cardiovascular cycle effects on both brightness judgments and auditory thresholds have all failed.

Some months after the first brightness judgment experiments, Subject KEL came back for a second series of alpha phase studies. The procedure was the same as before except that the stimuli were presented only when the required alpha phase occurred within 320 msec. after an ear lobe pulse. In no case have we seen synchronization of alpha with the EKG hold for more than 200 msec. after the Q wave, and the ear lobe pulse begins on an average of 250 msec. after the Q wave. Therefore, this procedure avoided times when EKG and alpha were likely to be synchronized.

The results are shown in Figure 4. Reaction times and brightness judgments follow an opposite course. In the harmonic dial, both brightness judgment and reaction time relationships are significant at better than the 1 per cent level of confidence. Although in the earlier series of experiments both brightness judg-

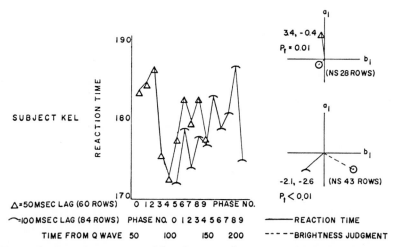

Figure 3. Reaction times and brightness judgments as functions of cardiac cycle.

ment and reaction time vectors lay in the same quadrant, we now find them at opposite poles. In the course of time, both reaction time and brightness judgment shifted with respect to alpha phase by approximately 45° and in opposite directions. However, it appears that alpha phase influences both reaction time and brightness judgment even when precautions are taken to rule out the interaction between alpha phase and cardiac cycle.

We may summarize the effects of the EEG alpha cycle on behavior as follows: 1) Alpha cycle influences vision alone; 2) It acts early in the course of neural events; 3) There is variability of phase—behavior relationships between and to some extent within subjects; 4) Alpha cycle influences brightness judgment; 5) Although alpha is time-locked to the cardiac cycle at about the time of mechanical systole, alpha phase—behavior effects can be demonstrated when stimuli are restricted to portions of the cardiac cycle where no alpha time-locking occurs.

All of this would suggest that recordable EEG alpha activity and its behavioral correlates are both related to some more funda-

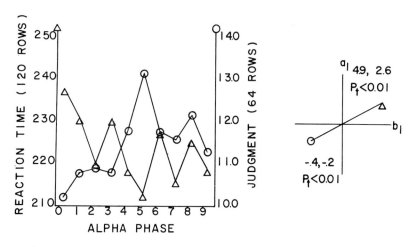

(ONLY DURING 320 MSEC FOLLOWING EAR PULSE)
REACTION TIMES AND JUDGMENTS TO SEPARATE STIMULI
SUBJECT KEL

Figure 4. Reaction times and brightness judgments as functions of alpha phase with cardiac cycle controlled.

mental underlying factor. One candidate would be Lindsley's alpha rhythm (Lindsley, 1958) which is postulated to exist even when EEG alpha is not recordable. By contrast, the autonomic cardiovascular cycle seems to fit a neurophysiological model without the necessity of an invisible intervening variable such as the unrecordable alpha rhythm. A brief consideration of this model may clarify the experiments to follow.

IV. THE AUTONOMIC CARDIOVASCULAR CYCLE THEORY

As blood pressure falls after mechanical systole, discharges from the carotid sinus and other pressure receptors diminish. Coincident with falling blood pressure, there tends to be a speeding of reaction time. Fastest reaction time ordinarily occurs just a little before the EKG Q wave—that is, during the time of minimal autonomic afferent discharge (Birren *et al.*, 1963). This reaction time effect can also be found using subjects with artificial pace-makers; therefore, we can discount the possibility of some intrinsic central rhythm both influencing reaction time and also triggering heart beats (Callaway, 1963).

Following the EKG Q wave there may be two or more bursts from the autonomic afferents; one reflecting electrical and/or mechanical systole, and another reflecting the arrival of the pulse wave at the carotid sinus. Although most of these afferents are inhibitory—at least in terms of sympathetic efferents —some are excitatory, and conduction velocities may vary from 6 to 30 meters per second (Uvnäs, 1960). EKG and alpha time-locking also occurs during the interval between the EKG Q wave and the carotid pulse. This added to the medley of discharging autonomic afferents makes the 250 msec. following the EKG Q wave a complex period. Relationships between reaction time and time from Q wave during this period are frequently of the form shown in Figure 3. Although not all subjects show this effect, a series of thirty-two studies showed it to be statistically significant.

V. PROCEDURE FOR STUDYING THE AUTONOMIC CARDIOVASCULAR CYCLE

It would appear that the cardiac cycle influences speed of motor discharge—that is, its effect occurs not upon stimulus presentation but only after the subject's reactions have been processed up to the point of being ready for motor discharge. This concept of action on speed of motor discharge was suggested by the work of the Laceys' (1958) and appeared to fit some earlier data.

To study this, we needed to present stimuli so that they would be processed to the point of motor discharge at about the time of systole—that is, from 0 to 300 msec. preceding the EKG Q wave. The subject was seated in a reclining chair in a sound deadened room; his EKG was used to step a 10 position beam switching tube. The operator could stop the beam switching tube to make adjustments, but ordinarily the 10 beat cycle was a recurring one. Six beats from this 10 beat cycle are diagrammed in Figure 5.

W refers to a warning click presented over loud speakers in the subject's room. W_1 warnings were presented at the Q wave of beat 5; W_2 warnings were presented at delay phi from beat 5. The stimulus was always presented after a delay of phi from beat 8. We used 5 phi values separated by 100 msec. steps. For each subject we tried to select phi values so that the largest phi would exceed the average time between pulse beats. For most subjects phi ranged from 500 to 900 msec.; for a few subjects it ranged from 400 to 800 msec. Phi values were written on cards and during an experimental sitting the cards were shuffled and stimuli

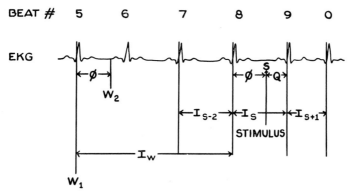

Figure 5. Sequence of events for study of cardiac cycle effect on reaction time.

were presented at all 5 phi values according to the order of the cards; then the cards; then the cards were reshuffled and the procedure was repeated.

The results of one stimulus presentation at each of the 5 phi values are referred to as a row. Data were collected one row at a time and the average sitting consisted of 30 rows. The time Q is the time from stimulus to the Q wave of beat 9. I stands for interval, with I_s being the interval between Q waves 8 and 9. When I_s is shorter than phi, Q becomes negative. However, in the experiments to be reported we discarded data with Q's less than 0. I_w is the warning interval—that is, the interval between Q waves 5 and 8. Stimuli were either brief flashes from a Strobe light mounted above the subject's head and shining on a wall 2 meters away, or else 1,000 cycles tones of between 60 and 70 db presented over loud speakers mounted on the wall of the subject's room. The tone stopped when the subject pressed the response key. Automatic recording machinery audibly printed out data whenever the subject responded. All data were punched on IBM cards. An individual card represented a single stimulus presentation and contained reaction time, phi, Q time, a subject and sitting code, the order of the row, form of stimulus, type of warning, and in most cases the interval I_w.

VI. THE INFLUENCE OF THE AUTONOMIC CARDIOVASCULAR CYCLE ON REACTION TIME LATE IN THE COURSE OF NEURAL EVENTS

With electrical systole, a series of inhibitory discharges start bombarding the medulla. With various perturbations, these reach a crescendo after the carotid pulse and fall to a minimum just before the next systole. These waves of inhibition are assumed to retard the discharge of motor reactions. If stimuli are presented so that the neural events leading to a response reach the motor end of things on the average as this wave of inhibition begins, then fast responses by arriving early would encounter the least inhibition and so would be discharged as action especially quickly, while responses that had been a little slow in getting to that stage would fall on the inhibited portion so that the final motor discharge would be slower. In such a case, mean reaction time might not change a great deal; variance, however, would. This led us to use an increase in variance as an indicator of the hypothetical onset of motor inhibition. We also predicted that when an experimental sitting is characterized by longer reaction times, the increase in variance will occur earlier since more time will be involved in the processing of neural data before the interaction with the wave of motor retardation.

To test this we sorted cards for each sitting according to Q time and set our computer to move a 20-card window across the data in 5-card steps calculating mean reaction time, variance of reaction time, variance of log reaction time, and mean Q time from the 20 cards at each step. The results from four subjects are shown in Figure 6. The curves show variance of log reaction time and are plotted on a log scale. Variance of log reaction time removes some of the correlations between reaction time and variance. However, the results would be essentially the same if

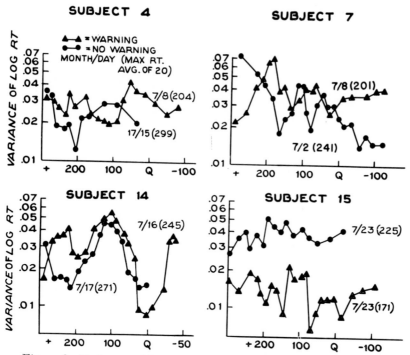

Figure 6. Variances of log reaction times as functions of "Q times."

simple variance of reaction time had been taken. The maximum mean reaction time encountered by the 20-card window is given. With warning, reaction times are faster and the variance increase, or "hump," occurs nearer to the next Q wave. This effect is seen in all four curves. Faster reaction times cause the motor end of the response to occur sooner after the stimulus. Hence with smaller reaction times, those stimuli that result in a variance hump will have smaller Q values (i.e., will have been delivered later with respect to the approaching systole). Thus, there should be a positive correlation between the Q at hump and reaction time.

For statistical purposes, we define a "hump" as the maximum variance of log reaction time calculated on steps having mean Q times between 50 and 300 msec. We used only data from subjects tested on tone stimulation, both with no warning and with warning at W_2. One subject was excluded because on one of his two sittings he had fewer than 20 Q times with values of less than 300 msec. Table I shows the correlation between variance humps and maximums of mean reaction times for the same sitting.

With no further stipulation the data are significant. However, the results are somewhat obscured by a few subjects who showed trivial variance humps and hence whose values selected by the criteria outlined are not meaningful. In this same Table we have also calculated rank order correlations excluding sittings when

TABLE 1
CORRELATIONS BETWEEN REACTION TIME AND VARIANCE "HUMP"

Subject	All Values		Only F 2.0	
	r	N	r	N
4	0.2	5	0.4	4
5	1.0	2		
7	1.0	4	1.0	4
10	−.2	4	1.0	3
11	1.0	2	1.0	2
14	1.0	2	1.0	2
15	1.0	2	1.0	2
16	1.0	2	1.0	2

r = rank order correlations across experiments.
n = number of experiments.

there was not a ratio of at least two between the hump value and some other variance of log reaction time from the same sitting. With this additional stipulation, all of the correlations become positive.

VII. CONFOUNDING OF AUTONOMIC CARDIOVASCULAR CYCLE INFLUENCES LATE IN THE CARDIAC CYCLE

Our experimental variables were selected so as to facilitate collecting data on reaction times to stimuli when Q ranged from about 300 msec. to 0. This particular interval produced maximum confounding effects of phi, I_w, I_s, and Q. The potential effects of these factors can be illustrated. Pooling data from all subjects under no warning conditions and excluding Q's less than 0, we computed reaction times by phase. The results are shown in Table II. Phase 4 is not shown because only a few subjects were given stimuli at phase 4. From phase 7 on, values drop out because of the requirement that Q be not less than 0. As the stimuli become closer to the Q wave, it is not the preceding interval phi but the following interval Q that determines reaction time. However, if we restrict our attention to phases 5 and 6 we find that reaction times to stimuli at phase 6 are shorter by 11 msec. than reaction times to stimuli at phase 5. The standard deviation of the difference between the means is 4.9, yielding a "t" of 2.2 which is significant at better than the 1 per cent level of confidence. This illustrates the effect of phi on reaction time.

In Table II, phi and Q are confounded for as phi increases, Q decreases. This table represents twelve runs on nine different subjects. For each phi on each run, rank correlations were run

TABLE 2
REACTION TIME AND Q AS FUNCTIONS OF ALPHA PHASE

Phase	5	6	7	8	9
Mean RT	254	243	250	255	270
SD of RT	63.5	61.8	66.6	63.3	72.2
Number	329	326	254	207	100
Mean Q	362	270	208	159	172

All subjects; Q >0; auditory stimulus with no warning.
Phase x 100 = phi in msec.

between Q and reaction time. Thus, there were twenty-four such correlations on phases 5 and 6. Of these, fifteen were negative indicating a tendency for short Q to go with long reaction time. This is not significant, probably due to counteractive I_s effects, but it is sufficient to demonstrate that the phi-reaction time effect is not an artifact due to a relationship between short Q and short reaction time.

With warning at W_2, I_w is the preparatory or warning interval. This effect is illustrated for the parameters of our experiment in Figure 7. As is well known, with random warning periods short warnings give long reaction time. In this particular experiment, a 1 beat per second metronome was substituted for the subject's pulse and warnings were presented at W_1 instead of at W_2. Phi values ranged from 500 to 900 msec. and 30 rows were collected.

One would intuitively expect I_w to be correlated with I_s since when an individual has three faster than average pulse beats, it is likely that his next pulse beat will also be faster than average. This suspected correlation has been found in every subject studied so far. In some subjects there is also a very strong tendency for I_s to correlate with reaction time in such a way that the faster the I_s, the faster the reaction time. Although this might be predicted on the basis of drowsy subjects showing simultaneous slowing of pulse rate and slowing of reaction times,

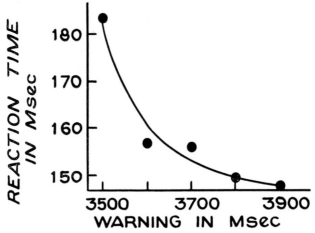

Figure 7. Effect of warning interval (I_w) on reaction time.

this does not seem to be the entire story. However, it is a some-what complex problem and will have to be the subject of a separate report (Buchsbaum and Callaway, to be published).

In an experiment on a 65-year-old pace-maker patient, I_s was held constant since all variables but one were fixed by the electronic pace-maker which controlled the patient's cardiac cycle. We used intervals of 50 msec. between phi values and used 10 phi's; stimuli were Strobe light flashes and warning was at W_2. Reaction times of over 500 msec were discarded in calculating the mean reaction times and the variance curves. Calculations were made for each phi value separately. There were 16 reaction times below 500 msec. for each phi value except for the ninth where there were fifteen.

The results are shown in Figure 8. The numbers above the mean reaction time curve indicate the total number of measure-

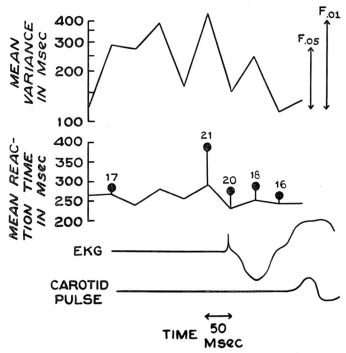

Figure 8.   Reaction time—cardiac cycle relationships in a pace-maker patient.

ments, including reaction times above 500 msec. The dot indicates what the mean reaction time would have been with all values included. The variance humps are striking. The first significant increase in variance occurs just long enough in advance of the pace-maker discharge so that the motor response to stimuli at that phi would coincide on an average with electrical systole. With reaction times over 500 msec. excluded, the highest mean reaction time precedes the pace-maker discharge. This is also the point of maximum variance and maximum number of reaction times over 500 msec. The pace-maker discharge precedes what would be analogous to the normal Q wave. Thus, if we restrict our attention to very small Q times, there is a tendency for slow reaction times to go with the smaller Q times.

We may now spell out the confounding of variables that complicates the use of simple reaction time in studying the autonomic cardiovascular cycle. Consider the situation *when I_s is constant.* The longer phi, the shorter Q; the longer phi, the shorter reaction time up to some value of Q; then the shorter Q, the longer reaction time. *When phi is constant,* I_s determines Q. Short I_s may yield short reaction time; short I_s yields short Q; yet for small Q, shorter Q yields longer reaction time. Finally, long I_w goes with long I_s; long I_w, if warning is included, yields short reaction time; yet long I_s is often associated with long reaction time. These strictures apply chiefly to the latter portion of the cardiac cycle.

VIII. CONCLUSION

The recordable alpha cycle seems too remote from its hypothetical underlying physiologically significant cycle for practical value. Not so for the autonomic cardiovascular cycle. The action of the autonomic cardiovascular cycle at the motor end of things, coupled with the complex interactions between pertinent variables just described produces complications. Nevertheless, the autonomic cardiovascular cycle effects can be held more or less constant for most reaction time studies by controlling for pulse rate and presenting stimuli about 300 msec. after the Q wave. This is to be recommended whenever variance of reaction time should be kept minimal and mean reaction time will not exceed I_s minus 300 msec.

The concept of action "at the motor end of things" may help explain the findings reported by Birren in this symposium. His young people showed reaction times of about 150 msec., the fastest reaction times being at the P wave. His older people had reaction times about 100 msec. longer and did not show fast reaction times at the P wave. The 100 msec. slower reaction times would be expected to displace the phase at stimulation for fast reaction times back 100 msec. This would take it out of Birren's "P" phase and put it into the "T—P" phase. There it would be obscured by being averaged with all the other conditions subsumed under T-P.

From a theoretical standpoint, the finding of action on motor readiness supports a set of concepts described by the Laceys in their report on "The Relationship between Autonomic Activity and Motor Impulsivity." The behavioral effects of the autonomic cardiovascular cycle may also be related to such diverse phenomena as the motor restlessness of patients in shock and the personalities characteristic of various cardiovascular disease states. The role of the autonomic cardiovascular cycle in changes with aging remains unexplored except for the pioneering investigations of Birren reported in this symposium.

SUMMARY

Alpha cycle influences responses to visual stimuli early in the course of neural events. It influences reaction time and brightness judgment, but the phase relationships are variable. By contrast, the autonomic cardiovascular cycle influences only reaction time and is independent of stimulus modality. It appears to reflect a wave of motor inhibition paralleling sinus and vagal autonomic afferent discharge.

REFERENCES

Bernhard, C. G.: (1940) Contributions to the nerophysiology of the optic pathway. *Acta Physiol. Scand.*, *1*:1-94.

Birren, J. E., Cardon, P. V. and Phillips, S. L.: (1963) Reaction time as a function of the cardiac cycle in young adults. *Science*, *140*:195-196.

Buchsbaum, M. and Callaway, E.: Heart rate, respiration and reaction time. (To be published.)

Callaway, E.: (1961) Day-to-day variability in relationship between electroencephalographic alpha phase and reaction time to visual stimuli. *Ann. NY Acad. Sci.*, 92:1183-1186.

Callaway, E.: (1962a) Factors influencing the relationship between alpha activity and visual reaction time. *Electroenceph. Clin. Neurophysiol.*, 14:674-682.

Callaway, E.: (1962b) A method for harmonic dial calculation. *Psychophysiol. Newsletter*, 8:3; 6-9.

Callaway, E.: (1963) Interaction between the visual evoked response and two spontaneous biological rhythms: the EEG alpha cycle and the cardiac arousal cycle. Proceedings of the Conference on the Sensory Evoked Responses in Man, *Ann. NY Acad. Sci.*, in press.

Callaway, E. and Yeager, C. L.: (1960) Relationship between reaction time and electroencephalographic alpha phase. *Science, 132:*1765.

Callaway, E. and Yeager, C. L.: (Sept. 1960) Relations between human reaction time and EEG alpha phase. Proceedings of the 7th International Congress of the Society for the Study of Biological Rhythms, *Minerva Medica.*

Lacey, J. I. and Lacey, B. C.: (1958) The relationship of resting autonomic activity to motor impulsivity. Chapter V in *The Brain and Human Behavior*, Vol. 36, Proc. A.R.N.M.D., Baltimore, Williams and Wilkins Co.

Uvnäs, B.: (1960) Central cardiovascular control. Chapter 44 in *Handbook of Physiology*, Vol. II. John Field, H. W. Magoun, Victor E. Hall, eds., Washington, Am. Physiol. Soc.

12

RELATIONSHIPS BETWEEN THE AUTONOMIC NERVOUS SYSTEM AND CENTRAL NERVOUS SYSTEM IN AGE DIFFERENCES IN BEHAVIOR[1]

B. M. Shmavonian, A. J. Yarmat and S. I. Cohen

INTRODUCTION

T HE PURPOSE of this paper is truly a comparative one. It is comparative in at least two dimensions: the first being the relationship of the different autonomic nervous system and central nervous system responses; the second being relationship between subject groups—that is, young men, young women and old men.

A. THE RELATIONSHIP OF AUTONOMIC NERVOUS SYSTEM AND CENTRAL NERVOUS SYSTEM RESPONSES

Although our colleagues in the Soviet Union have written a good deal about the role of the central nervous system in autonomic conditioning, at the present time the status of autonomic conditioning in the United States is somewhat obscured by large gaps in our understanding of the total process and in some cases doubt as to whether such conditioning is possible at all. Ever since the work of Pavlov (1928) on the conditioning of gastric secretions, autonomic conditioning has been assumed as a well

[1] This research was supported by Public Health Service research grants M-6022 and GM-05385 from National Institute of Health.

demonstrated fact. The actual experimental foundation for this assumption, however, is unsatisfactorily small. Most of the American work in the area was carried out in the early 1930's and has been rather sporadic and inconclusive. Some of the Russian work translated by Razran (1961) and by Gantt (1957) is unsatisfactory because of the complete absence of any reports of procedures or details of results, making it difficult to arrive at any definite conclusions.

As has been mentioned, there is general acceptance of the validity of the phenomena of autonomic conditioning, and men like Mowrer (1960) and Skinner (1938) have written at length about the two types of learning and their possible interaction. However, some investigators have taken an extreme view in another direction. K. Smith (1954), for example, has argued that autonomic conditioning is an impossibility and hypothesizes that all conditioning is a result of skeletal muscle conditioning which triggers autonomic responses and/or artifact.

The role of central nervous system in autonomic conditioning has had even less rigorous attention. Some recent work by Malmo (1959), Shmavonian and Busse (1963), Cohen, Silverman and Shmavonian (1961) and Silverman, Cohen and Shmavonian (1959) indicates that autonomic reactivity appears to be affected by central nervous system activation. Martin (1960) reported faster GRS conditioning in central nervous system activated subjects. Furthermore, reticular activation has been associated with peripheral sympathetic nervous system activity as a result of posterior hypothalamic discharge. Several studies by Elmadjian, Lamson and Neri (1956), Von Euler (1956) and Bergsman (1959) have suggested that urinary excretory levels of adrenaline and noradrenaline reflect activity at the sympathetic motor end plates as well as adrenal medullary discharge from sympathetic activity.

B. RELATIONSHIP BETWEEN SUBJECT GROUPS

Sex differences and similarities in autonomic nervous system and central nervous system activity is a relatively neglected area. For the purposes of this paper, we shall look at some findings without very much speculation.

Age differences, however, have been studied more intensively. Shmavonian and Busse (1963) and Cohen, Silverman and Shmavonian (1961) reviewed some of this literature and there is no need here to repeat more than a few of the directly relevant ones.

Kimble (1960) using the eyelid response, has noticed that in general the conditioned and unconditioned response in the elderly is of much smaller magnitude than in normal young adults. Furthermore, he has found that after several couplings of the conditioned and unconditioned stimuli, the response to the unconditioned stimulus disappears altogether; that is to say, the subject no longer blinks to a puff of air, which is coupled to a light. However, when the light is removed in this situation and the puff of air given alone, the response returns, indicating certain inhibitory influences with the periodic presentations of these stimuli. Botwinick and Kornetsky (1960) demonstrated differences in amplitude of GSR responses and rate of acquisition and extinction between young and aged subjects; the aged giving smaller GSR responses showing slower conditioning and faster extinction.

Histopathological studies have supported physiological evidence of autonomic nervous system changes associated with age. Kuntz (1938) found a progressive change in dendrites, reduction in chromidial substance and a deposition of melanotic pigment in autonomic ganglion cells associated with age. Andrew (1956) in an extensive study of structural alterations with aging, stated that the nuclei of the hypothalamus show perhaps the most impressive and striking incidents of specificity of age changes seen anywhere in the nervous system. He found an increase in cellular size to giant cell proportions, eight to ten times as large as comparable cells in young individuals.

Gellhorn, Nelson and Redgate (1956) pointed out that the diminution of the reflex involving the anterior or parasympathetic division was observed with increasing age and this was interpreted as being due to diminishing reactivity of the parasympathetic areas of the hypothalamus.

The above works raised questions as to the relationship of peripheral autonomic conditioned responses and central autonomic reactivity. Differences in autonomic reactivity and altered conditioning characteristics in young and aged subjects may be related to a change in the reactivity of hypothalamus in aged subjects.

Chow (1954) and Hernandes-Peon *et al.* (1956) have shown that partial destruction of hypothalamus or the mesencephalic reticular formation may abolish some autonomic conditioned reflexes but the corresponding unconditioned reflex persists. These subcortical structures are believed to play an important role in the elaboration of conditioned reflexes and behavior.

There is good evidence that the formation of conditioned reflexes involves and is facilitated by activation of the hypothalamic-cortical system. Most investigations point to the fact that conditioning is the result of an interaction between central excitatory processes (midbrain and hypothalamus) set up by conditioned and unconditioned stimuli. Without activation of mesencephalic and hypothalamic centers it is questionable if conditioning will occur. Furthermore, it has been suggested by Shmavonian (1959) and Martin (1960) that autonomic conditioning is dependent on general autonomic arousal and not merely changes produced in peripheral structures by unconditioned stimuli.

Our procedures, to be described below, allow comparison in young and old subjects of acquisition and extinction rates, latencies, relationships between blood flow, GSR and EEG and the investigation of phenomena observed by Kimble. Furthermore, catechol amine comparisons were made as a reflection of sympathetico-adrenal responsivity.

METHOD

Subjects

The subjects consisted of a total of thirty-three aged men, thirty young men and twenty-two young women. Of these, useable data was available on twenty-five aged, twenty-six young men and seventeen young women. From these groups there were occasional omissions of subjects due to artifact or instrumental failure on certain of the obtained measures or insufficient urine samples. Since the rest of their data was useable and since their addition or subtraction did not change the slopes of the obtained curves—there were never more than two such cases per specific measure—their data was included in all but the unuseable analyses.

The young subjects were all undergraduates at Duke University. Their mean age was twenty and the range was eighteen to twenty-two years. The aged subjects were recruited through the employment office. Their mean age was sixty-five with a range of fifty-nine to seventy-six years. The prerequisite conditions were: no cardiac or circulatory disorders or history of same; no illness at present; no gross hearing deficit; and, willingness to tolerate electric shock to the finger.

All subjects were asked not to participate in strenuous physical activity or sexual activity; not to use alcoholic beverages or eat bananas, for at least twelve hours immediately preceding the experiment. These precautions were particularly designed to avoid contamination in the assessment of the catechol amines.

Apparatus

A Grass Model IIID EEG polygraph with the appropriate AC and DC amplifiers, consisting of six channels of EEG and five channels of DC widesweep pens was used. The Burch EEG analyzer (described earlier by senior author (1963) and by Thompson and Obrist (1963) was also utilized.

The GSR amplifier used throughout most of this experiment was the Texas Biophysical Instrument Co., Inc. Model 201 amplifier. For the first few subjects an earlier prototype of this amplifier with the same twenty microampere induced current was used. The machines were, therefore, quite comparable, the main difference being in their automatic recentering devices. Silver chloride impregnated cloth foot electrodes were used throughout this experiment.

The respirometer was a simple rubber tube filled with copper sulfate and attached to the subject's chest. As the tube is stretched resistance increases and as it is released resistance decreases. This is amplified through a bridge and recorded on the polygraph.

The photocrystal finger plethysmograph has been described in detail by the senior author elsewhere.

The electric shock source was a 1,000 cycle DC shock amplifier developed in our laboratory.

Procedure

The subjects arrived at the laboratory and were asked to urinate; this urine was discarded. They were then given a glass of water to drink following which they were led into a dimly lit room and asked to rest on a comfortable cot for one hour. At the end of the hour they were asked to urinate again and this sample was retained for resting-level catechol amine determinations. They were given another glass of water and were led into the experimental chamber where they were seated in a comfortable chair and GSR electrodes, EEG leads, respirometer, plethysmograph and shock electrodes were attached to the subject. The 512 cycle mild tone was sounded to ascertain that it was audible to all the subjects. They were then told to remain seated for the rest of the experiment; that all communications would take place via the intercom and that they should try to remain awake, not move and to follow instructions.

The next step involved establishing of shock tolerance levels. All subjects were encouraged to take as much shock as they could tolerate. When the limit was reached they were given the shock for a five second period and then asked if they could tolerate a little more. If the answer was yes, it was increased five more volts. At this point they were told that there would be no more shocks for a while and they should relax and attend to the various stimuli. Adaptation trials were begun which consisted of sounding repeatedly the 512 cps tone for thirty trials or until the subjects showed no vasomotor response to the tone for five consecutive presentations. Those subjects who did not adapt in thirty trials were not included in the main body of this experiment although their conditioning curves did produce some interesting results. (When we have a large enough group of non-adaptors we perhaps will present a separate paper on that issue.)

Following adaptation, the conditioning period was begun which consisted of ten reinforced trials of a fifteen second tone with the last five seconds being overlapped by shock. After these ten reinforced trials, ten extinction trials were given which entailed the presentation of the tone without the shock. The presentation of the stimuli both during acquisition and during extinction was temporally varied from one to four minutes between trials.

RESULTS

1. Vasomotor Reactivity

As the acquisition curves of Figure 1 show, there were clearcut differences between the three groups. The young men show the highest amplitudes of vasomotor conditioning and most typical acquisition curves. The young women show smaller conditioned responses and a far more erratic conditioning curve. Although this erratic curve may be partially a result of the smaller number of young women subjects, our previous experiences have convinced us that this type of responsivity is characteristic of women subjects and it would be grossly erroneous to mix men and women

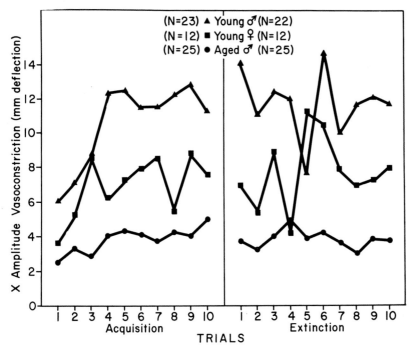

Figure 1. Vasomotor conditioned responses during ten seconds of conditioned stimulus (mm. of pen deflection).

subjects where physiological measures are being obtained. The aged subjects show the smallest vasomotor responsivity both in amplitude and in overall acquisition curves. There obviously is mild conditioning but below the levels of both younger groups. Table 1 shows the statistical comparison made both within groups (trial 1 vs. trial 10) and between groups, i.e., comparison of the three groups on the first and last conditioning trials.

The extinction curves of Figure 1 indicates that the ten trials were not sufficient for extinction to take place. In fact, both the young men and young women produced larger responses during extinction than they did during acquisition. This is most probably due to anticipation of further shock, boredom, fatigue and other centrally mediated factors. The aged subjects, however, after an initial rise do show an inhibitory trend toward extinction although even this group does not return to the same level as that of the first conditioning trial.

2. GSR Conditioning

Figure 2 shows the acquisition and extinction curves for the GSR. The conversion utilized here was differences in conductance (delta C) recommended by Edelberg (1960) which takes into account the level of conductance preceding each stimulus.

TABLE 1

STATISTICAL COMPARISON: WITHIN AND BETWEEN GROUPS
ON PLETHYSMOGRAPHIC CONDITIONING

Group	Trial	Mean Diff.	t	p	df
Aged Males	10-1	2.480	2.138	<.05	24
Young Males	10-1	5.239	3.745	<.005	22
Young Females	10-1	3.992	2.134	<.10	10
Aged Males-Young Males	1	3.52	2.207	<.05	46
Aged Males-Young Males	10	6.28	3.139	<.005	46
Aged Males-Young Females	1	1.116	.955	<.40	34*
Aged Males-Young Females	10	2.625	1.066	<.40	35
Young Males-Young Females	1	2.404	.993	<.40	32*
Young Males-Young Females	10	3.655	1.265	>.20	33

*No score for one female on Trial 1.

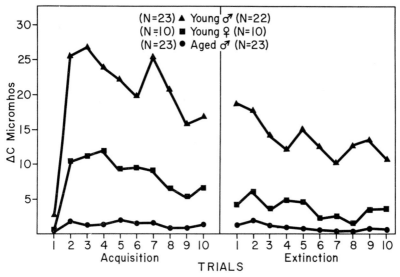

Figure 2. Mean amplitude GSR ($\triangle$C) per trial acquisition and extinction.

Here again, the young men show the largest conditioned responses and high overall conditioning. The young women are in the middle position again and the first to last trial comparison approaches but does not reach significance due to high variance, whereas the aged men with very small changes in delta C units show significant conditioning due to very low variance. In terms of between groups comparisons on the first trial the young men are significantly higher than aged men but young women are approximately at the same level as the aged. On the tenth trial, however, both younger groups were significantly higher than the aged, but not significantly different from each other. Table II shows these relationships and their statistical significance levels.

It should be noted that all three groups show typical extinction curves. None of the groups return to the original base level of acquisition trial 1; however, this obviously is due to the fact that ten extinction trials are not sufficient for complete extinction. It is also interesting to note that the relative positions of these curves remain unchanged in relation to each other as well as in their amplitude of response.

In order to better understand the role of sympathetic activation in GSR conditioning, basal conductance at the moment of the CS onset was plotted for the acquisition and extinction trials. Figure 3 shows these relationships graphically. Both the young groups are significantly higher in this activation level at the be-

TABLE 2

STATISTICAL COMPARISON: WITHIN AND BETWEEN GROUPS
ON GSR (DELTA C) CONDITIONING

Group	Trial	Mean Diff.	t	p	df
Aged Males	10-1	1.142	2.302	<.05	22
Young Males	10-1	13.966	4.397	<.001	22
Young Females	10-1	5.966	2.008	<.1	9
Aged Males-Young Males	1	2.406	2.543	<.025	44
Aged Males-Young Males	10	15.230	5.041	<.001	44
Aged Males-Young Females	1	0.322	1.013	<.4	31
Aged Males-Young Females	10	5.145	2.536	<.025	31
Young Males-Young Females	1	2.084	1.437	<.20	31
Young Males-Young Females	10	10.085	2.037	<.1	31

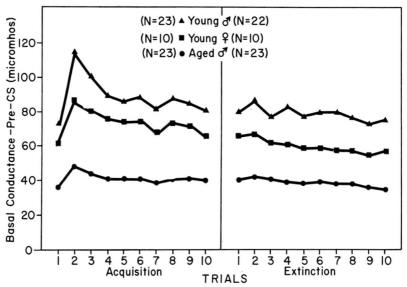

Figure 3. Basal conductance at time of conditioned stimulus onset.

ginning and at the end of conditioning (trials 1 and 10); however, they are not statistically different from each other. All three groups show a significant rise in activation levels after the first reinforcement. As the conditioning progresses this activation level shows a gradual decay or adaptation so that by the tenth reinforced trial the significant rise disappears and by the last extinction trial the young women and aged men are at or below the level of the first conditioning trial with the young men still slightly more aroused than on the first trial.

The importance of these curves cannot be overstated. It is clear that the sympathetic activation discussed above plays an important role in the determination of the conditioning curve. The large CRs obtained on second and third reinforcement are obviously greatly determined by this activation level and as the activation level drops the true CRs are obtained. Table III shows the statistical relationships in the basal conductance levels for within and between groups.

3. EEG

In the analysis of the EEG data it became obvious that delta and theta (.5-8cps) and alpha (8-12cps) activity did not change with the conditioning and also there were no group differences

TABLE 3
Statistical Comparison: Within and Between Groups
of Basal Conductance at Onset of CS

Group	Trial	Mean Diff.	t	p	df
Aged Males	2-1	10.682	2.12	$<.05$	22
Young Males	2-1	41.790	6.46	$<.001$	22
Young Females	2-1	25.156	2.48	$<.05$	9
Aged Males	10-1	3.681	1.88	$<.1$	22
Young Males	10-1	7.621	2.07	$<.06$	22
Young Females	10-1	4.41	1.10	$<.4$	9
Aged Males-Young Males	1	36.183	4.72	$<.001$	44
Aged Males-Young Males	10	40.124	4.85	$<.001$	44
Aged Males-Young Females	1	24.805	2.63	$<.025$	31
Aged Males-Young Females	10	25.533	2.45	$<.025$	31
Young Males-Young Females	1	11.378	0.917	$<.4$	31
Young Males-Young Females	10	14.591	1.052	$<.4$	31

between the young and aged subjects. (No statistical calculations were made for the young women since we had few adequate EEG records for this group.) The analysis of superimposed activity (wave complexity) only showed that there was a significant difference between the ten second pre-stimulus period and the ten second stimulus period for both groups. The levels were higher during the stimulus regardless of groups or trials.

The EEG conditioning and extinction data was analyzed using analysis of variance techniques described by Winer (1962). The measures were total count, beta, and superimposed activity mentioned above. Each of the analyses consisted of a 2 x 10 x 2 factorial design, with two factors having repeated measures. The analyses were carried out using the unweighted means solution given by Winer to adjust for the unequal group sizes. In some of the analyses it was necessary to estimate missing data. This was done according to the manner described by Li (1957).

Total Activity

The total activity refers to the analyzer channel which includes all of the theta-delta, alpha, and beta activity plus the superimposed activity (wave complexity). Figure 4 shows the mean number of total EEG activity ten seconds immediately pre CS and ten seconds during CS, for the acquisition and extinction trials. It is obvious that young and aged men vary dramatically in total EEG activity and that the aged show increases in this measure as the reinforced trials proceed both in the pre CS and in the CS periods, whereas the young subjects after an initial rise start showing adaptation. In the extinction, the trend is somewhat in the opposite direction. Table IV shows the total EEG activity analysis of variance for the acquisition period.

The data was coded for computation purposes by dividing each value by 10 and rounding to the nearest whole number. Four missing values were estimated.

Groups (A): There was a highly significant F value for the group main effect, with the aged men showing greater activity throughout the period.

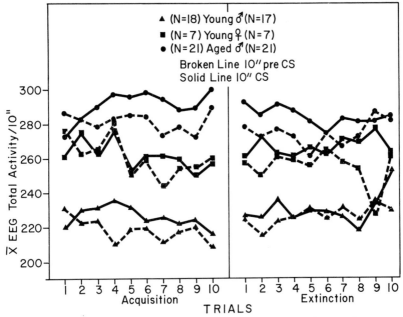

Figure 4. Mean number total EEG wave per ten second periods pre CS and during CS.

TABLE 4

ANALYSIS OF VARIANCE: EEG TOTAL COUNT
FOR ACQUISITION PERIOD

Source	df	ms	F	p
Between Subjects	38	7941.80	18.72	<.001
Groups (A)	1	424.17		
Error Between	37			
Within Subjects	741			
Trials (B)	9	4.84	<1	—
AB	9	14.29	1.71	<.10
Error	333	8.36		
Pre-During CS (C)	1	153.39	7.61	<.01
AC	1	1.97	<1	—
Error	37	20.15		
BC	9	15.31	3.52	<.001
ABC	9	3.03	<1	—
Error	333	4.35		

Trials (B): There was no significant effect of trials.

Groups x trials (AB): This interaction did reach the .10 level. Inspection of the curves show a tendency for the aged subjects to increase (both pre and during the CS) and the young men to decrease.

Pre-During CS (C): The F value was significant. CS values were higher than pre CS values except for trial 1.

Groups x pre-during CS (AC): This interaction was not significant indicating that the pre-during difference (summed over trials) was proportionately the same although the levels were higher for the aged subjects.

Trials x pre-during CS (BC): This interaction was significant indicating differential spread between pre-during CS values over trials regardless of groups. The data shows a drop in EEG total count from pre to during CS on the first trial, whereas trials 2-10 are characterized by increases from pre to during CS values.

Groups x trials x pre-during CS: This interaction was not significant.

Table V shows the analysis of variance of the EEG total count for the extinction period.

As in the acquisition period, the aged subjects were significantly higher than the young subjects in level of total activity. There

TABLE 5
ANALYSIS OF VARIANCE: EEG TOTAL COUNT
FOR EXTINCTION PERIOD

Source	df	ms	F	p
Between Subjects	37			
Groups (A)	1	4767.25	10.51	.005
Error	36	453.45		
Within Subjects	722			
Trials (B)	9	15.23	1.13	—
AB	9	7.43	<1	—
Error	324	13.44		
Pre-During CS (C)	1	82.48	4.15	<.05
AC	1	14.76	<1	—
Error	36	19.89		
BC	9	6.13	1.32	—
ABC	9	7.86	1.69	<.10
Error	324	4.64		

was no overall effect of trials. The trials by groups interaction was not significant. There was again a significant pre-during CS effect, with values during the CS generally higher than those for the pre CS period. The triple interaction approached significance, very close to the .10 level. Inspection of Figure 4 shows that for the young subjects the pre CS levels do fall below the CS levels at several points; whereas, for the aged subjects, this occurs only once, and that on trial 9 of the extinction.

Beta Activity

Figure 5 shows the beta activity for the acquisition and extinction periods. It is obvious that with no differences in the slower waves among the groups it is the beta activity that contributed so heavily to the differences (in this total activity) just discussed. Table VI shows the analysis of variance for the beta activity during the acquisition.

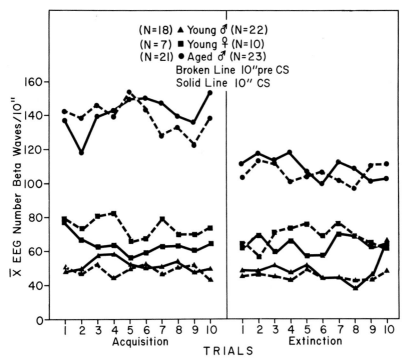

Figure 5. Mean number beta wave per ten second periods pre CS and during CS.

TABLE 6
ANALYSIS OF VARIANCE: EEG BETA ACTIVITY
FOR ACQUISITION PERIOD

Source	df	ms	F	p
Between Subjects	38	1,578,111.12	33.82	<.001
Groups (A)	1	46,656.16		
Error Between	37			
Within Subjects	741			
Trials (B)	9	1371.10	1.59	<.20
AB	9	1024.98	1.19	—
Error	333	861.73		
Pre-During CS (C)	1	1548.11	<1	—
AC	1	3.08	<1	—
Error	37	2206.00		
BC	9	753.56	1.62	<.20
ABC	9	817.91	1.76	<.10
Error	333	464.58		

As in the total activity of the EEG, there was a highly significant group effect, with the aged having almost three times as
much beta activity as the young. No other effect reached the .05
level of significance. However, the groups x trials x pre-during
CS (ABC) interaction reached the .10 level. The curves show
that beta activity during the CS increased over the pre CS period

TABLE 7
ANALYSIS OF VARIANCE: EEG BETA ACTIVITY
FOR THE EXTINCTION PERIOD

Source	df	ms	F	p
Between Subjects	37			
Groups (A)	1	706,324.17	23.11	<.001
Error	36	30,569.48		
Within Subjects	722			
Trials (B)	9	856.66	<1	—
AB	9	478.56	<1	—
Error	324	1270.89		
Pre-During CS (C)	1	1384.35	<1	—
AC	1	3.33	<1	—
Error	36	2000.25		
BC	9	294.43	<1	—
ABC	9	791.30	1.64	<.20
Error	324	482.87		

TABLE 8

CATECHOL AMINE EXCRETION LEVELS FOR 58 CONDITIONING SUBJECTS

| | Young Males (n =22) | | | | Young Females (n =14) | | | | Aged Males (n =22) | | | |
| | Pre | | Post | | Pre | | Post | | Pre | | Post | |
	χ	S.D.	χ	S.D.	χ	S.D.	χ	S.D.	χ	S.D.	χ	S.D.
Adrenaline	0.81	0.62	0.97	0.56	1.31	0.67	0.79	0.55	1.77	0.86	1.32	0.94
Noradrenaline	2.10	0.98	1.67	1.10	1.23	0.80	1.16	0.77	2.18	1.57	1.55	0.80
Total Amines	2.91		2.64		2.54		1.95		3.95		2.87	

earlier for the young subjects. However, once the aged subjects did show this increase they maintained it more consistently and with greater differentiation. Table VII shows the analysis of variance for beta activity during the extinction period.

The only results of the beta analysis for the extinction period was a highly significant F for groups with the aged again showing much more beta than the young. The triple interaction is still high however, at the .20 level of significance.

4. Catechol Amines

Although there were a higher number of subjects for the catechol amine analysis than the one presented below, some of these subjects did not complete the conditioning for a variety of reasons. The inclusion of these subjects would not have changed the significant findings at all, but, in fact, would have raised the significance levels in many cases. However, to be conservative, only the 58 subjects on whom conditioning data was available are presented here. Table VIII shows the mean catechol excretion levels for the three groups.

Analysis of variance was carried out and comparisons were made between young men and women, young men and aged men, and pre and post experimental levels of adrenaline and noradrenaline. Individual t-tests were made and will be indicated

TABLE 9

ANALYSIS OF VARIANCE: CATECHOL AMINE EXCRETION FOR
58 SUBJECTS FOR WHOM THERE WAS COMPLETE CONDITIONING DATA

Groups in Analysis	Source of Variance	df	Adrenaline			Noradrenaline		
			ms	F	p	ms	F	p
Young Males and Females	Sex (A)	1	.42	1.02	—	8.25	6.50	<.025
	Error	34	.41			1.27		
	Pre-Post (B)	1	.54	1.74	—	1.08	2.00	<.20
	AB	1	2.04	6.58	<.025	.58	1.07	—
	Error	34	.31			.54		
Young and Old Males	Age (A)	1	9.35	11.69	<.005	.01	<1	—
	Error	42	.80			1.64		
	Pre-Post (B)	1	.45	1.25	—	6.24	6.24	<.025
	AB	1	2.11	5.86	<.025	.21	<1	—
	Error	42	.36			1.00		

below. Table IX shows the analysis of variance of catechol excretion for the three groups.

Adrenaline

In the analysis of the adrenaline data for the young men and young women, the only significant F value was for the interactions. Comparison of the cell means shown in Table VIII were made by t-tests. The increase from pre to post in the young men approached significance ($p<.10$); the decrease shown by the women was highly significant with a p value of $<.001$. A comparison of the pre and post means showed the women to have a significantly higher pre level ($p<.05$), whereas the post means for the two groups were not significantly different.

The analysis for the young men and aged men shows a significant group difference as well as a significant interaction. Inspection of the means in Table VIII shows the aged men to have higher adrenaline excretion rates for both the pre and the post periods; the difference in pre means was highly significant ($p<.001$); as with the young men-young women comparison, the post difference was not ($p<.20$). The decrease from pre to post shown by the aged men was highly significant ($p<.001$). It might be pointed out that although the levels are different the young women and aged men show similar patterns of adrenaline excretory activity.

Noradrenaline

Analysis of the noradrenaline data for the young men and young women showed a significant group difference, with the women tending to have lower noradrenaline levels. The difference appears mainly to be due to the difference in the pre means ($p<.01$); although the difference at the post level is of clinically meaningful value, the p was only $<.20$. There was some general tendency for noradrenaline values to decrease as shown by the F values for pre-post; however, this was not consistent enough to attain significance ($p<.20$).

The only significant F in the analysis for the young men and aged men was that for pre-post, indicating an overall tendency for noradrenaline excretion to decrease from pre to post. Both groups showed significant decreases when t-tests were performed (young men p<.01, aged men p<.001).

DISCUSSION AND CONCLUSIONS

As mentioned in the introduction the comparison of the young women with the other two groups is a difficult one. Furthermore, this group with fewer subjects cannot be viewed conclusively. It is obvious from the data that at least in this experiment the young women comprise a distinct population and is consistently between the aged men and young men in all the measures. Also, the variability in the women was extremely high on all the measures. This may have been due to variation in the menstrual cycle. We have to admit ignorance as to why these differences exist; however, it would appear that an a priori pooling of young subjects, regardless of sex, in experiments utilizing physiological measures is not justifiable.

In the comparisons of young and aged men in the previous pages it is evident that as far as peripheral sympathetic conditioning is concerned the young men show much higher responsivity both in GSR and in peripheral blood flow and clearly manifest conditioning. The aged men also show conditioning but at a much lower level. It is also obvious that this conditioning is a function of a general sympathetic activation, where after the first CS-US coupling, the basal conductance of all the subjects increases significantly and then gradually gets back to the initial level by the end of the extinction period. Again this phenomena is present in the aged subjects as well, but at a much lower amplitude.

The EEG data, on the other hand, show a much higher activity level for the aged subjects versus the young. This is not a new finding and has been reported many times. The interesting point here is that the aged show conditioned activation as the CS-US presentations progress; whereas the young subjects show adaptation across trials.

The catechol amines also show differences between the aged and the young, the aged producing much higher total amines, during the resting period in particular. In this experiment adrenaline was the main contributor, whereas in a previous experiment reported by the senior author (1963) it was the noradrenaline. This difference was probably due mainly to instructional set, i.e., here they were promised shock and were perhaps somewhat fearful of it, whereas in the previous study they were reassured and promised no discomfort. The main thing to consider appears to be this high level of resting total amines reported in many studies. Apparently the aged organism reacts to a novel and possibly stressful situation with total mobilization of its biochemical defense by "giving it all its got," whereas the young men react more economically, i.e., by responding to the immediate situation rather than maintained vigil.

There are at least three ways to interpret these findings theoretically, the most obvious being that only peripheral factors involved in the sympathetic reactivity of the aged subjects, such as arteriosclerosis, drying of the skin and disruptions in sweat gland activity, contribute to these findings. One cannot deny that these peripheral factors do play a role; however, it would be simple-minded to ascribe all the differences to them, especially when there are such obvious central and biochemical differences as well.

The second interpretation is a typically Pavlovian one which would classify the aged subjects as inhibitory types who show autonomic inhibition to repeated CS-US presentations, and the young men as excitatory types manifesting autonomic activation. The EEG data would not be contradictory here as the Soviet neurophysiologist A. B. Kogan (1960) has demonstrated. He states:

> "The reaction of the alpha-rhythm blocking or the 'arousal response' cannot be identified with the general excitation process in the cortex. It rather expresses the fact of working desynchronisation of the cortical neurons which may result both in excitation and inhibition. The first case is observed for example, when the conditioned signal evokes an increase in the neuron excitability, the second—when we have the spread of the external inhibition which causes the reduction of neuron excitability. Under the action of afferent stimulation the desynchronisation and the changes in the excitability cover even

those cortical areas which are deprived by operation of direct connections with the subcortical structures of the brain. Hence, the corresponding nervous processes may spread along the nervous elements of the cortex (real cortex irradiation)."

This interpretation would therefore claim that the fast activity in the aged EEGs was actually inhibitory in nature and that the increased activity over the conditioning trials was an increase in the inhibitory process with further conditioned inhibition taking place; whereas the younger subjects with gradual decline of fast activity may actually be manifesting an excitatory process, which they certainly do, as far as autonomic activity is concerned. This interpretation is appealing in its simplicity and the existance of some supportive evidence for this point makes it difficult to completely disagree with it. However, it would take a good deal of semantic manipulation to fit the high catechol amine levels into this scheme.

The third interpretation, which appeals to us most, is less doctrainaire, possibly more speculative and, in a sense, a compromise between some of the above points. There is no question that the aged subjects show definite autonomic nervous system inhibitions and that this is at least partially due to peripheral factors, but Andrew's (1956) study shows that this is also partly due to hypothalamic degeneration which not only produces autonomic inhibition but may also produce emergency biochemical reactions disproportionate to the situation.

The type of classical conditioning described in this experiment is one of the simplest kinds of learning, and after initial activation and discrimination, conditioning can take place at a subcortical level with minimal cortical involvement in normal subjects. However, if there is hypothalamic insufficiency with resultant autonomic nervous system inhibition, the cortex may remain active and involved even in such a simple conditioning. It is quite probable that with complex discrimination, conditioning the young men would show continual cortical involvement as well as autonomic nervous system activation throughout the conditioning; whereas the aged subjects would completely block and show central nervous system and autonomic nervous system inhibition with severe rises in total catechol amines as the only biological defense remaining to the organism in stress.

REFERENCES

Andrew, W.: (1956) Structural alterations with aging in the nervous system. *J. Chro. Dis.*, 3:575.

Bergsman, M.: (1959) The urinary excretion of adrenaline and noradrenaline in some mental diseases. *Acta Psychiat. Scand., Supplementum, 133*:34.

Botwinick, J. and Kornetsky, C.: (1960) Age differences in the acquisition and extinction of the G.S.R. *J. Geront.*, 15:1:83-84.

Chow, K. L.: (1954) Lack of behavioral effects following destruction of some thalamic association nuclei in monkey. *Arch. Neurol. Psychiat., 71*:762.

Cohen, S. I., Silverman, A. J. and Shmavonian, B. M.: (1961) Influence of psychodynamic factors on central nervous system functioning in young and aged subjects. *Psychosom. Med.*, 23:2:123-137.

Elmadjian, F., Lamson, E. T. and Neri, R.: (1956) Excretion of adrenaline and noradrenaline in human subjects. *J. Clin. Endocr.*, 16:222-234.

Gantt, W. H., ed.: (1957) *The Cerebral Cortex and the Internal Organs.* New York, Chemical Publishing Co., Inc.

Gellhorn, E., Nelson, R. and Redgate, E.: (1956) The influence of lesions in the anterior and posterior hypothalamus on tonic and phasic autonomic reactions. *J. Physiol., 131*:402.

Kimble, Gregory: (1960) Eyelid conditioning in young and old human subjects. Personal communication.

Hernandes-Peon, R., Brust-Carmona, H., Eckhaus, E., Lopez-Mendoza, E. and Alcocercuaron, C.: (1956) *Fed. Proc.*, 15:91.

Kogan, A. B.: (1960) The manifestations of processes of higher nervous activity in the electrical potentials of the cortex during free behaviour of animals. Moscow Colloquium, *Electroenceph. Clin. Neurophysiol., Supplement No. 13.*

Kuntz, A.: (1938) Histological variations in autonomic ganglia and ganglion cells associated with age and disease. *Amer. J. Path., 14*:783.

Li, Jerome: (1957) *Introduction to Statistical Inference.* Ann Arbor, Michigan, Edwards Brothers, Inc.

Malmo, R. B.: (1959) Activation: a neuropsychological dimension. *Psychol. Rev.*, 66:6:367-386.

Martin, Irene: (1960) Variations in skin resistance and their relationship to G.S.R. conditioning. *J. Ment. Sci.*, 106:281-287.

Mowrer, O. H.: (1960) *Learning Theory and Behavior.* John Wiley & Sons.

Pavlov, I. P.: (1928) *Lectures on Conditioned Reflexes.* New York, Live-right.

Razran, G.: (1961) The observable unconscious and the inferable conscious in current Soviet psychophysiology: interoceptive conditioning, semantic conditioning and the orienting reflex. *Psychol. Rev.,* 68:81-147.

Shmavonian, B. M.: (1959) Methodological study of vasomotor conditioning in human subjects. *J. Comp. Physiol. Psychol.,* 52:315.

Shmavonian, B. M. and Busse, E. W.: (1963) The utilization of psychophysiological techniques in the study of the aged. *Processes of Aging—Social and Psychol. Perspectives,* R. H. Williams, Clark Tibbittes, and Wilma Donahue, eds., N. Y., Atherton Press, Vol. I., p. 160-183.

Silverman, A. J., Cohen, S. I. and Shmavonian, B. M.: (1959) Investigation of psychophysiological relationships with skin resistance measures. *J. Psychosom. Res.,* 4:65-87.

Skinner, B. F.: (1938) *The Behavior of Organisms. An Experimental Analysis.* New York, Appleton-Century-Crofts.

Smith, K.: (1954) Conditioning as an artifact. *Psychol. Rev.,* 61:217-225.

Thompson, L. and Obrist, W.: (1963) EEG correlates of verbal learning and over learning. *Electroenceph. Clin. Neurophysiol.,* 15.

von Euler, U. S.: (1956) *Noradrenaline.* Springfield, Charles C Thomas.

Winer, J. B.: (1962) *Statistical Principles in Experimental Design.* New York, McGraw Hill Book Co.

13

ELECTROENCEPHALOGRAPHIC APPROACH TO AGE CHANGES IN RESPONSE SPEED*

Walter D. Obrist

Several characteristics of the electroencephalogram (EEG) have been correlated with response speed, suggesting that electrocortical activity may influence the timing of neural events in the brain (Lindsley, 1958, 1960). The EEG has also been shown to undergo certain changes in later life, notably a shift to slower frequencies (Obrist and Busse, 1964). Given these findings, the question arises whether the EEG can contribute to an understanding of the central mechanisms underlying altered response speed in old age.

In spite of an increasing interest in geriatric electroencephalography, very little research has been concerned with the direct correlation of reaction time and EEG during senescence. Surwillo (1961, 1963) has undertaken the only systematic studies which, indeed, have demonstrated a significant relationship between brain wave frequency and simple reaction time. Because of the paucity of literature in this field, the present paper will discuss certain research possibilities, with the hope of stimulating interest in some of the unanswered questions.

THE SENESCENT ELECTROENCEPHALOGRAM

EEG findings on elderly people have been reviewed elsewhere (Obrist, 1964; Obrist and Busse, 1964), and will only be sum-

* Portions of this work were supported by USPHS Grants M-900 and HD 00668, National Institutes of Health.

marized here. The basic age-related change occurs along the frequency dimension. The dominant alpha rhythm (8-12 cps.) becomes slower, and there is an accompanying increase in still slower theta (4-7 cps.) and delta (1-3 cps.) activity. Although fast beta waves (13-25 cps.) are prevalent during early sene-scence, they undergo decline with advancing age. These changes are usually quite minimal in healthy old people, whose tracings are indistinguishable from young adults, except on a statistical basis. Elderly patients with various diseases of the nervous and cardiovascular systems, however, show more profound alterations. In such cases, the EEG may be dominated by slow, theta and delta activity, which is significantly associated with impaired cerebral circulation and intellectual deficit. The latter relation-ship has permitted the limited use of EEG as a diagnostic and prognostic indicator of senile mental deterioration.

Figure 1 compares the mean frequency spectra of two aged groups: healthy community volunteers and hospitalized patients with chronic brain syndrome. The healthy subjects have a pre-ponderance of alpha and beta activity, with few waves less than 8 cycles per second. Their spectrum is shifted slightly to the slow side, relative to the dominant frequency of young adults (vertical line). The patients, on the other hand, have considerably more theta and delta activity, their spectrum being displaced still further in the slow direction. Samples of the two types of tracings are also illustrated in Figure 1. Not all areas of the brain manifest equal degrees of frequency change. Focal slowing is particularly prevalent over the temporal lobe, even in relatively healthy old people. It is diffuse slow activity, however, that bears a close relation to intellectual impairment.

EEG AND REACTION TIME IN OLD AGE

The occurrence of senescent EEG changes makes it reasonable to inquire whether such alterations are related to the slowing of reaction time, commonly found among elderly people. As men-tioned above, few attempts have been made to correlate the two variables. In healthy old age, there is little or no relationship be-tween occipital alpha frequency and reaction time when the two are recorded separately (Obrist, 1963). Nor is there a correlation between alpha frequency and tapping speed (Mundy-Castle, 1962), despite positive findings on writing and tapping speed in younger subjects (Denier van der Gon and van Hinte, 1959; Mundy-Castle and Sugarman, 1960). Data on aged psychiatric patients have not been obtained. Recently, the author in collaboration with Dr. Carl Eisdorfer, investigated the relation between resting temporal lobe abnormalities and choice reaction time in community volunteers. Elderly subjects with severe temporal slowing had reliably longer choice times than those with normal EEGs. This finding is difficult to interpret, however, since the role of the temporal lobe in reaction time is obscure.

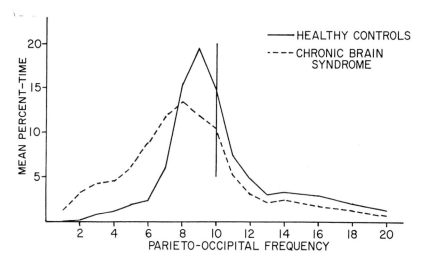

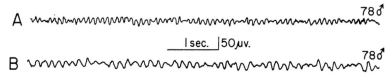

Figure 1. EEG frequency spectra for two groups of elderly subjects between sixty-five and ninety-four years of age: healthy community volunteers (N = 47) and hospitalized patients with chronic brain syndrome (N = 45). The curves indicate the mean percentage of time waves at a given frequency are present in the parieto-occipital tracing. The vertical line represents the peak frequency for young adults. Two EEG samples typical of each spectrum are illustrated below: A. healthy subject, and B. psychiatric patient. (Taken from Obrist, 1963; and Obrist and Henry, 1958.)

Of greater significance, are studies reported by Surwillo (1961, 1963), in which EEGs were recorded during the actual performance of a simple reaction time task. Occipital brain potentials were measured in the interval between an auditory stimulus and a digital response in 100 volunteers, ages 28-99. Low, but significant positive correlations (around .30 and .40) were obtained for individual subjects between the duration of waves and length of reaction time. When mean subject reaction time was correlated with mean duration of waves, a between-subjects coefficient of + .72 was found. Surwillo speculated that brain wave frequency is a factor in the longer reaction times of elderly people. His argument is based on the observation of a small positive correlation between reaction time and age, which becomes negative when EEG frequency is partialled out. In other words, the presence of slow brain potentials appears to be necessary for the occurrence of slow reaction times in old age. This intriguing concept deserves further investigation.

REACTION TIME AND THE ALPHA RHYTHM

A number of studies have presented evidence for a relationship between speed of response and specific characteristics of the alpha rhythm. Although none of these experiments has been performed on elderly people, the results are potentially relevant to research on aging.

Historically, the first EEG-reaction time studies involved the relation of response speed to the latent time of alpha blocking. (Travis, Knott and Griffith, 1937; Jasper and Cruikshank, 1937; Knott, 1939; Bakes, 1939). Significant positive correlations were obtained between the two variables for both visual and auditory stimulation. It should be noted, however, that reaction time is often shorter than blocking latency (Stamm, 1952), thus ruling out the possibility of a direct causal linkage between alpha desynchronization and motor response. Both events are probably influenced by a common neurophysiologic mechanism, possibly the reticular activating system discussed below.

According to Bernhard and Skoglund (1943), the latency of blocking in children is a function of alpha frequency, the slower rhythms giving rise to longer latencies. Comparable observations have not been made on elderly people, but longer latencies might be predicted as the alpha rhythm slows with advancing age. Whether the increased reaction times of senescence are paralleled by longer blocking latencies, is a question that remains unanswered.

In one of the classic experiments of the field, Lansing (1957) found significant variations in response speed for stimuli administered at different times in the alpha cycle. This finding was essentially confirmed by Callaway and co-workers (1960, 1962), who observed that individuals differ with respect to the particular alpha phase yielding the shortest reaction times. Lindsley (1958, 1960) interpreted these results in terms of a cortical excitability cycle which fluctuates with the voltage of spontaneous rhythms. Such a theory derives support from neurophysiologic evidence (Bishop and Clare, 1952; Chang, 1951, 1960; Bechtereva and Zontov, 1962).

Alpha phase has also been studied in relation to the time of onset of motor responses. Kibbler *et al.* (1949) and Bates (1951) reported that voluntary movement is initiated more often during certain phases of the alpha cycle than others, a finding consistent with a cortical excitability hypothesis. The relevance of these results for reaction time is suggested by the work of Venables (1960), who noted a periodicity in the occurrence of responses at approximately one-tenth of a second, the average duration of alpha waves.

The experiments just cited give rise to several questions concerning age changes in speed of response. Does the cortical excitability cycle vary with age, and if so, is it responsible for an increase in reaction time? According to such a hypothesis, the phase of maximal cortical excitability would occur less often in elderly people with slow rhythms, thus requiring more time, on the average, for a stimulus to trigger a response. Because the mean duration of alpha waves increases only 10 to 30 milliseconds during senescence, it seems unlikely that this hypothesis can account for more than a fraction of the reported slowing in reaction time.

An alternative explanation grows out of studies on reaction time and alpha desynchronization. Lansing, Schwartz and Lindsley (1959) observed significantly faster responses when the alpha rhythm was blocked (desynchronized) by a warning signal than when alpha activity persisted. Similar findings have been obtained by Fedio *et al.* (1961). In both studies, spontaneous blocking was not associated with faster responses, although recent evidence suggests that it might be (Dustman, Boswell and Porter, 1962). When alpha synchronization is enhanced, as in the case of certain conditioning procedures, reaction times are generally slower (Morrell and Ross, 1953). These experiments have been interpreted in terms of reticular activation theory, it being postulated that alpha desynchronization represents an excitatory state of the cortex produced by impulses arriving from the reticular system, and that alpha synchronization indicates a state of cortical inhibition. The facilitatory influence of reticular activation on reaction time has been demonstrated by Fuster and Uyeda (1962). They obtained shorter responses on a visual discrimination task during direct stimulation of the midbrain in monkeys.

The implication of these findings for senescent changes in response speed hinges upon the extent to which the aging cortex is capable of being activated by sensory stimulation via the reticular system. Experiments are reported in the following section which suggest that sensory stimulation is less effective in producing EEG desynchronization among elderly people than in young adults. If so, this might account for some of the longer reaction times encountered in older subjects.

ELECTROCORTICAL REACTIVITY IN SENESCENCE

The possibility exists that one of the factors underlying senescent changes in psychomotor performance is a lowered reactivity of the central nervous system to sensory input. In 1944, Liberson introduced the concept of "functional electroencephalography," which in contrast to the standard clinical evaluation of resting brain waves, attempted to assess cerebral dysfunction by analysing EEG responses to sensory stimulation. Of particular interest was the classical EEG reaction to light; namely, desynchronization of rhythmic alpha activity, commonly called an arousal response. Wells (1962, 1963) has recently reviewed the literature in this field, while presenting evidence that patients with brain disease show significantly less EEG reactivity to visual stimulation. He also demonstrated that the response in such patients becomes habituated (adapted) to repeated stimulation more rapidly than in normal controls.

There is some evidence that EEG reactivity declines in old age. Among psychiatric patients, Verdeaux and co-workers (1961) found that EEG responses to light were poorly developed after age seventy. Andermann and Stoller (1961) observed that elderly mental hospital patients showed less desynchronization than community subjects of the same age. Recently, Wilson and Obrist (1963) compared the EEG reactivity of healthy young and old community volunteers selected for superior intelligence. In spite of well preserved intellectual function, the elderly subjects were reliably less responsive to visual stimuli than the young controls.

Figure 2 is an illustration taken from the latter study. It shows desynchronization in response to the repetitive presentation of a steady light (on 3 seconds, off 9 seconds) during eye closure. The phenomenon of habituation is clearly seen in the decreasing effectiveness of the stimulus from trial 1 to 30, during which time the subject became almost completely habituated. Amplitude mea-

HABITUATION TO A REPEATED STMULUS

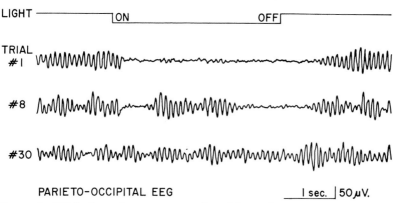

Figure 2. EEG desynchronization produced by a three-second visual stimulus presented at regular intervals for thirty trials. Note the habituation (diminished response) with repeated stimulation.

surements, integrated over each three second stimulus period, were subtracted from control values to obtain an index of de-synchronization based on voltage change. Habituation curves were then constructed by plotting the logarithm of voltage change against trials. Figure 3 compares the habituation curves of fifteen young and fifteen elderly subjects over twenty trials. Two parallel straight lines were obtained, with the elderly group showing significantly less voltage change, and hence less reactivity, than the young subjects. This suggested a similar *rate* of habituation, but a different response *magnitude*. It is as if the elderly person came into the experiment already partially adapted at a level corresponding to the tenth trial of the young group (see dashed line). Because the curves are based on group means, fluctuations in desynchronization characteristic of individual cases (Morrell and Morrell, 1962) are not apparent.

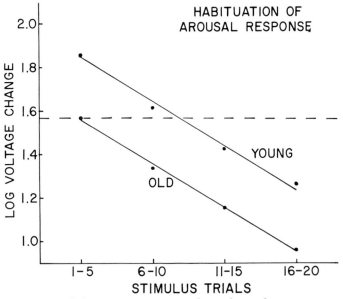

Figure 3. Mean habituation curves resulting from the repetitive visual stimulation of fifteen normal young (age 18-29) and fifteen normal old subjects (age 63-84). The degree of desynchronization was measured in terms of voltage change between control and stimulated portions of the tracing (see text), and plotted logarithmically for blocks of five stimulus trials. (From a study by Wilson and Obrist, 1963.)

The significance of these findings for senescent behavior is purely conjectural at the present time. If it is true that the aged individual is cortically less activated or aroused by sensory stimulation, such a fact would have important implications for psychomotor function in general, and speed of response in particular.

SPECULATIONS ON THE ROLE OF ANOXIA

The adverse effect of anoxia on speed of response has been known for many years. McFarland (1932, 1937) found that sudden ascents to high altitude resulted in slower reaction times. The rather extensive literature in this field has recently been reviewed by Van Liere and Stickney (1963).

There is also evidence (Obrist *et al.*, 1963; Obrist, 1964) that one of the important factors underlying senescent EEG changes is a reduction of cerebral oxygen uptake, a variable known to produce EEG slowing in a variety of clinical and experimental conditions (Gastaut and Meyer, 1961). In the light of the probable relationship between EEG and reaction time, it seems reasonable to speculate that cerebral anoxia may contribute to a slowing of response speed in old age by virtue of its effect on the electrical activity of the cortex. Much research is needed before etiologic questions of this type can be answered.

POSSIBILITIES FOR FUTURE RESEARCH

An attempt has been made to review the relevant literature on EEG and reaction time, with the hope of suggesting possible mechanisms for senescent changes in speed of response. Any hypothesis regarding such a mechanism must explain, not only the lengthening of reaction time, itself, but also the considerable increase in its *variability*, both within and between individuals. As reported previously (Obrist, 1953), the standard deviation representing individual differences in reaction time may be twice as great for elderly people than for young adults, while intra-individual variability increases 50 per cent. The question arises whether the large individual differences and moment to moment variations characteristic of the senescent EEG are related to the observed variability in reaction time.

An additional factor, not considered here, is the role of the autonomic nervous system in regulating both EEG potentials and speed of response. Studies on the relation of reaction time to cardiac cycle (Birren, Cardon and Phillips, 1963) might well tie in with the concepts of reticular activation and cortical excitability mentioned above.

Before definitive answers can be obtained, a more direct approach seems necessary. One possibility is the modification of EEG frequency by experimental procedures, while simultaneously measuring reaction time. Induced anoxia might be one such method. Other techniques for altering EEG frequency might also be used, such as photic driving (Mundy-Castle, 1953), sensory deprivation (Zubek and Welch, 1963), or prolonged body immobilization (Zubek and Welgosh, 1963). In this connection, Williams and associates (1962) have already demonstrated a high correlation between reaction time and EEG, when both variables are altered by sleep deprivation. The application of these specialized techniques to problems of aging is an intriguing challenge for future research.

REFERENCES

Andermann, K. and Stoller, A.: (1961) EEG patterns in hospitalized and non-hospitalized aged. *Electroenceph. Clin. Neuropshysiol., 13*:319.

Bakes, F. P.: (1939) Effect of response to auditory stimulation on the latent time of blocking of the Berger rhythm. *J. Exp. Psychol., 24*:406-418.

Bates, J. A. V.: (1951) Electrical activity of the cortex accompanying movement. *J. Physiol. (Lond.), 113*:240-257.

Bechtereva, N. P. and Zontov, V. V.: (1962) The relationship between certain forms of potentials and the variations in brain excitability (based on EEG, recorded during photic stimuli triggered by rhythmic brain potentials). *Electroenceph. Clin. Neurophysiol., 14*:320-330.

Bernhard, C. G. and Skoglund, C. R.: (1943) On the blocking time of the cortical alpha rhythm in children. *Acta Psychiat. Scand., 18*:159-170.

Birren, J. E., Cardon, P. V. and Phillips, S. L.: (1963) Reaction time as a function of the cardiac cycle in young adults. *Science, 140*:195-196.

Bishop, G. H. and Clare, M. H.: (1952) Relations between specifically evoked and "spontaneous" activity of optic cortex. *Electroenceph. Clin. Neurophysiol., 4*:321-330.

Callaway, E., III.: (1962) Factors influencing the relationship between alpha activity and visual reaction time. *Electroenceph. Clin. Neurophysiol., 14*:674-682.

Callaway, E., III, and Yeager, C. L.: (1960) Relationship between reaction time and electroencephalographic alpha phase. *Science, 132*:1765-1766.

Chang, H.-T.: (1951) Changes in excitability of cerebral cortex following single electric shock applied to cortical surface. *J. Neurophysiol., 14:* 95-111.

Chang, H.-T.: (1960) Some observations on the excitability changes of cortical and subcortical neurons and their possible significance in the process of conditioning. In H. H. Jasper and G. D. Smirnov, eds.: *The Moscow Colloquium on Electroencephalography of Higher Nervous Activity. Electroenceph. Clin. Neurophysiol., Suppl. 13*:39-49.

Denier van der Gon, J. J. and van Hinte, N.: (1959) The relation between the frequency of the alpha-rhythm and the speed of writing. *Electroenceph. Clin. Neurophysiol., 11*:669-674.

Dustman, R. E., Boswell, R. S. and Porter, P. B.: (1962) Beta brain waves as an index of alertness. *Science, 137*:533-534.

Fedio, R., Mirsky, A. F., Smith, W. J. and Parry, D.: (1961) Reaction time and EEG activation in normal and schizophrenic subjects. *Electroenceph. Clin. Neurophysiol., 13*:923-926.

Fuster, J. M. and Uyeda, A. A.: (1962) Facilitation of tachistoscopic performance by stimulation of midbrain tegmental points in the monkey. *Exp. Neurol., 6*:384-406.

Gastaut, H. and Meyer, J. S., eds.: (1961) *Cerebral Anoxia and the Electroencephalogram.* Springfield, Ill., C. C Thomas.

Jasper, H. H. and Cruikshank, R. M.: (1937) Electroencephalography: II. Visual stimulation and the after-image as affecting the occipital alpha rhythm. *J. Gen. Psychol., 17*:29-48.

Kibbler, G. O., Boreham, J. L. and Richter, D.: (1949) Relation of the alpha rhythm of the brain to psychomotor phenomena. *Nature (Lond.), 164*:371.

Knott, J. R.: (1939) Some effects of mental set upon the electrophysiological processes of the human cerebral cortex. *J. Exp. Psychol., 24*:384-405.

Lansing, R. W.: (1957) Relation of brain and tremor rhythms to visual reaction time. *Electroenceph. Clin. Neurophysiol., 9*:497-504.

Lansing, R. W., Schwartz, E. and Lindsley, D. B.: (1959) Reaction time and EEG activation. *J. Exp. Psychol., 58*:1-10.

Liberson, W. T.: (1944) Functional electroencephalography in mental disorders. *Dis. Nerv. Syst., 5*:357-364.

Lindsley, D. B.: (1958) The reticular system and perceptual discrimination. In H. H. Jasper, L. D. Proctor, R. S. Knighton, W. C. Noshay and R. T. Costello, eds.: *Reticular Formation of the Brain*, Boston, Little, Brown and Co., pp. 513-534.

Lindsley, D. B.: (1960) Attention, consciousness, sleep and wakefulness. In J. Field, H. W. Magoun and V. E. Hall, eds.: *Handbook of Physiology: Neurophysiology*, Washington, Amer. Physiol. Soc., Vol. III, pp. 1553-1593.

McFarland, R. A.: (1932) The psychological effects of oxygen deprivation (anoxemia) on human behavior. *Arch. Psychol.,* 22:145:1-135.

McFarland, R. A.: (1937) Psycho-physiological studies at high altitude in the Andes. IV. Sensory and circulatory responses of the Andean residents at 17,500 feet. *J. Comp. Psychol.,* 23:191-258.

Morrell, L. and Morrell, F.: (1962) Non-random oscillation in the response-duration curve of electrographic activation. *Electroenceph. Clin. Neurophysiol.,* 14:724-730.

Morrell, F. and Ross, M. H.: (1953) Central inhibition in cortical conditioned reflexes. *Arch. Neurol. Psychiat. (Chic.),* 70:611-616.

Mundy-Castle, A. C.: (1953) An analysis of central responses to photic stimulation in normal adults. *Electroenceph. Clin. Neurophysiol.,* 5:1-22.

Mundy-Castle, A. C.: (1962) Central excitability in the aged. In H. T. Blumenthal, ed.: *Medical and Clinical Aspects of Aging,* New York, Columbia Univ. Press, pp. 575-595.

Mundy-Castle, A. C. and Sugarman, L.: (1960) Factors influencing relations between tapping speed and alpha rhythm. *Electroenceph. Clin. Neurophysiol.,* 12:895-904.

Obrist, W. D.: (1953) Simple auditory reaction time in aged adults. *J. Psychol.,* 35:259-266.

Obrist, W. D.: (1963) The electroencephalogram of healthy aged males. In J. E. Birren, R. N. Butler, S. W. Greenhouse, L. Sokoloff and M. R. Yarrow, eds.: *Human Aging: A Biological and Behavioral Study,* PHS Publ. No. 986, Washington, U. S. Govt. Print. Off., pp. 79-93.

Obrist, W. D.: (1964, in press) Cerebral ischemia and the senescent electroencephalogram. In E. Simonson and T. H. McGavack, eds.: *Cerebral Ischemia,* Springfield, Ill., C. C Thomas.

Obrist, W. D. and Busse, E. W.: (1964, in press) The electroencephalogram in old age. In W. P. Wilson and E. W. Busse, eds.: *Applications of EEG in Psychiatry,* Durham, N. C., Duke Univ. Press.

Obrist, W. D. and Henry, C. E.: (1958) Electroencephalographic frequency analysis of aged psychiatric patients. *Electroenceph. Clin. Neurophysiol.,* 10:621-632.

Obrist, W. D., Sokoloff, L., Lassen, N. A., Lane, M. H., Butler, R. N. and Feinberg, I.: (1963) Relation of EEG to cerebral blood flow and metabolism in old age. *Electroenceph. Clin. Neurophysiol.,* 15:610-619.

Stamm, J. S.: (1952) On the relationship between reaction time to light and latency of blocking of the alpha rhythm. *Electroenceph. Clin. Neurophysiol.,* 4:61-68.

Surwillo, W. W.: (1961) Frequency of the "alpha" rhythm, reaction time and age. *Nature (Lond.),* 191:823-824.

Surwillo, W. W.: (1963) The relation of simple response time to brain-wave frequency and the effects of age. *Electroenceph. Clin. Neurophysiol.,* 15:105-114.

Travis, L. E., Knott, J. R. and Griffith, P. E.: (1937) Effect of response on the latency and frequency of the Berger rhythm. *J. Gen. Psychol.*, 16:391-401.

Van Liere, E. J. and Stickney, J. C.: (1963) *Hypoxia*. Chicago, Univ. Chicago Press.

Venables, P. H.: (1960) Periodicity in reaction time. *Brit. J. Psychol.*, 51: 37-43.

Verdeaux, G., Verdeaux, J. and Turmel, J.: (1961) Etude statistique de le frequence et de la reactivite des electroencephalogrammes chez les sujets ages. *Canad. Phychiat. Ass. J.*, 6:28-36.

Wells, C. E.: (1962) Response of alpha waves to light in neurologic disease. *Arch. Neurol. (Chic.)*, 6:478-491.

Wells, C. E.: (1963) Alpha wave responsiveness to light in man. In G. H. Glaser, ed.: *EEG and Behavior*, New York, Basic Books, pp. 27-59.

Williams, H. L., Granda, A. M., Jones, R. C., Lubin, A. and Armington, J. C.: (1962) EEG frequency and finger pulse volume as predictors of reaction time during sleep loss. *Electroenceph. Clin. Neurophysiol.*, 14: 64-70.

Wilson, S. and Obrist, W. D.: (1963) Age differences in EEG response to visual stimulation. Paper presented at the *Amer. EEG Soc.*, San Francisco. (Based on a doctoral dissertation by S. Wilson, George Peabody College, 1962.)

Zubek, J. P. and Welch, G.: (1963) Electroencephalographic changes after prolonged sensory and perceptual deprivation. *Science*, 139:1209-1210.

Zubek, J. P. and Welgosh, L.: (1963) Prolonged immobilization of the body: Changes in performance and in the electroencephalogram. *Science*, 140:306-308.

14

PHYSIOLOGICALLY INDUCED NEUROPSYCHOLOGICAL CHANGES AND AGING

Max Pollack

Longitudinal studies of aged normals as well as cross-sectional comparisons of aged persons with younger ones are in agreement that there are small but significant decrements in perceptual, perceptual-motor and intellectual functioning in the aged. Although there is a widely held belief that these changes are reflective of diffuse sub-clinical brain damage, understanding of the nature of the physiological basis is at present speculative. Electroencephalographic changes in the direction of increased slow wave activity reported in studies of aged persons is consistent with the concept of diffuse cerebral dysfunction (Obrist, 1954). However, in a sample of normal aged the EEG variables did not correlate significantly with intellectual performance (Obrist *et al.*, 1962). There is, however, a substantial correlation between EEG and psychological tests in aged persons with marked intellectual impairment associated with brain disease (Obrist *et al.*, 1962).

The induction of cerebral dysfunction through physiological techniques, e.g., drugs, may be of value in clarifying the nature of the biological basis underlying the subtle psychological changes in the aged. A body of knowledge now exists which demonstrates, through the study of simultaneous EEG recording and psychological performance, that the induction of cerebral changes characterized by increased EEG slowing is associated with perceptual-motor impairment and reduced alertness. The findings are similar for both non-physiological procedures, such as sleep loss (Williams *et al.*, 1962) and physiological ones, such as chlorpromazine (Mirsky and Cardon, 1962).

This report is concerned with the following:

1) A comparison of the changes in perceptual, perceptual-motor and intellectual functioning associated with two psychiatric treatments that induce different degrees of EEG slowing; severe (grand-mal convulsions) and mild (chlorpromazine).

2) The relation of these psychological changes to increased EEG slowing.

3) A comparison of these results with those changes found in the aged.

The choice of chlorpromazine is of particular interest to the purpose of this volume in that it is known for its property of retarding psychomotor functioning.

CHLORPROMAZINE

Method

In a voluntary psychiatric hospital, 144 patients consecutively referred for psychotropic drug therapy randomly received (in a double-blind design) a course of orally administered placebo, chlorpromazine or imipramine (Pollack *et al.*, in press). Dosages were increased to 1200 mg of chlorpromazine daily with 15 mg of procyclidine added to reduce "side-effects." Patients were tested in the week prior to drug administration and during the sixth week of placebo or chlorpromazine (1200 mg daily) medication. At time of retest there were forty-three placebo and forty-nine chlorpromazine treated patients. The mean age of the group was 31.1 years; mean education 12.6 years; mean full scale Wechsler-Bellevue I.Q. was 109.3. The diagnoses were as follows: schizophrenia (58%), psychotic depressions (25%), character disorders (9%) and psychoneurosis (8%). The group was alert and cooperative.

Statistical Analysis

A total of 16 different psychological tests and five EEG variables were investigated. The tests are outlined in Table 1.

Details conceiving test procedure have been described elsewhere (Pollack et al., in press). The chlorpromazine group was compared with the placebo by two techniques, univariate and multivariate analysis. In the univariate analysis the means for each of the variables for chlorpromazine and placebo groups were compared by analysis of covariance in which the on-drug scores were adjusted for pretreatment level, the adjusted on-drug means were then compared by the t test. Multivariance analysis was performed using a discriminant function analysis for the two groups (Rao, 1952).

TABLE 1
PSYCHOLOGICAL MEASURES

Area of Functioning	Tests	Response Measures
Perceptual	Critical flicker fusion	Threshold in cycles per second
	Rod and frame	Errors in degrees from vertical
	Delayed auditory feedback	Difference in seconds between reading under feedback and normal conditions
Visuomotor	Tapping rate	Taps per ten seconds
	Hand steadiness	Number of contacts in 15 seconds
	Two-hand coordination	Time on target in one minute
Cognitive	Wechsler-Bellevue, Form I Information Comprehension Similarities Arithmetic Digit Span Picture completion Block design Object assembly Digit symbol Picture arrangement	Weighted scores

TABLE 2

MEAN CHANGES AND RETEST CORRELATIONS OF PSYCHOLOGICAL
TESTS WITH PLACEBO TREATMENT (N = 43)

Test	Pretreatment Mean	SD	Placebo Mean	SD	Mean Diff.	t	Pre Drug On Drug r[1]
Critical Flicker Fusion	35.6	3.2	35.2	3.1	−0.4	1.54	.86
Steadiness	1.2	1.1	0.9	0.8	−0.3	.21	.47
Tapping	66.0	7.4	66.5	7.9	0.5	.64	.80
Two-Hand Coordination	15.2	7.8	20.2	10.8	5.0	5.15**	.82
Rod and Frame	14.2	8.5	13.2	8.3	−1.0	1.59	.88
Auditory Delayed Feedback	34.3	33.6	27.5	29.2	−6.8	1.21	.37
Wechsler-Bellevue, Form I							
Information	11.8	3.0	12.7	2.8	0.9	5.29**	.92
Comprehension	11.4	3.0	12.2	2.6	0.8	2.42*	.72
Similarities	12.8	3.1	13.0	2.9	0.2	.67	.79
Arithmetic	10.3	5.0	11.9	5.0	1.6	3.81**	.85
Digit Span	10.0	3.5	10.5	4.0	0.5	1.22	.77
Picture Arrangement	10.0	3.1	12.1	3.0	2.1	6.36**	.75
Picture Completion	10.7	3.0	11.9	2.7	1.2	3.53**	.72
Block Design	10.5	2.8	11.1	3.2	0.6	2.50*	.88
Object Assembly	10.9	2.9	11.6	3.1	0.7	2.50*	.82
Digit Symbol	10.8	3.4	12.1	3.6	1.3	4.64**	.90

[1] Product-Moment (Pearson) correlation—all correlations are significant at the .01 level except for auditory delayed feedback, $p < .05$.

*p = .05
**p = .01

UNIVARIATE ANALYSIS
EEG

Fink (1961) in our laboratory, employed an electronic frequency analyzer to measure the changes in the frequency spectra. Twenty-four frequencies from 3 to 33 cps were recorded. When compared with placebo the chlorpromazine group showed a statistically significant increase in mean delta (3.0-4.5 cps) and theta (5-7 cps) but not in alpha (8-12 cps), beta$_1$ (13.5-20 cps) or beta$_2$ (22-33 cps) frequencies.

Psychological Tests

The changes under the placebo condition and the retest correlations are shown in Table 2. Performance on nine tests showed a significant practice effect. There was no significant decline in performance on any test. Retest correlations were extremely high and did not differ from that obtained with normals (Karp et al., 1962).

Of these sixteen tests, chlorpromazine significantly affected performance in eight. They are listed in order of the significance of mean differences between drug and placebo groups (Table 3). Analysis of the results indicates that all the significant changes in visuomotor or cognitive tasks involved some aspects of timed performance or serial retention involving a time limit aspect. Of the perceptual tests only critical flicker fusion threshold was significantly decreased, the tests of sensory distortion, the rod and frame and delayed auditory feedback, did not differ significantly from placebo. The lack of sensitivity of auditory delayed feedback to chlorpromazine is of interest in that it is a test that was expected to be altered by cerebral dysfunction (Lindsley, 1961).

All of the visuomotor tests showed a significant change with decreased speed in digit symbol substitution and tapping speed and increased hand unsteadiness. Performance on tests requiring mental alertness, digit span and arithmetic, were also impaired. The tests involving verbal aspects such as information, comprehension or similarities were not significantly affected.

Of the Wechsler-Bellevue subtests, digit symbol substitution was most affected. Birren (1963) has noted that this test seems most associated with "aging" (p. 396).

The profile of changes is consistent with that found following acute administration of chlorpromazine in normal volunteers (Di Mascio et al., 1963, Lehmann and Csank 1957). These changes are also compatible with that reported by those workers using these or similar ones to measure changes in the aged (Birren, 1963; Jarvik et al., 1962; Loranger and Misiak, 1959).

Intercorrelations of Test Changes

Correlation coefficients between changes in chlorpromazine-altered psychological tests and changes in delta and theta EEG frequencies were with one exception not significant. Hand steadiness decreased with increased delta (r:.34, p<.05).

TABLE 3

SIGNIFICANT TEST CHANGES WITH CHLORPROMAZINE—
ANALYSIS OF COVARIANCE

	Mean Pre Drug	*Mean on Drug*	*t—values (one-tailed)*	*P*
Critical Flicker Fusion				
Placebo	35.6	35.2	5.04	.0005
Chlorpromazine	34.9	32.5		
Digit Symbol Substitution				
Placebo	10.7	12.1	4.15	.0005
Chlorpromazine	10.3	10.1		
Hand Steadiness				
Placebo	1.1	0.8	4.06	.0005
Chlorpromazine	1.2	2.0		
Tapping Rate				
Placebo	66.0	66.5	2.85	.005
Chlorpromazine	65.6	62.7		
Digit Span				
Placebo	9.9	10.5	2.84	.005
Chlorpromazine	10.0	9.1		
Arithmetic				
Placebo	10.3	11.8	2.73	.005
Chlorpromazine	10.0	10.1		
Block Design				
Placebo	10.4	11.0	1.77	.05
Chlorpromazine	9.4	9.4		
Two-Hand Coordination				
Placebo	15.1	20.1	1.77	.05
Chlorpromazine	14.1	16.8		

Of the psychological tests only CFF and digit symbol substitution were correlated significantly ($r = .30$, $p < .05$). The significant positive correlation between CFF and digit symbol has been reported in studies of the aged by Loranger and Misiak (1959).

MULTIVARIATE ANALYSIS

A discriminant function analysis using the Mahalonobis D^2 was employed using on-drug scores. The D^2 statistic provides a means of rank ordering all subjects along the dimension that maximally differentiates placebo from drug effects. It also determines the overlap between the two groups and gives an estimate (F value) of the likelihood that this overlap differs from chance. Therefore, it is possible to rank each patient from most placebo-like to most chlorpromazine-like. For the psychological variables, only those that by covariance analysis individually differentiated chlorpromazine from placebo were used. The F value was 9.13, $p < .01$, indicating the minimal degree of overlap between groups using these tests. For the EEG variables, the F value was 2.39, $p < .05$.

In order to correlate the psychological and EEG changes, a rank order correlation was performed for both the placebo and chlorpromazine groups employing the ranks provided by the D^2 analysis. For the chlorpromazine group the correlation of the psychological and EEG orderings was highly significant, the rho $= .71$, $p < .01$. For the placebo group it was .39, just failing significance at the .05 level. This indicates that there is an overall multivariate association between the chlorpromazine-induced EEG and psychological changes.

Summary: The pattern of psychological and EEG changes with chronic administration of a high dosage of chlorpromazine closely resembles that found with normal aged subjects. The absence of significant correlation between the psychological test changes and EEG variables using univariate analysis and the presence of a substantial relationship between these disparate measures using multivariate analysis raises the question of the utility of using single variables as adequate indicators of change in brain function.

CONVULSIVE THERAPY
Procedure

Thirty-six inpatients consecutively referred for grand-mal convulsive therapy were studied. In twenty-one patients the convulsions were induced by a Medcraft alternating current instrument, and in fifteen others by inhalation of hexafluorodiethyl. Details concerning the procedure are given in a previous report (Fink *et al.*, 1961). The patients were studied in the week prior to treatment, between the tenth and twelfth treatments and two weeks following the termination of the final treatment.

The mean age of the group was 37.8 years, education 11.6 years, mean I.Q. 104 (Verbal Scale, Wechsler-Bellevue); 42 per cent were diagnosed as schizophrenia, 28 per cent psychotic depression, 14 per cent as involutional disorder and 16 per cent as psychoneurosis.

Only one EEG variable was measured, the per cent time occupied by waves 6 cps or less in sixty-six seconds of recording from the anterior temporal vertex leads. Ten psychological variables were studied. These were the recognition of tachistoscopically presented pseudoisochromatic numbers (Pollack *et al.*, 1962), the rod and frame, delayed auditory feedback, reading time, two hand coordination, and five subtests of the Wechsler-Bellevue form I: information, comprehension, digit span, object assembly and digit symbol. With the exception of the tachistoscopic recognition test and reading time all tests have been outlined in Table 1.

RESULTS
EEG

The changes in slow-wave activity are shown in Table 4. By the tenth treatment increase in slow wave activity was very pronounced and the record appeared grossly abnormal. Clinically, the patients showed marked mental changes such as memory loss (they were amnestic for the pretreatment examinations), and disorientation for time or place. Older subjects showed a greater impairment clinically and this was reflected in the EEG. The correlation between age and increased EEG slowing was .41 ($p < .01$).

Psychological Performance

With treatment, performance on all tests except the rod and frame, delayed auditory feedback and two-hand coordination was significantly impaired when compared with pretreatment level (Table 5). The performance on the two-hand coordination test

TABLE 4

EFFECT OF CONVULSIVE THERAPY ON EEG SLOWING

(% 6 CPS OR SLOWER)

	Pre Treatment	10-12 Treatments	Pre Treatment	2 Weeks after Last Treatment
N	36	36	25	25
Mean	5.5	54.0	5.6	16.5
SD	4.4	22.0	4.3	10.0
Mean Diff.	48.5		10.9	
t	12.8**		4.8**	
r	.34*		.09	

*p <.05   **p <.001

TABLE 5

EFFECT OF CONVULSIVE THERAPY (CT)

ON TEST SCORES

	Pretreatment & 10-12 CTs		Pretreatment & 2 Weeks after Last Treatment	
	Mean Diff.	r	Mean Diff.	r
Tachistoscopic—PIN	+6.7**	.80**	−6.3**	.64**
Rod and Frame	−2.0*	.93**	−5.1**	.77**
Delayed Auditory Feedback	−11.1	.30	+5.4	.54*
Reading Time	+11.9*	.74**	+4.0	.79**
Two-Hand Coordination	−1.4	.76**	+4.3*	.90**
Wechsler-Bellevue Subtests				
Information	−1.9***	.80**	−0.4	.93**
Comprehension	−1.7**	.55**	+1.0*	.72**
Digit Span	−2.3***	.59**	−0.2	.75**
Object Assembly	−1.1*	.69**	+3.1***	.73**
Digit Symbol	−2.2***	.76**	+0.9*	.81**

*p <.05, **p <.01, ***p <.001.

was slowed significantly when compared with placebo or drug controls whereas neither the rod and frame nor the delayed auditory feedback tests differed from controls. With cessation of treatment, functioning on all tests returned to pretreatment level or showed improvement over pretreatment scores. The importance of the pretreatment level of functioning is illustrated by the high retest correlations.

Psychological Test Changes and EEG

Decrement in performance on four tests, (tachistoscopic recognition, and three Wechsler-Bellevue subtests, digit span, digit symbol and object assembly) correlated significantly with increased slow wave activity. All correlations were btween .4 and .6 ($p < .01$). It is of interest that although the verbal tests, information and comprehension, were significantly impaired by the convulsive therapy, these changes did not correlate significantly with EEG slowing. All of the tests that correlated significantly with EEG slowing involved functioning under time limit conditions or in the case of digit span had a time delay feature. Furthermore, in a factor analysis of pretreatment psychological variables, the three Wechsler-Bellevue subtests, digit span, digit symbol and object assembly loaded on one factor.

CONCLUSIONS

The changes in psychological test performance associated with induced mild and severe EEG slowing are similar to those found in studies of aged persons. The changes with chlorpromazine paralleled those reported for normal aged persons, while those with convulsive therapy resemble those of senile patients. The correlations of intellectual tasks with EEG also resemble the results obtained with normal and cerebrally-damaged aged. The high retest correlation under conditions of induced mild and severe diffuse brain dysfunction suggests the crucial importance of premorbid functioning.

The similarity of decrement in perceptual, perceptual-motor and cognitive functioning with normal aged and chlorpromazine-induced cerebral dysfunction suggests that in the aged these psychological changes reflect a variety of pathological alterations in brain function. Furthermore, the biological basis of aging may not be a unitary process but may consist of a variety of different pathological changes producing similar cerebral dysfunctions.

REFERENCES

Birren, J. E.: (1963) Research on the psychologic aspects of aging. *Geriatrics, 18:*393-403.

DiMascio, A., Havens, L. and Klerman, G. L.: (1963) The psychopharmacology of phenothiazine compounds: a comparative study of the effects of chlorpromazine, promethazine, trifluoperazine and perphenazine in normal males. *J. Nerv. Ment. Dis., 136:*15-28, 168-186.

Fink, M.: (1961) Quantitative electroencephalography and human psychopharmacology, I: frequency spectra and drug action. *Medicina Experimentalis, 5:*364-369.

Fink, M., Kahn, R. L., Karp, E., Pollack, M., Green, M. A., Alan, B. and Lefkowits, H. J.: (1961) Inhalant-induced convulsions. *Arch. Gen. Psychiat., 4:*256-266.

Karp, E., Pollack, M. and Fink, M.: (1962) Critical flicker frequency and EEG alpha. *Electroenceph. Clin. Neurophysiol., 14:*60-63.

Jarvik, L. F., Kallmann, F. J. and Falek, A.: (1962) Intellectual changes in aged twins. *J. Gerontol., 17:*289-294.

Lehmann, H. E. and Csank, J.: (1957) Differential screening of phrenotropic agents in man: psychophysiologic test data. *J. Clin. Psychopath., 18:*222-235.

Lindsley, D. B.: (1961) Common factors in sensory deprivation, sensory distortion and sensory overload. In *Sensory Deprivation,* J. Solomon, P. E. Kubzansky, P. H. Leiderman, J. H. Mendelson, R. Trumbull, and D. Wexler, eds., Cambridge, Mass., Harvard University Press, pp. 174-194.

Loranger, A. W. and Misiak, H.: (1959) Critical flicker frequency and some intellectual functions in old age. *J. Gerontol., 14:*323-327.

Mirsky, A. F. and Cardon, P. V.: (1962) A comparison of the behavioral and physiological changes accompanying sleep deprivation and chlorpromazine administration in man. *Electroenceph. Clin. Neurophysiol., 14:*1-10.

Obrist, W. D.: (1954) The electroencephalogram of normal aged adults. *Electroenceph. Clin. Neurophysiol., 6:*245-252.

Obrist, W. D., Busse, E. W., Eisdorfer and Kleemeier, R. W.: (1962) Relation of the electroencephalogram to intellectual function in senescence. *J. Geront., 17:*197-206.

Pollack, M., Kahn, R. L., Karp, E. and Fink, M.: (1962) Tachistoscopic perception after induced altered brain function: influence of mental set. *J. Nerv. Ment. Dis., 134:*422-430.

Pollack, M., Karp, E., Belmont, I., Willner, A., Klein, D. F. and Fink, M.:
(in press) Comparative studies of chlorpromazine and imipramine. II:
psychological performance profiles. Bradley, P., ed.: *Neuropsycho-
pharmacology*, 3, Amsterdam, Elsevier.

Rao, C. R.: (1952) *Advanced Statistical Methods in Biometric Research.*
New York, John Wiley & Sons.

Williams, H. L., Granda, A. M., Jones, R. C., Lubin, A. and Armington,
J. C.: (1962) EEG frequency and finger pulse volume as predictors of
reaction time during sleep loss. *Electroenceph. Clin. Neurophysiol., 14:*
64-70.

15

EXTRAPYRAMIDAL CONTROL OF THE SPEED OF BEHAVIOUR AND ITS CHANGE BY PRIMARY AGE PROCESSES

R. Hassler

Behavior in the strictest sense, that is excluding data obtained through introspective observation and verbal communication, is conceived as the way in which an individual moves and acts and hereby reveals some aspects of psychical processes. These movements or the permanent attitudes are controlled by two nervous apparatuses: the pyramidal and extrapyramidal motor systems. The expressive movements, the associated movements (Foerster, 1921), the primary and secondary automatisms (Vogt, 1911 and 1920) as well as the speed of movements (Hassler, 1957 and 1961) are effected through the extrapyramidal system. Therefore any study of behavioral changes due to ageing must deal with this very system. On the other hand, this system has a predisposition to age changes (Vogt, 1920; Spatz, 1927). There are a number of old-age disorders that are due to primary biological changes of the extrapyramidal system (Hassler, 1938; v. Braunmühl, 1957) without being expressive of psychical age disturbances. Thus, there are two reasons for our interest in the extrapyramidal system, the behavioural effects of its primary disorders and the disorders of expression of psychical age disturbances. Finally some information may be given about the primary age processes in this system and their individual differences.

284

The first point, which I want to demonstrate is the extrapyramidal control of expressive and associated movements. When an individual suffers from unilateral athetosis, the facial expressions and the gestures of the affected side are exaggerated and cramped (Oppenheimer, *et al.*, 1912). Sometimes these movements occur for no reason at all, not as expressions of any emotion. These are due to a lesion in the contralateral basal ganglia (Anton, 1896), particularly of the external part of the pallidum (Vogt, 1920; Hassler, 1953). If the right one is damaged in early life, there occur only on the left side exaggerated movements (Fig. 1). Contrariwise, if somebody becomes ill with Parkinson's disease, only on one side of the body, the first symptoms are the slowness of the voluntary and involuntary movements and the reduction of facial expression and gestures on the affected side (Kleist, 1918;

Figure 1. Exaggerated expressive movements on the left side of the face in a case of athetosis, due probably to a status marmoratus of the right putamen and outer segment of the pallidum. Before operation.

Foerster, 1921). The cerebral substratum of the unilateral mask like face is the loss of nerve cells in medial cell groups of the substantia nigra (Hassler, 1938) (Fig. 2), which is most often due to encephalitis passed through many years earlier.

Although **emotional experience** is an entirety, its behavioural manifestation or **expression** is produced for each of the two halves of the body **by a contralateral** circumscribed **extrapyramidal neuronal** chain.

Since the development of stereotactic brain operations we learned a little more about the pathways for the control of expressive and automatic movements. One of its most powerful inhibitory mechanisms, is localized in the rostral third of the caudate nucleus and putamen (Vogt, 1920; Jakob, 1923) (Fig. 3), which acts through the strio-nigral fibres on medial cell groups of the substantis nigra (Fig. 4). From here the excitatory pathway descends to the opposite peripheral motor apparatus of emotional expression. The rostral third of the caudate nucleus and putamen also influences through short fibres the rostral third of the external pallidum. The destruction of this part results in the demonstrated involuntary grimacing. That can be reduced or even abolished by a coagulation in the internal pallidum (Fig. 5) or in the next

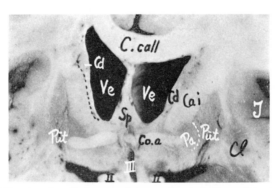

Figure 2. The heads of the caudate nucleus (cd) and putamen (pùt) are affected by a severe atrophy and consecutive shrinkage in a case of Huntington's Chorea. The most severe symptoms in the region of the mouth and face correspond to the most severe involvement of the head of the striatum in contrast to its more posterior parts. (Sp = Septum; Ve = lateral ventricle; III = third ventricle.)

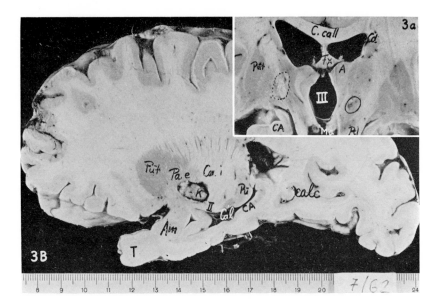

Figure 3a. A scar (marked by points) occupying the left anterior thalamus, the internal capsule and the inner segment of the pallidum has reduced the volume of the anterior thalamus. This scar is the consequence of a stereotactic coagulation one and a half years before death. In the right thalamus the base is occupied by a recently produced coagulation. Thereby the basal parts of V.o.a are destroyed. The left-sided coagulation abolished the tremor and rigidity in the right extremities and was followed by a mimical facial paresis on the right side.

Figure 3b. Sagittal section of a Parkinson brain with a coagulation of the inner segment of the pallidum produced eighteen days before death due to a lung embolus. The coagulation was followed by a relief of rigidity and reduction of tremor in the contralateral extremities. The coagulation focus stops abruptly in front of the internal capsule and above the optic tract. It spares the outer segment of the pallidum almost completely. Am: amygdaloid nucleus; Ca. i: internal capsule; calc: fissura calcarina; C A: Cornu Ammonis; G. 1: Geniculatum laterale; K: Coagulation; Pa. e: Pallidum externum; Pu: Pulvinar; Put: Putamen; T: Pole of the temporal lobe; Tri: trigonum of the lateral ventricle; II: optic tract.

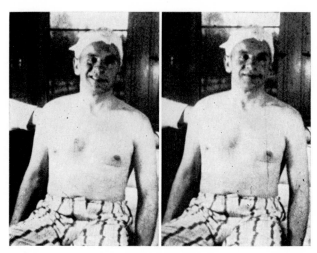

Figure 4. This patient with a postencephalitic Parkinsonism has a left side facial paresis for mimical movements only four days after coagulation of the right ventro-oral thalamic nuclei. No difference during voluntary pulling the corners of the mouth (right picture) in contrast to the failure of laughing on the left side (left picture).

neuronal station of this pathway: in the oral ventral nuclei of the thalamus (Fig. 6) (Hassler and Riechert, 1954).

These nuclei are the main site where the lesions are now made for the relief of involuntary movements or of Parkinson tremor and rigidity. The elimination of this basal part of VL (or V.o. a and V.o.p) by electrolysis, or high frequency current, by cold or by chemicals results, beyond the relief of motor-disturbances, in a contralateral **facial weakness** or paresis which is apparent only **during mimical expression** not during voluntary movements (Hassler, 1953, 1959) (Fig. 7). This is the most constant by-effect of the coagulation of these structures also in cases in which the mimical expression is not primarily disturbed. Therefore the facial expression needs for its appearance a normal neuronal pathway from the pallidum through V.o.a to the motor cortex, to which the V.o.a projects. If these thalamic nuclei are stimulated before coagulation, contralateral facial contractions can be elicited in the patients (Hassler and Riechert, 1954). But the mimical facial paresis after thalamic (V.o) coagulation disappears in almost all cases after

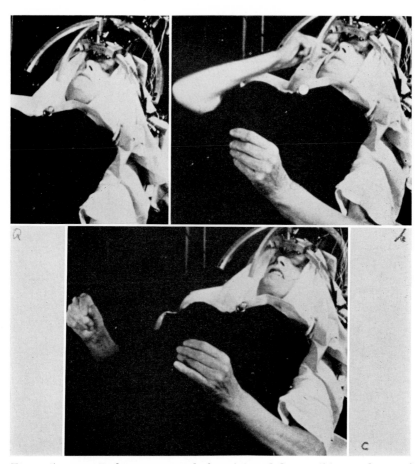

Figure 5 a — c. Parkinson-patient before (a) and during (b) stimulation of the left V.o.a with 50/sec. The patient turns the eyes to the contralateral side and raises the contralateral arm to point to the face. She began to utter unintelligible words during stimulation and continued to speak in a fast excited manner after the end of the stimulation (c) (Hassler, 1961).

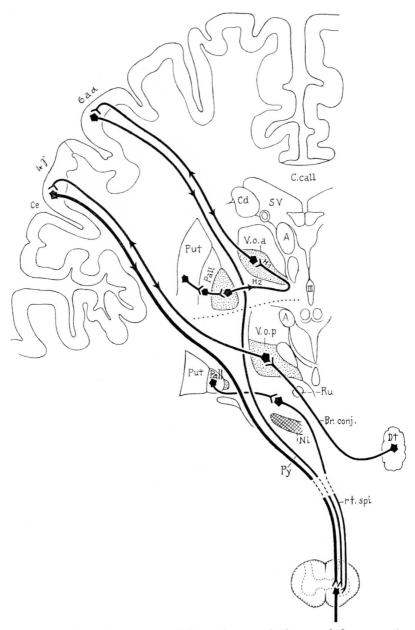

Figure 6. Schematic drawing of the pathways which control the expressive movements and the speed of movements. The neuronal chain from the putamen passes the external and internal segment of the pallidum (Pall), is

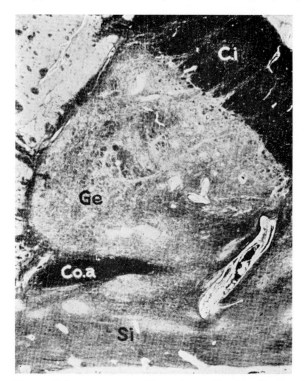

Figure 7a. The pallidum externum (Ge) of an old man of eighty-four years of age, without any neurological disturbances. In spite of this a severe état précriblé exists in the pallidum with perivascular tissue rarefication. The basal nucleus in the substantia innominata (Si) appears in the low power view (6:1) much less affected. The internal capsule (C.i) and Commissura anterior (C.o.a) are free from vascular damage.

---

continued through the bundle H_2 and H_1 to the thalamic nucleus V.o.a which is in two way connection with the premotor field 6 aα. The other neuronal chain originates from the dentate nucleus, crosses the midline, passes the thalamic nucleus V.o.p to reach the area 4γ. From the area 4γ and 6 aα arise cortico-spinal fibres (Pγ) to the peripheral motor apparatus. Voluntary movements can be accelerated by stimulation of V.o.p. After coagulation of V.o.a and V.o.p a contralateral paresis for expressive movements only occurs for a few weeks.

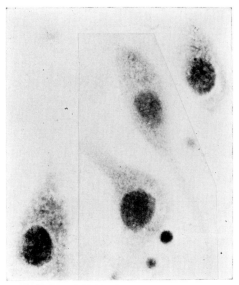

Figure 7b. The nerve cells of the pallidum externum of a patient, affected from senile dementia but free from Parkinson-symptoms show changes in the direction of ischemic cell disease (severe nuclear disease of Lewy). These cytopathologic alterations alone can not be the substratum of Parkinson-symptoms. In the middle of the picture the same cytopathologic alteration of pallidum nerve cells in a case of paralysis agitans (Hassler, 1938).

some weeks. So this afferent pathway to the contralateral motor cortex is not the single but only one of three substrata for contralateral expressive movements.

EMOTIONAL EFFECTS AND URGE TO SPEAK ELICITED BY DIENCEPHALIC STIMULATIONS

Stimulations of points a little more medial result beyond facial contractions in some cases in natural hearty **laughing** (Fig. 8) or in smiling (Hassler, 1957 and 1961), both mostly with the adequate affect. The patients afterwards say, they do not know, why all things seem to be so funny during the stimulation. Requested not to laugh during repetitive stimulation they try to do so, but the laughing movements and the **merry jovial** mood prevail after a few seconds of stimulation. Real emotions with pertaining expressions can be elicited in the clear-headed conscious patient by electrical stimulation in the oral ventral thalamic nuclei lateral to

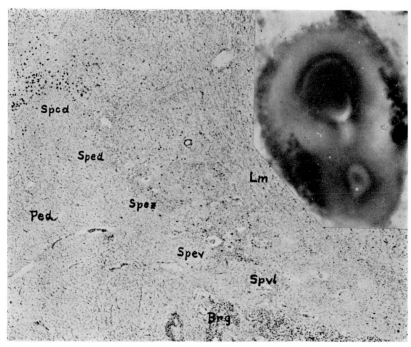

Figure 8a. Cell loss in the cell groups (Sped-Spv) of substantia nigra in a case of pure senile Parkinsonism, beginning in the eighty-fifth year of life. In accordance with the findings in all other kinds of Parkinsonism this is the substratum of Parkinson symptoms (Hassler, 1939). As an insert the argyrophilic cytoplasmatic inclusion body in a cell of the substantia nigra of hereditary Parkinsonism can be seen. The cell alteration occurs in senile Parkinsonism and without cell loss also in very old persons unaffected by Parkinson-symptoms.

the Lamella medialis. We know some but not all conditions for these laughing or smiling effects.

In front and also medial in the thalamus is another structure, the stimulation of which results in repeated **uttering of unintelligible** or queer **words** even when requested before stimulation to remain absolutely silent. The facial expression with dilated pupils, flushed face and high pitched voice are characteristic of somebody appealing in an excited manner to his surroundings. Sometimes the gaze deviates to the opposite side and the opposite arm is quickly raised or the hand grasps at the ear or the eye (Fig. 9). This complex effect is similar to that obtained in stimulation of

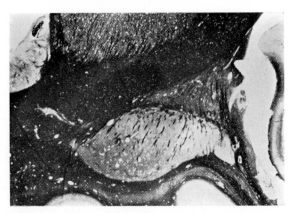

Figure 8b. État précriblé in the dorsal part of putamen in a case of senile essential tremor. This is the substratum of the single symptom of this disease (Hassler, 1939).

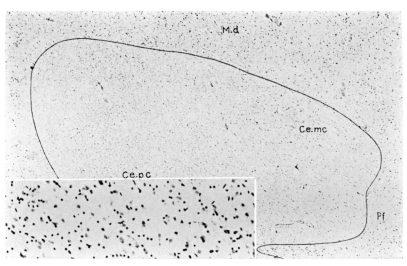

Figure 9 a + b. Cell shrinkage and atrophy in the centre médian of a neurologically normal person of eighty-two years of age in contrast to the normal cell preservation in the surrounding nuclei (M.d. = medio-dorsal nucleus, Pf = parafascicular nucleus). The insert in the left corner shows the cells in higher magnification of 200:1. No cell loss, but severe loss of stainability and shrinking of the nerve cells (C and O. Vogt, 1942).

the supplementary motor area on the medial aspect of the hemisphere, as reported by Penfield and Welch (1951). Probably the thalamic projection nucleus to this area is stimulated in the cases described (Hassler, 1961). Important seems to me, that the **urge to speak** quickly or to vocalize can be produced by a circumscribed thalamic stimulation which prevails over the intention not to speak, or the intention to speak something else, or to count slowly. The mechanism of urge to speak could be elicited separately from adversive movements. This effect has some local specificity. In a series of more than 500 patients we found that during stimulation of the pallidum internum spontaneous speaking or vocalization was three times less frequent than during rostral thalamic stimulation.

Pallidum stimulation never resulted in the complex effect with adversive movements. After destruction of these stimulation points by coagulation the patients may have a reduced drive to speak for some days or weeks and also after bilateral damage, passing disturbances of expressive aphasia.

ACCELERATION AND SLOWING OF MOVEMENTS AND SPEAKING

Belonging to the topic of this volume are also some stimulation effects which alter the speed of movements or of speaking. Regularly the patients are requested to count backwards during the stereotactic stimulation (Hassler and Riechert, 1954). The stimulation of oral ventral nuclei of the thalamus very often elicits an **acceleration of counting** or speaking with or without subsequent block. Most patients were aware of this afterwards and gave the following reasons: They felt urged, there was such a pressure to hurry, the thoughts were driven, even till complete interruption of thinking. The acceleration of counting by (oro-ventral) thalamic stimulation was 6 times more frequent, than by stimulation of the pallidum. Contrariwise the latter stimulation results more frequently in a **slowing down of counting,** sometimes till a total block. The reasons given herefore by the patients were not striking: My thoughts were half gone; I felt a little inhibited and could not think so well; the voice did not go as I want. The slowing of counting or speaking was twice and a half more fre-

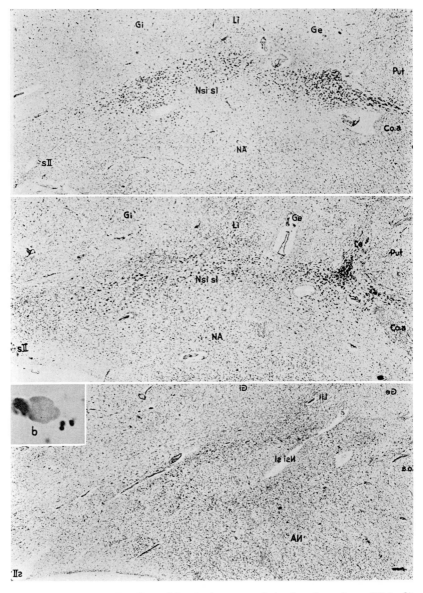

Figure 10 a – c. 10a The sublenticular part of the basal nucleus (Nsi. sl) in a normal brain. This is situated between the globus pallidus internus (Gi) and externus (Ge) above and the amygdaloid nucleus (NA) below. – *10 b* The same nucleus shows considerable cell loss in a normal person

quent during **pallidum stimulation** than during stimulation of the oral ventral nucleus of the thalamus.

In the same way the **speed of active movements** of the arms were altered during stimulation. To and fro movements of the forearms are frequently slowed down during pallidum stimulation. This occurred twice as often as during rostral thalamic stimulation. Contrariwise the rhythmic movements are in most cases **accelerated** during this thalamic stimulation; precisely: five times as often as during pallidum stimulation. When asked, the patients gave reasons as follows: "It goes faster all of itself. What's up with my hand? All things were faster; I had a respiration stop." This acceleration or slowing down was obtained independently from the spontaneous bradykinesia of Parkinsonian patients.

The interpretation of these accelerations of movements and of speaking is the following: The specific afferent fibers of the motor cortex are excited in ventral oral nuclei of the thalamus. If the stimulation is of higher frequency, than movements are spontaneously performed, the origin of the movements in the motor cortex is driven through physiological pathways (Fig. 10). An increase in the intensity of the stimulation interrupts the active movements earlier. The prevailing of the slowing down of movements by pallidum stimulation is remarkable. The pallidum internum sends its efferent fibers immediately to the oral ventral thalamic nuclei (Hassler, 1949). They seem to have an antagonistic action on these nuclei, so that the speed of active movements is opposed by excitement. Not too rarely the acceleration of movements by excitation is subjectively perceived as a pressure to hurry or as a feeling to be driven. This proves the subcortical influence on the speed of speaking and movements originating from the extrapyramidal structures. There is some extrapyramidal pace-maker for the intended movements.

---

of eighty-four years of age. — *10 c* (reversed for comparison with 10 a + b). The same nucleus has undergone almost complete cell loss in a case of familiar paralysis agitans, in spite of the age of sixty-six years. The insert shows the glassy cell disease of Lewy in a cell of the basal nucleus (Hassler, 1938).

CEREBRAL SUBSTRATUM OF PARKINSON-SYMPTOMS AND OF AGE CHANGES

The reduction of the speed of movements, of speaking, and of thinking is an outstanding age change of behaviour. The same symptom, more strongly marked, is one of the main symptoms of Parkinsonism (Kleist, 1918; Foerster, 1921). Because the old people frequently suffer also from a lack of spontaneous movements and from unsteadiness of movements or even shaking, many authors identified the motor disturbances of old people with Parkinson's disease. When Lewy (1923), Hunt (1917), C. and O. Vogt (1920), Bielschowsky (1922), and Jakob (1923) found senile alterations and vascular damage in the Putamen and Pallidum of Parkison patients, they were believed to provide the anatomical basic of Parkinson's disease as well as the substratum of senile behavioural changes.

In later investigations along these lines we found (Hassler, 1938-1939) that all the alterations in the Pallidum and Striatum of Parkinson patients were the same as found in older brains without Parkinson symptoms. Therefore we must distinguish between the average age changes in the extrapyramidal centres and the anatomo-pathological substratum of Parkinson symptoms. The latter are due in every case, which is adequately investigated in serial sections, to a loss of the black pigmented cells of the substantia nigra. This is not only true in postencephalitic cases, where it is accepted as the substratum since the early twenties (Spatz, 1923). The same is true also for the hereditary and idiopathic Parkinson disease which is mostly called Paralysis agitans (Fig. 11). Trétiakoff, 1919; Hassler, 1938).

The changes in the substantia nigra in postencephalitic and idiopathic cases can be differentiated by the characteristic distribution of the cell loss in the idiopathic cases, as well as by specific cytopathological alterations. These are restricted to the black pigmented cells in midbrain, pons and medulla oblongata. The cell destruction in the postencephalitic cases always occur by neuro-fibrillary changes of Alzheimer—also in young Parkinson patients under twenty years of age. These findings of Hallervorden (1933), Fenyes (1933), and myself (1938) have been confirmed in England by Greenfield and Bosanquet (1953). In hereditary and idiopathic Parkinsonism the black pigmented cells are destroyed by growing argyrophilic inclusion bodies (Fig. 12). Thus (Hassler, 1938; Beheim, 1956), the pathology of Parkinsonism of different etiology informs us, that the cell loss in the substantia nigra is the constant substratum of rigidity, tremor and perhaps of akinesis too.

The surgical therapy of Parkinson symptoms, mainly of rigidity and tremor at rest shows additionally that a pallidum destruction cannot be the patho-anatomical substratum of these symptoms. If the pallidum itself is coagulated in Parkinson patients the rigidity disappears immediately during the coagulation and in proportion to the extent of pallidum destruction. That is inconsistent with the long living pallidum-theory of Parkinsonism. Instead, the undestroyed pallidum systems are the pathways, that

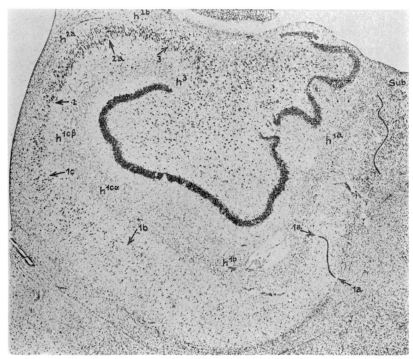

Figure 11. Extensive cell degeneration and cell loss in the field h¹ of the Ammonshorn in a case of senile dementia. The fields h² and h³ are much less affected by cell degeneration due to ageing (C. and O. Vogt, 1942).

are **necessary for the appearance** of Parkinson symptoms. Surgical pallidum destruction, in addition to the destruction of the substantia nigra can reduce or even abolish some Parkinson symptoms.

LOCALIZED CELL AGEING PROCESSES

The pathology of Parkinsonism, however, gives us further information about ageing. The **primary process of ageing** at time as well as premature ageing is not a generalized or diffuse phenomenon but appears localized and sometimes restricted to a single kind of neurons (Hassler, 1938; Vogt, 1942). The **neuro-fibrillary tangles** of Alzheimer in postencephalitic Parkinsonism are present only in the substantia nigra and in other types of cells of the brain stem which contain melanine. In the pure and not premature ageing of the nigra cells, these disintegrate only exceptionally by the formation of neuro-fibrillary tangles. Likewise in the idiopathic and hereditary Parkinsonism the cell destruction by the formation of **intraplasmatic argyrophilic inclusions** is also restricted to the neurons of the nigra and other nerve cells with melanine as in the locus caeruleus. In Parkinson cases they are never present in the nerve cells of the cerebral cortex. This kind of disintegration of black pigmented nerve cells is also an ageing process, although a precocious one. This kind of nerve cell ageing, however, can also be found in very old individuals which were clinically not Parkinsonistic. The **normal ageing of the nigra cells** shows the formation of the same **intraplasmatic inclusion** bodies, which are argyrophilic (Hassler, 1955; Beheim, 1956). If several nerve cells are destroyed by this pure senile process, a really senile Parkinsonism takes place which in my autopsy cases (1938 and 1939) began after the eightieth year. The same restriction of ageing processes to some neuronal systems is found in the brains of very old people without Parkinson symptoms.

The **ageing** of nerve cells **prefers** some **special neuronal** complexes. In the centre médian the nerve cells turn pale, so that in low power view this nucleus appears to have lost all nerve cells, in contrast to the surrounding nuclei (Vogt, 1942). Another predilection for systemic age changes of nerve cells is the inferior olive and the dentate nucleus. But each brain seems to have its own specific pattern of distribution of localized age changes (C. and O. Vogt, 1942).

In only one nucleus I found twenty-five years ago regularly age changes in all brains of individuals which had lived more than seventy years. This is the nucleus of Reichert's substance or the **basal nucleus,** which is continuous with the nucleus of the diagonal band of Broca. In contrast to the surrounding nerve cell aggregations of Putamen, Pallidum or supraoptic nucleus, these big nerve cells show always the **glassy cell disease** of Lewy (1923), and due to this, several of them undergo disintegration. This is of some interest because the same type of nerve cells shows an even more accelerated and intensified ageing process in idiopathic and hereditary Parkinsonism, so that the majority of nerve cells are lost.

Because these nerve cells of the basal nucleus have no relation to motor functions, their loss is supposed to be related to the most frequent psychical alteration in paralysis agitans, which is called **bradyphenia.** This is characterized by a slowing down of thinking, a delay and reduction of emotional reactions, a failure of distributive attention and difficulty of decision. The psychical changes in cases not complicated by cerebral arteriosclerosis are of the same kind, if the disorders of recent memory are at first neglected.

The system of Broca's diagonal band with its specific nerve cells seems to be one of the most important activation structures of the brain (Green *et al.*, 1954; Petsche *et al.*, 1962). If the structure is stimulated in the freely moving unrestrained cat, the animal looked there and back, in an excited manner with dilated pupils, as soon as the stimulation began (unpublished observations). Stumpf and Petsche (1962) found by single cell recordings that the cells of Broca's band are the pace maker for the hippocampus. If the diagonal band is destroyed, the theta waves in the hippocampus can no more be elicited by midbrain reticular stimulation (Green, 1954). Even the paradoxical phase of sleep (Jouvet, 1962) does no more occur after destruction of the rostral pontine reticular substance if both diagonal bands are coagulated. By way of the inferior thalamic peduncle the cells of Broca's band also influence the medial thalamic nucleus, which is the specific subcortical projection nucleus to the large prefrontal cortex of the human.

In the hippocampus itself, which is also a powerful activator of the cerebral cortex, the most constant age change is the cell loss of the II. pyramidal layer of field h 1 (C. and O. Vogt, 1942). According to many training experiments the hippocampus seems to bear importance for recent memory. Perhaps the loss of recent memory in old people is correlated with this cell loss due to age changes.

However, I now want to return to the extrapyramidal motor system and its age changes. The turning pale of centre médian cells can be considered as the substratum of sleep disturbances of aged people because this nucleus belongs to the thalamic hypnogenic zone of Hess (1929; 1944).

The **senile cell loss** in the **inferior olive** and **dentate nucleus** could be brought into correlation with the well known **ataxia** and **intention tremor** of the old aged. The pure senile or essential tremor however has its patho-anatomical substratum not in these changes but in a rarefaction of nerve cells around the capillaries in the Putamen and caudate nucleus (Hassler, 1939). This condition has been called the état précriblé for a long time. The same état précriblé is the substratum of hereditary or toxic essential tremor. The pure tremor of aged people has probably in each case its substratum in putamen and caudate nucleus.

The last system, which is a predilection focus of the ageing process, is the **pallidum.** In the first part it was established that the pallidum is not the patho-anatomical substratum of rigidity and tremor at rest. But what kind of age disturbances are correlated to the pallidum lesions often seen in the brains of aged people? The stimulation effect of the pallidum in the human (1957) as well as in the cat (with Montanelli, 1962) are adversive movements, regulary to the contralateral side with pupillodilatation (Fig. 13). These could no more be elicited by stimulation after coagulation of this structure. After unilateral pallidum coagulation in the human a slow wave delta focus appears in the frontal cortex for one to three months (Ganglberger, 1961). The single motor symptom which is not improved after pallidum co-agulation in Parkinson cases is the motor akinesis. Contrariwise, this is often increased after Pallidum coagulation, so that many patients show a contralateral **motor neglect** in the first weeks after coagulation which is exactly the reverse of the stimulation effect. The pallidum is more a psycho-motor than a somato-motor centre. The bilateral destruction of pallidum in stereotaxic operations induces a state of mental disturbance, or coma or an amential and delirious state. Akinesis and reduced psycho-motor activity is a prominent phenomenon of behavioural age changes and is probably correlated to the ageing of nerve cells and vessels in the pallidum.

SUMMARY

Summarizing it may be stated that there are two primary processes of ageing of nerve cells, **one diffuse** and spread all over the brain and the **other localized** in some special populations of neurons. The general assumption that ageing is the same process in all humans should be corrected. Everybody seems to have his own pattern of localized ageing in different areas of the brain. The consequence is that also the physiological and psychological phenomena of ageing are different in different individuals in spite of the fact that they often have some common characteristics. In the extrapyramidal structures, the primary ageing process prefers the **basal nucleus** and also the **pallidum** and the **centre median.** This type of ageing must be differentiated from the premature ageing in the idiopathic Parkinsonism; here the same cytopathological kind of ageing, by formation of intraplasmatic inclusion bodies, occurs as in very old normal subjects without Parkinsonism, but than without cell disintegration. The **speed** of active movements and of speaking can be **accelerated** by ventro-oral thalamic stimulation in the awake human, and **slowed down** by pallidum stimulation. The **urge to speak** can also be elicited by rostromedial thalamic stimulation. The facial expression of emotions is mediated by localized neuronal chains mainly from the rostral putamen and pallidum to the substantia nigra (medial cell groups).

REFERENCES

Anton, G.: Über die Beteiligung der großen basalen Gehirnganglien bei Bewegungsstörungen insbesondere bei Chorea. *Jahrb. Psychiat.*, *14*: 141-182, 1896.

Beheim-Schwarzbach, D.: Pathokline Niger-Veränderungen. *J. Hirnforsch.*, *2*:94-126, 1956.

Bielschowsky, M.: Weitere Bemerkungen zur normalen und pathologischen Histologie des striären Systems. *J. Psychol. u. Neurol.*, *27*:233-288, 1922.

Braunmühl, A. v.: Alterserkrankungen des Zentralnervensystems. Senile Involution. Senile Demenz. Alzheimersche Krankheit *Hdb. spez. pathol. Anat* XIII, 1 A: 337-539, 1957.

Brissaud, E.: *Leçons sur les Maladies Nerveuses*. Paris, 1895.

Foerster, Otfr.: Zur Analyse und Pathophysiologie der striären Bewegungsstörungen. *Z. Neur.*, *73*:1-169, 1921.

Ganglberger, J. A.: Vorübergehende Herdveränderungen im EEG nach stereotaktischen Operationen an den Basalganglien. *Arch.f.Psychiatr.*, *201*:528-548, 1961.

Green, J. D. and Arduini, A. A.: Hippocampal electrical activity in arousal. *J. Neurophysiol.*, *17*:533-557, 1954.

Greenfield, J. G. and Bosanquet, F. D.: The brainstem lesions in Parkinsonism. *J. of Neur. N.S.*, *16*:213-226, 1953.

Hallervorden, J.: Zur Pathogenese des postencephalitischen Parkinsonismus. *Klin. Wschr.*, *12*:692-695, 1933.

Hassler, R.: Zur Pathologie der Paralysis agitans und des postencephalitischen Parkinsonismus. *J. Psychol. u. Neurol.*, *48*:387-476, 1938.

Hassler, R.: Zur pathologischen Anatomie des senilen und parkinsonistischen Tremor. *J. Psychol. u. Neur.*, *49*:193-230, 1939.

Hassler, R.: Über die afferenten Bahnen und Thalamuskerne des motorischen Systems des Großhirns. I + II *Arch. f. Psychiatr.*, *182*:759-818, 1949.

Hassler, R.: Extrapyramidal-motorische Syndrome und Erkrankungen. *Hdb. inn Med.*, 4. Aufl. Bd. V, Teil 3:676-904, 1953.

Hassler, R.: The pathological and pathophysiological basis of tremor and Parkinsonism. *Proceed. II. Internat. Congr. Neuropath.* London *I*:29-40, 1955.

Hassler, R.: Über die Bedeutung der pallidären Systeme für Parkinsonsyndrom und Psychomotorik nach Erfahrungen bei gezielten Hirnoperationen. *Rapp. 1 Congr. Internat. Neurochir. Brüssel*: 174-178, 1957.

Hassler, R.: Stereotactic brain surgery for extrapyramidal motor disturbances. *In, Introduction to Stereotaxis with an Atlas of the human brain.* Edit. Schaltenbrand-Bailey, Stuttgart, 472-488, 1959.

Hassler, R.: Motorische und sensible Effekte umschriebener Reizungen und Ausschaltungen im menschlichen Zwischenhirn. *Dtsch. Z. Nervenheilk.*, *183*:148-171, 1961.

Hassler, R.: Affective and arousal effects elicited from distinctive nuclei of the human diencephalon. *EGG. Clin. Neurophysiol., 14:*422-423, 1962.

Hassler, R. and Riechert, T.: Indikationen und Lokalisationsmethode der gezielten Hirnoperationen. *Nervenarzt, 25:*441-447, 1954.

Hess, W. R.: Lokalisatorische Ergebnisse der Hirnreizversuche mit Schlaf-effekt. *Arch.f.Psychiatr., 88:*813-816, 1929.

Hess, W. R.: Das Schlafsyndrom als Folge diencephaler Reizung. *Helv. Physiol. Acta, 2:*305-344, 1944.

Hunt, J. R.: The syndrome of the Globus pallidus. *J. nerv. ment. Dis., 44:* 437-442, 1917.

Jakob, A.: *Die extrapyramidalen Erkrankungen.* Berlin, 1923.

Jouvet, M.: Sur l'existence d'un système hypnique pontolimbique; ses rapports avec l'activité onirique. *In, Physiologie de l'Hippocampe,* Montpellier, 297-330, 1962.

Jung, R. and Hassler R.: The extrapyramidal motor system. *Handbook Physiol.-Neurophysiol II:* 863-927, 1959.

Kleist, K.: *Untersuchungen zur Kenntnis der psychomotorischen Bewegungsstörungen bei Geisteskranken.* Leipzig, 1908.

Kleist, K.: Zur Auffassung der subcorticalen Bewegungsstörungen (Chorea, Athetose, Bewegungsausfall, Starre, Zittern) *Arch. f. Psychiatr., 59:*790-803, 1918.

Kleist, K.: *Gehirnpathologie.* Leipzig, 1934.

Lewy, F. H.: *Die Lehre vom Tonus und der Bewegung.* Berlin, 1923.

Lukisch, F. and Spatz, H.: Die Veränderungen im Zentralnervensystem bei Parkinsonismus in den Spätstadien der Encephalitis epidemica. *Münch. med. Wschr., 70:*1245, 1923.

Montanelli, R. P. and Hassler, R.: Stimulation effects of the globus pallidus and nucleus entopeduncularis of the cat. *Excerpta Med. Internat. Congr. Ser.* 48 Nr. 1091 XXII Intern. Congr. Physiol. Sci. Leiden, 1962.

Oppenheim, H. and Vogt, C.: Nature et localisation de la paralysie pseudo-bulbaire congénitale et infantile. *J. Psychol. u. Neur., 18:*293-308, 1912.

Penfield, W. and Welch, K.: The supplementary motor area of the cerebral cortex. *Arch. of Neur., 66:*289-317, 1951.

Petsche, H. and Stumpe, Ch. and Gogolak, G.: The significance of the rabbit's septum as a relay station between the midbrain and the hippocampus. I. The control of hippocampus arousal activity by the septum cells. *EEG Clin. Neurophysiol., 14:*202-211, 1962.

Spatz, H. Substantia nigra und das extrapyramidal-motorische System. *Dtsch. Z. Nervenheilk., 77:*275, 1923.

Spatz, H.: Physiologie und Pathologie der Stammganglien. *Hdb. norm. u. path. Physiol. X:*318-417, 1927.

TRÉTIAKOFF, C.: *Contribution à l'étude de l'anatomie pathologique du locus niger de Soemmering avec quelques déductions rélatives à la pathogénie des troubles du tonus musculaire de la maladie de Parkinson.* Thèse de Paris, 1919.

VOGT, C.: *Quelques considérations générales a propos du syndrome du corps strié. J. Psychol. u. Neur.,* 18:479-488, 1911.

VOGT, C. u. O.: Zur Lehre der Erkrankungen des striären Systems. *J. Psychol. u. Neur.,* 25, Erg. H. (1920) 631-846.

VOGT, C. u. O.: Sitz und Wesen der Krankheiten im Lichte der topistischen Hirnforschung u. des Variiierens der Tiere. I. *J. Psychol. u. Neur.,* 47: 237-457, 1937.

VOGT, C. u. O.: Morphologische Gestaltungen unter normalen und pathologischen Bedingungen. *J. Psychol. u. Neur.,* 50:161-524, 1942.

16

ON THE EYE

R. A. WEALE

It is perhaps fair to say that behaviour will depend at least in part on the information which reaches the subject. Such information is received via the special senses, and the following considerations are concerned particularly with problems of vision although some of the implications extend to other modalities of perception. It stands to reason that if the speed of behaviour is found to change with age, then every part of the loop, beginning with the most peripheral element of the afferent path and ending with the extreme part of the efferent route, must receive equally detailed consideration.

1. SOME OCULAR REFLEXES

To begin with, it may not be without interest to consider one or two of the ocular reflexes which are mediated by visual stimuli. The blink reflex springs to mind straightaway and when one considers how difficult it is to measure the latent period of blinking in a consistent manner, it will hardly come as a surprise that no study appears to have been made of the variation of this with age. In some preliminary experiments, we obtained an increase in the latent period of blinking with age, but the scatter of the data was such that it is doubtful if any significance can be attributed to the finding that the latent period at sixty is perhaps two or three times as long as that in the late teens.

The latent period of the pupillary reflex, i.e., the interval which elapses between the arrival of a photic stimulus at the retina and the onset of the constriction of the pupil, has recently been shown to be virtually independent of age (Kumnick, 1956a). This is not unexpected when it is remembered that the visual reaction time and therefore the visual latent period vary with age very slowly, and the pupillary reflex has a latent period of about 0.25 sec. Even so, when we recall that the iris tissues become more and more rigid as they age (Rones, 1938; Larsson and Österlind, 1943), it is perhaps a little surprising that there should be no frictional effects which would slow down the motion of the iris.

While the blink reflex and the pupillary reflex are unlikely to be of very great importance in a study of behaviour, this is hardly true of the third reflex to be considered in this context. This is the speed with which the eye can accommodate, i.e., adjust itself from distant to near vision and vice versa. It is obvious that this problem can be of critical importance, for instance, to motorists, engine drivers, and even pilots of aircraft. The physiologist may well regret that the gerontological aspect of this problem has not been tackled by objective means, but from the point of view of behaviour it is, of course, the attainment of subjective criteria which matters rather than the mechanism whereby the desired result is achieved. One study, due to Robertson, was published as long ago as 1937. He determined the average time (in seconds) required by people of various ages to obtain sharp vision when they directed their gaze from a point 33 cm. away to one 6 m. away, secondly from the latter to the former, and thirdly from near to far and back again to near. As expected, the time taken for these three tasks increased with age, but one of the results is not necessarily predicted on the basis of other experiments. When the former two times are added to each other; i.e., when the near to far and far to near tasks are added to one another, the sum accurately equals the value obtained for the near to far to near measurement (Fig. 1). When one thinks about the problem, this is rather surprising, because if—as it were—one instructs one's accommodative mechanism to relax accommodation until vision is sharp at a greater distance, and then instructs accommodation to work so that vision at a near distance becomes sharp again, quite clearly a period must elapse between the accomplishment of the first task and the beginning of the next. Of this period there is no trace in Robertson's results.

Another difficulty arising from these measurements is that when the latent period of accommodation is measured by objective means in the young eye, it is found to be about 0.4 sec. whereas Figure 1 shows that subjective accommodation takes just under half a second. This is surprising when one recalls that

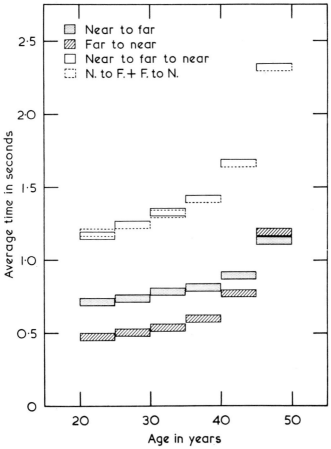

Figure 1. The speed of subjective accommodation and its relaxation. The dotted rectangles represent the sum of the shaded ones. Experimental data from Robertson, 1937.

visual reaction times are of the order of 0.2 sec. (cf. Fig. 2), and that in the experiments described by Robertson the observers were instructed to perform a motor response *when vision was sharp.* One might expect that the accommodation and reaction times would have summated so that the total time would have been about 0.6 sec. It is possible, however, that the two times might have overlapped in the sense that the observer has enough data on which to begin his decision to react, before the image becomes fully sharp.

Even if the detail of the results is in doubt, it is feasible to believe that the average time required to change the state of accommodation of the eye increases with age, although the physiological reasons as to why this should be so are not entirely clear. These doubts are accentuated by a study by Allen (1956) which was perhaps more detailed than Robertson's. The states of accommodation and of relaxation were measured as a function of time and of age, and it was shown that accommodation

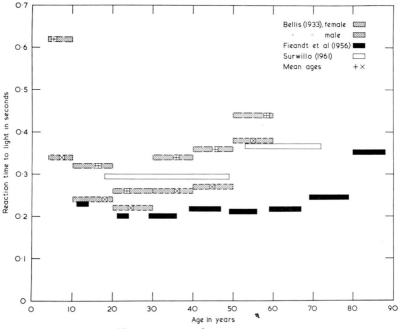

Figure 2. Visual reaction time.

and relaxation, so far from occupying a fraction of a second, go on for the better part of two seconds. These experiments again used subjective criteria. However, they illustrate a very remarkable point, namely that the relative speed of accommodation actually *increases* with age between the first and fourth decades of life. There is a sound anatomical basis for this finding, for Stieve (1949) has shown that the ciliary muscle goes on developing up to the fourth if not the fifth decade, becoming progressively stronger and embarking on its period of devolution only as we approach our fiftieth year.

We have to ask ourselves whether there is any means enabling us to decide between the two sets of experimental data just reviewed. The answer, I think, is provided by reference to other work which deals with the decrease of the amplitude of accommodation with age. It is a matter of common experience that, as one gets older, one's reading distance increases. This is only another way of saying that the ability of the eye to focus for very near distances decreases with age. We say that the eye becomes presbyopic. Several studies on the variation of amplitude of accommodation of the aging human eye have been published; one of the most recent being due to Brückner (1959). A combination of Brückner's and Robertson's data on the one hand, and Allen's results on the other, leads to the following picture.

In the early part of the third and the fifth decades, Robertson's results suggest that relative accommodation is complete before the measurements of Allen have even begun. While it is perfectly true to say that Allen's dioptric values are below average, a fact which may be attributed to his optical arrangement, one cannot help feeling that Allen's is the more likely result, and, on balance, his data would appear to command greater confidence. The question must be said to be open, and further research with unexceptionable techniques is required to clinch it. It is self-evident that the answer to this question is of some importance in the determination of the age variation of the speed of the visual behaviour, although one must not forget that the complicated question of the variation with age of visual acuity (cf. Weale, 1963) enters the problem just discussed, which is really very much more involved than the following problems amenable to relatively easy quantitative study.

2. MATTERS OF TIMING

It so happens that there are several temporal aspects to vision. One of them is connected with reaction time, defined simply as the interval elapsing between the arrival of the stimulus at the eye and the execution of the required response; another deals with properties of the eye itself and is familiar to experimental psychologists under the term of "flicker." Eye and brain are concerned in both these functions and it is noteworthy that there is ample evidence to suggest that the brain itself undergoes definite senile changes. One has to remember, however, that the relation between well-defined, morphological, cortical changes and the alteration of function is at best elusive and may well be non-existent. Our ideas regarding the localization of function are, of course, very much more fluid now than they were a few decades ago. There are two schools of thought as regards the question of whether the retina, after all part of the brain, is involved in senile changes or not. The majority of writers (Fischer, 1948; Kornzweig, 1954) believe that this tissue is extremely resistant to senile change. There are one or two, such as Hager (1959) and Pillat (1952), who think that it shows signs of decay which cannot be called physiological in nature. More recently, Streiff and Bakel (1963) have listed some histological changes of the fundus and retina: the distinction between normal and pathological aging is not well marked, and fogged even more by the authors' failure to examine probable causes for senile retinal dysfunction.

If there is some doubt about retinal stamina, there is none whatever about the events occurring at an even more peripheral stage. The structures referred to are the iris pupil and the crystalline lens, both of which are characterised by marked senile changes. The pupil and the lens govern the quantity and quality of the light reaching the retina, and will be of special significance in our enquiry regarding senile variations in visual response only if it can be shown that the temporal phenomena mentioned earlier on, namely reaction time and flicker, themselves depend on the amount of light which reaches the retina. For instance, there is no question but that the latent period of vision depends on the intensity of the stimulus (Bernhard, 1940; Arden and Weale, 1954). The latent period, t, i.e., the interval elapsing between the termination of the stimulating light and the beginning of discharge in the optic nerve, of course, forms only part of the reaction time, one might almost be tempted to say a neglibible part, were it not for the fact that at low intensities changes in latent period of up to a quarter or half a second have been recorded. (One is concerned with changes in latent period, for the absolute value cannot be measured in man without several assumptions being made.) Now it is important to preserve a sense of proportion in this connection because significant changes in t can be produced only by changes in light stimulus intensity amounting to factors of about 1,000 or even 10,000. It is easily shown that the normal aging eye cannot be subject to changes of this magnitude as a result of aging; that is to say, although for reasons mentioned below, the amount of light reaching the old retina is reduced by measurable and significant amounts in comparison with those reaching the retina in the young, we are concerned with factors not of 1,000 or 10,000 but rather those of the order of 3 or 4. It readily follows from this that the speed of behaviour, in so far as it may depend on the latent period, is not likely to be much affected by senile changes occurring in the eye. This theoretical prediction is confirmed by the experiments of Bellis (1933), Fieandt *et al.* (1956), and Surwillo (1961), in which the reaction time to light was measured in a variety of ways as a function of age (Fig. 2); although there is an indubitable rise in reaction time in the measurements of Bellis and also of Surwillo during the fifth decade and after, the more extensive measurements by Fieandt and his collaborators do not show any change until about the eighth decade. I think it is reasonable to conclude that these changes are unlikely to be due primarily to peripheral causes which arise much earlier in life. It is perhaps appropriate to recall the work of Birren and Botwinik (1955), who showed that the conduction time in the central nervous system does not vary appreciably with age.

As regards flicker, however, the story is entirely different. This sensation, produced by intermittent illumination, depends to a considerable extent on age and on the level of retinal illumination. The relation between the fusion frequency, i.e., the frequency at which flicker disappears, and intensity, is described within given limits by the well-known Ferry-Porter law, which has recently been generalised so as to include the variation of flicker fusion, not only with area, but also with retinal position (Weale, 1958; Angel *et al.*, 1959). If then, the fusion frequency depends considerably on the amount of light reaching the retina, one is faced with the question as to the extent to which the variation with age which many workers have observed in connection with fusion frequency (Fig. 3) can be predicted in terms of senile alterations in the pupil and lens respectively.

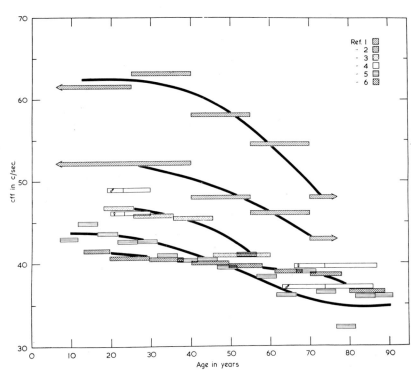

Figure 3. Critical flicker frequency as a function of age. References: 1) Hylkema (1944): retinal periphery; 2) Hylkema (1.c.): fovea; 3) Brozek and Keys (1945); 4) Misiak (1947); 5) Misiak (1951); 6) McFarland *et al.* (1958).

3. THE EFFECTS OF SENILE CHANGES IN THE IRIS AND THE CRYSTALLINE LENS

What are these senile alterations? In the first place, numerous workers have observed that owing to changes in the iris, the pupil area becomes smaller and smaller with age (Birren *et al.*, 1950; Kadlecová *et al.*, 1958; Leinhos, 1959;). There are, undoubtedly, old people who have juvenile pupils, just as there are young people who have apparently miotic senile pupils. But by and large, there is no getting away from the fact that the average pupil decreases in diameter with age. This means that the pupillary area decreases at a greater rate for it is proportional to the square of the diameter, and consequently the amount of light reaching the retina becomes progressively smaller as we get older (Fig. 4). In addition to the cutting down of the light quantity reaching the retina as a result of senile miosis or pupillary constriction, there is the quantitative and qualitative effect on light intensity as caused by the lens. The crystalline lens becomes not only less transparent throughout the whole spectrum (Said and Weale, 1959), but superimposed on this overall loss in transparency, which is also progressive, there is an enhanced

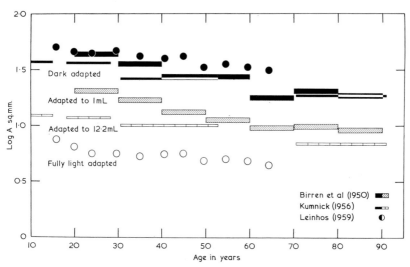

Figure 4. The senile variation of pupillary area and its dependence on the level of adaptation.

opacification in the blue part of the spectrum (Fig. 5), with the result that the lens becomes yellower as we get older. Consequently, it is not only the light quantity but also the spectral quality which changes with age. It may be mentioned in this connection that numerous measurements made of the absolute

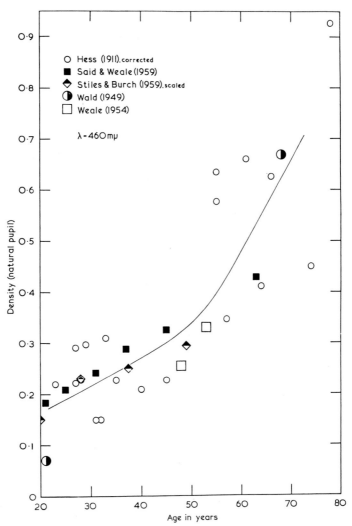

Figure 5. The photometric density of the human crystalline lens in the blue part of the spectrum. The data of Hess were originally related to yellow light: the present plot allows for this. The data of Stiles and Burch are relative, i.e., only their relative values can be moved by an arbitrary amount.

threshold of vision, under a variety of conditions, can be almost completely accounted for in terms of the senile changes of these two tissues. It is found, for instance, that the absolute threshold of vision, when measured with white light, rises in a manner which is approximately the reciprocal of the senile change in the average pupillary area (Robertson and Yudkin, 1944). Now white light is very suitable for the detection of changes in threshhold as due primarily to changes in pupillary diameter, for it minimises the senile effects as manifested by the yellowing of the lens (Gunkel and Gouras, 1963). On the other hand, if the pupillary diameter is controlled, for instance by the use of an artificial pupil or the use of a mydriatic, and the absolute threshold is measured, not with white light but say with blue or violet light, then a significant increase in threshold with age is observed once again (cf. Weale, 1961a). Clearly, this cannot be due to the effect of senile miosis, and it can be shown that the amount of lenticular yellowing accounts for the senile change in threshold observed under these conditions almost completely. As mentioned a little earlier, these considerations lead to the conclusion that the sixty-year-old retina receives only about one-third of the white light which reaches the twenty-year-old retina (Fig. 6), no matter whether the eye is light- or dark-adapted. Of course, if the eye is illuminated, not with white but with blue light, then the decrease in retinal illumination is much accentuated and can reach a factor of 8 or 9.

4. AN EXPLANATION OF WHY FUSION FREQUENCY DROPS AS WE AGE

These amounts are of significance when it comes to flicker because, as is well-known, a change in retinal illumination of about a factor of 10 can produce a change in flicker frequency of some 11 cycles/sec. It can be shown quite easily that the "senile" factor of 3 in illumination would be expected to produce a decline in fusion frequency of about 5 cycles/sec. Between the ages of twenty and sixty, the average decline in fusion frequency as estimated from results of a number of workers (Fig. 3) corresponds to about 7 cycles/sec. It follows that senile miosis can account for some 70 per cent of this decline found experimentally, lenticular opacification being able to account perhaps for another

10 per cent. Contrary to what Landis (1954) believes, it is fair to say that physical factors can account for the major part of the senile variation in flicker fusion. This is true of experiments done with the fovea, but not true when it comes to work done with the retinal periphery, where the change in fusion frequency observed experimentally is very much larger than in the fovea (Weekers and Roussel, 1946). It may well be that in these circumstances which involve observing a target extra-foveally, i.e., without actually looking at it, the question of perceptual skills and their variation with age has to be raised. These, as has been shown by Welford (1959) and other workers, fail with age and are taxed to the utmost when it comes to extra-foveal observation. Further evidence in favour of the view that the senile

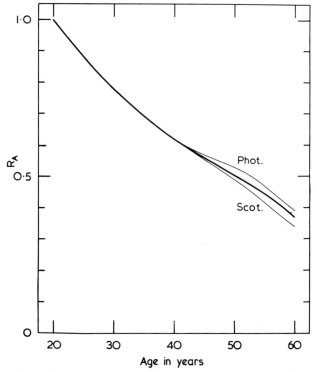

Figure 6. The relative amounts of effective light reaching the light-adapted (Phot.) or dark-adapted (Scot.) retina at various ages between twenty and sixty years (Weale, 1961b).

variation of flicker fusion is due largely to peripheral factors is obtained from the work by Weekers and Roussel (1946), who measured the fusion frequency as a function of age under two sets of conditions: a) when the pupil was natural, and b) when it was dilated, and therefore presumably maximal at all ages. The decline shown in the experiments with the natural pupil is not only delayed but also diminished when the pupil is dilated (Fig. 7). All these results suggest that, as regards the peripheral performance of the visual organ, such deterioration, as is observed in matters of speed or in factors which might affect speed, is almost wholly explicable in terms of the senility of two of the image forming devices, namely the pupil and the lens.

5. THE RATE OF DARK-ADAPTATION

The factor relating to the diminished retinal illumination as we age, namely the amount of 3 or 4 for white light, or of 8 or 9 for blue light, is only of importance when the eye is subjected to threshold conditions, and, in these circumstances, there can occur a situation in which the speed of behaviour is not determined at all by what might be called the dynamic processes of the eye, but purely and simply by an apparent slowing down of

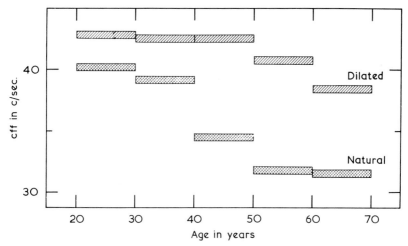

Figure 7. The effect of pupil size on the variation of critical flicker frequency with age (after Weekers and Roussel, 1946).

its adaptation to changes in illumination. This is illustrated in Figure 8 which shows typical dark-adaptation curves; in fact it represents a modification of a figure by Birren *et al.* (1950). There are, actually, three dark-adaptation curves, one on top of the other obtained for three different age groups. To a first approximation these three curves can be superimposed by shifting

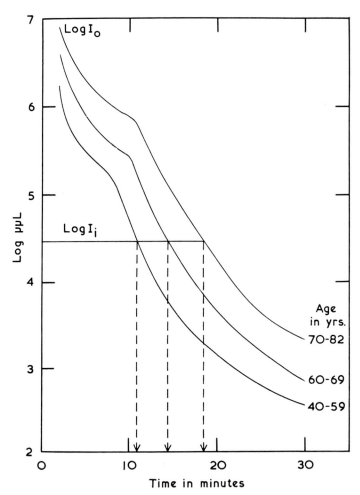

Figure 8. To show why older people take longer to reach a given level of dark-adaptation (after Birren and Shock, 1950).

them in a vertical direction, which is only another way of saying that as we age, so does the threshold rise. I am not here
concerned with the actual cause of the rise in threshold, but
with the demonstration that this rise may occasion a slowing
down in the speed of response. Supposing we have a mixed
population standing about in sunlight (I_0), and instruct them
to enter a cinema and to let us know when they can see the
faint light indicating the emergency exit. If they all enter the
cinema at once, then there is no doubt that the younger people
will spot the emergency light quite a few minutes before the
older ones, the luminance level of perception (I_i) being shown
in the afore-mentioned Figure. Although the rate of adaptation of
all people—subject to some remarks on this point which are
elaborated below—will at any time be independent of age (i. e.,
$\delta \log I/\delta t \neq F [A]$), the mere fact that the older people will
reach a given level of adaptation later than the younger ones will
cause a delay in their response, and this delay has to be distinguished carefully from the senile change in reaction time
mentioned earlier on. The delay in adaptation is due almost
wholly to changes in the quantity of light reaching the eye and
to the consequent apparent reduction in the rate of dark-adaptation. It should perhaps be mentioned in parentheses that this
delay in adaptation is not due to any neural or retinal factor.
Pillat, in particular, has suggested that the regeneration of visual
purple may be reduced as we get older, and, although this may
of course appear to be true when the rate of regeneration is measured by some of the means at our disposal, e.g., because of the
occasional senile scotoma, his view is quite unlikely to apply to
individual rods. There are sporadic measurements, due to Rushton (1961) and to Weale (1962), which show that an eye in its
sixth decade may regenerate its visual purple a little more slowly
than younger eyes in their twenties or thirties; but one cannot
exclude the possibility that this is due to one of the artefacts associated with Rushton's or with Weale's method (cf. Weale,
1962, 1964). It may be concluded that, to a first approximation,
there is no senile variation in the rate at which physiological dark-
adaptation takes place.

6. VISUAL ACUITY

Now not all visual behaviour, not all responses, take place under threshold intensity conditions. Most of the time when a visual performance is required the amount of light is adequate, not to say more than adequate, and the shortcomings of the aging eye as revealed under the rather stringent conditions of threshold experiments will be of little import in daylight and in circumstances of adequate artificial illumination. Nonetheless, even here it may be possible to detect a change in the speed of behaviour, and this may be due to a cause none other than a senile change in visual acuity. We have seen that the temporal resolving power is inherently age-stable and that such senile changes as are observed are explicable largely, if not wholly, in factors changing retinal illumination as we age. But this need not apply to visual acuity, although this function, sometimes referred to as the resolving power of the retina, also changes quite appreciably with retinal illumination. Even if one compensates for the factor of 3 or 4 mentioned earlier, if one increases the retinal illumination during measurements of visual acuity, one finds that the values obtained for visual acuity in the young are never reached in the old (Fankhauser and Schmidt, 1957; Ferree *et al.*, 1934).

The reasons here are a little sadder perhaps in their implications, because there is no remedy, and it is almost certain that visual acuity deteriorates in old age, not primarily because of retinal decay but because of the opacities, bubbles, and the like formed in the aging crystalline lens and vitreous humour. At present these are irreversible. They interfere with the smooth transmission of light across the dioptric media so that it gets scattered and the retinal image blurs, and no amount of additional illumination can compensate for the resulting loss in resolution. On the contrary, the more light that is pumped into the eye and passed through the lens, the greater the scatter with consequent discomfort for the subject under consideration. There is no evidence for a belief in impaired retinal resolution; but the latter can hardly excel if the retinal image formed is of poor quality. Unfortunately, it is not practicable or even meaningful to obtain a quantitative measure of the light scattered by the lens; that is to say, we cannot predict at present to what extent a given amount of scatter of light by the lens is going to interfere with visual resolving power. It is therefore impossible to make quantitative predictions of the extent to which visual acuity is going to suffer, contrary to what we have seen to be feasible in connection with conditions depending on the visual threshold. It is, nonetheless, plausible to suggest that if visual acuity is reduced, if for instance a scene has to be scanned for a prolonged period before a given decision can be reached, this is going to be manifested as a slowing down in the speed of behaviour.

7. CONCLUSION

I would be the last person to suggest that senile changes in behaviour are due wholly, or even mainly, to the sort of peripheral change which has been discussed. But I feel that one ought to insist on any reference to such senile changes in behaviour to be concerned with the aging of the whole of the afferent pathways in order to demonstrate that its effects are of no consequence as regards the overall picture, if this is indeed the case.

REFERENCES

Allen, M. J.: (1956) The influence of age on the speed of accommodation. *Amer. J. Optom.*, *33*:201-208.

Angel, A., Hems, D. A., Rouse, W., Woledge, R. C. and Weale, R. A.: (1959) Fusion frequency and light quantity. *Nature*, (*Lond.*), *184*: 1873-1874.

Arden, G. B. and Weale, R. A.: (1954) Variations of the latent period of vision. *Proc. Roy. Soc. BB.*, *142*:258-267.

Bellis, C. J.: (1933) Reaction time and chronological age. *Proc. Soc. Exp. Biol. Med.*, *30*:801-803.

Bernhard, C. G.: (1940) Contributions to the neurophysiology of the optic pathway. *Acta Physiol. Scand.*, *1*: Suppl. 1.

Birren, J. E. and Botwinick, J.: (1955) Age differences in finger, jaw and foot reaction time to auditory stimuli. *J. Geront.*, *10*:429-432.

Birren, J. E., Casperson, R. C. and Botwinick, J.: (1950) Age changes in pupil size. *J. Geront.*, *5*:216-221.

Birren, J. E. and Shock, N. W.: (1950) Age changes in rate and level of visual dark adaptation. *J. Appl. Physiol.*, *2*:407-411.

Brozek, J. and Keys, A.: (1945) Changes in flicker-fusion fusion frequency with age. *J. Consult. Psychol.*, *9*:87-90.

Brückner, R.: (1959) Über Methoden longitudinaler Altersforschung am Auge. *Ophthalmologica*, Basel, *138*:59-75.

Fankhauser, F. and Schmidt, Th.: (1957) Die Untersuchung der Funktionen des dunkeladaptierten Auges mit dem Adaptometer Goldmann-Weekers. *Ophthalmologica*, Basel, *133*:264-272.

Ferree, C. E., Rand, G. and Lewis, E. F.: (1934) The effect of increase of intensity of light and the visual acuity of presbyopic and non-presbyopic eyes. *Trans. Illum. Eng. Soc.*, *29*:296-313.

Fieandt, K. v., Huhtala, A., Kullberg, P. and Saar, K.: (1956) Personal tempo and phenomenal time at different age-levels. *Psychol. Inst.*, Univ. of Helsinki, Report No. 2.

Fischer, F. P.: (1948) Senescence of the eye. In *Modern Trends in Ophthalmology*, A. Sorsby, ed., London, Butterworth and Co., Vol. II.

Gunkel, R. D. and Gouras, P.: (1963) Changes in scotopic visibility thresholds with age. *Arch. Ophthal.*, *69*:4-9.

Hager, G.: (1959) Sehfunktionsänderungen beim physiologischen Altern. *Klin. Mbl. Augenheilk.*, *134*:609-615.

Hess, C.: (1911) *Gr. Saemisch Handb. Augenheilk.*, 3rd ed., pt. II, Ch. 9, 21-22.

Hylkema, B. S.: (1944) Klinische Anwendung der Bestimmung der Verschmelzungsfrequenz. *Graefe's Arch. Ophthal.*, *146*:110-127.

Kadlecová, V., Peleška, M. and Vaško, A.: (1958) Dependence on age of the diameter of the pupil in the dark. *Nature (Lond.)*, *182*:1520-1521.

Kornzweig, A. L.: (1954) Physiological effects of age on the visual process. *Sight-Saving Rev.*, *24*:130-138.

Kumnick, L. S.: (1956a) Aging and pupillary response to light and sound stimuli. *J. Geront.*, *11*:38-45.

Kumnick, L. S.: (1956b) Aging and the efficiency of the pupillary mechanism. *J. Geront.*, *11*:160-164.

Landis, C.: (1954) Determinants of the critical flicker-fusion threshold. *Physiol. Rev.*, *34*:259-286.

Larsson, S. and Österlind, G.: (1943) Studies in the causes of senile miosis and rigidity of the pupil. *Acta ophthal.*, *(Kbh.)*, *21*:1-25.

Leinhos, R.: (1959) Die Altersabhängigkeit des Augenpupillendurchmessers. *Optik*, *16*:669-671.

McFarland, R. A., Warren, A. B. and Karis, C.: (1958) Alterations in critical flicker frequency as a function of age and light:dark ratio. *J. Exp. Psychol.*, *56*:529-538.

Misiak, H.: (1947) Age and sex differences in critical flicker frequency. *J. Exp. Psychol.*, *37*:318-332.

Misiak, H.: (1951) The decrease of critical flicker frequency with age. *Science*, *113*:551-552.

Pillat, A.: (1952) Das Altern der Netzhaut des Menschen. *Klin. Wschr.*, *64*:856-857.

Robertson, C. J.: (1937) Effect of fatigue on the adjustment of the eye. *Arch. Ophthal.*, *17*:859-876.

Robertson, G. W. and Yudkin, J.: (1944) Effect of age upon dark adaptation. *J. Physiol.*, *103*:1-8.

Rones, B.: (1938) Senile changes and degeneration of the human eye. *Amer. J. Ophthal.*, *21*:239-255.

Rushton, W. A. H.: (1961) Dark-adaptation and the regeneration of rhodopsin. *J. Physiol.*, *156*:166-178.

Said, F. S. and Weale, R. A.: (1959) The variation with age of the spectral transmissivity of the living human crystalline lens. *Gerontologia*, *3*:213-231.

Stieve, R.: (1949) Über den Bau des menschlichen Ciliarmuskels, seine Veränderungen während des Lebens und seine Bedeutung für die Akkommodation. *Anat. Anz.*, *97*:69-79.

Stiles, W. S. and Burch, J. M.: (1959) N.P.L. Colour matching investigation: final report. *Optica Acta*, *6*:1-26.

Streiff, E. B. and Babel, J.: (1963) Gérontologie et gériatrie du fond de *l'oeil*. *Advances Ophthal.*, *13*:1-75.

Surwillo, W. W.: (1961) Frequency of the "alpha" rhythm, reaction time and age. *Nature*, (*Lond.*), *191*:823-824.

Wald, G.: (1949) The photochemistry of vision. *Docum. Ophthal.*, *3*:94-137.

Weale, R. A.: (1954) Light absorption by the lens of the human eye. *Optica Acta*, *1*:107-110.

Weale, R. A.: (1958) The effect of test size and adapting luminance on foveal critical fusion frequencies. *Nat. Phys. Lab. Symposium No. 8*, *2*:445-459.

Weale, R. A.: (1961a) Notes on the photometric significance of the human crystalline lens. *Vision Res.*, *1*:183-191.

Weale, R. A.: (1961b) Retinal illumination and age. *Trans. Illum. Eng. Soc.*, *26*:95-100.

Weale, R. A.: (1962) Photo-chemical changes in the dark-adapting human retina. *Vision Res.*, *2*:25-33.

Weale, R. A.: (1963) *The Aging Eye*. London, H. K. Lewis & Co., Ltd.

Weale, R. A.: Fundus reflectometry and vision. *Photochemistry and Photobiology*, in press.

Weekers, R. and Roussel, F.: (1946) Introduction à l'étude de la fréquence de fusion en clinique. *Ophthalmologica*, Basel, *112*:305-319.

Welford, A. T.: (1959) Psycho-motor performance. In *Handbook of Aging and the Individual*, J. E. Birren, ed., Chicago, University of Chicago Press.

17

LATENCY OF PUPILLARY REFLEX TO LIGHT STIMULATION AND ITS RELATIONSHIP TO AGING

RICHARD FEINBERG AND EDWARD PODOLAK

T HIS STUDY is concerned with the latency period of the pupillary contraction to light and the relationship of this latency period to aging. Some findings on pupillary latency periods related to light intensity, as well as to myopes with mydriasis and to an individual with nerve conduction disease, are described.

Analysis of the normal light reflex into its several components of speed and amplitude has been attempted for over 100 years. Techniques of pupillary measurement have been varied and have included: 1) entopic observation in which the observer subjectively measured his own pupillary diameter or reactions; 2) direct observation and measurement of the subject's pupil by ruler, scales, circles, holes, etc.; 3) photographic techniques, and, 4) pupillographs using various cinematographic or electronic devices. In 1956, Lowenstein and Loewenfeld developed the Electronic Pupillograph which was the prototype of the instrument used in this study. A typical curve of the signal output of the Electronic Pupillograph is shown in Figure 1.

In 1845, Listing with entopic observations determined that the latency period for pupillary contraction was about 0.4 second when the eye was opened suddenly, and that the contraction movement lasted about 0.5 second. Since then, numerous investigators have made determinations of the latency period and duration of contraction. Most of the investigators (Duke-Elder, 1949; Lowenstein and Loewenfeld, 1958, 1963; Shaknovitch; Talbot, 1938; Tschirren, 1947; Walsh, 1910; Weiler, 1910) agreed that the latency period of pupil contraction ranges from 0.2 to 0.3 second. Some authors, however, have reported shorter latency periods; for example, Fuchs (1903) reported 0.12 second, Dolének (1960) 0.126 to 0.295 second, and Gradle and Eisendraht (1923) 0.1875 second. At the other end of the time scale, von Arlt (1869) found the pupillary latency period to be 0.492 second and Donders (1864) 0.400 second.

There have been relatively few studies relating the pupillary latency period to other physiological factors. Schlesinger (1913) stated that it increased upon repeated stimulation; Loewenfeld and Lowenstein (1963) have maintained that it may vary among individuals and in the same individual under different experimental conditions.

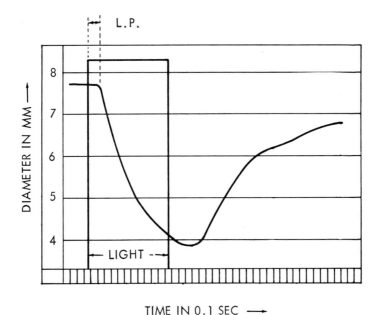

TIME IN 0.1 SEC ⟶

Figure 1. Diagram of pupillary reflex to light stimulus (after Lowenstein and Loewenfeld). L.P. = Latent Period in pupillary contraction.

Kumnick (1956) stated that the latency period of pupil constriction is *not* affected by increasing age[*] but is affected significantly by the pupillary conditions of restitution and decay of restitution at certain age levels.

METHOD

The over-all features of the instrumentation used for pupil latency measurements are shown in the block diagram of Figure 2 and the photograph of Figure 3. The basic instrument is the Electronic Pupillograph (10, 14). It consists of a scanner, an amplifier-detector assembly and a stimulator.

The scanning unit is a rotating drum with slits in its periphery through which a light beam is projected. This beam is divided into two identical paths which scan both irises in rectangular patterns, comprised of twelve horizontal lines, at a rate of sixty times per second. A Wratten 87C filter placed between the drum and the eye renders the scanning light invisible to the dark-adapted person. The light of the two scanning beams is reflected onto two photoelectric cells. The outputs of these cells are amplified in two identical channels and converted into DC analog voltages, whereby the voltage amplitudes are proportional to the largest horizontal diameters of the pupils.

The stimulator lamp energy is reflected from a mirror located just above the optical path of the infrared scanning unit. The same mirror is used to reflect a dim, red fixation light which is placed on the ceiling above the scanner at a distance of four feet. The line of regard and the direction of the stimulating light beam are 15° above horizontal.

The Grass Photic Stimulator (model PS-2) provided a high intensity flash of approximately one million peak candle power for 10 microseconds. The flash was seen by the left eye only, while measurements of latency period were obtained from the consensually reacting right pupil. For these measurements, the derivative of the Electronic Pupillograph scanner voltage was used rather than the analog voltage which represents the pupil

---

[*] Kumnick noted means of initial latency of pupil constriction to be 0.200 for age group 7.5—15.0 years; 0.222 for 18.1—28.2 years; 0.226 for 30.5—52.7 years; 0.226 for 70.4—90.8 years.

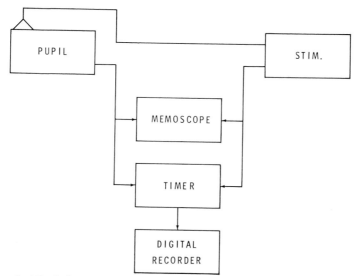

Figure 2. Block diagram of instrumentation for pupil latency measurement.

Figure 3. Photo of test apparatus.

diameter. The derivative voltage, representing the velocity of the pupil, was used as the following description indicates.

A signal coinciding with the stimulator light current is available at the External Monitor receptacle of the Grass Photic stimulator. This signal started both the sweep circuit of a Hughes Memoscope (model 105) and the "Start" circuit of a Beckman Berkeley Universal Timer (model 7350). The timer was stopped when the derivative pupil signal exceeded a pre-set voltage level of its "Stop" circuit. The time measured from the "Start" to the "Stop" signal was read out on a Digital Recorder (model 1452).

Initially, a comparison of the analog signal representing the pupil diameter and its derivative was made simultaneously to determine which of the two signals available from the Electronic Pupillograph was the more suitable for timing purposes. In this

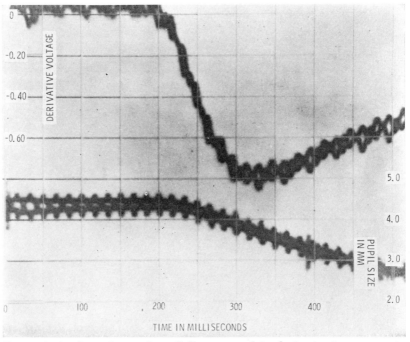

Figure 4. Analog voltage of pupil diameter and its derivative in response to high intensity light.

comparison for each flash of light from the Photic Stimulator two traces were generated on the dual beam Memoscope face, whereby the lower trace showed the analog voltage of the diameter, and the upper trace its derivative. It can be seen that the curve representing the derivative voltage has a much steeper slope than the analog signal of the diameter. The definition with which a single sweep can be resolved on the Memoscope is adequate for measurements within ± 3 milliseconds (Figure 5). The readings used for this study were taken from the Digital Recorder. For our purposes, this recorder had an accuracy of ± 0.0001 seconds. Figure 5 also shows that the 60 cycle per second scanning rate of the pupillograph modulates the derivative signal.

The timer has a crystal controlled oscillator operating at a frequency of 100,000 cycles per second; for the present application, a 10,000 cycles per second rate was used. A gate in the

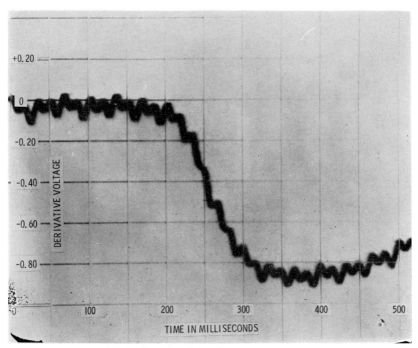

Figure 5. Definition of single sweep on memoscope.

timer was opened by the "Start" circuit when the Photo-Stimulator was triggered. The gate was closed by the timer "Stop" circuit when the voltage from the derivative signal exceeded a pre-set level of the "Stop" circuit. The counter, in the meantime, counted the number of cycles that passed from the crystal oscillator through the gate at a 10,000 cycle per second rate.

The "Stop" level of the timer was pre-set so that a derivative signal of -0.30 volts did not stop the timer, while -0.35 volts did stop it. A voltage of -0.35 was equivalent to a pupil contraction velocity of 3.5 mm. per second (manufacturer's specifications).

One of the advantages of using the derivative pupil signal is that the same "Stop" level on the timer can be used for all subjects. Once the diameter of the pupil attains equilibrium (in darkness), its derivative becomes zero and all measurements are taken from this zero point, i.e., *all measurements are independent of the initial absolute diameter of the pupil or of the iris color.*

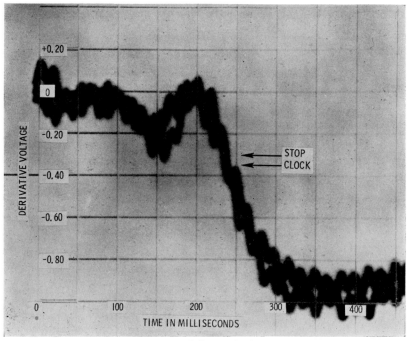

Figure 6. Presetting of "stop-clock" timing circuit.

RESULTS

Our sample consisted of 86 persons ranging from 14 to 67 years of age (Table 1). The average latency period in these subjects

TABLE 1
AGE OF SUBJECTS USED IN THIS EXPERIMENT

Age in Years	No. of Subjects
14-20	15
21-30	17
31-40	10
41-50	22
51-60	20
61+	2
	N=86

was 0.252 second, with a range from 0.214 to 0.314 second (Figure 7). It should be noted that the true latency periods are somewhat shorter than the values indicated in this communication. The latency period as determined in this experiment was the time interval from the start of stimulation to the moment when pupillary contraction had reached a speed of 3.5 mm. per

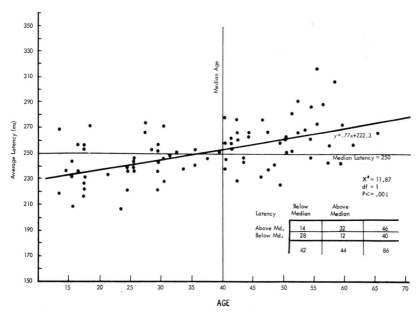

Figure 7. Scattergram of average pupil latency periods by age.

second. It is obvious that this time is longer than the period of pupillary inactivity that follows the initiation of stimulation. If we wish to redefine latency period as the time from photic stimulation to the first detectable response, we must re-examine our data. Figure 5 shows that the voltage level used for a single sample measurement was reached approximately 0.034 sec. after the moment of first noticeable change. Though it would have been preferable to trigger the "Stop" circuit of the counter by this first minute voltage change, it was necessary to chose the higher voltage in order to operate beyond the noise level of the system.

Consciously or unconsciously, most authors have run into similar difficulties. For example, it is impossible to detect with the unaided eye the exact moment of initiation of the contraction movement, especially when the stimulus intensity is low and the reactions shallow. Since, in addition, the latency period increases with decreasing stimulus brightness (Lowenfeld and Lowenstein, 1959), the large range of values for the pupillary latency period reported by competent authors is not surprising.

The prolongation of the latency period beyond its true value depends upon the steepness of the slope of increasing contraction velocity. For this reason mainly, we chose the maximal light intensity conveniently available for our experiment on aging. The values obtained on the readout of the Digital Recorder and those marked on the Memoscope at the −0.35 volt cutoff point agreed very well (maximal discrepancy ± 4 milliseconds), and since all of our normal subjects responded to the powerful light flashes by reactions with steep velocity slopes, the differences between the true latency periods and the mean times measured at the -0.35 volt cutoff point varied only little among individuals.

LATENCY PERIOD AND LIGHT INTENSITY

Even at the high brightness levels used in this experiment, the latency period tended to lengthen when the stimulus intensity was reduced. Figure 8 shows the responses of the pupil to five different flash light intensities ranging in intensity ratios from 1 to 80.

The logarithms of the relative intensities (10 log relative intensity in db) are 0, 6.0, 12.0, 16.8, and 19.0. Peak intensity

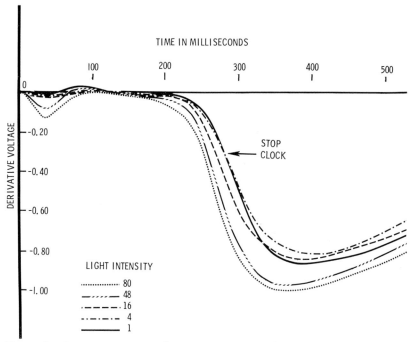

Figure 8. Composite curves of average response of pupil vs. light intensity.

with the highest setting is approximately one million peak candles measured on the axis of the parabola at a distance of 10 inches from the glass face plate. The latency values used at each intensity setting were means of 10 digital readings, a plot of which is shown in Figure 9. The standard deviation of the readings about each mean was approximately five milliseconds, and their standard deviations did not vary significantly from one intensity level to another.

LATENCY PERIOD OF PUPILLARY CONSTRICTION AND AGING

A scattergram (Fig. 7) of the average latency period by age shows a positive relationship ($r = .54$) between pupillary latency period and aging. As one grows older, his pupillary latency period increases. A chi-square of 11.87 (each variable split at the median) with one degree of freedom, a $p < .001$ shows that this is highly significant. The slope of this increase is shown by the regression equation $y = .77x + 222.3$.

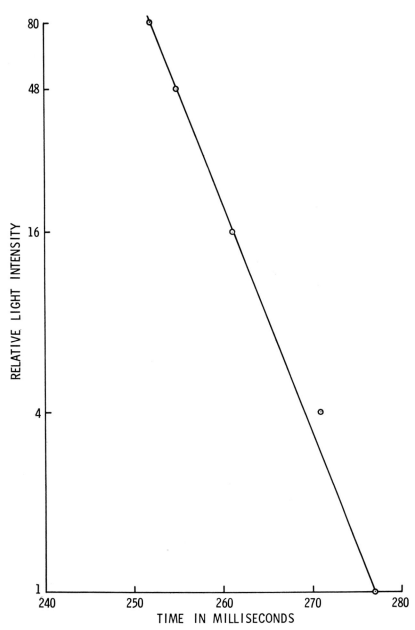

Figure 9. Means of pupillary latency vs. relative light intensity (one subject).

Moreover, if we compare the means for the extremes in the ages studied, namely, those under twenty-one and those over fifty years of age, we find that the older group definitely has a longer pupillary latency (0.273 sec.) than the younger group (0.238 sec.). Comparing the means of these two groups, a highly significant t value of 3.92 was found with 34 degrees of freedom. The probability that the two populations would have the same mean would be less than 1 in 1000.

If we compare the original pupil size and aging, we find that with aging, the pupil diameter decreases. Statistically, this may be expressed by a Pearsonian r of -0.55, a regression line $y = 0.36x + 7.5$, a chi-square of 11.20 (df $= 1$; $p < .001$).

The average latency of response to original pupil size in darkness shows a negative relationship.

A possible relationship between latency of response and myopia with mydriasis has been brought to our attention in five cases which we have studied. In each instance, regardless of age, the latency period has been longer than 0.260 sec. Whether these longer latency periods have occurred by chance or not will have to be determined by further studies.

Longer latency period in pupillary constriction as a possible correlate of nerve conduction disease was introduced to us by a physician, who, himself, was the victim of Charcot-Marie-Tooth disease, a progressive disorder that symmetrically affects only the distal muscles of the legs and occasionally the arms. It is associated with pathologic changes in the anterior horn cells, peripheral neuromuscular units, posterior columns and frequently other tracts of the spinal cord including the pyramidal (Baker, 1962). Our patient showed, at the age of fifty-one, a pupillary latency period of 0.299 sec.

CONCLUSIONS

1) A method is described for measuring pupillary contraction latency period regardless of initial absolute pupil diameter.

2) Pupillary contraction latency period increases with age. The data presented show that the normal pupil, as usually found in healthy young people, has a shorter latency than is found in older normal subjects.

3) Original pupil size decreases with age.

4) A limited number of subjects with myopia coupled with mydriasis had relatively long latency periods.

5) One subject with a nerve conduction disease was found to have a relatively long latency period.

REFERENCES

Adler, F. H.: (1953) *Physiology of the Eye*. Mosby and Co., p. 195.

van Arlt, F., Jr.: (1869) Beitrag zur Kentniss der Zeitverhältnisse bei den Bewegungen der Iris. *Graefe Arch. Ophthal.*, 15:294-317.

Baker, A. B., ed.: (1962) *Clinical Neurology*. New York, Hoeber-Harper, pp. 1760-61.

Bender, W. R. G.: (1933) The effect of pain and emotional stimuli and alcohol upon pupillary reflex activity. *Psychol. Monogr.*, 44:2:1-32.

Dolének, A.: (1960) Beitrag zur Pupillographie. *Ophthalmologica, 139*: 76-83.

Donders, F. C.: (1864) On the anomalies of accommodation and refraction of the eye. *The New Sydenham Soc. London*, 22:573-583.

Duke-Elder, Sir S. W.: (1949) *Textbook of Ophthalmology*, Vol. IV, pp. 371-376.

Fuchs, A.: (1903) Die Messung der Pupillengrösse und Zeitbestimmung der Licht-reaktion der Pupillen bein einzelnen Psychosen und Nerven-krankheiten. *Jahrbücher f. Psychiat.*, 24:326-458.

Gradle, H. S. and Eisendraht, E. B.: (1923) Die Reaktionszeit der norm-alen Pupille. *Vorlaufige Mitt. Hbl. Augenheilk.*, 71:311.

King, G. W.: (1959) Recording pupil changes for clinical diagnosis. *Electronics, 32:67*.

Kumnick, L. S.: (1956) Aging and the latency and duration of pupil con-striction in response to light and sound stimuli. *J. Geront., 11:391*.

Listing, J. B.: (——) Beitrag zur Physiologischen Optik. Besonderen Abdruck, aus d. Göttingen Studien; quoted after Loewenfeld.

Loewenfeld, I. E. and Lowenstein, O.: Personal communications.

Lowenstein, O. and Loewenfeld, I. E.: (July 1959) Scoptic and photopic thresholds of the pupillary light reflex in normal man. *Amer. J. Ophthal., 48:1*, Part II.

Lowenstein, O. and Loewenfeld, I. E.: (1958) Electronic pupillography. A new instrument and some clinical applications. *Arch. Ophth. (New York)*, 59:353-363.

Morone, G.: (1948) Ricerche pupillografiche nell'abbagliamento. *Boll. Oculist, 27:639-652*.

Acknowledgement: We are indebted to Miss Anne Alderman for her assistance in compiling the statistical data.

Ogle, K. and Burke, D.: Comparison of pupillary and visual light thresholds in the periphery. (Presentation at the 1963 Colloquium on the Pupil., N.Y.C.

Shaknovitch, V. R.: Cinematographic investigation of pupillary reaction to convergence. *J. Physiol. (USSR)*, 44:170-172.

Schlesinger, E.: (1913) Über den Schwellenwart der Pupillenreaktion und die Ausdehnung des pupillomotorischen Besirkes der Retina. Untersuchungen auf Grund einer neuen Methodik. *Deutsch. Med. Wschr.*, 163-165; *Neurol. Zbl.*, 316.

Smith-Kline Precision Co.: (1962) *Instruction Manual.* Aug. 20.

Talbot, S. A.: (1938) Cinematography of the pupil. *Amer. J. Physiol.*, 123:200.

Tschirren, B.: (1947) Die fortlaufende Registrierung des Pupillen-reflexes. *Helv. Physiol. Pharmacol. Acta*, 5:C57-C58.

Walsh, F. G.: (1910) *Clinical Neuroophthalmology.* Williams & Wilkins, pp. 152-154.

Weiler, K.: (1910) *Untersuchungen der Pupille und der Irisbewegungen beim Menschen.* Berlin. Also *Zeitschr. Ges. Neurol. Psychiat. II:*101-274.

18

FUNCTIONAL AND STRUCTURAL CHANGES IN MOTOR NEURONS WITH AGE

Ernest Retzlaff and Joan Fontaine

INTRODUCTION

IT IS postulated that physiological aging in the central and peripheral nervous system is a uniform process throughout the life span of the mammalian organism and that the normal aging process results in a final breakdown of nervous integrative mechanisms. In addition, it is hypothesized that controlled exercise exerts a beneficial effect on the organism and delays the onset of physiological aging enabling the organism to function in an optimal manner for a greater part of its life span than when no special exercise is performed. While a controlled exercise program may only slightly increase the total life span of the organism, it will effectively increase the functional capacity of the mammal for a greater proportion of its total life.

In order to study the effects of the normal aging process on the function and structure of the nervous system, a longitudinal study was started in 1957 using the Sprague-Dawley albino rat as the experimental animal. The work presented in this paper is based primarily on the results obtained from litter mate studies. The research plan includes two variables, age and exercise. The exercise program consists of dividing each litter into two groups; one group having only cage activity and a second group being exercised. A motor-driven, variable-speed, stainless-steel, four-

340

compartment, drum-exerciser holding 12-15 rats has been constructed in our instrument shop (Fig. 1). Two daily exercise periods of ten minutes each is designated as exercise. The rats readily learn to run in the drum and no training period is reqiured. The total distance traveled by the rats during each ten minute period is 115 meters.

ANIMAL COLONY

The conditions under which these rats live are the most important factor in establishing the reliability of the experimental results. A population of 450 to 500 rats is housed in a specially constructed isolation room which is completely separate from other animal rooms. With the exception of the original breeding stock, no new animals have been added to the colony. The animals are not removed from this room until actually used in

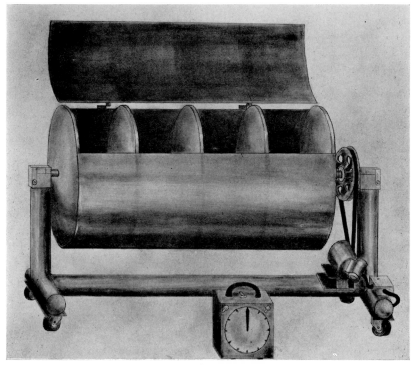

Figure 1. Rat exerciser.

an experiment, nor are they returned after leaving. The rat diet consists of an *ad libitum* diet of Rockland D-free ration with a supplement of apples and oranges fed on alternate days. The room temperature is maintained at 76° F. (± 0.5° F.) with a relative humidity of 50 per cent by means of an air-conditioning unit (heating and cooling) which uses 100 per cent filtered outside air. Apparently, the rats thrive under these controlled conditions as evidenced by the general health of the colony.

A light-dark cycle of twelve hours each is controlled by an automatic programming clock. All work is done during the light part of the time schedule which allows a period of at least twelve hours that the animals are undisturbed. Loud noises and other disturbances are minimized by limiting access to the room to authorized personnel. Special precautions are taken to avoid infection of the aging colony rats by contact with other animals or direct contact with the skin of humans touching the rats. There have been no deaths that can be attributed to respiratory infection. While the colony is not germ-free, it is considered to be essentially free of respiratory disease.

The rats are housed in stainless steel cages which hold four to eight rats. The cages and their mobile racks are washed and steam sterilized every second day. Smaller cages of stainless steel are used as delivery cages and to house the mother and pups until weaning (30 days). All work is done by biology or preprofessional school students. At the age of thirty days, each rat is numbered using a combination ear punch-tattoo system. Each litter is divided into exercise and no exercise groups and the experimental use of each animal is determined.

The data obtained from the rats in the aging colony is being recorded on McBee Keysort cards which provide a convenient and accurate means of keeping the history of each animal. An identification card is made for each rat which gives its number, sex, date of birth, date and cause of death, number of male and female pups in its litter, parentage (including age of parents and number of litters delivered before) and the planned experimental use. Additional data recorded on this card includes weekly (or more often if required) weight records, and the exercise group to which the animal belongs (Fig. 2).

Otitis Media

We completed a study concerning the incidence and the control of *Otitis media* which was a potential problem in our colony and is reported to be of major concern in similar colonies (Retzlaff, 1960). The organism isolated from the infected middle ear has been tentatively identified as belong to the genus *Streptobaccilus.* The blood from these animals yielded an organism identified as *Staphyloccus aureus.* It is proposed that the infection in the isolated rat colony was brought in by a natural skin microflora present on the hands of the animal handlers. As a method for control of the infection, all persons who touch the rats directly or indirectly are required to wear autoclavable rubber surgical gloves. The introduction of this simple control

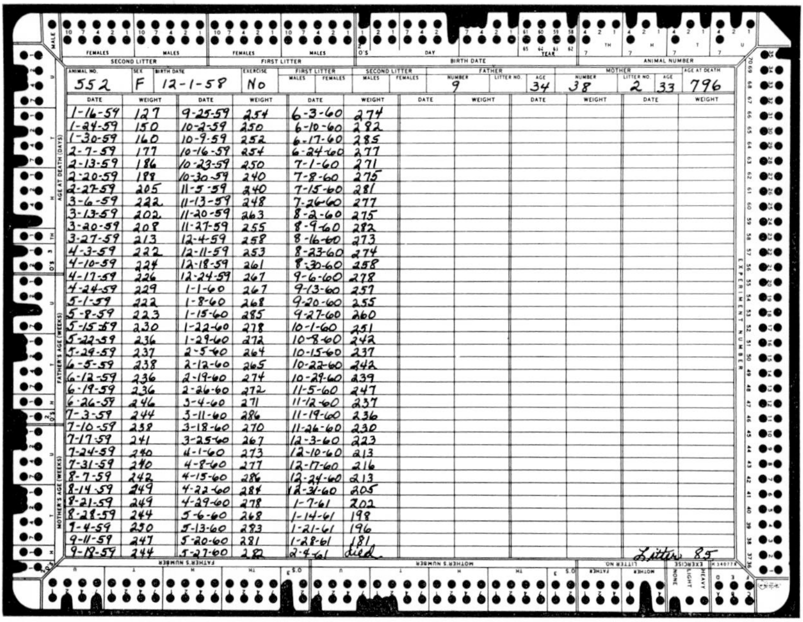

ANIMAL NO.	SEX	BIRTH DATE	EXERCISE	FIRST LITTER MALES	FIRST LITTER FEMALES	SECOND LITTER MALES	SECOND LITTER FEMALES	FATHER NUMBER	FATHER LITTER NO.	FATHER AGE	MOTHER NUMBER	MOTHER LITTER NO.	MOTHER AGE	AGE AT DEATH
552	F	12-1-58	No					9		34	38	2	33	796

DATE	WEIGHT	DATE	WEIGHT	DATE	WEIGHT	DATE	WEIGHT	DATE	WEIGHT	DATE	WEIGHT
1-16-59	127	9-25-59	254	6-3-60	274						
1-24-59	150	10-2-59	250	6-10-60	282						
1-30-59	160	10-9-59	252	6-17-60	285						
2-7-59	177	10-16-59	254	6-24-60	277						
2-13-59	186	10-23-59	250	7-1-60	271						
2-20-59	188	10-30-59	240	7-8-60	275						
2-27-59	205	11-5-59	240	7-15-60	281						
3-6-59	222	11-13-59	248	7-26-60	277						
3-13-59	202	11-20-59	263	8-2-60	275						
3-20-59	208	11-27-59	255	8-9-60	282						
3-27-59	213	12-4-59	258	8-16-60	273						
4-3-59	222	12-11-59	253	8-23-60	274						
4-10-59	224	12-18-59	261	8-30-60	258						
4-17-59	226	12-24-59	267	9-6-60	278						
4-24-59	229	1-1-60	267	9-13-60	257						
5-1-59	222	1-8-60	268	9-20-60	255						
5-8-59	223	1-15-60	285	9-27-60	260						
5-15-59	230	1-22-60	278	10-1-60	251						
5-22-59	236	1-29-60	272	10-8-60	242						
5-29-59	237	2-5-60	264	10-15-60	237						
6-5-59	238	2-12-60	265	10-22-60	242						
6-12-59	236	2-19-60	274	10-29-60	239						
6-19-59	236	2-26-60	272	11-5-60	247						
6-26-59	246	3-4-60	271	11-12-60	237						
7-3-59	244	3-11-60	286	11-19-60	236						
7-10-59	238	3-18-60	270	11-26-60	230						
7-17-59	241	3-25-60	267	12-3-60	223						
7-24-59	240	4-1-60	273	12-10-60	213						
7-31-59	240	4-8-60	277	12-17-60	216						
8-7-59	242	4-15-60	286	12-24-60	213						
8-14-59	249	4-22-60	284	12-31-60	205						
8-21-59	249	4-29-60	278	1-7-61	202						
8-28-59	244	5-6-60	268	1-14-61	198						
9-4-59	250	5-13-60	283	1-21-61	196						
9-11-59	247	5-20-60	281	1-28-61	181						
9-18-59	244	5-27-60	282	2-4-61	died						

Litter 85

Figure 2. McBee Keysort Card. The identification card made for each rat gives its number, sex, date of birth, date and cause of death, number of male and female pups in its litter, parentage (including age of parents and number of litters delivered before) and the planned experimental use. Additional data recorded on this card includes weekly (or more often if required) weight records and the exercise group to which the animal belongs.

method has reduced the incidence of infection from roughly 10 per cent of the animals between six to eight months of age to 0 per cent in a period of ninety days. Apparently the rats in the age group of six to eight months are the most susceptible to this infection. Also, it was found that the animals receiving exercise each day were more naturally resistant while those living a sedentary cage-life were more susceptible to the infection. Since this colony is housed in an isolation room and is self-perpetuating, there is no possibility of infection from other animals. The incidence of *Otitis media* is zero and the incidence of respiratory infection is less than 0.5 per cent per month.

NEUROHISTOLOGICAL STUDIES

The 100 male and female rats used in this study have an age span of 60 to 720 days and are representatives of the no exercise and exercise groups. The animals were preselected from the total population to avoid bias.

A method has been developed which permits the preservation of the entire rat carcass for future study by qualified investigators supported by NIH aging research grants. Briefly, the method involves the surgical removal of the desired tissue from the anesthetized rats (Urethane-Chlorolose) for processing by the freeze-dehydration method (Retzlaff, 1960a) and then, after ligating the cut blood vessels, the entire rat is perfused via the heart. The initial perfusate is chilled (5° C) isotonic saline solution containing 5 per cent (w/v) chloral hydrate. This solution serves to rapidly cool the animal and flush the circulatory system. The chloral hydrate has a vasodilatory effect. This perfusion is followed by a fixing solution of either 10 per cent formalin or Bouin's solution, also at 5° C.

The chemically fixed tissues are dehydrated in dioxane and infiltrated with a mixture of 75 per cent Harleco paraffin and 25 per cent Fisher tissue mat (52° C. melting point) using an Autotechnicon to facilitate this aspect of the work. The frozen-dried tissues are infiltrated using the same paraffin mixture but no chemical dehydrant is required. The tissues are embedded and stored in 24mm Peel-A-Way plastic embedding molds.

In this study, the lumbar spinal enlargement is sectioned serially, mounted on glass slides and differentially stained in batches of 400 to 500 slides using the protargol method.

Deparaffinized sections, after hydration in 3 changes of distilled water, 2 minutes each, are placed in freshly prepared 0.5% aqueous protargol with a 2 x 2 inch copper plate in the glass container. Incubate in a 37° C oven 18-24 hours. Wash 10 minutes in running water, 2 changes of distilled water, 5 minutes each, and one change of buffered* water for 2 minutes. Reduce in silver gelatin** mixture for 30 seconds. Wash in 4 changes of distilled water, 5 minutes each. Tone in 0.2% gold chloride 2 minutes. Wash in 2 changes distilled water, 5 minutes each. Place in 2% oxalic acid for 15 seconds, wash in 2 changes distilled water, 5 minutes each and finally treat in 5% sodium thiosulfate, 2 changes, 5 minutes each. Wash in running water for 5 minutes, dehydrate and cover.

*Buffered water—17 ml of 5M Acetic Acid (12 ml to 1000 ml distilled water) added to 3 ml of sodium acetate (16 grams to 1000 ml distilled water). Take 14 ml of stock buffer to 1000 ml distilled water. The pH is approximately 4.1.

**The silver gelatin reducing solution, using buffered water, is prepared as follows:
(1) 400 ml 3% gelatin heated to 70° C.
(2) 100 ml 2% AgNO$_3$
(3) 40 ml 1% hydroquinone
Stir (2) and (3) together and add to (1) immediately before use.

Bodian, D.: *J. Comp. Neurol.,* 68:117, 1937.
Pearson, A., and O'Neil, S. L.: *Anat. Rec.,* 95:297, 1946.

The entire central nervous system of 100 rats has been embedded and stored in paraffin as have fifty-three representative tissue samples from thirty-one rats. In all cases the entire remaining rat carcass is wet stored for possible future study.

Results of the neurohistological study suggests that the differential staining of motor neurons is dependent upon both the age of the rat and the exercise group to which it belongs. These results support the hypothesis that aging is a gradual process which is characterized by a gradual reduction of the reflex response and that exercise delays the onset of this aging process. Our studies have shown that there is a loss of both sensory and motor neuron large fibers and that there is an infiltration of the spinal roots by connective tissue.

Neurohistological studies of protargol stained lumbar spinal motor neurons from rats of different ages and exercise groups show that age and exercise alter the staining reaction of these neurons. Figure 3, a low power photomicrograph of the lumbar motor cells, demonstrates the typical staining seen in rats up to 14 months of age whether exercised or not. In this instance, some motor cells have deeply stained dendrites and cell bodies and a lightly colored axon hillock and proximal portion of the axon. In contrast, other motor cells have lightly stained dendrites and cell bodies and a deeply colored axonal end of the cell. We propose that this differential staining reaction is an indication of normal functioning motor neurons.

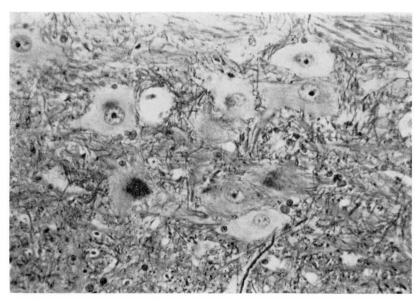

Figure 3. Spinal motor cells seen in rats aged up to 14 months showing typical light and dark differential staining reaction to protargol.   200X

A typical picture of the effects of exercise on the motor neuron staining reaction from a rat twenty months of age is seen in Figure 4. Here the differential staining reaction is evident in the two motor cells.

Motor cells from a rat of comparable age receiving no special exercise are shown in Figure 5. Differential staining does not occur in these cells. It should be noted that the neurons seen in both Figures 4 and 5 have synaptic endings on their surfaces. A high magnification photograph of a ventral horn cell (Fig. 6) from a senile male rat over 900 days of age shows a large number of afferent fiber end boutons on its surface.

These results show that rats, whether exercised or not, display differentially stained motor neurons up to fourteen months of age. In contrast, rats older than twenty months in the no exercise group have few differentially stained neurons while the motor cells of the exercise group of the same age are similar to those seen in the younger rats.

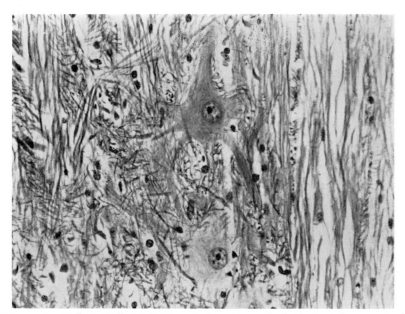

Figure 4. Differentially stained spinal motor cells from heavily exercised male rat, age twenty months, protargol.   300X

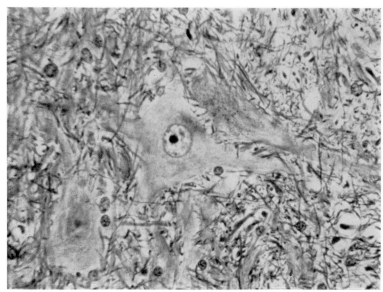

Figure 5. Non-differentially stained spinal motor cells from no exercise male rat, age twenty months. Note synaptic endings. Protargol.   300X

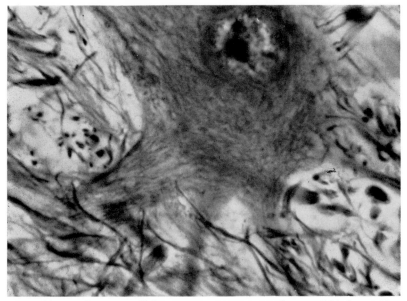

Figure 6. Spinal motor cell from rat, no exercise male, age 900 days. Note the synaptic endings. Protargol.   900X

From these results and from work previously reported (Retzlaff, 1960b, 1960c, 1962, 1963) the differential staining reaction of motor neurons is an indication of neuronal excitation and inhibition. Motor integration is dependent upon the ability of the neurons involved to be either excited or inhibited. Thus, as part of the normal aging process the nerve structures involved lose their ability to respond to normal levels of excitatory or inhibitory stimulus. It is suggested that controlled exercise delays the onset of physiological aging.

CONDUCTION VELOCITY

Sciatic nerve conduction velocity measurements have been done on litter mate male rats of the no exercise and exercise groups. These animals are anesthetized by using a mixture consisting of 5 grams Urethane and 0.25 gram alpha chlorolose in 5 cc of isotonic saline containing 5 per cent dextrose at 37° C. Anesthesia is induced by intraperitoneal injection of 2.2 cc K of body weight. For rats weighing over 500 grams, it is necessary to reduce the volume of the anesthetic by one-third.

Bipolar platinum stimulating and recording electrodes in an adjustable plastic holder are used in the conduction velocity measurements. The nerve potentials, after amplification, are photographed from a dual trace cathode ray oscilloscope. During the entire procedure, the body temperature of the rat is maintained at 38°C.

Results of a study on a group of sixteen litter mate male exercise and no exercise rats show that the exercised rats sixteen months of age have a large fiber sciatic nerve conduction velocity range of 86 to 52 m/sec with an average velocity of 70 m/sec. In contrast, the most rapid conducting fibers in the no exercise rats ranged from 85 to 37 m/sec with an average of 51 m/sec. The slower conducting fibers in both the exercised and no exercise rats have a conduction velocity of 13 m/sec. This suggests that exercise has no effect on the conduction velocity of the smaller diameter sciatic nerve axons.

These data are in agreement with Birren and Wall (1956) in their study of sciatic nerve conduction velocities in that they obtained a mean value of 59 m/sec in rats 350 days of age. How-

ever, in results of a more limited sample of older rats, we find
that the fastest conducting fibers average 20 m/sec at 900 days in
the no exercise group while the exercise group have an average
velocity of 45 m/sec.

AVERAGE LIFE SPAN

In a study involving the life span of fifty heavy and no exercise litter mate male rats, we find that exercised rats have a
higher average life span than the no exercise animals. These
animals died from natural causes with no detectable gross
pathology or respiratory infection. The results of this work are
summarized below:

	Age at Death (Days)	Age at Peak Weight (Days)	Peak Weight (Grams)
Heavy Exercise			
Range	336-773	247-673	331-611
Average	549	390	440
No Exercise			
Range	276-769	210-525	290-475
Average	494	339	411

It is evident from this litter mate sample that exercise is effective in increasing the average life span of these rats but it should
be noted that the total life span is only slightly increased. However, even a few days increase is notable at the extreme end of
the age curve.

The significance of the peak weight and the age at which it is
reached lies in the fact that in our colony the animal weight is a
reliable index of the general condition of the rats and may provide a means for predicting the life expectancy of the rat. The
observation that the exercised rats attain a peak weight at a
later date than the no exercise rats is important in that it is a reflection of muscular development of the rat and probably is significant in the functioning of the neuromuscular mechanisms. A subjective comparison of litter mates in exercise and no exercise
groups shows that the exercise animals are more alert and more

active when handled. Evidently, the amount of stimulation provided by our exercise program has a beneficial effect on the physical and psychological development of these rats (Fig. 7).

The results of these studies on the physiological aging process in the disease free albino rat indicate that controlled exercise exerts a beneficial effect on this mammalian organism in that it enhances the spinal motor neuron integrative capacity, increases the motor axon large fiber conduction velocity and increases the average life span.

The authors gratefully acknowledge the technical assistant of Wilmer Furuta, Kenneth Laudenbach, Allen Prebus, Charles Lachmeyer, Sidney Lee and Erna Palmer. Dr. Chauncey D. Leake's interest and encouragement has been of inestimable value in completion of these studies.

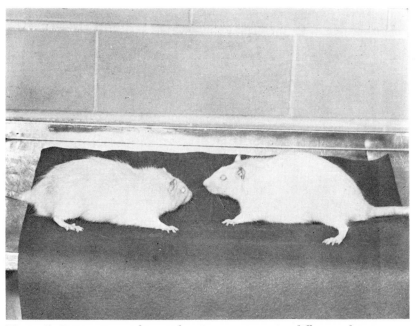

Figure 7. Litter mate male rats showing apparent size difference between no exercise and exercise. Exercised rat (right) weighs 445 grams while the no exercise rat weighs 370 grams.

REFERENCES CITED

Retzlaff, E., Rogols, S. and Pasamanick, B.: (1960a) *Otitis media* in aging albino rats. *Geriatrics, 15:*205-209.

———— and Fontaine, Joan: (1960b) Differential staining reaction demonstrating reciprocal activity in Mauthner's Cells. *Experientia, 16:*359-364.

———— and Fontaine, Joan: (1960c) Reciprocal inhibition as indicated by a differential staining reaction. *Science, 131:*104-105.

————, Fontaine, J., Pasamanick, B. and Leake, C. D.: (1963) Structural and functional changes in reciprocal innervation produced by localized tetanus in the albino rat. *Fed. Proc., 22:*280.

————, Fontaine, Joan and Pasamanick, Benjamin: (1962) Differential staining in aging motor neurons. *J. Geront., 17:*458.

Birren, James E. and Wall, Patrick D.: (1956) Age changes in conduction velocity, refractory period, number of fibers, connective tissue space, and blood vessels in sciatic nerve of rats. *J. Comp. Neurol., 104:*1-16.

GENERAL REFERENCES

Handbook of Aging and the Individual. James E. Birren, ed., Chicago, University of Chicago Press, 1959, 939 pages.

Medical and Clinical Aspects of Aging. Herman T. Blumenthal, ed., New York, Columbia Univ. Press, 1962, 690 pages.

Biological Aspects of Aging. Nathan B. Shock, ed., New York, Columbia Univ. Press, 1962, 391 pages.

This work was supported in part by NIH Grants M-4592 and MH 07871.

19

THE ROLE OF SIMPLE TESTS MEASURING SPEED OF PERFORMANCE IN THE ASSESSMENT OF BIOLOGICAL VIGOUR: A FACTORIAL STUDY IN ELDERLY WOMEN

Eeva Jalavisto

It is obvious that the vigour of people varies and is differently affected by aging. It would certainly be desirable to predict or to assess the deterioration brought about by the aging process, but so far no relevant method is available. The problem has usually been attacked by studying various tests of function in healthy people of differing age. It is then postulated (implicitly or explicitly) that if a test correlates with age and an individual shows better than average performance in such a test he is biologically younger than someone whose performance is less good (*Murray,* 1951). However, there is no criterion according to which the relative value of such tests could be evaluated. The long-term approach with follow-up and retesting of the subjects, is on the other hand very tedious and extremely time consuming. I started my studies in the hope of overcoming the difficulty inherent in the longitudinal approach by analyzing factorially the scores of many tests and variables characterizing the experimental subjects. I thought that if among the variables were included one such as familial longevity (or parental age at death) which is particularly often associated with long life (see *Dublin, Lotka* and *Spiegelman,* 1949), I might obtain "a familial longevity factor" which then would represent a factor of "biological vigour."

The rôle of those tests which load on this factor would then more likely be of greater importance for assessment of biological vigour than tests which do not load on the factor. If, on the other hand, no such factor comes out, we might get at least an *ageing factor* indicating which tests are connected with the deterioration of function with age.

One of the problems when dealing with ageing is the multitude of disease conditions in the aged. According to a Finnish survey some 67 per cent of people over sixty-five years of age complain of ill-health (Anon. 1953). However, there are nearly always constitutional factors involved in disease. Thus, if we examine only the one-third of old people who are healthy we probably lose much of the constitutional variation which affects ageing. One of the merits of a factorial study is that it makes a primary selection of "healthy" subjects unnecessary—in fact it makes it necessary *not* to make such a selection. This again has a further advantage. Very often when one has found that a test connected with sensory, motor or general central nervous system function, shows obvious deterioration, one is intrigued by the question: does this poor performance perhaps result from some general impairment, let us say, circulatory or respiratory insufficiency? This question has been dealt with by *Simonson* in regard to flicker fusion frequency (*Enzer, Simonson* and *Blakenstein,* 1941) and motor performance (*Simonson* and *Enzer,* 1941) and by *Birren* and *Spieth* (1962) in regard to response speed. The factorial approach offers the possibility of comparing the loadings of many tests at the same time on factors representing some disease entities such as hypertension, encephalopathy etc., and biological relationships. It thus permits evaluation of the roles of specific conditions in determining performance.

A difficulty in ageing studies is the interplay of bad living habits and their sequalae with ageing proper. That smoking means an obvious health hazard cannot be doubted and it may influence, e.g., respiratory function tests to an extent that it would be desirable to perform the studies on non-smokers only. But if we do this we may introduce unknown biasses in our sample since non-smokers and smokers may differ in other characteristics as well. There is only one possibility to avoid such bias while dealing with non-smokers only. It is to have old *women* as experimental subjects since because (at least in Finland) they very rarely smoke.

It is a well-known observation that everything requiring speed, be it an intellectual or motor performance, is usually impaired in old people. The question naturally arises whether there is some *fundamental common prosess which is slowed down with ageing.* Particularly clear is the slowing of more complicated mental tests. But even simpler acts, e.g., the simple reaction time usually increases with age. However, the slowing effect of ageing seems to become less as one proceeds from more complicated situations to simple reflex acts. Thus, for example, *Hügin, Norris* and *Shock* (1962) showed that the plantar flexion reflex time does not increase with age whereas the reaction time to visual stimuli or touch does do so. We noticed in a previous study that the reaction time was shortened, and approached the plantar reflex time, if the reaction time was recorded with a falling ruler and the subject, instead of seeing that the ruler fall, could feel it fall, i.e., a proprioceptive-tactile stimulus was substituted for the visual. However, the difference between the old and young age groups persisted (*Jalavisto, Forsén, Lindqvist, Makkonen* and *Tallqvist,* 1962.)

The assumption that there is a common process affecting speed of behavior implies that all tests which require speed should be intercorrelated. However, because they are all age-dependent, crude correlation coefficients are not informative. One could, naturally, calculate the partial correlation coefficients with elimination of the age dimension, but the factorial approach is probably more efficient. In factor analysis, intercorrelation if genuine, would manifest itself in a "speed-factor." Again, if the slowing of response time is an outcome of some pathologic circulatory or respiratory impairment becoming more common in the old, the "speed-tests" would load on the respective "disease"-factor.

MATERIALS AND METHODS

The purpose of the present paper is to deal with tests in which speed of response is required. To this category obviously belong tests of maximal tapping rate, reaction time to light stimuli and reaction time in grasping a falling ruler. Although less obviously, the flicker fusion frequency might be included in this category of tests. Tentatively, and for comparison, a test in which the frequency of change per minute in right and left eye dominance is recorded, i.e., the so-called "retinal rivalry"—test (*Eysenck, Granger* and *Brengelmann*, 1957), and a measurement of hearing loss (decibels, 4000 cps.) were included.

The subjects were 130 women aged 40-93 years, inmates in old peoples homes and members of certain women's clubs (e.g., "mothers' clubs"). All were ambulant and not acutely ill. A few hospitalized senile patients were included. Height, weight, blood pressure (systolic, diastolic and pulse pressures) vital capacity, determination of swaying amplitude, of the duration of spiral aftereffect, memory for simple picture patterns (Meumann-test), memory for numbers (reversed order), abstracting ability (series of pictures with increasing difficulty of concept formation) were recorded for all subjects. A thorough medical history was also taken for each subject and rated so that the highest score (4) indicated absence of any history of disease. The age at death of both parents was noted, and questions were asked about relatives on both paternal and maternal sides who had attained the age of eighty years and over. On these data "familial longevity" was rated so that the highest score (3) was given when there were relatives eighty years and over in both parental lines. The presence or absence in the subject of headache, dizziness and sleeplessness were each recorded. The socio-economic status was rated by giving scores in which the highest score (3) indicated middle class standards and the score (1) lowest economic and cultural level.

Product moment correlations were calculated between each of the twenty-five variables mentioned above. Six factors were extracted and the orthogonal rotations were performed by applying the "Varimax" criterion which is an analytical principal axes method. The highest correlation coefficient of each variable was taken as the estimate of communality. The "Elliott 803" computer was used for making the calculations.

In a smaller series (n = 91) more variables and tests including psychological questionnaires constructed to reveal agressiveness, emotionality, fears, compulsions, sociability, dependency and ambitions were applied and analyzed to yield eight factors

(*Jalavisto, Lindqvist, Makkonen,* to be published). In that paper further particulars of the methods used will be given.

RESULTS

The correlations of the various tests scores with age are shown in Table 1. The coefficients for the "speed-tests," memory and other psychological tests are shown in the first column, those of the cardiovascular-pulmonary and constitutional variables in the second and the rest in the third column.

The only variable in the second and third column which equals the general level of the correlation coefficients in the speed and mental capacity tests is *vital capacity.* Most of the tests in the group of mental and speed tests and vital capacity are also intercorrelated as shown by Table 2. Some of the correlations such as

TABLE 1

	r age		r age		r age
Memory, pictures	—.55	Vital capacity	—.54	Socio-economic status	—.27
Hearing loss, 4000 cps.	.55	Pulse pressure	.34	Swaying amplitude	.25
Flicker fusion f.		Sy. B.P.	.35	Familial longevity	—.24
(CFF)	—.48	Height	—.30	Medical history	—.20
Reaction time, ruler	.48	Di. B.P.	.10	(lack of)	
"Retinal rivalry"	—.47	Overweight (%)	.07	Dizziness	.18
Abstracting ability	—.44			Sleeplessness	.18
Max. tapping speed	—.44			Spiral after-effect	.18
Memory, numbers,				(duration)	
(reversed order)	—.41			Parental longevity	.01
Reaction time, light	.35			Headache	—.01

TABLE 2

INTERCORRELATION BETWEEN VITAL CAPACITY (1), AGE (3) AND SOME OTHER TESTS (2)
r13 = —.54

2	r12	r23	Age partialled out r12,3
R T, ruler	—.59	.48	—.45
R T, light	—.46	.35	—.34
CFF	.51	—.48	.34
Memory, pictures	.54	—.55	.34
Tapping rate	.48	—.44	.32
Abstracting ability	.42	—.44	.24
Memory, numbers	.40	—.41	.23
Hearing loss	—.46	.55	—.23
"Retinal rivalry"	.40	—.47	.20
Spiral after-effect	.22	—.18	.15

those for hearing loss and 'retinal rivalry" drop to insignificant levels if age is partialled out, but most of the intercorrelations remain significant so that we do not get rid of the vital capacity variable as related to the "speed-tests."

The result is exactly the same when the factorial structure is considered. The first factor obtained after rotation (Table 3a) could just as well be named an *ageing* factor as a speed or a *memory* factor since the loadings of all these variables differed very little from each other. Vital capacity loads as highly as any of them. Obviously this factor collects nearly all the variance due to age (89%) and it is not likely that increasing the number of factors extracted would materially change the picture. As a matter of fact, we first tried with eight factors and the result is seen in Table 3b (the number of subjects was less and the number of variables more, however). As may be seen the structure of the first factor is not much different in spite of these differences.

The main loadings on other factors are shown in Table 4.

The second factor is of little interest, especially in this context. It could be called "pulse pressure—factor" on which the pulse

TABLE 3

LOADIINGS ON FACTOR I (AGEING, SPEED, MEMORY)

a		b	
n=132 6 Factors		n=91 8 Factors	
Memory, pictures	—.72	Vital capacity	—.71
Age	+.70	Tapping speed	—.71
Tapping speed	—.68	Age	+.68
Vital capacity	—.67	RT, ruler	+.67
RT, ruler	+.65	Memory, pictures	—.60
Hearing loss (400 cps)	+.65	"Retinal rivalry,"	—.60
CFF	—.63	(frequency of change)	
Memory, numbers	—.61	CFF	—.56
RT, light	+.60	Hearing loss	+.53
Abstracting ability	—.56	RT, light	+.51
Retinal rivalry,	—.50	Memory, numbers	—.49
(frequency of change)		Abstracting ability	—.46
Socio-economic status	—.41	Maximum ventilatory capacity	—.43
Swaying amplitude	+.37	Swaying amplitude	+.30
Height	—.26	Parental longevity	—.30
Sleeplessness	—.26	Duration of spiral after-effect	—.30
Familial longevity	—.23	Socio-economic status	—.29
		Height	—.29
		Pulse wave velocity	—.28

pressure and systolic blood pressure load highly and nothing else, does so appreciably.

The third factor is, on the contrary, interesting. It is obviously the same factor that we have previously called "brain impairment factor" (*Jalavisto, Makkonen,* 1963 b). The highest loadings on

TABLE 4

LOADINGS ON FACTORS II, III, IV, V AND VI

Factor II (Pulse and systolic pressure)

Pulse pressure	0.85
Systolic blood pressure	0.73
Abstracting ability	—0.27
Familial longevity	+0.25
Sway amplitude	—0.20

Factor III (Brain impairment, encephalopathy)

Dizziness	0.61
Headache	0.50
Medical history (lack of)	—0.47
Sleeplessness	0.37
CFF	—0.31
Socio-economic status	—0.31
Memory, numbers	—0.29
Abstracting ability	—0.25
RT, ruler	0.23

Factor IV, (Overweight)

Overweight	0.57
Height	—0.54
Vital capacity	—0.34
Medical history (lack of)	—0.29
Systolic blood pressure	0.26
Duration of spiral after-effect	0.24
"Retinal rivalry"	—0.24
RT, ruler	0.20

Factor V. (Parental longevity)

Parental longevity	0.50
Abstracting ability	0.46
Duration of spiral after-effect	0.37
Memory, pictures	0.34
Memory, numbers	0.34
Familial longevity	0.30
Socio-economic status	0.29
Headache	—0.25

Factor VI. (Hypertension)

Diastolic blood pressure	0.75
Systolic blood pressure	0.50
Sleeplessness	0.40
Medical history (lack of)	—0.29
Familial longevity	—0.25

this factor are for the symptoms of dizziness, headache, medical history (much illness), sleeplessness and from the speed tests CFF with a moderate loading, and, with a slightly lower loading reaction time (ruler). Memory for numbers and abstracting ability have moderate negative loadings. It is obvious that the "speed-tests" are not as a group affected by the presence of encephalopathy, but as in former studies (*Jalavisto, Makkonen,* 1963 b) the CFF is involved.

The fourth factor is an "overweight-factor" with no special interest in this context. The fifth factor likewise has no connection with tests requiring speed, but it is interesting in other ways. It could be named a *"parental longevity factor."* The only loadings worth mentioning are for the tests of abstracting ability, memory for pictures and numbers and, interestingly enough, duration of spiral after-effect which is sometimes considered to be related to memory (*Freeman* and *Josey,* 1949). The considerable loading of socio-economic status on this "parental longevity factor" is of interest because of the correlation which has often been found between intelligence, socio-economic level and longevity (*Rose* and *Cummings,* 1963).

The sixth factor is clearly a "clinical hypertension" factor with high loadings on diastolic and systolic blood pressure, sleeplessness etc. and very low loadings or none at all on the speed tests.

In concluding the description of the factors, it may be mentioned that age has no loading on any factor other than the first except a low one on the factor of overweight.

DISCUSSION

One of the difficulties in the factorial approach is that the factors to be extracted are dependent both on the properties of the population sample and on the variable. For a factor of, let us say, "brain impairment" to manifest itself there must be "brain impaired" individuals in the population sample, and variables related to that condition. If, for instance, such variables as symptoms of dizziness, headache and sleeplessness are not recorded, there is no criterion to identify the factor.

It is interesting to note that both times a "brain impairment" factor has been found (*Jalavisto, Makkonen,* 1963, and this study) the CFF loaded on it. The first time duration of spiral after-effect likewise had a moderate loading, but it was not found this time. Whether a modification of the testing procedure (increased rate of revolutions, different form of the spiral) could account for this discrepancy, cannot be settled without further experiments. However, from the point of view of the present problem it is quite evident that the speed tests do not all behave uniformly: CFF and reaction time (ruler) load on this "brain impairment factor," whereas tapping speed and reaction time (light) do not. It is thus improbable that performance in the "speed tests" depends on the speed of one and the same fundamental process.

The lack of, or the very low, loadings of the "speed tests" on the hypertension factor, which is not related to age, is quite plausible and in conformity with the assumption that age is the common denominator in determining the level of performance in the speed tests. Thus the speed-tests are quite good indicators of age changes. Whether they are as good indicators of "biological vigour" and potential longevity is questionable. If the factor of "parental longevity" really represents, as hypothesized, a factor of "biological vigour" then the speed tests have no bearing on it. I intend to follow the fate of the subjects in order to see whether death rate is related to any of the variables, especially those loading on the "parental longevity" factor, i.e., memory and abstracting ability.

It has been shown that the relationship between age and some neurological functions diminished when intelligence level is kept constant. (Reaction time: *Heron*, personal communication, 1962; CFF: *Colgan*, 1954; *Loranger* and *Misiak*, 1959; *Landis* and *Hamwi*, 1956). If, however, we suppose that many age-dependent variables become age-independent if the intellectual level is not impaired, this may mean two things: 1) impaired general intelligence is a hindrance to good performance in the tests 2) impaired intelligence is a symptom of old age deterioration, i.e., of biological senility, in which case keeping the intelligence level constant actually means considering "biologically young" people only. The high loadings of abstracting ability and memory tests on the factor of "parental longevity" speaks in favour of the second proposition. This interpretation has quite recently received support from the longitudinal study reported by *Dr. Birren* in his paper in this volume. *Kallman* and *Jarvik* (1959) and *Jarvik* (1963) mention a fact which likewise could be interpreted as an indication of longer survival of the more intelligent: the survivors in 1955 of a population originally tested in 1944 achieved higher mean scores on all tests than the original total test population.

The fact that I have restricted my studies to elderly women only, perhaps deserves some comment. If the population to be investigated includes young persons, one of the variables that correlates negatively with age is height. This is probably an indication of a difference between the standards of living of the youth of to-day and of half a century ago. If the height of, say, twenty to forty year old people some thirty years ago is compared with the height of fifty to seventy years old now, there is no difference (*Jalavisto, Makkonen*, 1963 a). If the differing standard of living reduces growth it may have other physiological influences as well and *the young and old do not represent two comparable populations*. It is therefore preferable to reduce the age span of the population sample in order to minimize such secondary differences. As is seen from the present results this does not destroy the correlation of the test results with age. A further advantage is that most of the age-dependent variables which, if the total age span is considered, show curvilinearity, are practically linearly related to age if the later ages only are concerned.

Interpretation of the result concerning vital capacity, is not easy. Vital capacity is correlated with height, but if height is partialled out the coefficient of correlation between age and vital capacity still amounts to —.47. Thus the negative correlation with age, which is well known, does not depend on the difference in height. The intercorrelation with other age-related tests even after age is partialled out, is quite clear. Whether this finding should be interpreted to mean that respiratory function is impaired in the old to such an extent that it affects the performance of mental and speed tests is not clear. It is true that if the old live in a constant hypoxia, sensory and mental performance could deteriorate as postulated by *McFarland* (1961) in regard to dark adaptation, but another interpretation should perhaps also be taken into account. The determination of vital capacity requires a muscular effort and the result is thus only partly dependent upon the condition of the lungs. Because of this muscular effort, the determination of vital capacity determination necessitates cooperation and strong motivation of the experimental subject. If the aging process impaires the strength of motivation the result would be age-dependent deterioration of practically all functions requiring active cooperation, vital capacity among others. On the other hand, lack of motivation could also result from a hypoxic condition. *Dastur et al.* (1963) have, as a matter of fact, noted that healthy elderly men and elderly men with miscellaneous asymptomatic disease in the age of sixty-five to ninety-four years, very often show definitely lowered arterial O_2-saturations. This is in accordance with the findings of *Dill et al.* (1940): "elderly people at rest live, as it were, at an altitude of 1500-2000 m." The matter obviously deserves much more investigation.

SUMMARY

Tests of various functions were applied to 130 elderly women aged forty to ninety-three years. The tests included determinations of maximal tapping rate, reaction time in grasping a falling ruler, reaction time to visual stimuli, critical flicker fusion frequency, together called "speed tests." They further included determinations of hearing loss (audiometry, 4000 cps) blood pressure, vital capacity, over-weight etc. "Familial longevity" was rated and the variable was assumed to represent "biological vigour." Tests of memory and abstracting ability were included in the test battery, and ratings were made of the presence of symptoms such as headache, dizziness, sleeplessness.

The results were factorially analyzed. Six factors were extracted after orthogonal rotation according to the "Varimax" criterion. The following factors were identified.

I. Aging. This factor represented about 55 per cent of the total variance. The following tests loaded highest on this factor: memory for simple geometric figures, age, tapping rate, vital capacity, reaction time (ruler), hearing loss, CFF, memory for numbers (reversed order), abstracting ability, frequency of change in retinal dominance.

II. Pulse and Systolic Pressure. This factor was of little interest in the present connection. The "speed-tests" did not load on it.

III. "Brain Impairment." The highest loadings on this factor were symptoms of dizziness, headache, sleeplessness, CFF, memory for numbers, abstractive ability, reaction time (ruler).

IV. Overweight. This factor was of little interest in the present connection.

V. "Parental Longevity." The highest loadings on this factor were the familial and parental longevity, abstracting ability, memory for geometrical figures and numbers and duration of spiral after-effect. The "speed-tests" hardly loaded on it at all.

VI. Hypertension. The highest positive loadings on this factor were diastolic blood pressure, sleeplessness, medical history. It had negative loading in the familial longevity. No relation to the "speed-tests" was noted.

It was concluded that the "speed tests" are fairly good indicators of age-induced deterioration. The lack of uniformity in the ways the various "speed tests" load on the different factors makes it improbable, however, that there is a common process the slowing of which could explain the age changes in all these "speed tests." Nor is it probable that speed tests have any role as indicators of "biological vigour."

REFERENCES

Anonymous: (1953) Les conditions des vieillards l'automne 1950. Enquêtes spéciales sur les affaires sociales. 20. S.V.T. XXXII, Helsinki.

Birren, J. E., Butler, R. N., Greenhouse, S. W., Sokoloff, L. and Yarrow, M. R., eds.: (1963) *Human Aging.* U. S. Public Health Service Publication No. 986.

Birren, J. E. and Spieth, W.: (1962) Age, response speed, and cardiovascular functions. *J. Geront.,* 17:390-391.

Colgan, C. M.: (1954) Critical flicker frequency, age and intelligence. *Amer. J. Psychol.,* 67:711-713.

Dastur, D. K., Lane, M. H., Hansen, D. B., Kety, S. S., Butler, R. N., Perlin, S. and Sokoloff, L.: (1963) Effects of aging on cerebral circulation and metabolism in man. In Birren *et al.,* eds.: *Human Aging.* U. S. Public Health Service Publication No. 986.

Dill, D. B., Graybiel, A., Hurtado, A. and Taquini, A. C.: (1940) Der Gasautausch in den Lungen im Alter. *Z. Alternsforsch.,* 2:20-33.

Dublin, L. I., Lotka, A. J. and Spiegelman, M.: (1949) *Length of Life.* New York, Ronald Press.

Enzer, N., Simonson, E. and Blakenstein, S. S.: (1941) Fatigue of patients with circulatory insufficiency investigated by means of the fusion frequency of flicker. *Ann. Intern. Med., 16:*701-707.

Eysenck, H. J., Granger, G. W. and Brengelmann, J. C.: (1957) *Perceptual Processes and Mental Illness.* London, Chapman and Hall.

McFarland, R. A.: (1962) Experimental studies of sensory functions in relation to age. *Ergonomics, 5:*12-131.

Freeman, E. and Josey, W. E.: (1949) Quantitative visual index to memory impairment. *Arch. Neurol. Psychiat., 62:*794-797.

Hügin, F., Norris, A. H. and Shock, N. W.: (1960) Skin reflex and voluntary reaction times in young and old males. *J. Geront., 15:*388-391.

Jalavisto, Eeva and Makkonen, T.: (1963a) On the assessment of biological age I. Factor analysis of physiological measurements in old and young women. *Ann. Acad. Sci. fenn. A.V.* 1-38.

Jalavisto, E. and Makkonen, T.: (1963) On assessment of biological age II. A factorial study of aging in postmenopausal women. *Ann. Acad. Sci. fenn. 101:*1-15.

Jalavisto, Eeva, Forsén, A., Lindqvist, Carita, Makkonen, T. and Tallqvist, Merit: (1962) Age and the simple reaction time in response to visual, tactile and proprioceptive stimuli. *Ann. Acad. Sci. Fenn., 96:1-12.*

Jalavisto, E., Lindqvist, Carita and Makkonen, T.: (To be published).

Jarvik, L. F.: The experimental psychology of aging. Intellectual performance, survival and chromosomes. VIth Int. Congr. Gerontol. Copenhagen, 1963, *Excerpta Med. Internat. Congr., Series, 57:*20.

Kallman, F. J. and Jarvik, L. F.: (1959) Individual differences in constitution and genetic background. In *Handbook of Aging and the Individual,* J. E. Birren, ed., Chicago, University of Chicago Press, pp. 216-257.

Landis, C. and Hamwi, V.: (1956) Critical flicker frequency, age and intelligence. *Amer. J. Psychol., 69:*459-461.

Loranger, A. W. and Misiak, H.: (1959) Critical flicker frequency and some intellectual functions in old age. *J. Geront., 14:*323-327.

Murray, I. M.: (1951) Assessment of physiologic age by combination of several criteria—vision, hearing, blood pressure, and muscle force. *J. Geront., 6:*120-126.

Rose, C. L. and Cummins, J. F.: (1963) Social correlates of longevity. A study of Spanish-American war veteranes. Paper circulated as *VIth Intern. Congr. Geront. (Copenhagen).*

Simonson, E. and Enzer, N.: (1941) State of motor centers in circulatory insufficiency. *Arch. Intern. Med., 68:*498-512.

20

SLOWNESS OF TASK PERFORMANCE
AND CARDIOVASCULAR DISEASES

WALTER SPIETH

IN STUDYING the psychology of aging it is important to distinguish between the effects of aging *per se,* and the effects of controllable diseases which often, but not inevitably, accompany chronological age. The data discussed in this paper indicate that middle-aged men who are living normal lives and are in nominally "normal" health, but who have mild to moderate degrees of cardiovascular symptoms, without evidence of cerebro-vascular impairment, show slowed performance on psychological speed tests, including tests known to be good indices of organic brain dysfunction.

The data further confirm several other studies in the literature which indicate that middle-aged individuals with heart disease perform more poorly than like-aged controls on a variety of psychological tests and tasks, probably even when there is no independent evidence of cerebro-vascular impairment. Enzer, Simonson, and Blankstein (1942) reported that individuals with essential hypertension, coronary disease or both have a lower (poorer) visual flicker fusion threshold and lower maximum tapping rate (Simonson and Enzer, 1941) than healthy subjects of like age, and ascribed this to circulatory insufficiency. Krasno and Ivy (1950) obtained results similar to those of Enzer, Simonson and Blankstein, and also found that administration of a vaso-dilative drug, nitroglycerine, raised the flicker fusion threshold in cardiovascular disease patients and others believed to have insufficient circulation, and lowered it in normal subjects. Anderson (1963) found a reliable inferiority of middle-aged and older coronary heart diseased men to healthy men of like age and occupation in a one-hour speed test of solving simple but rather "tricky" arithmetic problems. Even while working more slowly, the coronary diseased subjects made more errors. This tends to indicate that these performance deficits are somehow "basic," and not just a matter of more judicious self-pacing on the part of the diseased subject. Anderson also found the threshold of flicker fusion to be significantly poorer in the subjects with coronary heart disease.

Apter, Halstead, and Heimburger (1951) found that Essential Hypertensives showed significantly higher indices of organic brain impairment than controls, using the highly valid Halstead Impairment Index Battery, and Reitan (1954) concluded that many essential hypertensive subjects' Rorschach profiles show substantial signs of brain dysfunction. Birren (1963) also reports that elderly hypertensives showed slower multiple-choice serial reaction times than more healthy old subjects. Reitan and Shipley (1963) reported a relationship between test-retest improvement on a battery known to be a good indicator of organic brain impairment, and diminution of hypercholesteremia over the test-retest interval, in middle-aged men enrolled in an executive health program.

Minc, Sinclair, and Taft (1963) measured a large number of variables on coronary artery disease convalescents and controls who had previously been hospitalized for non-cardiovascular illnesses. Their CAD group showed, at the 0.01 level of confidence, higher serum cholesterol levels and more family histories of CAD, and more seconds of high voltage ($> 50 \mu$ V) EEG Alpha waves in a one minute period of observation. The two groups demonstrated differences, significant at the 0.05 level of confidence, in two psychometric measures of personality. The CAD group was lower, but at less than the 0.05 level of statistical significance, on CFF thresholds, speed on a clerical checking task, speed of reactions to stimulus words, and frequency of EEG Alpha waves during the one minute period of observation. Apparently, there were no performance or cortical function measures on which their CAD group scored better than the comparison group. Considering the very conservative comparison group used, I feel that these findings are substantially in accord with the other studies cited above.

Most of the subjects in the studies cited above were at least ambulatory and apparently many were regularly employed or otherwise leading reasonably normal lives. It also appears that many of the subjects would not be counted as normal in a careful study of aging.

A RECENT STUDY

Our results (Spieth, 1964) extend the gist of the above findings to men who had only mild or moderate degrees of cardiovascular symptoms, being classified as 1A or 1B in the American Heart Association system, in which "1" indicates "ordinary physical activity causes no discomfort," A indicates "ordinary physical activity needs no restriction," and B indicates the same except that "patient should be advised against unusually severe or competitive efforts." Nearly all of the "pathological" cases in this study were recovered from disability and fully employed at the time of the examination, and most would be counted as "normals" in any performance study that did not include a careful physical examination. They are from a fairly homogeneous subpopulation: most are present or former military or civil air pilots, or air traffic controllers or both, and most are Federal Civil Servants of middle or upper rank. Nearly all are above average in intelligence and educational-occupational status. Most were once in very good health, the majority having been screened repeatedly by air pilot or air traffic controller physical examinations.

Ours is a Federal medical examination clinic with powers to grant or withhold a patient's medical certification to fly or control air traffic. The certificate must be renewed by annual examination. This may be done for fee by any of 6,000 physicians licensed to do this, or without charge at this clinic. Each man was told, truthfully, that the psychological tests were purely for research purposes and had nothing to do with the certification process and was asked to volunteer for them. Very few declined to volunteer. Most healthy patients elected to come to our clinic for their annual physical examinations, while most of the pathological patients were referred here for further evaluation by a physician in the field or sometimes by their Air Line employer's medical staff. Some thus appeared for a "medical appeal" under quite stressful circumstances. When a man appeared to be emotionally distressed by the medical findings or by the general circumstances he was not given psychological tests. The most serious artifact in this situation was that pathological cases were likely to be here under more stressful circumstances than most of the healthy men. In order to control for this variable, we recruited as many volunteer cardiovascular disease cases as possible from a Federal executive health program, men who did not require medical certification and who were given only the psychological tests in circumstances kept as informal as possible. About half of these "outside volunteers" also are former pilots or air traffic controllers or both, and all were of better than average educational-occupational level.

The following groups were formed, all men, aged thirty-five to fifty-nine.

Ia: 338 healthy subjects.

Ib: Sixteen "false-positive" subjects, who were examined while under serious threat of revocation of medical certification but were judged healthy enough to retain their certification by a panel which met after all testing had been completed.

II: twenty-two subjects with mild or moderate congenital or rheumatic heart defects, some of whom were subsequently denied certification. Many probably were under more situational stress than group Ia.

IIIa: Forty-six subjects with arteriosclerotic or coronary disease without hypertension, AHA Class IA or IB, not on medication for some time before the examination. The majority had had myocardial infarctions from six months to several years previously. Many presumably were under considerable situational stress.

IIIb: Twelve subjects with arteriosclerotic or coronary heart diseases without hypertension, AHA Class IA or IB, not on medication for some time before examination. A majority had evidence of old myocardial infarctions. They were "outside volunteers" and not under certification stress.

IVa: seventeen subjects with essential hypertension or other cardiovascular disease with hypertension, not on medication for some time before examination, subject to certification stress.

IVb: Thirteen subjects with hypertensive diseases, but with blood pressure maintained at normotensive levels by medication, "outside volunteers" not under stress of certification.

V: Nine subjects with history or physical evidence of cerebro-vascular diseases or old cerebrovascular accident.

These individuals were given a battery of tests consisting of: a) a series of stimulus-matching tasks on the Psychomet test apparatus (Birren, Reigel, and Morrison, 1962) which is best described as a ten-choice serial reaction time task. The apparatus consists of ten stimulus windows in a row, and a response button several inches below each stimulus window. Each button has its own removable code label. In the simplest test, the subject simply strikes the button under whichever light is lit. This act immediately switches on another stimulus light, the subject then strikes the button under the second light, and so on, as fast as possible. In the more complicated versions, a symbol appears in the lighted stimulus window and the subject must hunt among the response button-labels to find the correct button to strike. The Psychomet battery in this study (Spieth, 1964) differed from the battery described by Birren, Reigel, and Morrison; b) The WAIS Digit-Symbol Substitution Test, pencil and paper (Wechsler, 1955); c) The Trails Making Tests, pencil and paper (Reitan, 1958). Scores from all tests in a, b, and c were combined into a single "composite speed score" for each individual. d) The Halstead Tactual Performance Test, in which the subject must place geometrically-shaped blocks in an uptitled board while blindfolded, with his right hand, again with his left hand, and then with both hands, as fast as possible, and finally draw what he can recall of the shapes and locations after the board and blindfold have been removed, without time stress; e) the WAIS Block Design Test (Wechsler, 1955).

Results

The composite speed scores of all healthy cases less than age sixty are shown in Figure 1, together with groups IIIa and IIIb combined, and groups IVa and IVb. The differences among all groups are shown in Table 1. These statistics were computed by drawing the best straight-line fit to the means of the healthy group's scores for ages thirty-five through fifty-nine. This straight line was assigned the value of zero, and the variance of healthy scores around this line was set to 1.00. The means and standard durations for each subgroup were computed in these terms. This

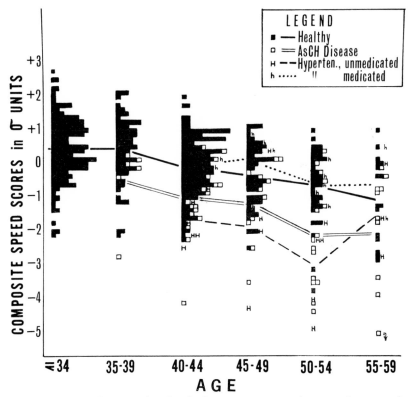

Figure 1. Distribution of individual composite speed scores by age, for healthy subjects, for groups IIIa and IIIb combined, and for groups IVa and IVb.

automatically incorporates age adjustments into all scores, using the linear age trend of the healthy cases.

Groups IIIa and IIIb were both significantly slower than the healthy group. Group IIIb, although presumably tested in less stressful circumstances than group IIIa, performed insignificantly more slowly than group IIIa. This fact, plus the fact that the presumably highly stressed subjects of group Ib performed as well as the healthy group, imply that either performance on these tasks is not penalized by stressful circumstances, or that the circumstances were not differently stressful among the normotensive groups.

The performance of the two hypertensive groups permits no simple conclusions because situational stress and vasodilative

TABLE 1
AGE-ADJUSTED COMPOSITE SPEED-TEST SCORES
FOR ALL SUBJECTS AGED 35-59

	Group	N	M	σ	p
Ia	Healthy, regular referrals	388	0.00	1.00	
Ib	"False positives," maximally stressed healthy cases	16	−0.06	0.98	0.50
II	Rheumatic or congenital defects, AHA class Ia	22	−0.38	1.07	0.10
IIIa	Arteriosclerotic cardiovascular disease, AHA class Ia or Ib (mild or moderate symptoms), not medicated, some situational stress	46	−0.95	1.43	0.001
IIIb	Arteriosclerotic cardiovascular disease, AHA class Ia or Ib, not medicated, volunteers not under situational stress	12	−1.54	1.53	0.01
IVa	Essential hypertension, AHA class Ia or Ib, not medicated, some situational stress	17	−1.74	1.40	0.001
IVb	Essential hypertension, AHA class Ia or Ib, medicated, volunteers not under situational stress	13	+0.24	0.77	0.10
V	Individuals displaying history or physical evidence of cerebro-vascular disease, mild to moderate, recovered and without clinically overt mental or behavioral deficits	9	−1.97	1.24	0.01

medication are confounded. We can only say that presumed stress plus elevated blood pressure (group IVa) lead to markedly slow performance—almost as slow as the cerebrovascular disease cases of group V—while the hypertensives (group IVb) whose blood pressure was maintained within normotensive limits by vasodilative medication and who presumably were under less situational stress performed insignificantly better than the healthy patients. Group II, the relatively mild and compensated heart-defect group, performed about like the healthy group, as would be expected, while the cerebrovascular damage cases (group V) were the poorest, as would be expected.

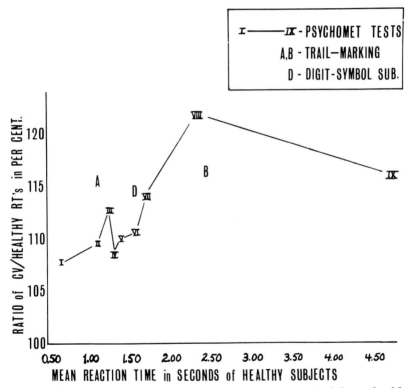

Figure 2. The abscissa represents the mean time required by a healthy subject per reaction in a serial choice reaction time test, or per response in a paper and pencil test. The mean time per reaction by subjects in groups IIIa, IIIb and IVa combined, is plotted as a per cent of the mean time per reaction on the test by a healthy subject.

Groups IIIa, IIIb, and IVa were combined into a single "pathology group" and compared with the healthy cases in regard to the relative amounts of time taken per response in the various speed tests. The results are shown in Figure 2. As may be seen, the pathology groups were relatively least slow on the simpler tests and proportionately more slow on the more complex, time consuming tests, relative to the healthy group.

The differences among these groups were less clear cut on the WAIS Block Design and Halstead Tactual Performance Test. Groups IIIa, IIIb, and IVa were combined and compared with the healthy group. The combined "pathology group" was reliably slower on these tests but at the less dramatic significance levels ranging from about p=.03 to p=.01. The Halstead test has one feature of particular interest here: everyone is required to reach the same criterion of tactual performance, after which he is given an untimed recall test. This gives a well controlled test of recall abilities independent of performance speed or time stress. The combined pathology group was insignificantly poorer at recalling the shapes dealt with ($.10 > p > .05$) and significantly poorer at recalling block locations ($p < .02$).

I think these performance differences were not simply a matter of more "cautiousness" or more sedate self-pacing by the pathological subjects. A simple motor slowness in the Psychomet series would have caused the proportionality curve in Figure 2 to fall toward the right, because the same oculomotor and arm-motor responses are required by all tests. Because Figure 2 rises toward the right, that is, because the pathological group was disproportionately slower on the more complex tests, it would appear that their slowness was not in the "doing" but in the "deciding what to do." They were also poorer on the time-free recall part of the Tactual Performance Test. Also, Anderson's finding that his coronary heart disease subjects made more errors while working more slowly suggests that such individuals do not have a tendency to value accuracy abnormally at the expense of speed.

The studies reviewed, taken together, demonstrate quite conclusively that subjects suffering arteriosclerosic coronary heart disease or who show evidence of old myocardial infarctions, and those with essential hypertension, will perform more poorly than reasonably well matched healthy subjects on a wide variety of self-paced tasks in which sheer physical effort is minimal; and that this is true of those who are recovered from acute symptoms and who have these diseases in relatively moderate degree.

SOME POSSIBLE CAUSES OF THE POORER PERFORMANCES

In enumerating some of the differences among the healthy and pathological groups which might explain the performance differences, I have attempted to impose some simplicity by grouping the facts and speculations around two orthogonal questions: to what extent are the performance differences contingent upon the effects of the disease in its clinically manifest state and to what extent upon individual characteristics which might produce the disease and also the poor performance? Secondly, to what extent are these causes of poor performance "biological," and to what extent are they "psychological" or "psychophysiological"? By the latter two terms, I mean states or behavioral dispositions which could be manipulated by stimulus, social, incentive, temporal (adaptational or habituational) or other situational variables.

CNS Circulatory Insufficiencies and Brain Dysfunction

The most parsimonious single explanation for the performance differences is a straightforward biological one: that these patients are suffering from a chronic insufficiency of oxygen transport to or uptake in at least some parts of the central nervous system. Krasno and Ivy (1950) attributed the improvement in flicker fusion threshold in their nitroglycerine-treated cardiovascular-disease patients to improved circulation in the retina, although the circulation in the central nervous system probably was improved also, in these patients. They attributed the opposite effect of nitroglycerine in normal subjects to a disruption of optimum circulation.*

---

* It seems just possible that an additional mechanism exists which could be involved in producing these results: if the autonomic nervous system dynamics in cardiovascular-disease patients differed from the dynamics in normals in a way such that nitroglycerine had a dilative effect on the pupils of the cardiovascular-disease patients relative to its effect on the pupils of normal subjects, then this would help produce these results, because the larger the pupil, the more light is focused on the retina, and the higher will be the threshold of flicker-fusion. However, we know of no data on the existence of such autonomic differences.

In autopsy, the amount of atherosclerosis—the most common form of arteriosclerosis—in the coronary arteries is positively correlated with amount of atherosclerosis in the cerebral arteries: Young, Gofman, Tandy, Malamud, and Waters (1960) found $r=.54$ for ninety-five cases, aged sixty to ninety, and Mathur, Kashyap, and Kumar (1963), examining 200 cases of accidental or traumatic death in Indians, found $r=.67$ for the entire group and $r=.68$ for the sixty-seven cases who were more than forty years old. Young, Gofman, and Tandy also reported $r=.89$ to .95 between amount of atherosclerosis in one cerebral artery and in all cerebral arteries considered together. Thus, given an amount of atherosclerosis in the coronary arteries sufficient to produce myocardial infarction or other pronounced symptoms, there is almost certainly some atherosclerosis in at least one of the cerebral arteries. The degre of cerebral atherosclerosis need not be great to affect the brain; a single atherosclerotic plaque in an artery can plug it as effectively as a series of plaques. In regard to this problem, Kety (1960) states: "studies upon patients with cerebral arteriosclerosis have demonstrated a significant decrease in the cerebral circulation and oxygen consumption of the brain when compared to values found in healthy young men. The restriction of cerebral blood flow is upon the basis of an increased cerebrovascular resistance which was found to be about twice the normal value and which represents a physiological confirmation during life of the well known sclerotic changes observed post-mortem." Of course, circulation in a local area can be blocked completely even when total brain circulation is normal. This altered cerebral circulation could explain the poorer task performances of the arteriosclerotics.

In addition, most of the arteriosclerotic subjects in the Spieth (1964) study, and probably the majority of those reported in the other studies, had suffered myocardial infarctions. Some infarctions have been reported to be relatively "silent," but many others are associated with profound arrhythmias such as ventricular tachycardia, and a greatly diminished output resulting in hypotension, with disruption of adequate blood supply to some areas of the brain. This might result in some permanent brain damage, because interruption of oxygen to brain tissue for only a few minutes is thought to produce irreversible disability or death to the nerve cells (Sokoloff, 1959). There may also be permanent damage due to edema produced by acute hypotension in some arterioles. Part of the anoxic damage may be due to congestion of the microcirculation by an agglutination of red corpuscles with blocking of flow (Finckelstein, Woerner, Smith, Bayles, Levine, and Kwork, 1963). This traumatic disruption of the brain circulation with myocardial infarct occurs in a person whose CNS vasculature is probably already damaged by atherosclerosis or by the hypertension which often precedes the infarction. Melikova, as reviewed by Simonson (1958) states that in lethal acute myocardial infarction in man, vascular changes, with resulting damage to the brain tissue, are always present, probably because of secondary cerebral ischemia.

One strongly suspected cause of atherosclerosis, hypercholesteremia, may or may not be negatively correlated with performance level. In a previous study of the strictly healthy men seen in our clinic, we (Birren and Spieth, 1962) found no relationship between cholesterol level in the blood and performance. As a check on this, I examined these two variables for eighty-eight healthy cases aged forty-five to fifty-four (about half of whom had been included in the earlier study), eighteen of whom had serum cholesterol levels greater than 300 mg/100 cc, and again found no relationship. Reitan and Shipley (1963) found a greater improvement in performance on a battery of tests in those who had succeeded in reducing their high cholesterol levels than in those who had not. Our single cholesterol determinations were undoubtedly substantially less reliable than Reitan and Shipley's multiple determinations, and we suspect that some of the poor performers in their study would not have been classified as strictly healthy by the quite stringent criteria used in our aviation examination clinic. There is even a possibility that poor mean group performance, as well as high cholesterol levels, could be caused by a fatty diet, because Swank (1954) has shown that a heavy, high-fat meal causes an agglutination of blood cells and marked slowing of flow in capillaries, the flow being slowest several hours after the meal.

The notion of "circulatory insufficiency" has somewhat less

direct applicability in explaining the poorer performance by the essential hypertensive cases. Since essential hypertension tends to go with, and sometimes be caused in part by, arterioslerotic diseases, it can be assumed that there is some cerebral sclerosis in a good many cases. However, in the case of fairly mild or early essential hypertension, the dysfunctions hypothesized in the central nervous system should be functionally somewhat reversible, because, for example, in the Spieth (1964) study the group of essential hypertensive cases whose blood pressures were maintained at normotensive levels by medications performed fully as well as healthy men of like age, while relatively mild essential hypertensive cases whose blood pressures were high on the day of testing were markedly slower and poorer, although there was a psychophysiological basis for the difference also, the latter group being under more situational stress. Hypertension, by itself, does not reduce blood flow through the brain. According to Kety (1960), "this disease is characterized by an elevation in mean arterial pressure and a corresponding increase in the tone of the cerebral vessels with the result that the cerebral circulation remains within normal limits. This indicates that the vessels of the brain partake in the generalized vasoconstriction which occurs in this condition."

"It has also been demonstrated that in essential hypertension, uncomplicated by cerebral arteriosclerosis, the narrowing of the vessels is a functional one which is capable of relaxation should the arterial pressure of the patient be reduced. Thus, the increased cerebral vascular resistance is not the result of permanent structural change. Since it is not reduced by stellate ganglion blockade, it is probably not sympathetic in origin. Although some unidentified vasoconstrictor circulating in the blood has often been postulated in this disease, the sudden relaxation in response to a fall in arterial pressure, however achieved, is not easily explained in terms of a circulating humoral agent. The observations generally give most support to the hypothesis that the cerebral vasoconstriction is a compensatory adjustment to the hypertension and may be achieved by the homeostatic effects of the local concentration of carbon dioxide on cerebral vessels." The disruption of blood flow and/or oxygenation of the brain tissues in essential hypertension is usually assumed on the basis of transitory alterations of behavior and nervous function known to coincide with acute elevation of blood pressure in essential hypertensives.

According to Fishberg (1939) these effects include transitory hemiplegias, monoplegia, aphasias, local anesthesias and pains, and blurred vision or even blindness, sometimes with visible spasm of the retinal arteries, suggesting that angiospasm and also local hypotensive edemas will occur in the brain as well. Accord-to Kety (1960), "the possibility of spasm of cerebral vessels, often suggested by certain syndromes and beautifully demonstrated by cerebral embolization in animals, has not yet been definitely demonstrated in man. Although arteriographic evidence sugges-tive of spasm has been obtained, such studies are hard to control rigorously. Most of the clinical evidence for spasm is equally compatible with an explanation on the basis of multiple minor thromboses or transitory systemic hypotension in a critically narrowed vessel."

It is likely that the stressfulness of the testing situation will have more effect on the circulatory dynamics and thus the per-formance levels of hypertensives than on non-hypertensives. Both hypertensives and many normotensives are known to show eleva-tions of blood pressure in stressful or arousing situations (Malmo and Shagass, 1951) (Schnore, 1959) (Schneider and Zangari, 1951) (Hokanson and Shetler, 1961) (Hickham, Cargell, and Golden, 1948), and essential hypertensives may show a dis-proportionate further elevation of blood pressure in response to stress (Imhof, Hurlimann, and Steinmann, 1957). This situational rise in blood pressure would have a particularly deleterious effect on the cortical functioning of the subject whose blood pressure is already high. In the Spieth study, we observed that at least three of the seventeen unmedicated, stressed hypertensives showed a rare behavior pattern on the Halstead Tactual Per-formance Test: whereas, almost all of the hundreds of men tested by us on this task showed improvement from the first to the second trials and a considerable improvement on the third trial, these three hypertensives got progressively worse, and within fifteen minutes after beginning showed a peculiar pattern of distressed, listless ineptitude which caused us to halt the task short of completion. In these hypertensives, and others, there may be a progressive intra-task disability when the task is arduous or given under stressful conditions. Most people, probably, show some rise in blood pressure when engaged in an arduous or challenging task, but in the hypertensive this further rise, which is likely to be large (Imhof, Hurlimann, and Steinmann, 1957), should be deleterious to performance when it would not be deleterious in the normotensive individual.

Some Other Differences in Nervous Function

So far, we have considered the poor task performance of the cardiovascular diseased as an effect of central nervous system dysfunction caused in turn by circulatory and vascular pathology. The relationship between both the central and autonomic nervous system and circulatory changes is undoubtedly circular, so that performance changes and cardiovascular diseases could also be viewed, to some extent, as common effects of central nervous changes. There is much evidence that once cardiovascular disease has developed there is poorer regulation of the cardiovascular system. Simonson (1958) provides an extensive review of Russian work with conditioned vascular reflexes, in which the response measured is usually vasoconstriction or dilation of the hand or forearm, the unconditioned stimulus is usually warm or cold water applied to the opposite hand, and a variety of signals —often tone and a light—are used as positive and negative conditioned stimuli.

The gist of a score or more of studies on this reflex reviewed by Simonson indicates that, in relation to healthy individuals, the reflexes of patients suffering coronary insufficiency are usually hyporeactive or sometimes hyperreactive, exaggerated fluctuations are sometimes seen, and that frequently vasoconstriction occurs in response to heat as well as cold (the normal response to heat being vasodilation). In the early stages of hypertension, there was little abnormality in the reflexes, but in later stages the responses tend to become hyporeactive, with occasional reversal of effect (dilitation to cold, constriction to heat). Conversely, pathology or disturbances in the central nervous system are associated with abnormal vascular conditioned reflexes. Psychiatric disorders—schizophrenia and "hypochondriac psychoses"—were associated with hyporeactive responses, and in forty-nine patients with hemiplegia, unconditioned and conditioned responses were more pronounced on the normal side. Involvement of the more complex perceptual functions of the cortex was demonstrated in other subjects by the finding that the response, conditioned to loud sound or electrical shock to the skin, could be abolished by suggestion under hypnosis that the pain or noise was absent.

Aging also decreases the control of autonomically-regulated functions. Hellon and Lynd (1956) found a much slower onset of sweating in response to heat in middle aged men than in young men, and in the middle aged men the changes in sweating in response to changes in the heat load were much slower. They also found (Lynd and Hellon, 1963) in coal miners, all presumably reasonably healthy and well adapted to the working situation, that the older men sweated relatively less during a work stint and relatively more in the rest period that followed, and that the older men's peripheral blood flow remained relatively much higher during the post-work rest period. Frolkis (1962) reports that blood pressure, which rises in response to an irritating stimulus, returns to normal in about 50″ in the young adult rabbit but only after about 540″ in the older rabbit. Frolkis attributes this both to differences in adrenaline output and in central nervous system regulation.

It seems worth conjecturing that in periods of stress and effort a person who is developing hypertension has a cortex which sends a sub-optimum pattern of instructions to the hypothalamic area and other lower centers and has a different pattern of input to the cortex, both from the hypothalamic and ascending reticular activating system and from the autonomically and/or humorally controlled events in the rest of the organism. Something similar might be said of the individual who is in the process of developing atherosclerosis and/or coronary heart disease, although the dynamics of the signal-neuro-cardiovascular loops are probably not the same. Poor psychological performance and cardiovascular diseases often might be parallel effects of antecedent neurological changes. Both brain and psychic stimulations of certain kinds enhance production of both arteriosclerotic heart disease and sustained hypertension. Gunn, Friedman, and Byers (1960) demonstrated that in rabbits a combination of fatty diet plus electrical stimulation of the ventral medial nucleus and other portions of the diencephalon, at stimulus levels just above those necessary to produce pupillary dilatation and other signs of sympathetic activity, produced gross hypercholesteremia and a great degree of coronary atherosclerosis. The fatty diet alone, while producing gross hypercholesteremia, produced much less atherosclerosis. Stimulation alone produced no changes.

Uhley and Friedman (1959) procured similar results in rats, using "psychological" stress (conditioned avoidance of shock) instead of direct hypothalamic stimulation. None of these treatments produced more than transient hypertension or any changes in corticosteroid levels. A similar effect in hypercholesteremic rabbits is produced by vagal stimulation (Yushchenko, as reported by Simonson, 1960) and also by phenamine, while the atherosclerosis is reduced by barbiturates, when the drugs are administered over a period of time (Myaskinov, 1958). Glaser and Griffin (1960) demonstrated that small bilateral lesions in the frontal cortex of the rat prevented habituation of accelerated heart rate response to a cold stimulus, while unilateral frontal lesions or lesions in the occipito-parietal area did not. In this regard, Shock (1963) pointed out that bilateral cortical ablations and topectomics in psychiatric and neuropathological human patients are not notable as precursors of cardiovascular diseases.

Gellhorn and Loofbourrow (1963) give extensive discussion to the neruophysiological mechanisms in the production and maintenance of hypertension and say "in the light of the role of the hypothalamus in the emotions it is suggested that increasing hypothalamic sympathetic discharges play a dominant role in initiating processes which eventually lead to hypertension. The sympathetically induced renal ischemia (which leads to the production of vasopressor agents) is one of the consequences of these central autonomic discharges." These authors note that hypothalamic stimulation also involves secretion of vasopressor substances from the hypothalamus and related hypophysis. In the same source, Gellhorn also cites his own experimental finding that repeated stimulation of the sympathetic division of the hypothalamus may alter the autonomic balance so as to increase sympathetic reactivity and rate of discharge and reciprocally diminish the activity of the parasympathetic system, and points out that increased sympathetic reactivity in hypertensives has been reasonably well established both clinically and experimentally.

According to Simonson and Brozek (1959) there is a strong consensus among the Russians that arterial hypertension is initiated by disturbances of the normal regulatory effect of the cerebral cortex on the hypothalamic vasomotor centers; the resulting increased excitability of the vasomotor centers exaggerates pressor responses, first producing periods of transient increases of blood pressure due to spastic contraction of arterioles. Renal, cardiac, cerebral, and endocrine involvement is considered to be of secondary but increasing importance in the later phases of hypertension. The initial cerebral cortical failure to inhibit the hypothalamic vasomotor centers results from prolonged psychic stress, particularly suppressed "negative" emotions. There is a large body of experimental and clinical evidence which supports the gist of the foregoing ideas, although other interpretations are possible.

Simonson and Brozek (1959) review a body of Russian work indicating that lesions in and trauma to various regions of the cortex of animals and humans produced elevated blood pressure, usually unilaterally on the side contralateral to the hemisphere involved, and that prolonged increased blood pressure occurs in humans when the middle hypothalamic region has been irritated. Simonson and Brozek also review Magnitskii's particularly interesting finding that when the rabbit's posterior hypothalamic region is electrically stimulated, the blood pressure increases considerably, and that when weak and normally ineffectual sensory stimuli are superimposed on this electrical stimulation, a strong pressor response is observed and that this effect increases with repetition. This is in accord with the facts about the hypothalamic contribution to the ascending reticular activating system to the cortex. Apparently, these procedures are not reported as producing chronic hypertension. In the Gunn, Friedman, and Byers (1960) experiment, stimulation of the rabbits' posterior hypothalamic regions produced transient elevated blood pressures but no chronic elevation.

Wilkins' (1954) report of the control of essential hypertension by the central depressant Rauwolfia also indicates the causal role of the CNS.

Situational Stresses and Cardiovascular Diseases

Since Cannon's (1920) classical demonstrations of the massive sympathetically mediated physiological arousal in cats in response to barking dogs and other stimuli, there have been demonstrations that a variety of external unconditioned sensory stimuli produce increased blood pressure, in some cases sustained hypertension with extensively chronic stimulation. Schunk (1954) produced sustained hypertension in about one-half of cats exposed daily to barking dogs for several months, and Minimoshvili (1960) was able to produce sustained hypertension in a small sample of monkeys by isolating them within sight of others kept in groups, and feeding the others first, within sight of the isolated monkey. Usievich, Strakhov, Iaroshevski, Gavlichek, and Napalkov and Karas, as reported by Simonson (1958), also produced sustained hypertension by Pavlovian conditioning techniques, and Blomstrand and Lofgren (1956) exposed cats to the barking of dogs and found that this produced renal ischemia, which in turn produced a release of renal vasoconstrictive agents. This renal mechanism is one well-known cause of hypertension.

The relationship between situational-responsive and sustained hypertensive disease is not known completely, but those who demonstrate transient elevation of blood pressure in physical examinations are about fifteen times as likely to develop sustained hypertension eventually as those who do not (Levy, Hillman, Stroud, and White, 1944). There is also a good deal of less direct evidence that certain kinds of chronic or relatively prolonged stressful features in the human's environment are associated with the development of cardiovascular diseases or states predisposing to the diseases, where the individuals have not selected the stressful situation for themselves. Kraus and Lilienfeld (1959) found the death rate from cardiovascular diseases to be several to many times higher among the young widowed group than among the married of like age. In ages twenty to twenty-four, twenty-five to thirty-four, and thirty-five to forty-four respectively, widowed women had about 14.4, 6.0, and 2.8 times as much arteriosclerotic heart disease or general arteriosclerosis, and widowed men had about 10.0, 4.9, and 1.9 times as much.

For hypertension with heart disease, the ratios were 18.4, 4.7, and 3.6 for women and 1.0, 10.8, and 4.6 for men. For vascular diseases of the central nervous system the ratios were similarly high. The authors discuss the artifact that unhealthy people are probably less likely to re-enter the married category than the more healthy, and demonstrate that this artifact could not account for more than a part of these differences. Relatively persistant hyptertension has been found to be abnormally common in large groups following combat (Graham, 1945) and a natural disaster (Ruskin, Beard, and Shaffer, 1948). Young men with coronary artery disease are much more likely than controls to have a work history of long hours in demanding situations: Russek and Zohman (1958) found that seventy-one of 100 younger men with coronary artery disease either worked at two jobs or more than sixty hours at one job, while this was true of fewer than twenty of the 100 control subjects. It is not clear whether the stressful work pattern or the personal characteristics and behaviors associated with selection of this work pattern is the more important causal factor. There are several longitudinal studies showing that both young and older men show a considerable rise in cholesterol levels and blood clotting speed as critical "test" situations approach—tax deadlines for tax accountants (Friedman, Rosenman, and Carroll, 1958), and final examinations for medical students (Wertlake, Wilcox, Haley, and Peterson, 1958) (Thomas and Murphy, 1958) (Grundy and Griffin, 1959).

Thus, there is good reason to assume that essential hypertension and perhaps a good many cases of arteriosclerosis also, are preceded by fairly sustained states of autonomic hyperreactivity, and that this hyperreactivity is maintained, in the hypertensive at least, after the disease has developed. Could hypertension and poor performance be to some extent parallel effects of this hypothalamic-sympathetic hyperreactivity? I have been unable to find any data on the direct effects of increased hypothalamic-sympathetic activity on performances of the kind reviewed in this paper, independent of external stimuli—fear, shock, pain, annoyance, and "heckling," of humans by the examiner, etc., which would have task-interference as well as physiological arousal properties. I was unable to find any data on the direct effects of increased blood pressure on task performance where the means of raising the blood pressure are independent of the task and do not distract from the performance of the task. One might regard worries, and other internal symbolic activities, as the "effective conditioned stimuli" which are built into the subject, but these are chronic or recurrent stimuli producing chronic or recurrent physiological responses, whose effect in disrupting task performance is undoubtedly different and probably less than would be the effects of acute stimuli and responses. We need research on individuals in which certain autonomic states or levels are present more or less chronically, and in which the stimuli or events which arouse or maintain these states are not directly competing with the task stimuli and are not contingent upon task reponses.

"Anxiety" and Task Performances

Hypertensives are markedly more anxious and obsessive-compulsive and show less ability to express aggression than normals or even pychiatric patients (Gressel, Shope, Saslow, DuBois, and Shroeder, 1949), and they show these characteristics more than other kinds of psychosomatic patients (Gildea, 1949). It would be reasonable to assume that individuals with other dangerous cardiovascular diseases would be more anxious also, although Gildea (1949); Miles, Waldfogel, Barrabee, and Cobb (1954); Friedman and Rosenman (1959); and others indicate that coronary disease patients have personalities quite different from hypertensives, and not too different from normal controls, except that the coronary disease patients tend to be ambitious, striving hard workers, less contemplative and more action-oriented, and perhaps a little mor sociable and well-liked than normals.

There is an extensive literature organized around the rubric of "task performance as a function of anxiety." In regard to the tasks reviewed in this paper, Goldstone (1955) found that highly anxious psychiatric outpatients had significantly poorer flicker fusion thresholds than psychiatric outpatients who were rated as less anxious, and many studies—some of which will be discussed in the paragraphs to follow—indicate interactions between kind and circumstances of task and psychometrically defined anxiety level. On the other hand, Cohen and White (1951) investigated, after twenty years, 273 individuals who had been diagnosed with the more or less interchangeable labels of neurocirculatory asthenia, neurasthenia, effort syndrome, or anxiety neurosis, and found no more than the expected incidence of hypertension, heart diseases, or several other disorders thought to be especially psychosomatic in origin. In fact, only eighteen of these cases died of anything, where 34.6 was the actuarially expected number.

Since anxiety neurotics are often the implicit or explicit criterial groups for defining anxiety—particularly psychometrically measured anxiety—it would appear that much of the psychological literature on "anxiety and performance" would have to be applied with great caution in accounting for the performance differences related to cardiovascular disease states. While there are other interesting personality differences between normal controls and coronary or arteriosclerotic heart disease patients, and between both of them and essential hypertensives, we will dwell primarily on the possibility that differences in "anxiety" caused the performance differences described in this paper, for the simple reason that "anxiety" is the only emotional-disruption or distraction type of personal variable which has been studied extensively relative to task performances in reasonably "normal," non-psychiatric subjects.

In examining the possibility that the performance differences we are trying to account for were due to some kind of emotional disruption or distraction or some other difference in the attitudinal-motivational area, we have some bits and pieces to go on:

As described previously (Spieth, 1964), we found that among the "volunteer" non-hypertensive arteriosclerotic and coronary heart disease cases, the "outside volunteer" cases (group IIIb) who presumably were under less situational stress than the main group of patients, performed somewhat more poorly than the latter group. We also found that the highly-stressed "false positive" cases performed as well as the healthy cases. Thus, we conclude that this testing situation and these tests were not particularly stressful and/or that the performances of arteriosclerotic cardiovascular disease cases are not especially prone to situational anxiety.

It is important to note that all of the tasks in the studies reviewed in this paper were self-paced. Tasks can have three levels of "pacing stress": first, the self-paced task in which the subject is "stressed" by exhortation to perform rapidly on a task which "stands still" for the subject; secondly, there are "step-paced" tasks—typified by the memory drum—in which the response to a unit or item must be made within a time limit, and where a wrong or omitted response does not change the nature of the remainder of the task; thirdly, there is the "super-paced" task— typified by many continuous tracking tasks—in which a segment of incorrect performance makes the next segment more difficult to achieve, and so on, so that the task tends to "get out of control" when errors are made. One would expect a person who is especially susceptible to "emotional disorganization" to be least penalized by the self-paced task and most penalized by the super-paced task. There is unpublished evidence that this is true: in a program of research in which I participated under the direction of Prof. Don Lewis, about 1950, we gave three tasks to a large number of college students whose scores on the Taylor Manifest Anxiety Scale (1953) were available. All three tasks involved complex perceptual-motor coordination skills. The first was self-paced, the second was a tracking task, but a rather slow one with a "natural" or expected relationship between the controls and the target-follower, and the third was a tracking task with the relationship between control and target-follower movements of the position-velocity type with some difficult inertial, backlash, and accelerative characteristics also. Few ever mastered this beast. In contrasting the performances of the psychometrically "highly anxious" with the "less anxious" subjects, I found a clear-cut interaction, the anxious subjects being clearly superior on the self-paced task and somewhat inferior on the third, with the two groups performing similarly on the second task.*

There is a considerable body of facts concerning psycho-metrically measured anxiety—proneness and task performance, which is described in reviews by Taylor (1956), Sarason (1960), and Martin (1961). Most of the work has been done with psycho-metrically highly anxious and less anxious college students, and most has been concerned with step-paced verbal learning tasks. The gist of many studies is that there is an interaction between anxiety, and task difficulty, intra-task confusability, speed of presentation, or stress induced in the situation by a variety of means. Usually, it is found that anxious students will be superior or equal to the less anxious on simpler, less stressful, unpaced or less rapidly paced tasks, and tend to be inferior on the faster paced, more stressed, or more confusing task versions. In attempting to apply these rules of thumb to the task situations reviewed in this paper, it should be noted that hypertensive and other cardiovascular diseased people have been found slower and poorer on a wide range of unpaced tasks, varying from unhurried judgments of flicker fusion threshold and finger tapping to the rather tricky mental arithmetic problems used by Anderson and the difficult but untimed Halstead Categories Test. There was some indication of a complexity-by-deficit interaction, in that the pathological subjects did relatively less poorly on the simpler than on the more complicated stimulus-matching tests on the Psychomet. However, on the most complicated speeded tests— The Block Design and Tactual Performance Tests—the patho-logical cases were not disproportionately slower than on the bulk of the Psychomet tests.

To recapitulate, the studies reviewed in this paper concern differences in performance on unpaced tasks which should, if any-

---

* The interpretation of these data was made difficult because the design called for running each subject to a performance criterion, *or* for *n* trials. Contrary to expectation, a large number of subjects did not reach the performance criterion in *n* trials on one or another of the tasks. In my analysis of the data (which differed from that performed by other members of the project) I retained all cases and assigned conservatively extrapolated scores to those who had met a criterion in the number of trials allowed. With these estimated scores to fill the gaps, the anxiety-by-task interaction was unmistakably significant.

thing, give the advantage to the anxious individual. Performance differences were found on tasks varying widely in complexity, where the simpler would not penalize, or might favor, the anxious individual; and in the one study which appeared to have two degrees of general situational stress built into it (Spieth, 1964), the presumably less stressed non-hypertensive pathological cases did at least as poorly as the presumably more stressed, while there was a possibility, obscured by the confounding of situational stress and hypotensive medication, that essential hypertensives performed more poorly than they might in a more casual situation.

The problem of "biological" versus "psychological" causes of the performance differences could be partly solved by running normal and pathological subjects in repeated sessions with maximal opportunity for emotional adaptation and habituation to take place. If the differences reviewed in this paper reflect "psychological" or transient "dynamic" differences, the performance differences should disappear across several testing sessions.

Other Personal Variables and Task Performance

Deeply depressed individuals are slow at tasks, and acute myocardial infarction patients are sometimes quite depressed at the time, but after recovery from acute clinical symptoms these individuals show no evidence of deep depression (Miles, *et al.,* 1954; Gildea, 1949), nor do hypertensives (Gildea).

Finally, there is one special kind of possible "motivational" cause of the performance differences which can be ruled out: Anderson found that his coronary heart disease patients made more errors, even while working more slowly, which shows that their slowness did not represent a differential preoccupation with accuracy at the expense of speed.

Some personality characteristics predict the development of clinical symptoms of coronary heart disease: Brozek and Keys (1963), who had administered the Minnesota Multiphasic Personality Inventory and the Thurstone Temperament Schedules to 258 business and professional men reported in a fourteen year follow-up that thirty-one had developed coronary heart disease and 138 remained healthy throughout. The coronary group gave significantly more "hypochondriasis" responses, which could be interpreted as self-recognition of the early stages of real disease. The coronary group also showed significantly more masculine interests. In the Thurstone schedule, they scored significantly higher on the "activity drive" scale, indicating significantly greater tendencies to eat, talk, walk, and drive fast. I have not found any data on how these personality characteristics might affect performance. Some of the personal characteristics associated with arteriosclerotic and coronary diseases are the tendency to be descended from or related to victims of these diseases, to be obese, to eat fatty foods, and to smoke (Russek and Zohman, 1958). Individual measures which predict essential hypertension include blood pressure lability as described earlier, and a familial correlation. Also, the markedly "subnormal assertiveness" and marked obsessive-compulsive behavior of hypertensives would seem to be the kind of stable personality patterns which, in some degree, very probably predate the clinical manifestations of the disease.

I have not been able to find correlations between any of these personal factors and speed of performance on self-paced psychological tests. However, I expect to run correlations between performance and obesity, familial disease history, smoking, blood pressure, cholesterol level, and combinations of these, among our non-pathological cases, as my next project.

SCIENTIFIC IMPLICATIONS OF SLOW PERFORMANCE

How much do differences in speed of performance tell us about individuals? Perhaps they could tell us much more than we psychologists realize. A rule of thumb has gained currency among psychologists to the effect that "verbal abilities tend to increase with adult age while performance abilities decline." This is true only when the verbal abilities are in untimed "tests" depending largely upon previously verbal learning. When a verbal test is stringently timed, the adult age trend is downward: the most precipitous "age decline" that we have been able to find in the literature was on a speeded test of choosing verbal analogies. This same study reported that in a companion speeded information inventory, the number of items attempted dropped progressively with age while the percentage of attempted items gotten correctly rose progressively with age, the scores of total correct remaining almost constant over the adult age range studied, which was eighteen to sixty years (Jones, 1959).

Williams, Lubin, and Gieseking (1959) and Lubin, Gieseking and Williams (1962) report results with speeded tests which suggest a logical parallel to the age-speed problem. In re-administering an Army Classification Battery of stringently timed tests to sixty-four subjects who had suffered traumatic brain injury after the first administration of the Battery, to 159 who had developed schizophrenia subsequent to the first administration, and to 162 controls, they found the relative deficit scores of both impaired groups to be fairly uniform across tests differing widely in content and in degree of pre-existing knowledge tapped. The clerical speed task scores showed large declines in both impaired groups. It seems likely that the "speededness" of tests rather than their "content" is the critical factor in producing differences between normals and many different kinds of impaired subpopulations. Confusion could be avoided if leniently timed "knowledge inventories" were called that, rather than "tests." When a test requires either speed or efficient dealing with fairly difficult and fairly novel relationships, the adult age-trend of performance is always downward beyond early middle age if not earlier.

The major import of the present results is that a great deal of mean "age changes" in cross-sectional studies of psychological performance might better be attributed to disease processes which are not inexorably bound up with age, but are merely positively correlated with age. The incidence of cardiovascular diseases and their increase with age are high enough to account for much of the reported downward trends of mean psychological test scores with age. For example, White, Edwards, and Dry (1950) report important degrees of coronary arteriosclerosis in about 20 per cent of males aged thirty-five, 50 per cent of those aged forty-five, and about 75 per cent of those aged fifty-five. After that the incidence curve declines with age, due to a rampant death rate. Elsewhere, it is shown that the incidence of substantial degrees of ballistocardiographic anomalies among males is near zero at age thirty, about 50 per cent at age fifty-two, and 100 per cent at age seventy-five (Scarborough, Davis, Baker, Mason, Singewald, Lore, and Fox, 1953); however, Scarborough, in a personal communication, warns that the clinical significance of these anomalies is somewhat controversial. We need assume only that the progressively older age samples in a typical study of psychological performance contain increasing percentages of the kind of mild-to-moderate cardiovascular disease cases studies here, in order to predict many typical "aging effects."

For the sake of the argument, let us conjecture that advanced chronological age "per se" has little effect on mental efficiency. Figure 3 illustrates this notion: assume that the health composition of the whole population changes with age somewhat in the manner of the upper graph. Assume further, as in the middle graph, that each level of impairment has its own bell-shaped distribution of performance levels, but that age *per se* has no effect. If we were to draw samples of various ages from this population and exclude only the frankly impaired or disabled, we would get performance score distributions like those shown in the bottom graph. In the youngest samples we would get unimpaired performances, at the next older age we would get mostly unimpaired performances with some impaired ones, so that the distribution of scores would be negatively skewed; with a still older age group we would get a bell-shaped distribution of scores with enlarged variance and lower mean, and, finally, in a quite elderly sample, we would get a positively skewed score distribution of quite low mean.

We have been able to find only one published study giving the distributions of scores for large samples of adult individuals of a wide age range: this is the study of Birren and Botwinick (1951). Figure 4 reproduces their figure. Note the pronounced trends mentioned above: the variance increasing through middle age and then decreasing, the shapes of the distributions going from bell-shaped to negatively skewed to bell-shaped again, and then to positively skewed, with the means showing the typical age curve reported in many studies.

There is undoubtedly a great deal more to aging than cardiovascular or other particular diseases. This is implied by Figure 1, which shows a significant downtrend of speed with age among

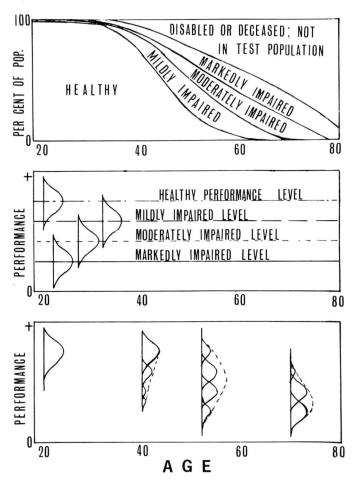

Figure 3. Illustration of the manner in which age decrements found in a cross-sectional study might be accounted for. The top graph represents changes in the hypothetical health status of a population with age; the middle graph represents hypothetical distributions of response speeds associated with each health state; the bottom graph represents the distributions of response speeds that would be expected if the top and middle graphs were true and samples of individuals were drawn from all health levels that did not show gross or obvious impairment or disability.

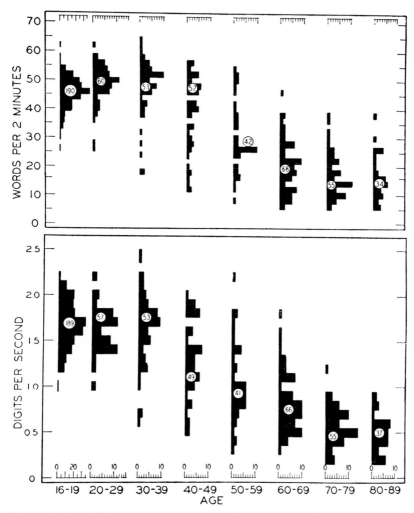

Figure 4. Age differences in writing speed. Frequency polygons are shown for each age group. The total number of subjects in each age group is indicated in each individual distribution (after Birren and Botwinick, 1957). Note the resemblance of these two graphs to the bottom graph of Figure 3.

the healthy group of rather superior individuals. However, it also would be very profitable, when studying differences between older and younger age groups, to examine the subjects' cardiovascular health status.

REFERENCES

Anderson, Duane: (1963) An evaluation of the fusion frequency of flicker and related phenomena as indices of sedentary fatigue and/or levels of excitability of the central nervous system. Ph.D. Thesis, U. of Minnesota.

Apter, N. S., Halstead, W. C. and Heimburger, R. F.: (1951) Impaired cerebral functions in essential hypertension, *Am. J. Psychiat.*, 107:808-813.

Birren, J. E.: (1963) Psychophysiological Relations. In *Human Aging: A Biological and Behavioral Study*, Birren, et al., eds., U. S. Public Health Service Pub. No. 986, Washington, D. C., p. 292.

Birren, J. E. and Botwinick, J.: (1951) The relation of writing speed to age in the senile psychoses. *J. Consult. Psychol.*, 15:243-249.

Birren, J. E., Riegel, K. F. and Morrison, D. F.: (1962) Age differences in response speed as a function of controlled variations of stimulus conditions: evidence of a general speed factor, *Gerontologia*, 6:1-18.

Birren, J. E. and Spieth, W.: (1962) Age, response speed, and cardiovascular functions. *J. Geront.*, 17:390-391.

Blomstrand, R. and Lofgren, F.: (1956) Influence of emotional stress on the renal circulation. *Psychosom. Med.*, 18:420-426.

Brozek, J. and Keys, A.: (1963) Scores on personality inventories in the prediction of the development of coronary heart disease (abstract No. 468). Sixth International Congress of Gerontology, *Excerpta Med.*, 57:193.

Cannon, W. B.: (1920) *Bodily Changes in Pain, Hunger, Fear and Rage.* New York, Appleton-Century-Crofts.

Cohen, M. E. and White, P. D.: (1951) Life situations, emotions, and neurocirculatory asthenia (anxiety neurosis, neurasthenia, effort syndrome). *Psychosom. Med.*, 13:335-355.

Enzer, N., Simonson, E. and Blankstein, S. S.: (1942) Fatigue of patients with circulatory insufficiency, investigated by means of fusion frequency of flicker. *Ann. Intern. Med.*, 16:701-707.

Finkelstein, A. E., Woerner, T. E., Smith, J. C., Bayles, T. B., Levine, H. D. and Kwork, G.: (1963) Abnormal globulins in myocardial infarction with special reference to a material coating erythrocytes and a cold-insoluble protein. *Amer. J. Med.*, 35:163-168.

Fishberg, A. M.: (1939) *Hypertension and Nephritis.* Philadelphia, Lea & Febinger, p. 289ff.

Friedman, M. and Rosenman, R. H.: (1959) Association of specific overt behavior pattern with blood and cardiovascular findings, *J. A. M. A., 169*:1286-1296.

Friedman, M., Rosenman, R. H. and Carroll, V.: (1958) Changes in the serum cholesterol and blood clotting time in men subjected to cyclic variation of occupational stress. *Circulation, 17*:852-861.

Frolkis, V. V.: (1962) Peculiarities of the reflex regulation of the activity of the cardiovascular system during the senescence of the organism. *Medical and Clinical Aspects of Aging,* H. Blumenthal, ed., New York, Columbia U. Press, pp. 440-445.

Gellhorn, E. and Loofbourrow, G. N.: (1963) *Emotions and Emotional Disorders; a Neurophysiological Study.* New York, Hoeber Div., Harper & Row.

Gildea, E. F.: (1949) Special features of personality which are common to certain psychosomatic disorders. *Psychosom. Med., 11*:273.

Glaser, E. M. and Griffen, J. P.: (March 1962) Influence of the cerebral cortex on habituation. *J. Physiol., 160*:429-445.

Goldstone, S.: (1955) Flicker fusion measurements and anxiety level. *J. Exp. Psychol., 49*:200-202.

Graham, J. D. P.: (1945) High blood pressure after battle. *Lancet, 1*:239.

Gressel, G. C., Shobe, F. O., Saslow, G., DuBois, P. H. and Schroeder, H. A.: (1949) Personality factors in essential hypertension. *J. A. M. A., 140*:265-268.

Grundy, S. M. and Griffen, A. C.: (1959) Effects of periodic mental stress in serum cholesterol levels. *Circulation, 19*:496.

Gunn, C. G., Friedman, M. and Byers, S. O.: (1960) Effect of chronic hypothalamic stimulation on cholesterol-induced atherosclerosis in the rabbit. *J. Clin. Invest., 39*:1963-1972.

Halstead, W. C.: (1947) *Brain and Intelligence.* Chicago, U. Chicago Press.

Hellon, R. F. and Lind, A. R.: (1956) Observations on the activity of sweat glands with special reference to the influence of aging. *J. Physiol., (London), 133*:132.

Hickham, J. B., Cargell, W. H. and Golden, A.: (1948) Cardiovascular reactions to emotional stimuli: effect on cardiac output, AV oxygen difference, arterial pressure, and peripheral resistance. *J. Clin. Invest., 27*:290.

Hokanson, J. E. and Shetler, S.: (1961) The effect of overt aggression on physiological arousal level. *J. Soc. Abnorm. Psychol., 63*:446-448.

Imhof, P., Hürlimann, A. and Steinmann, B.: (1957) Über blutdruck-steigerung bei psychischen belastung. *Cardiologia, 31*:272.

Jolliffe, N.: (1959) Fats, cholesterol, and coronary heart disease. *Circulation, 20*:109.

Jones, H. E.: (1959) Intelligence and problem solving. Chap. 22 in *Handbook of Aging and the Individual,* J. E. Birren, ed., Chicago, U. Chicago Press, pp. 724-725.

Kety, S.: (1960) The cerebral circulation. *Neurophysiology,* Handbook of Physiology, Amer. Physiol. Soc., Baltimore, Williams & Williams Co., Vol. III, Sec. 1, Chapter LXXI.

Krasno, L. R. and Ivy, A. C.: (1950) The Response of the Flicker Fusion Threshold to Nitroglycerine and Its Potential Value in the Diagnosis, Prognosis, and Therapy of Subclinical and Clinical Cardiovascular Disease. *Circulation, 1:*1267-1276.

Kraus, A. S. and Lilienfeld, A. M.: (1959) Some epidemiologic aspects of the high mortality rate in the young widowed group. *J. Chron. Dis., 10:*207-217.

Levy, R. L., Hillman, O. C., Stroud, W. D. and White, P. D.: (1944) Transient hypertension: its significance in terms of later development of sustained hypertension and cardiovascular-renal disease. *J. A. M. A., 126:*829-831.

Lind, A. R. and Hellon, R. F.: (1962) *Changes in Thermoregulatory Process in Man Due to Aging; Biological Aspects of Aging.* N. Shock, ed., New York, Columbia U. Press, p. 208.

Lubin, A., Gieseking, C. F. and Williams, H. L.: (1962) Direct measurement of cognitive deficit in schizophrenia. *J. Consult. Psychol., 26:* 139-143.

Malmo, R. B. and Shagass, C.: (1952) Studies of blood pressure in psychiatric patients under stress. *Psychosom. Med., 14:*82-93.

Martin, B.: (1961) The assessment of anxiety by physiological behavioral measures. *Psychol. Bull., 58:*234-255.

Mathur, K. S., Kashyap, S. K. and Kumar, V.: (1963) Correlation of the extent and severity of atherosclerosis in the coronary and cerebral arteries. *Circulation, 27:*929-934.

Miles, H. W.: Waldfogel, S., Barrabee, E. L. and Cobb, S.: (1954) Psychosomatic study of 46 young men with coronary artery disease. *Psychosom. Med., 16:*455-477.

Minc, S., Sinclair, G. and Taft, R.: (1963) Some psychological factors in coronary heart disease. *Psychosom. Med., 25:*133-139.

Minimoshvili, D. I., with Magakian, G. O., and Kokaia, I.: (1960) Experimental neurosis in monkeys, and attempts to obtain a model of hypertension and coronary insufficiency in monkeys. In *Theoretical and Practical Problems of Medicine and Biology in Experiments on Monkeys,* I. A. Utkin, ed., New York, Pergamon.

Myaskinov, A. L.: (1958) Influence of some factors on development of experimental cholesterol atherosclerosis. *Circulation, 17:*99.

Reitan, R. M.: (1954) Intellectual and affective changes in essential hypertension. *Amer. J. Psychiat., 110:*817-824.

Reitan, R. M.: (1958) Validity of the trail marking test as an indication of organic brain damage. *Perceptual and Motor Skills*, 8:271-276.

Reitan, R. M. and Shipley, R. E.: (1963) The relationship of serum cholesterol changes to psychological abilities. *J. Geront.*, 18:350-357.

Ruskin, A., Beard, C. W. and Shaffer, R. C.: (1948) Blast hypertension: elevated arterial pressure and victims of the Texas City disaster. *Am. J. Med.*, 4: 228.

Russek, H. I. and Zohman, E. I.: (1958) Relative significance of heredity, diet, and occupational stress in coronary heart disease of young adults. *Am. J. Med. Sci.*, 235:266-275.

Sarason, I. G.: (1960) Empirical findings and theoretical problems in the use of anxiety scales. *Psychol. Bull.*, 57:403-415.

Scarborough, W. R., Davis, F. W., Baker, B. M., Mason, R. E., Singewald, M. D., Lore, S. A. and Fox, C. M.: (1953) A ballistocardiographic study of 369 apparently normal persons. *Amer. Heart J.*, 45:161.

Schneider, R. A. and Zangari, V. M.: (1951) Variations in clotting time relative viscosity and other physiochemical properties of blood accompanying physical and emotional stress in normotensive and hypertensive subjects. *Psychosom. Med.*, 13:289-303.

Schnore, M. M.: (1959) Individual patterns of physiological activity as a function of task differences and degree of arousal. *J. Exp. Psychol.*, 58: 117-127.

Schunk, J.: (1954) Emotionale faktoren in der pathogenese der essentiellen hypertonie. *Z. Klin. Med.*, 152:251-280.

Shock, N.: Personal communication.

Simonson, E.: (1958) Russian physiology (cardiovascular aspects). *Ann. Rev. Physiol.*, 20.

Simonson, E.: (1960) Russian research on the role of visceral reflexes in coronary insufficiency. *Circulation*, 22:1179-1184.

Simonson, E. and Brozek, J.: (1959) Russian research on arterial hypertension. *Ann. Intern. Med.*, 50:129.

Simsonson, E. and Enzer, N.: (1941) State of motor centers in circulatory insufficiency. *Arch. Intern. Med.*, 68:498-512.

Sokoloff, L.: (1959) Circulation and metabolism of brain in relation to the process of aging. Chap. 10 in *The Process of Aging in the Nervous System*, J. E. Birren, H. I. Imus, and W. F. Windle, eds., Springfield, Thomas.

Spieth, W.: (1964, in press) Cardiovascular health status, age, and psychological performance. *J. Geront.*

Swank, R. L.: (1954) Effect of high fat feedings on the viscosity of the blood. *Science*, 120:427-428, Sept. 10.

Taylor, J. A.: (1953) A personality scale of manifest anxiety. *J. Abnorm. Soc. Psychol.*, 48:285-290.

Thomas, C. B. and Murphy, E. A.: (1958) Further studies in cholesterol levels in The Johns Hopkins medical students: effects of stress at examinations. *J. Chron. Dis.*, 8:661.

Uhley, H. N. and Friedman, M.: (1959) Blood lipids, clotting, and coronary atherosclerosis in rats exposed to a particular form of stress. *Am. J. Physiol.*, 197:396.

Wechsler Adult Intelligence Scales: (1947, 1955) The Psychological Corp., 304 East 45th Street, New York 17, New York.

Wertlake, P. T., Wilcox, A. A., Haley, M. I. and Peterson, J. E.: (1958) Relationship of mental and emotional stress to serum cholesterol levels. *Proc. Soc. Exp. Med. Biol.*, 97:163-165.

White, N. K., Edwards, J. E. and Dry, T. J.: (1950) The relationship of the degree of coronary atherosclerosis with age, in men. *Circulation*, 1:645.

Wilkins, R. W.: (1954) Rauwolfia in the treatment of essential hypertension. *Am. J. Med.*, 17:703.

Williams, H. L., Lubin, A. and Gieseking, C. F. (1959) Direct measurement of cognitive deficit in brain-injured patients. *J. Consult. Psychol.*, 23:300-305.

Young, W., Gofman, J. W., Tandy, R. Malamud, N. and Waters, E. S. G.: (1960) The quantitation of artherosclerosis III: the extent of correlation of degree of atherosclerosis within and between the coronary and cerebral vascular beds. *Am. J. Cardiol.*, 6:300-308.

21

PERFORMANCE AS A FUNCTION OF AGE AND CARDIOVASCULAR DISEASE[1]

Ernst Simonson

INTRODUCTION

T HE EFFECT of age and cardiovascular disease on performance involves a multitude of aspects and problems. There are different types of work, dependent on different physiological functions and affected by age and cardiovascular disease in a different way. There are also various types of cardiovascular disease which have to be considered in relation to the stage of disease. Cardiovascular disease also secondarily involves other organs and functions which affect performance in a "vicious circle." Last but not least, age trends in the various tissues, organs and functions in the resting condition are pertinent. For instance, the decrease of the skeletal muscle mass with age explains to a large degree the decrease of musclar strength. On the other hand, the decrease with age of cardiac minute volume at rest is comparatively slight and parallels the decrease of the basal metabolic rate, so that the decrease of cardiac work capacity with age is mainly due to a loss of capacity to increase heart rate and cardiac minute volume with increasing oxygen demand. Determination of this important function at rest, therefore, does not reveal its limitation during work.

[1] In part, supported by Grants NB01859 and HE06314, National Institutes of Health, Bethesda, Md.

The literature on the effect of cardiovascular disease on performance is extensive: In a previous review (Simonson and Enzer, 1942) twenty years ago, 287 references were listed; since that time, the number of investigations has substantially increased. The literature on the effect of age on performance is also extensive but does not approach the number of publications on work performance in cardiovascular disease. In general, age effects have been studied in a larger number of types of performance, while cardiovascular disease has been studied analytically in a greater number of circulatory, respiratory and metabolic functions.

In spite of the voluminous literature, important problems still need further exploration. Most of the types of performance extensively studied were moderately heavy or strenuous exercise which depend on oxygen transport. Types of work which depend mainly on central nervous system (C.N.S.) functions have been less extensively studied but are in the foreground of interest in this volume. However, general cardiovascular impairment will

TABLE 1

Type of Work Performance	Function, System Involved
Severe dynamic (Running bicycle ergometer)	Oxygen transport, pulmonary capacity; heart output; ability to accumulate oxygen debt, or lactic acid
Moderate dynamic (Walking; arm-ergometer)	Energetics (mechanical efficiency); circulation; motor-coordination
Recovery speed of oxygen debt	1st part: circulation; 2nd part: metabolic (muscle, liver)
Static Work (weight holding) (endurance at 50% maximum load)	Resistance against peripheral sensations and peripheral ischemia
Speed; single movements	Muscle force (isotonic): Muscle viscosity; central nervous system
Repeated movements (tapping rate)	Chronaxie, refractory period of motor centers
Strength test (dynamometer)	Muscle force (isometric); central nervous system
Motor reaction time	Sensory-motor synapses
Flicker fusion frequency	Refractory period of visual (sensory) centers
Precision work	Motor coordination

affect also the C.N.S. and, therefore, cardiopulmonary and metabolic functions must be considered in the integrated analysis of
performance impairment.

The multitude of aspects, problems and results concerned with
the impairment of work capacity with age and in cardiovascular
disease cannot be presented in the limitation of this article. In
addition to a condensed presentation of experimental data, I will

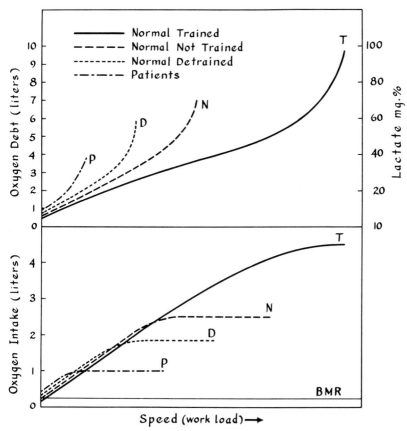

Figure 1. *Lower Part:* Schematic diagram of increase of oxygen and its
maximum level attained in trained young men (T), average healthy young
men (N), detrained or older men (D), and heart patients (P) with increasing work load—absolute and with reference to the basal metabolic
rate (BMR). *Upper Part:* Concomitant increase of oxygen debt (left ordi-
ate) and blood lactate (right ordinate).

try to outline briefly the mechanisms of impairment of performance, discuss in some greater detail the role of the C.N.S., and
attempt to give some perspectives for further research.

COMPARISON OF PERFORMANCE DROP WITH AGE
AND IN CARDIOVASCULAR DISEASE

Table 1 lists several types of performance with the critical
physiological functions. The capacity for types of heavy prolonged (aerobic) work and for strenuous (anaerobic) work depends on the maximum oxygen intake. This is illustrated in
Diagram 1, based on available information from numerous studies.
With general increase of load, the oxygen demand (and consumption) increases until it approaches a plateau, characterizing
the maximum possible oxygen intake, i.e., the maximum energy
which can be made available for physical work. It is increased by
training and decreased with age, lack of exercise and in cardiovascular disease. Below the level of maximum oxygen intake, the
oxygen requirement can be met so that sustained performance
is possible. With heavy loads approaching or exceeding the level
of maximum oxygen intake, the oxygen requirement cannot be
adequately met, resulting in rapid accumulation of metabolic
products (best characterized by blood lactate) and oxygen debt.
Work loads exceeding the maximum level of oxygen intake are,
therefore, called "anaerobic," and those below this level "aerobic."
However, the transition from aerobic to anaerobic work with
increasing work load is gradual rather than a sharp delineation,
as schematically illustrated in Figure 2. The maximum oxygen
intake, therefore, is (with certain limitations, Müller, 1961) the
best available method to determine the reserve capacity for
physical work. The lower the oxygen intake for a given type of
work below the maximum intake, the greater is the reserve capacity which determines also endurance in moderately heavy work.
This correlation, however, decreases after the age of thirty years
(Müller, 1961). According to Christensen (1962) a level of
about 50 per cent of the maximum O_2 intake approximates the
limit for performance continued over several hours. With reduction of the maximum oxygen intake, the load level for sustained
work is correspondingly reduced, and in some ambulatory cardiac

patients even the smallest load is performed under partially anaerobic conditions so that endurance for sustained work is practically reduced to zero.

The correlation between maximum oxygen intake and endurance in submaximum aerobic work may be expected to decrease with the load and level of oxygen consumption. It is dubious whether there is any correlation at lower levels. E. A. Müller has for a long time differentiated between capacity for short strenuous work and for prolonged performance. In his most recent publication on this subject, the discrepancy is demonstrated for people over thirty years (1961). It should be noted that occupational or recreational activity in older men rarely approaches the level of maximum oxygen intake. With prolongation of work, motivation, deterioration of motor coordination or muscular fatigue sensation may limit endurance.

In occupational work, uninterrupted work is a rare exception and, therefore, the effect of short pauses (several seconds to several minutes) must be considered for endurance. Interrup-

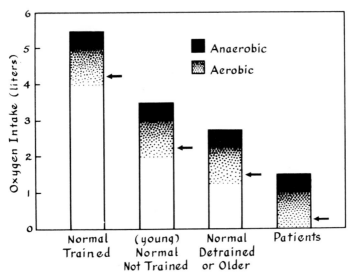

Figure 2. Working capacity in terms of maximum oxygen intake (margin of black areas) depending on physical condition. Stippled areas show transition from aerobic to anaerobic condition. (Reproduced from Simonson, 1958, *Journal of Gerontol.*, *13*, Suppl. No. 2: 18, "Fig. 6").

tion of work (weight lifting) intervals of two minutes by pauses of one minute resulted in a steady state of oxygen consumption (continuous with minor variations through work intervals and pauses) at a lower level than in uninterrupted work (Simonson, 1938). Therefore, pauses decrease the effective metabolic load. The mechanical efficiency was increased in another series of the same type of work with pauses of 1.5 seconds between movements of 1.5 seconds, and the oxygen debt decreased (Simonson and Enzer, 1914A). The improvement of the efficiency is due to increase of the aerobic phase and reduction of the anaerobic phase. While weight lifting is moderately heavy work with loads of 4 and 6 Kilograms, Christensen (1962) confirmed the beneficial effect of short interruptions of strenuous work. Strenuous anaero-

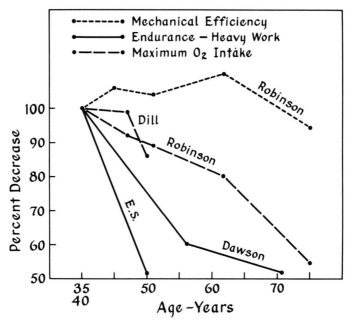

Figure 3. Effect of age on endurance in heavy aerobic work (Dawson and Hellebrandt, 1945) on the maximum O₂ intake in anaerobic work (Dill, 1942; Robinson, 1938) and mechanical efficiency in moderate aerobic work (Robinson, 1938) expressed in per cent of peak performance between thirty and forty years. (Reproduced from *Journal of Gerontol., 13,* Suppl. No. 2:18 "Fig. 5").

bic work with fatigue occurring within a few minutes was converted into moderately heavy aerobic work which could be continued for thirty minutes and longer, with corresponding low
values of blood lactate and oxygen debt.

The diagram in Figure 1 does not apply to the mechanical
efficiency (ratio of work performed and calories expended, calculated from the oxygen consumption). Mechanical efficiency
shows in most types of work an optimum at medium speed
(Atzler, 1927). In general, the optimum contraction speed is
about 0.5 to 0.75 sec. Simonson and Enzer (1941A) found the
mechanical efficiency at contraction speed of lm/0.75 sec. about
60 per cent better than at a contraction speed of lm/3 sec. The
increase of energy expenditure is very steep at fast contraction
speeds below 0.5 sec.

Figure 3 shows the decrease of several types of performance
and functions with age. The decline with age, in per cent of the
peak performance between thirty and forty years, is greatest
for endurance in heavy aerobic work (Dawson and Hellebrandt,
1945, Simonson *et al.*, 1943) the decline of the maximum oxygen
intake is profound but somewhat less steep (Robinson, 1938, Dill,
1942), at least for mechanical efficiency in moderate aerobic
work performed at a steady state of oxygen intake well below the
level of maximum oxygen intake (Robinson, 1938). All types of
work in Figure 3 are continuous performance. It must be expected that the effect of short pauses will be more beneficial for
older people and for heart patients than for healthy persons because their recovery speed is delayed. However, no experimental
data on this important aspect have been reported. It is of great
interest that Durkin and Mikulicic (1956) found no difference
of oxygen consumption, respiratory efficiency and heart rate
between young and older men in arm ergometer work but significantly higher values of older men in walking on the treadmill
at 3.7 m.p.h. The energy expenditure (approximately 6 K cal/
min) was similar for both types of work, i.e., the difference
could not be explained on account of the general metabolic load.
The steep decrease of endurance in heavy, aerobic work with age
may be, in part, due to a change of motivation. Unfortunately,
all endurance tests depend on motivation, while maximum oxygen
intake and mechanical efficiency are objective tests.

In Table 2 (modified Table 6 of a previous publication—Simonson, 1957), the effect of age and cardiovascular disease on various types of performance is compared. The references given in Table 1 are representative and far from complete. The majority of the patients summarized in Table 2 had valvular heart disease or arterial hypertension and were compensated or slightly decompensated (Simonson and Gollwitzer-Mexer, 1930; Simonson and Enzer, 1942). There is a striking similarity between the effect of age and heart disease, implying that impairment of cardiovascular functions is to a large degree responsible for the general decline of performance capacity with age. This, however, applies only to types of work depending on oxygen transport. In this connection, Meerson's (1962) recent results are of great interest. He found that the biochemical changes in the hearts of animals in the compensatory phase of experimental aortic stenosis and senile myocardial changes are strikingly similar: decrease of protein synthesis, decrease in DNA, decrease in oxidative phosphorylation, etc.

The measurement of muscle strength is essential for a general evaluation of physical capacity. It does not depend on the circulatory or metabolic reserve capacity but on the muscular cross section involved and the ability to activate a maximum number of muscle fibers. The handgrip dynamometer is most frequently used, but measurement of the strength of back muscles is preferable because of the much greater muscle mass involved (in addition to back muscles also arm and leg muscles). The person pulls, from bent-over position, the dynamometer grip upward, to more erect position. This test was used in 1836 by Quetelet who found a pronounced decrease of muscle strength with age. In contrast, it is not or only slightly affected in heart disease (Panfilov, 1963). Endurance for static work is usually tested by graphic recording of the drop of muscle tension at one half of the maximum strength and shows no significant age trend (Simonson *et al.*, 1943). According to Müller, endurance is indefinite at 15 per cent of the maximum strength (1961). There is, however, an age trend when endurance is tested at maximum strength (Burke *et al.*, 1953). Critical factors for this type of endurance are interference of peripheral circulation by contracted muscles (Lind-

TABLE 2
Effect of Older Age and Heart Disease on Various Types of Performance and Related Physiologic Functions

Performance, Physiologic Functions	Age	Cardiovascular Disease
Max. O₂ intake	Decreased 1)	Decreased 2)
Speed of initial increase of O₂ cons. in work	Delayed 1)	Delayed 2), 3)
Oxidative recovery	Delayed 1), 4), 20)	Delayed 2), 3)
Mechanical efficiency	Unchanged or moderately decreased at higher age 1), 5)	Unchanged or moderately decreased dependent on degree of decompensation and load 2)
Respiratory efficiency	Decreased 1), 5), 20)	Decreased 2)
Cardiac stroke volume	Decreased 6)	Decreased 2), 6)
Pulse rate recovery	Delayed 1), 20)	Delayed 2)
Endurance, moderately heavy work	Decreased 7), 8)	Decreased 2)
Endurance, static work	Unchanged 9)	Probably little change
Muscle strength	Decreased 10), 11), 12)	Unchanged or slightly decreased 13)
Speed repet. Movements, small muscles	Slightly decreased 14)	Moderately decreased 15)
Motor coordination, small muscles	Unchanged 14), 16), 17), 18)	Probably unchanged
larger muscles	Well maintained 19), 21)	Probably little changed

1) Robinson, 1938
2) Reviewed in Simonson and Enzer, 1942
3) Meakins and Long, 1927
4) König et al., 1962
5) Durkin and Mikulicic, 1956
6) Landowne et al., 1955
7) Dawson and Hellebrandt, 1945
8) Burke et al., 1953
9) Simonson et al., 1943
10) Quetelet, 1836
11) Reijs, 1921
12) Fisher and Birren, 1947
13) Panfilov, 1963
14) Kossoris, 1940
15) Simonson and Enzer, 1941
16) Ascher and Baumgarten, 1925
17) Berg, 1947
18) Stieglitz, 1941
19) Jokl, 1954
20) Frol'kis et al., 1962
21) Smith, 1938

hard, 1920) and tolerance of the C.N.S. to peripheral sensation elicited by accumulating waste products, including possibly a pain producing substance. This test has not been applied to cardiac patients. There is no reason to expect a decrement in cardiovascular patients, except by a change of the C.N.S. sensory thresholds.

Motor coordination, according to available evidence, is well maintained with age (Ascher and Baumgarten, 1925; Berg, 1947; Kossoris, 1940; Jokl, 1954; Miles, 1943; Stieglitz, 1947) and probably also not or only slightly impaired in cardiovascular patients. However, to my knowledge, refined methods such as electromyograms (EMG) or detailed motion analysis have not yet been employed in cardiovascular patients.

Motor coordination deserves much further attention, since deterioration of muscle coordination in fatigue has been known for a long time as main reason for deterioration of mechanical efficiency, due to involvement of auxiliary muscle groups (Atzler, 1928; Simonson, 1930; Simonson *et al.*, 1934; Simonson, 1935). In fatigue, the gross deterioration of muscle coordination can easily be demonstrated with simple methods. Deterioration of the mechanical efficiency (i.e., increase of oxygen consumption) in moderate work is an objective, though indirect criterion for the deterioration of muscle coordination in moderately heavy work in fatigue, but sensitive direct methods would be preferable. The EMG of antagonistic and synergistic muscles show a different phase relationship in fatigue, and this method could also be used in types of light muscular work. Changes of EMG in static work with heavy load is associated, according to Wachholder (1933) with increase of action currents and localized, pronounced sensation of fatigue. The work, however, can be repeated within a short interval. Increase of EMG emplitudes corresponds to increased voluntary impulse strength. With light load, fatigue sensation is dull, the work cannot be repeated for hours or on the same day, and the EMG decreases, possibly due to dissipation of motor impulses over a larger cortical area.

SOME MECHANISMS INVOLVED IN FATIGUE

The discussion of motor coordination leads to discussion of some more general aspects of fatigue. Performance clearly cannot be separated from fatigue, which is, like performance, a complex problem involving many aspects and mechanisms. This author reviewed the physiology of fatigue in 1935; the essential points of the discussion still appear to be valid, aithough, of course, much additional information is now available. Fatigue in man is always a subjective phenomenon. It was suggested that the basis for subjective fatigue is a disproportion between the strength of effort, i. e., of motor impulses and the resulting work. It is still easier to rule out involvement of various functions and factors in fatigue of the whole organism (particularly in man) than to demonstrate specific mechanisms of fatigue. Accumulation of waste products, for instance, is not the determining factor (Simonson and Sirkina, 1936). The C.N.S. appears to be the limiting factor not only in man for any type of work, but also for animals so low on a comparative phylogenetic scale as frogs. Muscles from frogs exhausted by reflex stimulation (i.e. unable to move on strong pain stimuli) respond immediately, i.e., a few seconds after removal, to direct and indirect electrical stimulation (Simonson, 1942). However, the contraction was diminished as compared to the contralateral muscle with section of the sciatic nerve before the exhausting reflex stimulation, so that some peripheral muscular fatigue was also present. In rats, it is difficult to produce fatigue by rhythmic tetanic direct or indirect muscle stimulation—even with continued tetanic stimulation it may take one hour or more to produce complete fatigue (Simonson, Omachi and Visscher, 1946). In man, direct electrical stimulation produces contractions immediately after complete fatigue with the Mosso finger-ergograph.

The limiting factor of the C.N.S. for performance in heavy aerobic and anaerobic work has been demonstrated in man by experiments with hypnosis. Schattenstein and Njemtsova (Proceed. 15th Intern. Physiol. Congress, Leningrad 1935, p. 444, quoted from E. Simonson, 1935) found that hypnotic suggestion of a lighter load than actually performed on the bicycle ergometer decreased the oxygen consumption from 15 to 43 per cent and delayed the onset of fatigue, while suggestion of a heavier load had the opposite effect. In experiments of this reviewer, hypnotic suggestion improved (i.e., shortened) the time for the 100 meter dash in well-trained athletes, below the value ever attained by the same athletes before or after these experiments (Simonson, 1937). This does not contradict the importance of oxygen transport as discussed before but shows that for the performance in man the C.N.S. cannot be ignored for fatigue and endurance even in types of heavy muscular work. It has not been shown, however, that the maximum oxygen intake can be increased by hypnotic suggestion; obviously it is the tolerance to physico-chemical changes in heavy work which can be affected by the C.N.S.

These results are probably pertinent for the effect of motivation, in that they show this effect in an exaggerated way. The motivation for heavy muscular work is depressed in older people, and this may be, in part, responsible for the pronounced drop of endurance in heavy work, exceeding that of the maximum oxygen intake.

Two observations by Russian physiologists are particularly pertinent for fatigue of motor performance. About sixty years ago, Vedenskii stimulated an afferent nerve (N. peroneus) recording the reflex muscle contraction. At the moment of complete fatigue, stimulation of the efferent motor nerve, superimposed on the continued stimulation of the N. peroneus, produced contraction again. The same result was obtained with superimposed stimulation of a second afferent nerve (N. tibialis). (The same reflex-contraction can be produced by stimulation of different afferent nerves, since they are connected with different spinal motor neurons through intraspinal pathways.) Therefore, reflex fatigue is located in the neurons of the stimulated afferent nerve.

It has been demonstrated by these simple experiments that sensory centers are more sensitive to fatigue than motor centers, and this has been supported by further experimental evidence. It probably applies also to circulatory disturbance producing cerebral hypoxia or ischemia. The fact that immediately after complete fatigue in static work the same muscles, in a different functional combination, are capable to perform other types of (particularly dynamic) work also speaks for primary fatigue of sensory centers (Simonson, 1935).

Coordinated performance involves sensory as well as motor centers and pathways, and thus, study of the various sensory receptors, particularly skin and muscle receptors and visual pathways, are as important as the study of motor centers and pathways for analysis of performance and fatigue, and as basis for age trends and effects of cardiovascular disease.

In our experience, the decrement of a sensitive visual function, the flicker fusion frequency (FFF) with age (Simonson *et al.*, 1941) and in heart disease (Enzer, Simonson and Blankstein, 1942) is more pronounced and consistent than the decrement of motor function (Simonson and Enzer, 1941).

The other observation is Orbeli's restitution effect. Muscle fatigue was produced by stimulation of the anterior spinal roots; superimposed stimulation of the sympathetic chain restored muscle contraction (Orbeli, 1932; Ginezinski, 1923, Tonkikh, 1927). Asher (1931) and his associates (Maibach, 1928; Labhart, 1929) confirmed this phenomenon in extensive investigations, but most interesting is its reproduction by O. Lowenstein (1937) and Lowenstein and Loewenfeld (1952) in the restitution of the fatigued pupillary reflex in man by strong acoustic or skin stimuli. Lowenstein and Loewenfeld (1952) demonstrated that this phenomenon is involved in the spontaneous restitution in fatigue. Therefore, Orbeli's restitution effect is important for maintenance of continued performance, by overcoming fatigue.

Studies of the effect of Pervitin (Desoxyephedrine) and Benzedrine (Amphetamine) on the tapping rate may be related to the Orbeli phenomenon, since both drugs are central sympathetic stimulants. Benzedrine increases the maximum attainable tapping frequency (Simonson, Enzer and Blankstein, 1941), while Pervitin improves the endurance (Simonson and Enzer, 1942). Both effects were statistically significant.

There is evidence, based on cardiovascular reflexes (heart rate and blood pressure) that the response to sympathicomimetic and sympathicolytic, and to vagomimetic and vagolytic drugs is decreased with age (Frolkis, 1962) in man, and observations on circulatory postural reflexes (Simonson, 1959) are in the same line. A decrease in the range of heart rate produced by nitroglycerin (increase) and breathing of NH_3 fumes (bradycardia) has been demonstrated in experimental aortic stenosis by Meerson (1961), reviewed by Simonson and Lieberman (1963).

The general decreased reactivity of the autonomic nervous

system with age and in heart disease limits the range of physio-logical adaptation to work and reduces the efficiency of Orbeli's restitution effect. In this connection, it is of interest that failure to increase the heart rate is by most investigators (since Dill and Robinson) held as the limiting factor for performance capacity in heavy work. A decreased effect of Orbeli's phenomenon with age has not yet been demonstrated by comparison of young and older animals, but it appears reasonable to expect it. Thus, one of the physiological mechanisms important for overcoming fatigue and for endurance (acting as feed-back mechanism) is probably less effective in older people.

The effect of strong sensory stimuli on endurance is known for a long time. Feré (1904) increased substantially finger-ergograph performance with different sensory stimuli. Most likely, the effect of sensory stimuli is mediated through the sympathetic nervous system.

MECHANISMS OF CIRCULATORY IMPAIRMENT

Circulatory limiting factors for work performance are 1) gen-eral circulatory-respiratory capacity for oxygen transport; 2) car-diovascular reflex regulations; and 3) localized ischemia. These three types of limitations may occur single or combined.

1) Circulatory-respiratory capacity sets, as was discussed, the limit for all types of work with oxygen demand close to the maxi-mum oxygen intake and somewhat below this level. The C.N.S. is involved, as discussed in the preceding section, as far as the tolerance to physico-chemical changes in exercise is concerned, but, of course, cannot compensate for inadequate oxygenation. In general, cardiac capacity is more important than pulmonary capacity, although cardiac decompensation may involve secon-darily pulmonary capacity or vice versa, for instance in em-physema. In most patients who are able to walk, circulatory-respiratory capacity is not a limiting factor for types of sedentary work, since the oxygen consumption is substantially below that required for walking. In some patients, however, the circulatory-respiratory capacity is so low that it limits the performance even for light work. Patients with slight decompensation (or cardiac insufficiency only at work, but not at rest), due to valvular heart

disease or hypertension, fall into this group, but cardiac decompensation may develop also in pulmonary, metabolic or infectious diseases. For instance, the post-exercise oxidative recovery is prolonged after infectious diseases (E. Simonson and C. Gollwitzer-Meier 1931), and the reduction of work capacity in various diseases by reducing speed and limit of oxidations and associated cardiovascular functions is well documented (Simonson and Enzer, 1942).

2) Cardiovascular regulations, important for circulatory adaptation to work, may be affected by age. This has been demonstrated for the postural adjustment of peripheral circulation, reducing the capacity of older people for work performed in standing positions (Simonson, 1959).

3) Most important, however, is localized ischemia due to atherosclerosis, in the heart (coronary heart disease), in the brain (cerebral ischemia), in the peripheral arteries, or in the kidneys. Renal atherosclerosis produces secondary arterial hypertension and cardiac involvement, but will not be discussed here.

Localized myocardial ischemia producing angina of effort due to coronary insufficiency is clinically the most important limitation of work capacity in the elderly. Angina pectoris occurs when the oxygen consumption exceeds a critical level for the oxygen requirement of the heart, usually far below the otherwise attainable level of oxygen intake. Below this critical level, the cardiovascular and metabolic processes of patients with coronary heart disease are similar to that of healthy subjects. The critical level shows considerable interindividual and intraindividual variation, but for most patients with coronary disease, the clinically used electrocardiographic exercise tests exceed it, so that an abnormal response of the electrocardiogram (ECG) results. An abnormal exercise test may actually precede by several years the development of clinical coronary heart disease.

The typical abnormal response to exercise in coronary insufficiency is characterized by depression of the S-T segment and inversion of the T wave (so-called "ischemic response"). It is shown in Figure 4 C and cannot be reproduced in healthy persons by severe anaerobic work (Fig. 4 N) which produces entirely different ECG changes, most typical an increase of the T wave.

This type of response, however, was found in patients with aortic insufficiency (Fig. 4 A) at a much lower level of exercise, probably indicating relative cardiac work insufficiency. In healthy persons, the changes of the ECG at moderate work, such as used for exercise tests in patients with suspected coronary heart disease, are minor.

The state of peripheral circulation in the legs is important for work capacity involving locomotion since peripheral atherosclerosis is much more common in leg arteries than in arm arteries.

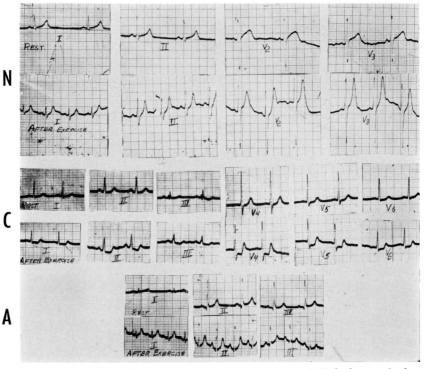

Figure 4. Electrocardiogram of a healthy young man (N) before and after severe work (running at a speed of 7 m.p.h. at 10% grade). Note the large increase of T waves. A similar response is shown in a patient with aortic insufficiency (A) at moderate work (walking at 3 m.p.h.). The typical abnormal (ischemic) response of a patient with coronary insufficiency (C) is entirely different (S-T depression with diphasic T). (Reproduced from Simonson, E. "Differentiation between normal and abnormal in electrocardiography," C. V. Mosby, 1961, Fig. 41.)

This can be evaluated by plethysmographic methods. Photo-electric toe-pulse records or impedance-plethysmography reveal early insufficiency of peripheral circulation, often long before appearance of clinical symptoms (Simonson, *et al.*, 1955). We prefer impedance-plethysmography because it is not limited to transparent tissues. Impedance-plethysmography is based on different conductivity of blood from most other tissues and a record can be obtained within a few minutes. As a functional test, we found reactive hyperemia after arterial occlusion by cuff pressure for five minutes to be useful. Figure 5 shows an example of a healthy person and a patient with peripheral atherosclerosis. The up- and downstroke of the pulse is slower in the patient and the reactive hyperemia is missing. Most important for motor co-ordination and motor performance in light muscular work is localized ischemia of the brain. There is reason to believe that cerebral ischemia in elderly is nearly as widespread as coronary insufficiency, although it is clinically asymptomatic in a larger

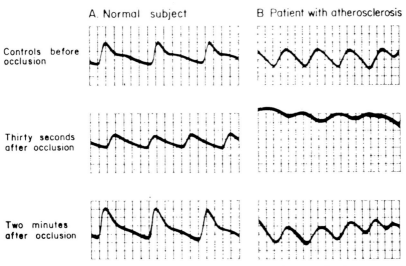

Figure 5. Photoelectrically recorded toe pulse before and after arterial occlusion (inflation of a cuff above systolic blood pressure for five minutes) in a normal subject (A) and a patient with peripheral atherosclerosis (B). In the patient, the upstroke is slower; the dicrotic notch and reactive hyperemia are absent. (Reproduced from Simonson, E., 1956, *Geriatrics*, 11:425).

number of people (Simonson, E., 1963). Table 3 shows a comparison of the drop of the flicker fusion frequency (FFF) with age compiled from the data of several investigators (Simonson, Enzer and Blankstein, 1941; Brozek and Keys, 1945; Misiak, 1947; Coppinger, 1955) and decrease of cerebral blood flow determined with Kety and Schmidt's method (Kety, 1955). The parallelism is striking but doesn't necessarily imply a direct causal relationship. However, most likely the drop of cerebral blood flow with age is involved in the drop of the FFF.* The FFF is decreased in cardiac patients and in hypoxia (literature reviewed by Simonson and Brozek, 1952). It is also lower in elderly people in sitting rather than in supine position (Keys and Simonson, 1952) reflecting the change in cerebral blood flow.

Cerebral ischemia may be due to intracranial atherosclerosis or changes in blood vessels supplying the brain or may be due secondarily to cardiac or pulmonary insufficiency. The various

TABLE 3

CHANGES OF CEREBRAL BLOOD FLOW AND
FLICKER FUSION FREQUENCY WITH AGE

Function	Average at Age 20	Decrease at Age 30	40	50	60	70
Cerebral blood flow (Kety, 1955)	60.0	−6	−10	−12	−14	−16
Flicker fusion frequency*	46.0	−1.3	− 2.8	− 4.5	− 5.8	− 9.0

*Average of various authors. Simonson *et al.*, 1941; Brozek and Keys, 1945; Misiak, 1947; Simonson and Brozek, 1952; Coppinger, 1955.

---

* In a particularly highly selected group (only 27 to 54 male subjects over 65 years met the exacting requirements of second-stage evaluation, as free of any apparent disease as possible), the cerebral blood flow was essentially the same as in 15 healthy young subjects (age difference 50 years). The slight decrease of 7 percent was statistically not significant (Effects of Aging on Cerebral Circulation and Metabolism in Man, D. K. Dastur, M. H. Lane, D. B. Hansen, S. S. Kety, R. N. Butler, S. Perlin, L. Sokoloff, "Human Aging" National Institute of Mental Health, Bethesda, Maryland Pp. 59-78, 1963.) The descrepancy to other investigations may well be due to greater incidence of asymptomatic cerebrovascular disease in older subjects. The samples for the studies on age trends of FFF were less rigidly selected but correspond more closely to "average" healthy population.

mechanisms and effects of cerebral have been reviewed recently (Simonson and McGavack, 1963). It may interfere with performance at different levels: motivation, general tolerance to fatigue, motor coordination, sensory pathways involved in coordinated motor performance and motor centers.

Horiuchi (1929) demonstrated experimentally the effect of progressive cerebral ischemia on the work performance in dogs. After occlusion of the vertebral arteries, partial constriction of the carotid arteries increased the energy expenditure in running at different speeds and grades on the treadmill, and the increase during the performance was steeper. This is truly a vicious circle: with cerebral ischemia, the strength and spread of motor impulses is increased, typical for fatigue, and the resulting increase of energy expenditure occurs in the condition of decreased capacity for cerebral oxygen supply. This is one of the most important experimental documentations of the effect of cerebral ischemia on performance, the more so, as the motor centers are probably the latest to be affected by cerebral ischemia (see preceeding section). However, the functional depression of motor centers with age and in cardiovascular disease has been demonstrated also with other and more direct methods.

TAPPING RATE

The maximum frequency of impulses a center can receive or emit is an expression of its functional state (Vedenskii, 1901). It is related to the chronaxie (studied in fatigue by Bourguignon and Laugier, 1928) except that the chronaxie is determined with a single impulse, while the maximum frequency is determined with a series of impulses. It has been extensively used as criterion of excitability by Russian workers under the term "lability" (Vedenskii, 1901; Ukhtomskii, 1927). The FFF is actually the same type of criterion and has been used in various stresses and diseases (Simonson and Brozek, 1952).

While in animals this function can be tested by electrical stimulation of spinal and cerebral motor centers, in investigations in man an indirect method has to be used. The maximum frequency of voluntary movements depends both on the functional state of the motor centers and on properties of the muscles investigated. With increasing weight of the limb or limb segment investigated, the maximum frequency of voluntary movements is determined by the inertia. Therefore, only by investigation of the smallest segments, such as fingers or hand, gives this test some approximation to an estimate of the functional state of the motor centers. Lehmann (1928) has shown that the number of motor impulses is proportional to the speed of finger movements. The actual frequency of motor impulses in voluntary movements is, of course, higher (about 1.5 times, Simpson and Derbyshire, 1934, to 5 times, Bouman and van Rijnberk, 1938) than could be revealed by this method. The tapping test, preferably performed with a finger (although hand movements are also involved) appears to be the method of choice. Tapping can be performed with a stylus (one metal plate is preferable to alternating tapping on two plates because of smaller inertia) or with a pushbutton contact.

The tapping rate was studied for a period of sixty seconds and measured in intervals of ten seconds in forty-two healthy subjects

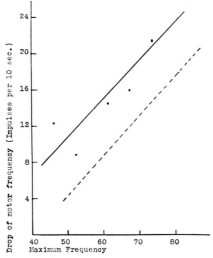

Figure 6. Drop in the frequency of motor impulses dependent on the maximum frequency of impulses. The broken line indicates the values for a group of forty-two normal subjects, and the unbroken line signifies the values for a group of twenty-three patients with hypertension or heart disease. (Reproduced from Simonson and Enzer, 1941B, *Arch. Int. Med.,* 68:498, Fig. 1.)

and in twenty-three patients with heart disease (arterial hypertension, coronary heart disease, valvular heart disease). The test was repeated after an interval of one minute. The age distribution of patients and the normal control group was similar. The test was performed with the right as well as the left hand (Simonson and Enzer, 1941). The frequency of movements drops sharply during the performance and the drop is more pronounced the higher the maximum frequency. Figure 6 shows the drop of frequency in normal subjects and in cardiovascular patients. Both regression lines are parallel, but the values of the patients are substantially higher, indicating more pronounced fatigue of motor centers.

In 97 per cent of healthy subjects the initial frequency was the highest as compared to 43.5 per cent in patients. The different trend is shown in Figure 7. In the normal subjects, the motor centers are in the highest functional state at the start of the test; in the patients, they reach it only during the performance due to adaptation processes. The improvement of the functional state cannot be due to improvement of circulation, because of the short interval from ten to thirty seconds and therefore must be due to central facilitation.

Comparison of the first and second performance gives some

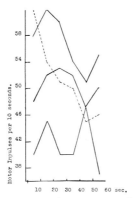

Figure 7. Drop in the frequency of motor impulses during a sixty second performance. The broken line indicates the values for a normal subject, and the unbroken lines signify the values for three patients with hypertension or heart disease. (Reproduced from Simonson and Enzer, 1941B, *Arch. Int. Med.*, 68:498, Fig. 2.)

information about the speed of recovery and adaptation loss during the pause of one minute. The second performance was better maintained in normal subjects than in patients, probably due to better maintenance of adaptation of motor centers to work performance. In several patients, there was a correlation between the clinical condition and the tapping rate. There was no correlation between the FFF and the tapping rate in normal subjects as well as in the cardiac patients, although both were depressed in the patients.

HORMONAL INVOLVEMENT

There is some indirect evidence that reduced sex hormone production may be involved in the drop of performance with age. Treatment of six older, clinically asymptomatic men, with methyltestosterone (up to 40 weeks) in a double blind test increased endurance in dynamic work (lifting of 16 lbs.) by 73 per cent, endurance in static work (weight holding) by 51 per cent and back muscle strength by 47 per cent. Handgrip strength was increased only by 5 per cent. The greater effect on back muscle than on handgrip strength is of interest, because the decline of back muscle strength is more pronounced with age (Rejs, 1921). The performance tests were separated by an interval of several weeks in order to eliminate training and practice effects. The placebo control periods showed that no training trends were present. The tapping rate was not affected, (Simonson, Kearns, and Enzer, 1944). This was a preselected group since all six subjects complained of fatiguability. Methyltestosterone treatment improved also the performance of various types of work in four eunochoids and castrates (age 21 to 47 years): fingererograph by 45 per cent, weight lifting by 68.5 per cent, static work (weight holding) by 41 per cent, back muscle strength by 8 per cent (Simonson, Kearns and Enzer, 1941). In contrast, Samuels, Henschel and Keys (1942) found that methyltestosterne had no effect on work performance in four healthy young men. The results were discussed in greater detail previously (Simonson, 1952).

There is also a possibility that a reduction of thyroid hormone may be involved in the deterioration of performance with age.

Figure 8 shows a significantly greater drop of tapping rate in thirteen patients with hypothyroidism (dots) (Enzer, Simonson and Blankstein, 1941) as compared to the normal subjects (solid line). The antithyroid treatment of patients with coronary heart disease, although less frequent than ten years ago, is of interest in this connection.

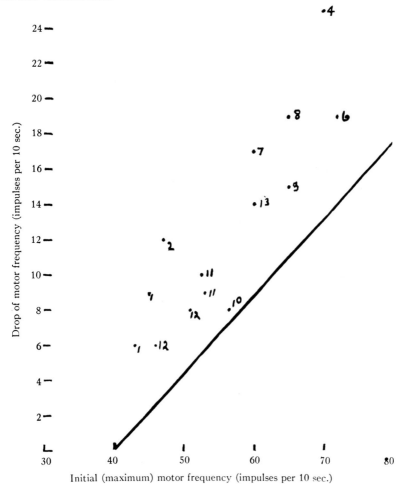

Figure 8. Drop of motor frequency during the performance (right hand) dependent on the initial value in normal subjects (drawn in full line: average of 45 subjects) and of patients with hypothyroidism (dots). (Reproduced from Enzer, Simonson and Blankstein 1941, *Am. Int. Med., 15:* 659, Fig. 1.)

MAXIMUM SPEED OF MOVEMENT

Ideally, for a systematic evaluation of performance, all functions and pathways involved should be studied. Aside from the auxiliary but important cardiovascular-pulmonary functions involved in oxygen transport, the sensory-motor pathways should be investigated (see p.   ). It may be advisable to take the effector organ, i.e., the state of the skeletal muscle, into consideration first. Impairment of the muscle, for instance, by atrophic degeneration or in myasthenia gravis would make all other tests superfluous.

The testing of muscle strength (i.e., isometric contraction) is of primary importance but is not adequate for testing of isotonic maximum capacity. Although both performance tests depend on the excitation of the maximum number of muscle fibers, there is little correlation between maximum speed and maximum strength. Summation of impulses occurs in isometric contraction while speed of performance, i.e., isotonic contraction, depends on the ability to activate the maximum number of fibers simultaneously precluding summation effects. In addition, the properties of the muscle are involved; it is known for a long time that the microscopic structure and functional properties of muscles involved in tonic contraction (red muscles) is different from that of (white) muscles usually involved in fast movements (Wachholder, 1930, 1931).

Therefore, a simple functional test developed by this reviewer may merit attention. The arm (or foot) rests on a plate which breaks an electrical circuit. The subject is requested, on signal, to lift the arm or leg with maximum speed. Removal from the contact plate opens a circuit which is broken by a lever set across the pathway of movement at angles from 10° to 120°. Usually we used an arc for arm movement of 45° and for leg movement of 90.° During the time of current flow, a condenser is charged and later discharged through a ballistic galvanometer calibrated in milliseconds. Thus, the angular speed can be determined in terms of degree/m. sec. This speed test does not involve any reaction time, since the circuit closes only after the movement has started. No significant practice effects were observed (Brozek, Simonson, Keys and Snowden, 1952). The leg speed test was performed without load and with a load of 10 lbs. A statistically significant increase of time (about 10 per cent) occurred in thiamine deficiency and a pronounced increment in six months of semistarvation (with 10 lbs. load) from a control value of 114 m. sec. to 170.5 m. sec. (32 young men). The results are encouraging for use of this test in research in aging and various types of disease.

SPEED OF WRITING

Birren and Botwinick (1951) found a significant age trend in the speed of writing. One digit numbers arranged in twelve rows (8 numbers in each row, total of 96 numbers) are copied as fast as possible below the printed rows. This test involves motor and eye-hand coordination, but the accuracy of coordination is not controlled (i.e., quality of written numbers). The speed is far below the maximum frequency of motor impulses emitted from the motor centers. Physiologically and psychologically the test is quite complex but technically very simple. We applied this test to a sample of 289 men including thirty-seven patients with arterial hypertension and twenty-nine patients with heart disease (mostly atherosclerotic heart disease). The normal sample of 221 men was subdivided into three occupational groups: sixty-four laborers, sixty-seven clerical workers and ninety executives. The executive group included professional men (lawyers, physicians) and the clerical group included a few salesmen. The age span extended from thirty-six to sixty-eight years; most of the executive group were over sixty years. Thus analysis of age effects is limited in scope as compared to Birren and Botwinick's group with an age range from sixteen to eighty-nine years. The results are summarized in Table 4.

There is no significant effect of heart disease and arterial hypertension on the speed of writing. It should be noted that the "patients" were fully compensated and (except a few who were retired) were working. The decrease of the maximum tapping rate was found in *hospitalized* patients and, therefore, may well be due to poorer clinical condition than in the sample with determination of the speed of writing. However, it is also possible that the maximum tapping rate is more sensitive to detect latent cerebral ischemia due to cardiovascular disease.

There was a statistically significant difference between laborers and clerical workers, between laborers and executives, but not between clerical workers and executives. The laborers obviously have not acquired the same degree of fine coordination in writing as the sedentary workers so that their speed is substantially slower.

The occupational and educational background, therefore, must be considered in any evaluation of the test. Since clerical workers and executives did not show a significant difference, they were combined for age trend analysis. Table 5 shows that, in spite of the limited age range, there is a highly significant age trend, in confirmation of Birren and Botwinick's results. No significant age trend was seen in the laborers possibly due to greater variation

TABLE 4

MEANS AND STANDARD DEVIATIONS FOR "COPYING TIME" IN
NORMALS (N): A (EXECUTIVES, SUPERVISORS); B (CLERICAL WORKERS);
C (WORKERS WHO HAVE HIGH LEVEL OF PHYSICAL ACTIVITY);
H (HYPERTENSIVES); D (SUBJECTS WITH HEART DISEASE)

	#	$\overline{x}$	SD	Normals	#	X	SD
N	221	70.5	20.7	A	90	66.7	17.7
H	37	70.6	26.1	B	67	65.4	15.0
D	29	72.1	16.2	C	64	81.3	25.5

		Group Differences				
	$\triangle$	$+$			$\triangle$	t^1
$\overline{X}_H - \overline{X}_N$	0.1	0.03	$\overline{X}_A - \overline{X}_B$		1.3	0.5
$\overline{X}_D - \overline{X}_N$	1.6	0.40	$\overline{X}_C - \overline{X}_A$		14.6	4.2***
$\overline{X}_D - \overline{X}_H$	1.5	0.79	$\overline{X}_C - \overline{X}_B$		15.9	4.4***

1)*** $= p \leq .0001$

TABLE 5

FREQUENCY DISTRIBUTION OF AGE FOR GROUP (A+B) AND GROUP C
AND COEFFICIENT OF CORRELATION (r) OF AGE WITH "SPEED OF COPYING"

	Age: Interval	Distribution: <45	45-50	51-55	56-60	61-65	>65	r
A+B	37-69	12	5	10	13	76	41	.26**
C	36-69	4	11	15	15	16	3	.03

(standard deviation) and smaller sample size. These results are preliminary and sampling is being continued.

INTEGRATED PERFORMANCE PROFILE

The complexity of human performance and involvement of various functions in different types of work demands use of a battery of tests designed to give an integrated picture of performance capacity. While a great variety of physiological functions have been studied in exercise, usually the authors have concentrated on one or a few closely related tests. It would be important, however, to use the same battery of tests in the same subjects under different conditions or in comparison of different groups.

The potentialities of such an integrated approach is demonstrated by previous investigations at this Laboratory in three

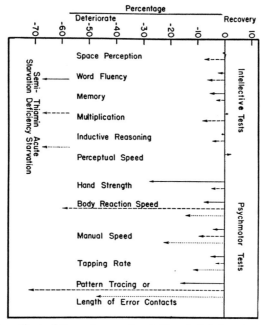

Figure 9. The effect of three types of nutritional deficiencies on intellective and psychomotor tests (Keys *et al.*, 1950; Brozek *et al.*, 1946; Taylor *et al.*, 1945). (Reproduced from Simonson, 1951, *Nutrition Fronts in Public Health*, Nat. Vit. Found., New York, 1951, Fig. 7.)

different types of nutritional deficiencies, acute complete starvation for four to five days (Taylor *et al.*, 1945) semi-starvation over six months resulting in loss of 25 per cent body weight (Keys *et al.*, 1950) experimental and thiamine deficiency (Brozek *et al.*, 1946) in young men.

The results were summarized by this reviewer (1951) in two diagrams (Figs. 9 and 10). They show quite different response of the various tests employed in different types of nutritional deficiencies. The effect of prolonged semi-starvation may have some bearing on changes with age, because loss of muscle mass occurs in both conditions (however, much more pronounced in semi-starvation). The main reason for reproduction of the dia-

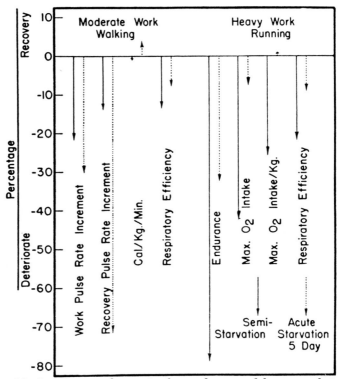

Figure 10. Impairment of capacity for moderate and heavy work in semi-starvation (Keys *et al.*, 1950) and acute starvation (Henschel *et al.*, 1959). (Reproduced from Simonson, 1951, *Nutrition Fronts in Public Health*, Nat. Vit. Found., New York, 1951, Fig. 8.)

grams here is the example of a performance profile, which will show typical characteristics for different types of stresses or samples of subjects investigated. It is not implied that the performance types investigated are the best possible selection for a performance profile; they were not designed for this purpose. However, as an example, this integrated approach and presentation holds some promise, particularly if agreement can be reached between several groups of investigators as to test selection preferably on an international scale.

BIBLIOGRAPHY

Ascher, L. and Baumgarten, P.: (1925) Beiträge zur Kenntnis der körperlichen Beschaffenheit der arbeitenden Bevölkerung. *Veröff. Med. Verwalt.*, 19:487.

Asher, L.: (1931) Wirkungsorte und Wirkungsart des Sympathicus an der Peripherie. *Klin. Wschr.*, 10:865.

Atzler, E.: (1927) *Körper und Arbeit.* Leipzig, Thieme Verlag.

Atzler, E.: (1928) Probleme und Aufgaben der Arbeitsphysiologie. *Ergebn. Physiol.*, 27:709.

Berg, W. E.: (1947) Individual differences in respiratory gas exchange during recovery from moderate exercise. *Am. J. Physiol.*, 149:597.

Birren, J. E. and Botwinick, J.: (1951) The relation of writing speed to age and to the senile psychoses. *J. Consult. Psychol.*, 15:243.

Bourguignon, G. L. and Laugier, H.: (1928) Variations de la Chronaxie dans la fatigue par contraction volontaire soutenue, chez l'homme. *Compt. Rend. Acad. Sc.*, 187:846-848.

Bouman, H. D. and van Rijnberk, G.: (1938) On muscle sound produced during voluntary contraction in man. *Arch. Neerl. Physiol.*, 23:34.

Brozek, J., Guetzkow, H. Mickelsen, O. and Keys, A.: (1946) Motor performance of normal young men maintained on restricted intakes of vitamin B complex. *J. Appl. Physiol.*, 30:359.

Brozek, J. and Keys, A.: (1945) Changes in flicker fusion frequency with age. *J. Consult. Psychol.*, 9:87.

Brozek, J., Simonson, E., Keys, A. and Snowden, A.: (1952) A test of speed of leg and arm movements. *J. Appl. Physiol.*, 4:753.

Enzer, N., Simonson, E. and Blankstein, S.: (1941) The state of sensory and motor centers in patients with hypothyroidism. *Ann. Intern. Med.*, 15:659.

Burke, W. E., Tuttle, W. W., Thompson, C. W., Janney, D. C. and Weber, R. J.: (1953) The relation of grip strength and grip strength endurance to age. *J. Appl. Physiol.*, 5:628-630.

Christensen, E. H.: (1962) Muscular work and fatigue. In Rodahl, K. and Horvath, S. M.: *Muscle as a Tissue,* New York, McGraw Hill Co., p. 176.

Coppinger, N. W.: (1955) The relationship between critical flicker frequency and chronological age for varying levels of stimulus brightness. *J. Geront., 10*:48.

Dawson, P. M. and Hellebrandt, F. A.: (1945) The influence of aging in man upon his capacity for physical work and upon his cardiovascular responses to exercise. *Am. J. Physiol., 143*:420.

Dill, D. B.: (1942) Effects of physical strain and high altitude on heart and circulation. *Am. Heart J., 23*:441.

Durnin, J., and Mikulicic, V.: (1956) The influence of graded exercises on the oxygen consumption, pulmonary ventilation and heart rate of young and elderly men. *Quart. J. Exp. Physiol., 41*:442.

Enzer, N., Simonson, E. and Blankstein, S. S.: (1942) Fatigue of patients with circulatory insufficiency, investigated by means of the fusion frequency of flicker. *Ann. Intern. Med., 16*:701.

Feré, L.: (1904) *Travail et plaisir,* Paris.

Fisher, M. B. and Birren, J.: (1947) Age and strength. *J. Appl. Psychol., 31*: 490.

Frolkis, V. V.: (1962) Changes of the cardiac reactivity with age. In *Voprosy Gerontologii i Geriatrii,* Kiev, p. 40 (Russian).

Frolkis, V. V., Golovchenko, S. F., Dukhovichnyi, S. M. and Tranin, S. A.: (1962) Functional changes of blood circulation and respiration associated with aging. *Klin. Med., 40*:12:87.

Ginezinski, A.: (1923) Effect of sympathetic nervous system on the function of striated muscles. *Fiziol. Zh.* (U.S.S.R.), 6:139.

Henschel, A., Taylor, H. L. and Keys, A.: (1954) Performance capacity in acute starvation with hard work. *J. Appl. Physiol., 6*:624.

Horiuchi, K.: (1929) Über den Einfluss oler Gehirndurchblutung auf die Ermüdung. *Arbeitsphysiol., 1*:75.

Jokl, E.: (1954) *Alter und Leistung.* Berlin, Springer-Verlag, 75 pp.

Kety, S. S.: (1955) Changes in cerebral circulation and oxygen consumption which accompany maturation and aging. In Waelsch, H.: *Biochemistry of the Developing Nervous System,* New York, Academic Press, pp. 208-217.

Keys, A., Brozek, J., Henschel, A., Mickelsen, O., Taylor, H., Simonson, E., Skinner, A. and Wells, S.: (1950) *The Biology of Human Starvation.* Minneapolis, Univ. of Minn. Press, 1384 pp.

Keys, A., and Simonson, E.: (1952) The flicker fusion frequency and its response to nitroglycerin in normal subjects and in patients with cardiovascular disease. *Circulation, 5*:215-224.

König, K., Reindell, H. and Roskann, H.: (——) Das Herzvolumen und die Leistungsfähigkeit bei 60-75 jährigen gesunden Männern. *Arch. Kreislaufforsch., 39*:143.

Kossoris, M. D.: (1940) Relation of age to industrial injuries. *Monthly Labor Rev.*, 51:789-799.

Labhart, F.: (1929) Fortgesetzte Untersuchungen über den Einfluss des Nervus sympathicus auf die Ermüdung des quergestreiften Muskels. *Z. Biol.*, 89:217.

Landowne, M., Brandfonbrener, M. and Shock, N. W.: (1955) The relation of age to certain measures of performance of the heart and circulation. *Circulation*, 12:567-576.

Lehmann, G.: (1928) Ueber den Mechanismus bei Willkürbewegung. *Arbeitsphysiol.*, 1:1.

Lindhard, J.: (1920) Untersuchungen über statische Muskelarbeit. *Scand. Arch. Physiol.*, 40:145.

Lowenstein, O.: (1937) Der Psychische Restitutionseffekt. Das Prinzip der psychisch bedingten Wiederherstellung der ermüdeten der erschöpften und der erkrankten Funktion. Basel, Schwabe & Co.

Lowenstein, O. and Loewenfeld, I. E.: (1952) Disintegration of central autonomic regulation during fatigue and its reintegration by psychosensory controlling mechanisms. *J. Nerv. Ment. Dis.*, 115:1-21.

Maibach, C.: (1928) Untersuchungen zur Frage des Einflusses des Sympathikus auf die Ermüdung der quergestreiften Muskulatur. *Z. Biol.*, 88:207-226.

Meakins, J. and Long, C. N. A.: (1927) Oxygen consumption, oxygen debt and lactic acid in circulatory failure. *J. Clin. Invest.*, 4:273.

Meerson, F. Z.: (1962) Senile changes in the compensatory cardiac hyperfunction and their experimental prevention. *Zh. Obshei Biologii.*, 23:2: 114, (Russian).

Miles, W. R.: (1943) Performance in relation to age. *Pub. Health Rep.*, *Suppl. No. 168*:34 pp.

Misiak, H.: (1947) Age and sex differences in critical flicker frequency. *J. Exp. Psychol.*, 37:318-332.

Müller, E. A.: (1961) Die ärztliche Beurteilung der körperlichen Dauer-Leistungsfähigkeit im Beruf. *Deutsch. Med. Wschr.*, 86:2272.

Orbeli, L. A.: (1932) Review of the sympathetic in innervation of skeletal muscles, organs, and the central nervous system. *Fiziol. Zh. (U.S.S.R.)*, 15:1.

Panfilov, B. K.: (1963) The functional state of the skeletal musculature in patients with aortic stenosis. *Ter. Arkh.*, 35:4:86.

Quetelet, A.: (1836) *Sur l'Homme et le Developement de ses Facultés.* Brussels, L. Hauman and Cie.

Rejs, J. H. O.: (1921) Über die Veränderung der Kraft während der Bewegung. *Arch. Ges. Physiol.*, 191:234-257.

Robinson, S.: (1938) Experimental studies of physical fitness in relation to age. *Arbeitsphysiol.*, 10:251.

Samuels, L. T., Henschel, A. F. and Keys, A.: (1942) Influence of methyl-testosterone on muscular work and creatin metabolism in normal young men. *J. Clin. Endocr.,* 2:649.

Simonson, E.: (1930) Umsatz bei koerperlicher Arbeit. Handb. d. normalen u. pathol. *Physiologie,* Berlin, Springer-Verlag, Vol. 15.

Simonson, E.: (1935) Der heutige Stand der Theorie der Ermuedung. *Ergebn. Physiol.,* 37:299.

Simonson, E.: (1937) Recherches sur la physiologie de la course. *Travail Humain,* 5:3:1-20.

Simonson, E.: (1938) Quelques questions concernant les échanges au cours du travail musculaire. *Travail Humain,* 6:4:385.

Simonson, E.: (1924) Unpublished.

Simonson, E.: (1951) Influence of nutrition on work performance. *Nutrition Fronts in Public Health,* New York, Nat. Vitamin Found., p. 72.

Simonson, E.: (1956) Photoelectric plethysmography: methods, normal standards and clinical application. *Geriatrics, 11:*425.

Simonson, E.: (1957) Changes in physical fitness and cardiovascular functions with age. *Geriatrics, 12:*28.

Simonson, E.: (1952) Endocrinologic aspects of aging and the muscular and nervous system in man. *J. Geront.,* 7:2.

Simonson, E.: (1959) Effect of age and coronary artery disease on the postural adjustment of peripheral circulation. *Circulation Research,* 7: 422.

Simonson, E.: (1958) Functional capacities of older individuals. *J. Geront., Suppl. No.* 2:13:18.

Simonson, E.: (1963 in press) Introduction. *Cerebral Ischemia.* Springfield, Illinois, Charles C Thomas.

Simonson, E. and Brozek, J.: (1952) Flicker fusion frequency. *Physiol. Rev.,* 32:349.

Simonson, E. and Enzer, N.: (1941a) Effect of short rest pauses in standing and sitting position on the efficiency of muscular work. *J. Indus. Hygiene & Toxicol.,* 23:106.

Simonson, E. and Enzer, N.: (1941a) The state of motor centers in circulatory insufficiency. *Arch. Intern. Med.,* 68:498.

Simonson, E. and Enzer, N.: (1942) Physiology of muscular exercise and fatigue in disease. *Medicine, 21:*345.

Simonson, E. and Enzer, N.: (1942a) Effect of Pervitin (Desoxyephedrine) on fatigue of the central nervous system. *J. Indus Hygiene & Toxicol.,* 24:205.

Simonson, E., Enzer, N. and Benton, R. W.: (1943) The influence of muscular work and fatigue on the state of the central nervous system. *J. Lab. Clin. Med.,* 38:1555.

Simonson, E., Enzer, N. and Blankstein, S.: (1941) Influence of age on the fusion frequency of flicker. *J. Exp. Psychol.,* 29:252.

Simonson, E., Enzer, N. and Blankstein, S. S.: (1941) Effect of amphetamine (benzedrine) on fatigue of the central nervous system. *War Medicine, 1:*690.

Simonson, E. and Gollwitzer-Meier, C.: (1930) Über den Arbeitsumsatz bei Herzinsuffizienz. *Ztschr. Ges. Exp. Med., 73:*25.

Simonson, E. and Gollwitzer-Meier, C.: (1931) Über den Arbeitsumsatz bei Grippe-Rekonvalescenz. *Ztschr. Ges. Exp. Med., 75:*330.

Simonson, E., Kearns, W. M. and Enzer, N.: (1941) Effect of oral administration of meethyltestosterone on fatigue of eunuchoids and castrates. *Endocrinology, 28:*506-512.

Simonson, E., Kearns, W. N. and Enzer, N.: (1944) Effect of methyltestosterone treatment on muscular performance and the central nervous system of older men. *J. Clin. Endocr., 4:*528.

Simonson, E., Koff, S. and Keys, A.: (1955) Contour of the toe pulse, reactive hyperemia, and pulse transmission velocity: group and repeat variability, effect of age, exercise, and disease. *Am. Heart J., 50:*260.

Simonson, E. and Lieberman, A.: (1963) Russian research on cardiac compensation and decompensation. *Am. Heart J., 65:*687.

Simonson, E. and McGavack, T. H., eds.: in press, *Cerebral Ischemia.* Springfield, Ill., Charles C Thomas.

Simonson, E., Omachi, A. and Visscher, M. B.: (1946) Excitability of muscle to direct and indirect stimulation during prolonged stimulation. *Proc. Soc. Exp. Biol. Med., 61:*91.

Simonson, E., Simonson, S. and Sokolow, A.: (1934) Beiträge zur Physiologie der motorischen Koordination. *Arbeitsphysiol., 7:*577.

Simonson, E. and Sirkina, G.: (1936) Gaswechsel bei ermuedender Arbeit. *Arbeitsphysiol., 9:*153.

Simpson, H. N. and Derbyshire, A. J.: (1934) Electrical activity of the motor cortex during cerebral anemia. *Am. J. Physiol., 109:*99.

Smith, K. R.: (1938) Age and performance in a repetitive manual task. *J. Appl. Psychol., 22:*295-306.

Stieglitz, E. J.: (1941) Aging as industrial health program. *J. A. M. A., 116:* 1383-1387.

Taylor, H. L., Brozek, J., Henschel, A., Mickelsen, O. and Keys, A.: (1945) The effect of successive fasts on the ability of men to withstand fasting during hard work. *Am. J. Physiol., 143:*148.

Tonkikh, A.: (1927) The role of the sympathetic nervous system in the Sechenov inhibition. *Fiziol. Zh. (U.S.S.R.), 10:*85.

Ukhtomskii, A. A.: (1927) *Physiology of Motor Apparatus.* Leningrad. (Russian).

Vedenskii, N. E.: (1901) *Excitation, Inhibition and Anesthesia (Vosbuzhdenye, Tormozhenye i narkoz).* St. Petersburg; republished, Vedenskii: *Collection of Publications,* Leningrad, Medgiz, 1935, Vol. 4.

Wachholder, K.: (1930) Untersuchungen über tonische and nicht tonische Wirbeltiermuskeln; verschiedenes Verhalten bei ermüdender Reizung. *Arch. Ges. Physiol., 226*:274.

Wachholder, K.: (1931) Weitere Untersuchungen über das Verhalten "tonischer" und "nicht tonischer" Muskeln bei ermüdender Reizung. *Arch. Ges. Physiol., 229*:133.

Wachholder, K.: (1933) Die allgemeinen physiologischen Grundlagen der Neurologie; allgemeine Physiologie des Zentralnervensystems. *Fortschr. Neurol. Psychiat., 5*:43.

22

THE EFFECT OF ORGAN EXTRACTS ON BEHAVIOR OF OLD RATS

KARL BÄTTIG AND ETIENNE GRANDJEAN

C{\scriptsize AVIEZEL} AND J{\scriptsize ASINSKI} (1962) reported that they were able to increase length of life in rats by a treatment consisting of extracts from bone, liver and stomach enriched by Vitamin B_{12}. On the basis of these results we planned to investigate whether this treatment could also postpone the onset of behavioral age changes in the rat. The behavioral measures used in this study were selected on the basis of their sensitivity to the influence of age. In a first phase of our study we measured swimming performance which has been demonstrated (Kay and Birren, 1958) to decline in old age, and avoidance learning which has been shown in an own study (1959) and by Denenberg and Kline (1958) to slow down in old rats. In a second phase of the study we used a modification of the "closed field test" developed by *Hebb and Williams* (1946) which seemed especially suitable for our purposes because of its underlying basic psychological functions.

Experiment 1
METHOD
Animals and Treatment

A group of forty female rats twenty-eight months old at the beginning of the experiments was divided into the four subgroups G_1, G_2, G_3 and G_4 of treated animals and the four subgroups

435

C_1, C_2, C_3 and C_4 of untreated control animals. The treated rats were given daily 50 mg of a combined organ extract (GER) consisting of bone extract (3 parts), liver extract (3 parts), stomach extract (2 parts) and Vitamin B_{12} (2 μg). This preparation was given in oatmeal porridge. Treatment was given 11 months before and during the experiments. The control rats received oatmeal porridge alone. Normal food consisted of laboratory chows, which were withdrawn daily eight hours before giving the treatment.

TESTS

a) Swimming Performance

A 12 ft. long, 16″ deep and 6″ wide metal alley was half-filled with water of 20°C. The inside of the alley was painted black and the top, except for the start and goal sections, was covered with black plastic cloth. An escape ladder at the goal end was the motivation for the rat to swim through the alley. A 70 W lamp at the start end and an air blow parallel to the water surface provided additional motivation for swimming. The animals could be required to work harder by fixing to their tail a thin nylon thread which was connected over a simple set of pulleys outside the alley to a load of 27 g. A session was terminated after ten single runs or ten minutes, whichever occurred first. The first three days of training were used as an adaptation period without using the pulleys and without further evaluation of the data. From the fourth day the pulleys were used in alternate runs. Additional methodological details are given by Bättig (1961).

b) Avoidance Conditioning

A wooden box (20″ x 8″ x 6″) was divided into two equal compartments by a partition with a metal sliding door. An electrically isolated metal grid served as floor, hardware cloth as cover. In each compartment a 4 V lamp above the sliding door was used in combination with a phone buzzer outside the box as the conditioning stimulus. Switching on the buzzer and the lamp of one compartment was followed after a short pre-selected delay by electrically charging the metal grid of the same compartment. As a consequence, the rat learned to leave the compartment through the door at the onset of the conditioning stimulus

(CS) in order to avoid the painful shocks (US) to the feet. The electric shock consisted of 120 V, 3 cps condenser discharges of 2 ms duration. These shocks produced no real pain but a rather sharp and uncomfortable "needling." Single trials were given at intervals of .5 minute. A session was terminated after fifteen single trials or ten minutes, whichever occurred first. The CS-US interval was kept at .025 minute, as long as the response time to the CS was longer than .05 minute in more than 75 percent of all single trials. CS-US interval was increased to .05 minute as soon as this criterion was passed. CS or CS + US were turned off only after the animal had moved into the other compartment, except when the rat did not leave the electrically charged grid within three minutes. Response time was defined as the time from the onset of the CS until the animal had left the compartment, regardless of whether it received a shock or not. Further details are given by Bättig and Grandjean (1957).

c) Open-field Behavior

A hexagonal open field with sides 2′ long and side walls 14″ high was used. The entire area and the side walls were painted black and illuminated by a dim light from above. The open field was marked off into thirteen areas of equal size. Rats were put in a corner of the open field and the number of areas entered during three minutes was recorded.

Experimental Design

Series I of the experiment consisted in testing the subgroups G_1, G_2, C_1 and C_2 on swimming performance, and the subgroups G_3, G_4, C_3 and C_4 on avoidance behavior and open-field behavior simultaneously. In series II the subgroups G_1, G_2, C_1 and C_2 were tested on avoidance behavior and open-field behavior, whereas the subgroups G_3, G_4, C_3 and C_4 were tested on swimming performance. Swimming performance and avoidance behavior of all rats were tested in one half of the sessions before and in the other half of the sessions after giving the treatment. Open-field behavior was measured only after giving the treatment. Each testing series lasted three weeks, with five sessions weekly per test.

RESULTS

During the six weeks of Experiment 1 four animals died due to infections of the respiratory tract. The other animals showed no signs of illness. Weight remained fairly constant in both groups throughout the tests.

The data on *swimming performance* are summarized in Table 1. Considering the total average for all experimental groups it must be concluded that the performance of the old animals was very poor. In earlier studies (Bättig 1961) we observed a far better performance in younger animals. Comparison of the means from one day to another revealed that performance improved signifi-

TABLE 1

THE EFFECT OF GER ON SWIMMING PERFORMANCE

(a) AVERAGE SWIMMING TIMES WITHOUT LOAD IN MINUTES
(b) AVERAGE SWIMMING TIMES WITH LOAD IN MINUTES
(c) AVERAGE NUMBER OF INCORRECT RUNS PER SESSION

SIGNIFICANTLY DIFFERENT VALUES ARE ITALICIZED

Total average =	.260 (a) .461 (b) 1.02 (c)

Series I	=	.263 (a) .480 (b) *1.31* (c)	Series II	=	.256 (a) .442 (b) *0.72* (c)
GER	=	.277 (a) .476 (b) 1.01 (c)	Placebo	=	*.243* (a) .446 (b) 1.02 (c)
Application before testing	=	.256 (a) .458 (b) 1.02 (c)	Application after testing	=	.264 (a) .464 (b) 1.01 (c)

Series I:				Series II:			
GER =	*.299*(a) *.550*(b) *1.55* (c)	Placebo =	.227(a) *.411*(b) *1.07* (c)	GER =	.254(a) *.402*(b) *0.49* (c)	Placebo =	.258(a) *.481*(b) *0.94* (c)

GER given:				Placebo given:			
before testing	.268(a) .463(b) 0.96 (c)	after testing	.285(a) .489(b) 1.06 (c)	before testing	.243(a) .453(b) 1.07 (c)	after testing	.243(a) .439(b) 0.96 (c)

Swimming times were compared by analysis of variance and group averages by the Duncan test. Numbers of incorrect runs were compared by means of the Wilcoxon ranking test.

cantly during testing, so that learning was still taking place beyond the preliminary three days of training. In the earlier studies learning was appreciable only during the first few days.

The groups tested in series I performed somewhat better than those tested in series II. For both series together, according to the data represented in the second row of Table 1, GER seemed to have a negative influence on swimming performance. Swimming times with load were slightly inferior in the treated groups than in the controls. Giving the treatment before or after testing made no difference at all.

More conclusive are the data on interaction between series and treatment, and between application and treatment as reported in the last two columns of the table. GER definitely impaired performance of the subgroups tested in series I, whereas, it definitely improved performance of the subgroups tested in series II. Since the animals tested in series II had had previous testing in avoidance behavior and the animals tested in series I had had no previous behavioral training at all, it could be concluded that treated animals derived more profit from previous experience than did the controls. The inferiority of the GER groups in series I was due to the fact that their initial performance in the first few days was clearly inferior to that of the controls. However, on the following days the GER treated animals showed a non significant tendency to improve their performance faster than the controls, so that the difference between the treated and untreated groups was smaller at the end of series I than at the beginning.

The data of *avoidance conditioning* are summarized in Table 2. At a first glance the result is very similar. As in swimming performance, the training success of these old animals was generally very poor. In an earlier study (1959) we investigated the effect of age on speed of avoidance learning. The performance measured in the oldest animals (about 2 years old) was about as poor as the performance of the animals of this new study. Performance improved again significantly during the three weeks of testing. The total mean of the response times was longer than the CS-US interval which was kept at .05 minute. This represents the fact that most responses occurred only after the onset of the US. The performance in series II was again better than in series I, but the difference between the two series was more pronounced than in the previous swimming test. In series II the avoidance responses were significantly more frequent, response time was significantly shorter and the amount of defecation was significantly lower than in series I. With respect to treatment, there was a tendency for better performance in the GER groups than in the controls which, however, was not significant for both groups taken together. Defecation was generally less frequent with GER than with Placebo. Giving the treatment before the test had a tendency to improve performance and to increase defecation. The interactions series x treatment and application

TABLE 2

THE EFFECT OF GER ON AVOIDANCE BEHAVIOR

(a) AVERAGE NUMBER OF AVOIDANCE RESPONSES PER SESSION
(b) AVERAGE RESPONSE TIMES IN MINUTES
(c) AVERAGE NUMBER OF FAECES PER SESSION

SIGNIFICANTLY DIFFERENT VALUES ARE ITALICIZED

	Total average =	1.68 (a) .080 (b) 4.56 (c)	

	Series I	0.68 (a) = .088 (b) 4.76 (c)		Series II	2.68 (a) = .071 (b) 4.36 (c)

	GER	1.79 (a) = 0.77 (b) 4.27 (c)		Placebo	1.56 (a) = .083 (b) 4.85 (c)

Application = before testing	1.49 (a) .075 (b) 4.75 (c)		Application = after testing	1.86 (a) .085 (b) 4.37 (c)

Series I:

GER =	0.34 (a) .088(b) 4.41 (c)	Placebo =	1.02 (a) .089(b) 5.12 (c)

Series II:

GER =	3.25 (a) .065(b) 4.13 (c)	Placebo =	2.11 (a) .077(b) 4.58 (c)

GER given:

before = testing	1.76 (a) .072(b) 4.36 (c)	after = testing	1.83 (a) .081(b) 4.18 (c)

Placebo given:

before = testing	1.23 (a) .078(b) 5.15 (c)	after = testing	1.90 (a) .088(b) 4.56 (c)

Numbers of avoidance responses were compared by means of 2 x 2 χ^2 tests.

Response times and numbers of faeces were compared by analysis of variance and group averages by the Duncan test.

x treatment point again in the same direction as the results of the swimming test. Within series I, the performance of the GER treated rats was poorer than that of the controls. This general tendency was significant with respect to the number of avoidance responses. Within series II GER improved performance significantly as regards both response time and number of avoidance responses. Amount of defecation again tended to be negatively correlated with the other measures. Performance tended to be poorer when measured after the treatment than before. This tendency was significant in the case of Placebo for the number of avoidance responses. Although not significant, the amount of defecation was again higher after than before giving the treatment. This could be due to the fact that treatment involved the ingestion of a considerable amount of food (about two tablespoons of oatmeal porridge) into a stomach probably almost empty, since the rats were deprived of food for about nine hours before testing.

As a whole these results suggest the same conclusion as the swimming test. GER treated rats derived more profit from previous test experience than did controls, and again performed worse than controls if they had no previous testing experience.

The data on *open-field behavior* are represented in Table 3. In this test neither the fact of being tested in series I or II nor the treatment with GER or Placebo had any effect on the measures.

Since the results of swimming performance and avoidance performance seemed to point to similar conclusions, and since fre-

TABLE 3

THE EFFECT OF GER ON OPEN FIELD BEHAVIOR
AVERAGE NUMBER OF AREAS ENTERED PER SESSION

Total average = 10.14	
Series I = 10.13	Series II = 10.15
GER = 9.96	Placebo = 10.32
Series I:	Series II:
GER = 10.15 Placebo = 10.10	GER = 9.77 Placebo = 10.53

Numbers of entries were compared by analysis of variance. No significant differences were found.

quency of defecation seemed to be higher with poorer avoidance performance, we calculated the ranking correlations between all these measures using Spearman's technique. These
correlation coefficients are set out in Table 4. Within the swimming test all measures are highly correlated. Within avoidance
behavior only the number of avoidance responses and the response times are correlated, whereas the number of defecations
showed no significant correlations with the other two measures.
Between different tests we found that open-field behavior was not
correlated with any other measure. The same holds for defecation. The number of correct runs in the swimming test but not
the swimming times were significantly correlated with both
avoidance measures.

These correlations indicate that reservations must be made
as to the possible conclusions of experiment 1. Both tests of this
experiment suggest a better transfer of the GER treated animals
from the first to the second given test. However, since the results of these two tests are at least partially correlated, this
evidence cannot be taken as independent. This fact led us to
plan a second experiment which was set up especially to test
transfer in a more critical way.

TABLE 4

RANKING CORRELATIONS BETWEEN DIFFERENT BEHAVIORAL MEASURES
SPEARMAN'S R. SIGNIFICANT CORRELATIONS ARE ITALICIZED

	I	IIa	IIb	IIc	IIIa	IIIb	IIIc
I. *Open field behavior*							
Nr. of areas entered	—	−.236	.261	.071	.160	.273	.266
II. *Avoidance behavior*							
a) Nr. of faeces	.236	—	.103	.228	−.147	−.183	−.003
b) Response time	.261	.103	—	*.599*	.219	.301	*.522*
c) Nr. of avoidance responses	.071	.228	*.599*	—	.196	.256	*.441*
III. *Swimming performance*							
a) Swimming time with load	.160	−.147	.219	.196	—	*.781*	*.606*
b) Swimming time without load	.273	−.183	.302	.256	*.781*	—	*.798*
c) Nr. of correct runs	.266	−.003	*.522*	*.441*	*.606*	*.798*	—

METHOD

Animals and Treatment

Fifty male rats fifteen months old were used. Half the animals received a powder diet with an addition of 0.25 per cent GER, the other half the same diet without GER. In this experiment treatment was given only during the tests.

Test

We used a square water basin of 5 x 5 ft with side walls 1 ft high. The basin was filled to a depth of 8″ with water of 20°C and covered with a glass plate. This plate was marked off into thirty-six square areas of equal size. These areas served as markers for placing barriers into the basin and also for measuring the length of a rat's run by counting the number of traversed areas. The inside of the basin was painted black. The task of the animals was to cross the basin from one corner to the diagonally opposite one. An entrance alley was situated in an extension of the diagonal at one corner and an exit alley in a similar extension at the other. A ladder situated in the exit alley allowed the rats to escape from the water.

The test consisted of three phases. In a preliminary adaptation phase (phase I) the rats were simply dropped into the entrance alley in order to adapt them to the new situation and teach them to search for the exit. As soon as the rats chose the shortest way toward the escape alley, the problems A to F of the original procedure described by *Rabinovitch and Rosvold* (1959) were applied (phase II). They consisted in blocking the straight diagonal run by inserting barriers of the same height as the side walls. These problems A to F served only to adapt the rats to the presence of barriers. After this second phase, the main problems one to twelve of the original test were used (phase III). They consisted of more complicated arrangements of the barriers. Training success was evaluated by counting the number of areas traversed on the way from the entrance to the exit alley. The difference between the minimal number of areas necessary to reach the exit alley and the number of areas traversed was defined as "error-score." Therefore, a score of "O errors" meant that a rat reached the exit alley with minimal length of detours.

Experimental Design

Training in phase I was continued until 75 per cent of the rats reached the exit alley straight along the diagonal. This goal was reached after six training days with four runs per rat. Then training in phase II was performed until again 75 per cent of the rats reached the exit alley with minimal detours. At this stage, the rats were divided into two equal groups matched for comparable training success in the two preceding test phases. One group received from now on GER, while the other group served as control. It was planned to give the following twelve main problems of phase III at intervals over a period from three to five weeks. However, the last three problems had to be given in almost immediate succession, because by then there was a considerable loss of animals from spontaneous death.

The duration of treatment preceding each problem was as follows: Problem 1: 32 days; problem 2: 61 days; problem 3: 115 days; problem 4: 144 days; problem 5: 173 days; problem 6: 191 days; problem 7: 231 days; problem 8: 250 days; problem 9: 268 days; problem 10: 270 days; problem 11: 273 days; problem 12: 277 days. Two sessions with 4 runs each were given for the problems 1 to 11. In problem twelve three sets of two sessions each were given, because no rat had reached criterion in the first two sessions. These three sets are referred to as "problem 12a, 12b, and 12c."

RESULTS

During the nine test months, thirteen out of the twenty-two rats treated with GER died, while out of the twenty-four control animals twelve died in the same period. This difference in favor of the control rats was not significant. The cause of death has not been verified histologically in this experiment as it had been done in the first one. The weight curves of both groups showed almost no difference. There was a small but non-significant weight gain in both groups from an average of about 440 g at the beginning to about 465 g at the end of the experiment.

The average number of error scores made in each problem of the test is shown in Figure 1. These values are based on the records of all animals, including the ones who died during the experiment. The means of the later problems are therefore based on fewer animals than those of the earlier ones. This was done because there were only very small differences between the mean values of all animals and the mean values of the animals who survived. There was little difference between the performances of the two groups on problems 1 to 5. The inferiority of the GER treated group in problem 6 was significant at the $p < 0.01$ level.

From problem 7 on up to the end of the test the GER treated animals made on the average fewer "error scores" than the controls. These differences were significant for the problems 7, 9, 12a, 12b, and 12c. Therefore, after problem 6 the GER treated animals remained superior for a row of eight problems, if the problems 12a, 12b and 12c are considered as independent. Sequential analysis indicates that a sequence of this length could not be due to chance. If, however, problems 12a, 12b and 12c are regarded as one, the GER groups were superior for a row of six problems only, and this could have been due to chance. There is some reason for considering the problems 12a, 12b and 12c

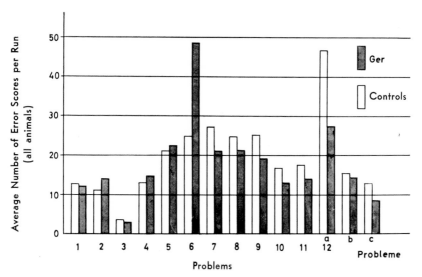

Figure 1. Performance in the twelve problems of the Hebb-Williams test. The height of the columns indicates the average number of "error scores" per run for all animals. Dark columns: treated rats; white columns: control rats. Numbers of errors were compared by means of the 2x2 χ^2 test.

as independent, because the animals solved problem 12 by "steps" rather than with a continuous decrease in the number of errors. Usually as a first step a preliminary solution involving an unnecessary detour was achieved, followed by an improved solution with a shorter detour, etc. Only in a second stage of learning were these preliminary solutions dropped in favor of the correct solution.

DISCUSSION

The behavioral results of the study confirm earlier findings about the poorer performance of old rats (Hubbert, 1915; Liu, 1928; Stone, 1929). Although there was no direct control of the age factor by using young animals too, sufficient data from earlier work allow an estimation of the amount of the behavioral deficit found with some of the tests in old rats. In the first experiment twenty-nine months old rats were used. They took on the average .26 minute for swimming over a distance of 4 metres without pulling a load, and .46 minute for swimming the same distance with a load. On several occasions we have measured swimming performance of rats less than a year old (*Bättig* 1961, 1963a, 1963b) and have never found average swimming times of more than .15 minute without load and .25 with load. In avoidance conditioning the old rats of the present study avoided only about 1.7 of the fifteen electric shocks given during a session. This result is very similar to the one obtained earlier (*Bättig and Grandjean* 1959) in nineteen and twenty-four month old rats. On the other hand, we have no direct comparison for the data on open-field behavior and defecation in the avoidance test. With reference to the Hebb-Williams test unpublished data on behavior of young rats suggest that the performances of the old rats of the present study were inferior.

The question of direct interest in this study is whether the treatment postponed the onset of the behavioral decrement in the old rats or not. The results suggest that the control rats showed a poorer transfer from one test to another than the treated rats. This holds for the second test in Experiment 1 and for the second half of the twelve standard problems in the Hebb-Williams test. This would suggest a beneficial effect of the treatment on the old rats. Signs of a beneficial effect of organ extract have already been found in other studies. As mentioned at the beginning of this paper, Caviezel and Jasinski (1962) found with the same preparation a longer life time in rats. Grandjean (1963) found an increased resistance to the cholesterol over-feeding with respect to rate of survival, weight, and swimming performance. Gotti and Nicolaj (1957), Cornet-Jaquemoud (1945), Jasinski (1957), Vaccari and Fantin (1959), Roth (1954) found clinically an improvement with the same organ extract in dystrophic disorders.

The present study gives no evidence with respect to the dura-tion of treatment necessary to produce such effects. In Experi-ment 1 a treatment of fixed duration preceded testing. In Experi-ment 2 testing was continued over several months of treatment, and the difference in favor of the treated group could be seen after about six months. However, this does not mean that a treatment of six months would be necessary to produce this effect. The result could as well be due to the fact that, by that time, the behavior of the controls had started to deteriorate, whereas the same effect was postponed in the treated rats. This hypothesis could be tested by comparing the treatment effect in old rats and in young and healthy rats.

With respect to the biological mechanism of the treatment little information is gained from the present study. Experiment 1 showed that the effect cannot be an immediate one since testing before or after the daily administration of the treatment makes no difference. With respect to the question whether the treat-ment effect was of a specific nature or not, only speculations can be made. The already mentioned increased resistance against the consequences of cholesterol overfeeding in rats and the im-provement of dystrophic disorders in man would rather suggest a non-specific mode of action.

SUMMARY

Eighteen rats were pre-treated with organ extracts during eleven months and eighteen rats served as controls. At the age of twenty-nine months all rats were tested on avoidance learning and on performance and learning to swim over a distance of 4 metres. In half the animals swimming performance and learning were measured first and in the other half of the animals avoidance learning. The controls were significantly inferior to the treated rats in the second test, suggesting a poorer transfer from test to test. In a second experiment twenty-five controls and twenty-five treated rats were given the twelve problems of the Hebb-Williams closed-field test between the age of fifteen and twenty-four months. From the age of twenty-one months on up to the end of the testing period, after a treatment of six months, the control rats remained significantly inferior to the treated rats. This suggests, similarly to the first experiment, an earlier loss of learning transfer in the controls than in the treated rats.

REFERENCES

Bättig, K. and Grandjean, E.: (1957) Der zeitliche Ablauf einer bedingten Fluchtreaktion bei der Ratte. *Arch. Exp. Path. Pharmakol.*, 231:119-132.

Bättig, K. and Grandjean, E.: (1959) Beziehungen zwischen Alter und Erlernen einer bedingten Fluchtreaktion bei der weissen Ratte. *Gerontologia*, 3:266-276.

Bättig, K.: (1961) Das Schwimmen von Ratten durch einen Wasserkanal. Methodische und pharmakologische Einflüsse auf Leistung und Ermüdung. *Helv. Physiol. Pharmacol. Acta*, 19:384-398.

Bättig, K.: (1963a) Differential psychopharmacological patterns of action in rats. In Votava, Z., Horvath, M. and Vinar, O.: *Methodology of the Study of Effects of Psychotropic Drugs on Higher Nervous Activity*, Oxford, Pergamon Press.

Bättig, K.: (1963b) Die Wirkung von Training und Amphetamin auf Ausdauer und Geschwindigkeit der Schwimmleistung der Ratte. *Psychopharmacologia*, 4:15-27.

Caviezel, R. and Jasinski, B.: (1962) Der Einfluss eines Organpräparates auf die Lebensdauer im Tierversuch. *Med. Exp.*, 6:249-253.

Cornet-Jaquemoud, C.: (1954) Die therapeutische Verwendung eines Knochenvollpräparates bei Kindern. *Mod. Probl. Paediat.*, I:245.

Denenberg, V. H. and Kline, N. J.: (1958) The relationship between age and avoidance learning in the hooded rat. *J. Comp. Physiol.*, 51:488-491.

Gotti, D. and Nicolaj, P.: (1957) Der Einfluss eines Knochenvollpräparates auf das Wachstum dystrophischer Kinder. *Clin. Pediat.*, 33.

Hebb, D. O. and Williams, K.: (1946) A method of rating animal intelligence. *J. Genet. Psychol.*, 34:59-65.

Hubbert, H. B.: (1915) The effect of age on habit formation in the albino rat. *Behav. Monogr.*, 2:55.

Jasinski, B.: (1957) Die Therapie chronischer Leberparenchymerkrankungen mit einem peroral wirksamen Leberextrakt. *Schweiz. Med. Wschr.*, 87:144.

Kay, H. and Birren, J. E.: (1958) Swimming speed of the albino rat. II. Fatigue practice and drug effects on age and sex differences. *J. Geront.*, 13:378-385.

Liu, S. Y.: (1928) The relation of age to the learning ability of the white rat. *J. Comp. Psychol.*, 8:75-85.

Rabinovitch, M. S. and Rosvold, H. E.: (1951) A closed field intelligence test for rats. *Canad. J. Psychol.*, 5:122-128.

Roth, O.: (1954) Dix ans d'expérience avec le Robuden. Résultats expérimentaux et cliniques. *Gastroenterologia*, 81:257.

Stone, C. P.: (1929) The age factor in animal learning. I. Rats in the problem box and maze. *Genet. Psychol. Monogr.*, 5:1. II. Rats on a multiple light discrimination box. *Génet. Psychol. Monogr.*, 6:2.

Vaccari, G. L. and Fantin, V.: (1959) Die Behandlung leichter und mittelschwerer Hepatopathien mit einem peroral verabreichten Leber-Totalextrakt. *Clin. Therapeut.*, 17:284.

23

RADIATION AS A TOOL IN STUDIES OF BEHAVIORAL AGE CHANGES*

Ernest Furchtgott

GENERAL BIOLOGICAL CONSIDERATIONS

During the course of the recent extensive research on the biological effects of ionizing radiation it has been observed that animals which had been irradiated and which had recovered from the acute effects had a shorter life span than control animals. Furthermore, the causes of death in these animals were similar to those observed in nonirradiated animals, i.e., the same kinds of degenerative diseases produced death in both irradiated as well as in nonirradiated groups. Nephrosclerosis, leukemia, arteriolocapillary fibrosis, hypertensive encephalopathy as well as external signs of aging, such as greying of the hair, all appear earlier in irradiated than in control animals. Plotting of mortality rates for the irradiated groups shows that the curve is displaced forwards in time, so that during the period of irradiation the animal "seems to age" and from then on the curve for the treated animals parallels that of the normal group. Since radiation is a very powerful mutagenic agent, the previously mentioned observations have led to the theory that aging is the result of somatic mutations. While it is true that certain objections have been

* Supported by Public Health Service research career program award No. K3-MH-16, 416-01, National Institute of Mental Health and by Research Grant RH65 from the Division of Radiological Health, Bureau of State Service.

raised against a genetic theory of aging (Strehler, 1960), these are based primarily on quantitative differences between the effects of radiation and aging, and one can argue that the objections are not fundamentally incompatible with the mutagenic theory. This is, however, not the place to examine this problem. Let us instead look at some recent evidence cited in support of at least a limited mutagenic theory. The account is based on Curtis' (1963) recent review of the theory.

One obvious approach to this problem is to compare the radiation-induced aging hypothesis with another popular hypothesis according to which aging is the cumulative result of the stresses and strains that the organism has during its life span (Selye and Prioreschi, 1960). According to this theory cumulative effects of diseases, accidents, and other stressors will shorten the life span. A recent series of experiments at the Brookhaven Laboratories by Curtis and co-workers has attempted to test this wear-and-tear theory and to contrast it with the muagenic theory. Mice were kept very sick for very large fractions of their life span by the injection of tetanus toxin, typhoid toxoid, subcutaneous intraperitoneal injections of turpentine, and other similar noxious agents. None of the stressors apparently had any effect on the life span. Curtis and co-workers concluded, therefore, that non-specific stress or the wear-and-tear theory does not explain all aging phenomena. However, in earlier experiments they did find that animals given small doses of mercuric chloride which damages the kidney selectively does shorten the life span. It should be noted here that kidney cells have the power to divide rapidly. The fact that the various injurious stressors did not shorten life span, whereas radiation did, led Curtis to the conclusion that radiation-life-shortening is not due to the general stress produced by radiation but rather to somatic mutations.

In further support of the theory of somatic mutations, Stevenson and Curtis found that chromosome aberrations in liver cells in normal mice increase with age and that radiation induces a very large increase in these aberrations. Also, the Brookhaven group has shown that chromosome aberrations develop much more rapidly as a function of age in short-lived than in long-lived strains of mice.

Furthermore, according to Curtis, in rapidly dividing cells mutation should cause relatively little damage because the affected cell will either die directly or be replaced. On the other hand, in slowly- or nondividing cells the defective cell will be retained indefinitely and thus contribute to the malfunctioning of the organ. Thus the neuro-muscular system, and especially the central nervous system consisting of relatively infrequently dividing cells, should exhibit relatively profound age changes, as indeed they do.

RADIATION AND THE NERVOUS SYSTEM

Since behavior is most intimately related to the functioning of the nervous system, it behooves us to examine radiation effects on this system. Classically it has been believed that the nervous system is highly reistant to radiation. In a large number of earlier studies it was shown that relatively large doses of radiation, well above the total-body lethal dose, have no structural effects. Most of the older studies used "survival of cells" as an indicator of neuronal radio-sensitivity. Actually, this criterion is of only limited value. A more useful index is *radiosensitivity* which denotes the degree of responsiveness of a cell or organism to radiation as a stimulus. There are various responses which may be measured, such as pathomorphological, physiological, psychological, etc. The responses within these broad categories may, of course, be further subdivided.

Using these criteria, recent research has shown that relatively small doses, even in the range below one Roentgen (R), may produce a variety of physiological and behavioral changes which may be detected by measuring electroencephalographic, heart rate, respiration, electro-retinographic changes, and radiation may act as an unconditioned stimulus in an avoidance conditioning paradigm. These changes are temporary; in many instances they do not last beyond a few minutes after the initiation of radiation, and frequently there is no dose effect relationship.

Radiobiologists are still in the dark about the mechanisms which produce these physiological changes at relatively low dose levels. It has been suggested by some that the observed changes are secondary effects inducd by the vascular system. The vascular endothelial cells which have a relatively high mitotic or molting rate are highly sensitive to radiation. Thus damage to the blood vessels has an indirect effect on the neuron. In addition, it has been hypothesized that cells injured by radiation release histamin or necrotoxins which initiate a chain of reactions leading to necrosis.

A variety of radiation-induced vascular reactions appear in all parts of the body including the nervous system. Hypotension, erythema, electrolyte imbalance, edema, and accelerated development of arterio-sclerosis have been reported following radiation. Slow progressing accelerated "aging" of vessels following irradiation is a fairly well-established phenomenon. It has also been assumed that "aging cannot validly be assumed to be operative in any organ or tissue profused by blood without evidence to exclude the causative role of circulatory alterations" (Landowne and Stanley, 1960, p. 160). Thus there seems to be a relationship between circulatory changes induced by radiation and aging.

A number of studies have shown that there are delayed degenerative changes in the nervous system following radiation, and in many of these, vascular degenerations have been assigned as a major causative factor. At the present time it is, therefore, very difficult to untangle the vascular from the possibly direct neural changes following radiation.

While neural tissue *per se* may be relatively resistant to the effect of radiation, when we study physiological or behavioral variables in assessing the functioning of the nervous system, other systems also enter into the picture. It is well known that a variety of internal homeostatic mechanisms are highly sensitive to radiation and these in turn may affect performance, measured either physiologically or behaviorally, of an organism following irradiation. It should come, therefore, as no surprise that radiation may indeed affect a variety of physiological or behavioral variables which may be a reflection not so much of a direct effect on neural tissues, but rather the secondary or indirect effect via a variety of changes in internal homeostatic mechanisms.

BEHAVIORAL STUDIES

So far there have been no longitudinal studies of irradiated animals. There have been, however, several attempts to test for possible delayed behavioral effects in animals which had been subjected to irradiation.

Cynomologus monkeys which had received 200 R gamma or x-radiation to the sides of the head showned no deficits in conditioned avoidance responses two weeks after irradiation even though at this time a homolateral EEG hypersynchrony was noted (Riopelle, 1962). Two to 3½ months postirradiation, however, the same Ss did show deficits, in visual discrimination tasks involving form, color, and size problems. The controls averaged 97 per cent correct solutions on the last six trials of the problem while the x-irradiates averaged 93 per cent, and the gamma-irradiates 85 per cent.

In the only published report using adult chimpanzees five animals which had received 375-400 R gamma irradiation were tested two to four years after irradiation on fourteen tests involving various types of discrimination learning, operant conditioning, social behavior, problem solving, etc. On eleven tests no differences were observed between the control and irradiated Ss. Three tests (4-choice oddity, visual acuity, and size discrimination) revealed deficits in the irradiated Ss. Whether these differences should be attributed to irradiation, characteristics of the particular small sample, or pure chance could not be answered (Riopelle, 1962).

Another long-term project has been in progress at the Radiobiological Laboratory at the Univerity of Texas. Data are now available for a seven-and-one-half-year postirradiation period. Early visual acuity testing established a definite deficit during the first year following the radiation exposure only in those irradiated monkeys exposed to the highest dose (616 rep.). This deficit in visual acuity was still evident three years after exposure. Monkeys receiving an intermediate dose (308 rep) showed no visual acuity changes during the first year after exposure, but such a deficit was observed three years after exposure (Brown and McDowell, 1960).

Davis (1963) observed deficits in discrimination learning involving original learning, but not in transfer of training in rhesus monkeys several years after they had received 1100 R (spaced) of whole body x-irradiation. On a test in which the animal had to shift successively from a double alteration to an object-quantity discrimination problem, there was actually a tendency for the irradiated Ss to show more frequent shifts, but the small size of the sample resulted in inconclusive data.

Davis (1962) reported that during a seven-year span following a total dose of 1100 R six monkeys showed a striking increment in self-involved behavior and a drop in social behavior.

The primate data obtained so far are too scant to arrive at definitive conclusions. There is some evidence for delayed behavioral changes in irradiated animals which seem to be most pronounced in the perceptual domain and in motivational variables. Insofar as the latter enter into a variety of behavioral functions, they may affect a whole host of measures.

For the last nine years we have been investigating the effects of prenatal x-irradiation on subsequent behavioral development in rats. To test for possible longitudinal radiation changes, animals in some of the experiments were tested throughout their life span. Since matched controls also had to be tested, this experimental design permitted us to investigate not only longitudinal age changes in irradiated animals, but also normal age changes in rats as well, and it also provided an opportunity to test the radiation-induced or mimicking aging hypothesis.

In one study, (Wechkin, Elder and Furchtgott, 1961), the rat's ability to climb an inclined plane was studied. Ninety-three Ss, approximately one-half of them having received 200 R on the 16th to 18th day of gestation and the others controls, were tested at the age of four to five months, fifteen months, or twenty to twenty-one months. The performance of the irradiated Ss was significantly inferior to the controls at all age levels, and age was inversely related to the ability to climb the inclined plane. The age x-irradiation interaction was not significant. The decline with age in the control groups was paralleled by a similar decline in the irradiated animals. The rate of decline was not greater in the latter.

In another study (Furchtgott and Wechkin, 1962) animals which had been irradiated with 200 R on the sixteenth day of gestation were compared with normal animals in a Miller-Mowrer avoidance conditioning situation. Animals were tested at the ages of three to four, fourteen, or twenty months. Approximately half of the 105 Ss were control and the other half irradiated animals. Speed of conditioning was inversely related to age, but the irradiated animals conditioned more rapidly than the controls. The most plausible hypothesis to account for the latter effect is the greater fearfulness of the irradiated rats, the latter having been established in several previous studies. According to drive theory, fearful Ss should show more rapid avoidance conditioning. The treatment $\times$ age interaction was not significant.

To digress here from a consideration of the radiation-induced aging hypothesis the finding that avoidance conditioning decreases significantly with age is noteworthy since it contrasts with many studies with rats which have shown that learning is not affected by age. It should be noted here, however, that avoidance conditioning in the Mowrer-Miller hurdle apparatus depends a great deal upon speed of performance. Accordingly an analysis of covariance with adjustment for response speed computed from the onset of the CS to the time that S landed on the non-electrified side, was performed. The resulting analysis produced an F of 17.58 for the irradiation variable, but the F for age was not significant at the .05 level. Thus, the difference in the number of trials to criterion between the three age groups could be best accounted for by decrements in response speed.

In several unpublished studies open field locomotion and sniffing at objects were measured in prenatally x-irradiated and in normal rats. The age decrements which were previously observed in young animals (Furchtgott, Wechkin and Dees, 1961) were equally apparent in the irradiated Ss.

In another study (Furchtgott and Tacker, 1963) the adjustment to food deprivation cycles was studied in rats which had been irradiated *in utero* with doses of 100 to 200 R between days fourteen and eighteen of the gestation period and in control animals. One hundred and three animals, approximately one-half of them controls, were tested at the age of seventy-five to ninety-four days, 380 to 397 days, or 629 to 735 days. Animals were placed on a twenty-two-hour food deprivation schedule with water available ad lib. The subjects were weighed during the twenty-first hour of the deprivation cycle. Adjustment to deprivation was determined in the terms of the days necessary to reach asymptotic weight. Figure 1 presents the results. It may be seen that adjustment to the deprivation schedule was inversely related to age. Also, in all three age controls the irradiated rats lost more weight than the controls. The initial greater weight and excess body fat of the older animals probably accounts for their slow adjustment to the deprivation schedule. Of course, one can also hypothesize that central nervous system (CNS) factors, which play an important role in feeding, are less efficient in older subjects. However, this is a rather tenuous hypothesis in the absence of well-defined CNS changes with age. The greater loss in body weight and slower adjustment of the irradiated rats at every age level came somewhat as a surprise since in every group

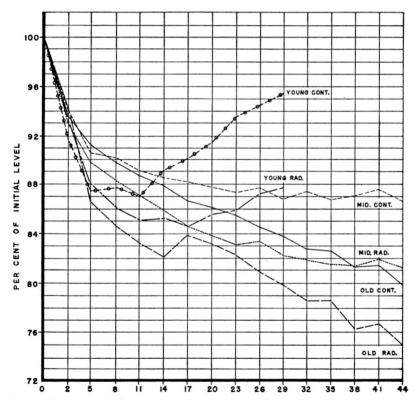

Figure 1. Mean body weights of young, middle aged, and old rats on a twenty-two-hour food deprivation schedule.

they weighed initially less than the controls and thus it might be assumed that they had a greater caloric need. It would seem plausible, therefore, to invoke CNS deficiencies as a major factor retarding the animals' adjustment to the feeding regimen. So far this experiment has provided probably the best evidence for a radiation-induced or mimicking aging hypothesis.

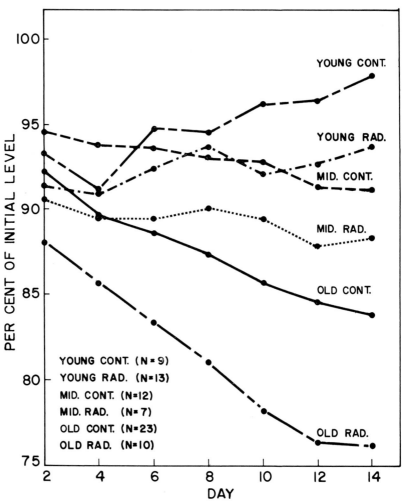

Figure 2. Mean body weights of young, middle aged, and old rats on a twenty-two-hour water deprivation schedule.

A similar experiment was performed on adjustment to water deprivation using different animals. Figure 2 presents these data. Results here were essentially identical with those on adjustment to food deprivation.

DISCUSSION AND SUMMARY

While there have been very few studies to test specifically the mutation theory of aging and no data directly supporting such a theory in the behavioral domain, we have some findings which are relevant to an analysis of the problem. On several performance measures in which after puberty there is a decline with age, prenatally irradiated animals exhibited a greater decline than normals. In all of the data which we have collected, the rate of decline does not show an acceleration in the treated animals. It seems rather that the irradiated animal "is older" in terms of the behavioral indices used by approximately the same constant at each chronological stage which we have tested.

We also have some evidence that delayed deficits occur in animals irradiated during adulthood, especially when motivational variables are measured. Whether these delayed changes are similar to those observed in normal aging processes has not been established as yet. Since neural functioning is affected by a host of internal metabolic factors and many of these in turn are relatively radiosensitive, we would expect that those behavioral functions which are most intimately related to metabolic factors, such as drive states, should also be most affected by radiation. This actually is the case. It would seem that an analogous situation exists when one examines behavioral age changes in non-irradiated organisms. The neuroanatomical and peripheral conduction age-induced changes are minor in comparison to the behavioral changes. The most pronounced peripheral neural age changes detected so far have occurred in the measurement of synaptic delay, and it is well known that the synapse is very sensitive to changes in the internal millieu. In animal learning studies drive and activity are probably the most potent age dependent variables. Thus from the standpoint of radiation-induced mutation as well as aging, one should examine those behavioral functions which are most closely associated with internal extra-neural homeostatic mechanisms.

In general, much more research is needed before we can arrive at more definite conclusions about the somatic theory of aging in the behavioral domain. In the meantime, however, the research efforts in the area are providing us with information of potentially great value in the modern atomic era on radiation effects at various age levels.

REFERENCES

Brown, W. L. and McDowell, A. A.: (1959) Visual acuity performance of normal and chronic irradiated monkeys. *J. Gen. Psychol., 61*:113-119.

Curtis, H. J.: (1963) Biological mechanisms underlying the aging process. *Science, 141*:686-694.

Davis, R. T.: (1962) Supplementary report: Effects of age and radiation on gross behavior of monkeys. *Psychol. Rep., 11*:738-740.

Davis, R. T.: (1963) Chronic effects of ionizing radiations and the hypothesis that irradiation produces aging-like changes in behavior. *J. Genet. Psychol., 102*:311-324.

Furchtgott, E. and Wechkin, S.: (1962) Avoidance conditioning as a function of prenatal irradiation and age. *J. Comp. Physiol. Psychol., 55*: 69-72.

Furchtgott, E., Wechkin, S. and Dees, J.: (1961) Open-field exploration as a function of age. *J. Comp. Physiol. Psychol.,* 386-388.

Landowne, M. and Stanley, J.: (1960) Aging and the cardiovascular system. In N. W. Shock, ed.: *Aging, Some Social and Biological Aspects,* Washington, AAAS, pp. 159-188.

Riopelle, A. J.: (1960) Some behavioral effects of ionizing radiation on primates. In T. J. Haley and R. S. Snider, eds.: *Response of the Nervous System to Ionizing Radiation,* N. Y., Academic Press, pp. 719-728.

Selye, H. and Prioreschi, P.: (1960) Stress theory of aging. In N. W. Shock, ed.: *Aging, Some Social and Biological Aspects,* Washington, AAAS, pp. 261-272.

Strehler, B. L.: (1960) Dynamic theory of aging. In N. W. Shock, ed.: *Aging, Some Social and Biological Aspects,* Washington, AAAS, pp. 273-304.

Tacker, R. S. and Furchtgott, E.: (1963) Adjustment to food deprivation cycles as a function of aging and prenatal X-irradiation. *J. Genet. Psychol., 102*:257-260.

Wechkin, S., Elder, R. and Furchtgott, E.: (1961) Motor performance in the rat as a function of age and prenatal X-irradiation. *J. Comp. Physiol. Psychol., 54*:658-659.

24

FACTORS INFLUENCING PERFORMANCE IN PSYCHOLOGICAL TESTING OF THE AGED

L. J. Hurwitz and R. S. Allison

Discussing the mental changes associated with old age, Rolleston (1932) remarks "In what may be regarded as normal old age physical activity diminishes . . . not only do initiative, elasticity, originality and the sense of humour fail, but new ideas and fresh lines of thought are assimilated with difficulty; hence the old are commonly conservative and *laudatores temporis acti*." This is the generally accepted view of what happens with normal ageing. However, there is difficulty in deciding by any form of testing which elderly subjects may be regarded as normal. Chapman and Wolff (1958) made a study of the intellectual performance of patients in whom the extent of brain injury was precisely known. They found that although the site of damage to the cerebral cortex was important as regards its effects on sensory and motor function and on speech, impairment of the highest integrative functions was dependent upon the extent of the lesion. This is the human counterpart to the "mass action" theory described in rats by Lashley (1929). Thus, the excision of small amounts of brain tissue, e.g., 30 grams led to changes which, if occurring in an old person, might be attributed to the effect of ageing, with reduction in versatility and of the capacity to function under stress, loss of spontaneity or "sparkle" and diminished drive or initiative. Subjects so affected complained of feeling

461

tired when attempting to learn new skills and preferred familiar activities which were well within their capacity. Relatives of elderly patients are inclined to attribute any change in behaviour to the "natural" effects of ageing; it is only when more pronounced aberrations occur that the possibility of disease is given thought. Indeed, so long as a man can go on working, deterioration of intellect may pass unnoticed, that is provided his work is chiefly routine in nature and workmates are prepared to help by "covering up" mistakes. It would appear, therefore, that there is some connection between the ability of such a subject to keep going and his adherence to routine and the avoidance of novel situations.

So, whilst going along with the proposition that in old age speed of performance is diminished we would qualify it by adding that in many cases this is due to organic brain changes which, although present, may not be apparent. A comparison of the few octo- and nonagenarians in whom intellectual activity is still undiminished with the large number of people between the ages of fifty and seventy who show blunting of intellect due to known brain disease supports the view that physiological ageing must surely be as rare as is physiological dying.

MATERIAL AND METHODS

The clinical material upon which our observations are based consists of over 200 patients in later life with organic mental states. In over 80 per cent of these the nature of the disease process was known, having been proved either at autopsy or surgical operation or by special investigation, such as arteriography or air pictures. About one-quarter had space-occupying lesions, one-third cerebro-vascular disease, and the rest a wide variety of disease entities including the primary dementias, anoxia, trauma, neurosyphilis, hypoglycaemia, parkinsonism and dementia, endocrine disturbance and hepatic encephalopathy. The aspects of intellect examined were:

1. Behaviour and mood.
2. Insight.
3. Series (forward and backward).
4. Registration and recall.

5. Memory for past events.
6. Orientation: spatial, temporal, bodily.
7. Speech and language.
8. Calculation.
9. Gnosis: visual, auditory, colour, tactile, picture.
10. Praxis: ideomotor and constructional.

The tests used were clinical and qualitative. In addition, all our patients were given quantitative psychological tests in the Department of Psychology of the Queen's University of Belfast. In this paper we will discuss the experience gained from the qualitative tests which, from a clinical point of view, were the more helpful.

GENERAL INFLUENCES AFFECTING PERFORMANCE
Traditions and Habit

One of the chief difficulties in assessing the results of tests for intellectual loss is the attitude of elderly people in many of whom there is a superficial desire to please and a tendency to act the part and do what they think is expected of an old person. Others may appear to cooperate well and to be intensely interested in what they are required to do but give the impression that they are not putting their maximal effort into the set task. They welcome the interviewer as a break in monotony and preface their attempts to respond with remarks like "I was better at doing this when I was a child and I am getting old now." One should never accept a poor performance uncritically and this rule applies particularly to timed tests. Often with encouragement and subtle cajolement a good performance can be obtained. This could in the psychological sense be related partly to elderly persons having atained their life's goal or effected some compromise to enable them to feel a sense of achievement at having lived so long. They congratulate themselves on the mere passage of time. They may well say with the poet "what I aspired to be and was not, comforts me." Their environment requires them to conform to certain conventional patterns inseparable from the popular concept of old age and horizons become narrowed in proportion to the degree to which they conform.

In a few patients a "don't want to do it" attitude is found and they feel it unreasonable to be required to undergo tests. (Adams and Hurwitz 1963). These patients will say they are well and in good spirits but just cannot abide with people who ask awkward questions. Although there are some ageing persons who never feel this sense of completeness and continue to show interest in exploring new situations, for many this is not so.

Effect of Automations

With advancing years, experience and repetition, many intellectual activities tend to become stylized into automations. This happens with speech and language and in such specialized activities as driving a motor car. Memory may become conditioned so that selective stimuli are needed to bring the mechanism of recall into play. Indeed, it is possible that many elderly people may feel little inclination to recall past events unless both the need and occasion arise. In the strange setting of the hospital or laboratory, when novel tests are presented and the usual stimuli are lacking, the effort of recalling names or events in the past or even topographical detail may present difficulty. For example, it is not uncommon to find a patient unable to fix the position of his home on a street map or to trace on a map how he would make his way to it from hospital. Yet, the same person may have no difficulty whatever in describing verbally the route he would take or in finding his way unaccompanied through the streets. Thus, the phenomenon of automation may introduce a variable by allowing the speed of performance to vary according to whether the test happens to be an appropriate stimulus to that individual.

Obsessive Tendencies

The mood and behaviour of an elderly person depends to some extent on the amount of brain damage, the previous personality and temperament, the kind of situation with which he is faced and on the rate of dissolution. Frankly obsessive tendencies are more common in slowly evolving primary and arteriosclerotic dementias than they are with space-occupying lesions. As Goldstein (1942) has pointed out, these attitudes lead to evasions and stratagems to cover up defects. Patients may even adopt a number of minor rituals such as making notes on pieces of paper, always arranging their belongings in the same order or depositing them in the same place. Such attitudes create difficulties in the use of tests designed to measure speed of performance, for no task, however straightforward, will be undertaken or completed until it has first been cautiously surveyed as fully as possible.

Gentle prompting by the examiner that speed is important may even be sufficient to induce catastrophic reactions. In one of our patients obsessive features became so prominent as virtually to exclude psychometric testing, although clinically there was little evidence of dementia:

> This was a woman, aged eighty-five years, who had recently begun to complain of feeling tense and jittery. She could not sleep at night and on advice took a warm drink of malted milk at bedtime. This helped but for weeks afterwards she would keep asking her daughter or her visitors "What was it the doctor recommended?" When she was told she would write down the name of the beverage in red ink on a piece of paper so that before long there was scarcely a room in the house left undecorated by these notices. She went on to make an excellent recovery and lost all these obsessional tendencies, psychological testing then showing little abnormality.

INFLUENCES RELATED TO BRAIN DYSFUNCTION
Perseveration

The word was first used by Neisser in 1894 and it has been applied since then in widely differing contexts so that it does not always have the same meaning. Psychologists have found that the tests employed for perserveration are open to differing interpretations, so that a great deal of their attitude is dependent on which theory and definition is espoused (Yates 1960). The neurologist acknowledges the presence of perserveration when the subject responds appropriately to a stimulus and then continues to make the same response after the stimulus is withdrawn and another presented in its place. Rarely one finds a single perseveratory activity occurring clinically in pure form (confined either to action, speech or thought); more usual is it to find signs in combination. A simple way of demonstrating perserveration of action is to ask the patient to put out his tongue and when he has done this then to close his eyes. Perseveration is shown by his carrying out the first request correctly but then repeating it when attempting to comply with the second. In speech it is readily demonstrated by the use of series tests, the patient being first asked to count from one to ten and then to repeat the days of the week or vice-versa. Perseveration in thought—which we may regard as showing a persistent type of "set"—is brought out in conversation. One engages in small talk with the patient, say about the weather, but when the subject is changed, his answers continue to be more appropriate to the former topic.

In recovery from unconsciousness from whatever cause (injury, epileptic fit, anoxia, electric shock treatment, etc.) perseveration is often found as a transient sign and may persist as the last recognisable indication of the disturbed mental state until full consciousness is regained. This pattern is consistently found even in previously healthy persons.

In our series of patients perseveration was a common symptom and often could be demonstrated repeatedly over a long period of time. Further, in many patients it was a more pronounced feature than might have been expected from consideration solely of their level of consciousness, as indicated by the relative preservation of memory and capacity for attention. Indeed, there appeared to be no constancy between the degree of perserveration and the extent of brain dysfunction (the former not necessarily being found only in those whose brain disease was the greatest).

The phenomenon was also variable in its occurrence, on some days being more pronounced than on others. If an interval of time were allowed to elapse between tests it did not occur, the relationship of the time interval between successive tests being of especial significance. It was found both with focal and with diffuse cerebral lesions, although in patients with focal lesions of the dominant hemisphere affecting the speech area, perseveration was sometimes related only to speech.

Perseveration is not limited in its occurrence to elderly brain-injured subjects. It is also seen in healthy young children and we have observed it in apparently normal old people. The following is an example:

Mrs. T., aged ninety-three years, widow of a professional man, had been in hospital for two years on account of increasing weakness of the legs, recurring bronchopneumonia and pyelitis. Despite being confined to bed she took the paper each day and read some at least of the news. Her mood was friendly and warm and she was interested in her surroundings, activities of the nurses, and had a good memory for names, places, and the sequence of events in the past. She commented one day on how important it was to keep her mind active, so, the opportunity was taken of suggesting that she should be tested. To this she readily agreed and the following conversation ensued:

Exam. "Give me the name of a town or city—anywhere—beginning with the letter "L."

Pt.   "London."

Exam. "Now, taking the last letter of the word 'London,' give me the name of another town beginning with it."

Pt.   (pauses, shifts her gaze) . . . "Northern Ireland . . . no, that wouldn't do, would it? . . . You want the name of a town! (smiling).

Exam. "That's right . . . the name of a town beginning with 'N' . . . what about Newry? Wouldn't that do?"

Pt.   "Yes, of course, Newry."

Exam. "Now, go on, another town, the name of which begins with the last letter."

Pt.   (thinking hard) . . . "that's difficult . . . I can't think of any town beginning with 'Y.'"

Exam. "'York,' wouldn't that do?"

Pt.   "I hadn't thought of that. I have been trying to think of a town in Northern Ireland."

It will be noted that she had no difficulty in registering, and that perseveration occurred solely in thought.

In the following instance, although there was no perseveration in motor activities, it was so pronounced in thought as to make any form of mental testing difficult, if not impossible to interpret.

The patient, Mrs. G., a married woman aged sixty-one years, had had steatorrhoea and metabolic bone disease for 8 years. Progressive intellectual deterioration had been noticed by relatives, especially in the six months preceding her examination. She herself had no complaints and in hospital always appeared to be alert, sitting up in bed and looking about her. When given a newspaper or illustrated magazine she immediately put on her glasses and appeared to be reading. But, one day, when she was glancing over a copy of "Woman," and she was asked what she was reading, she looked at the examiner whimsically and replied "you never read this . . . this is Woman . . . Woman you know . . . Woman!!," after which the conversation went something like as follows:

Q. How are you?
A. "This is Woman, you know, Doctor."
Q. What is the name of this place?
A. "Well, it is not what you would read."
Q. What day is it?
A. "I told you, you would never read it."

She was able to register and recall a name and an address when this was the first test used and it was the same with all other tests. There was no difficulty provided at the time of presentation no other "contaminating thought" was present (Brain 1962). Thus, she could draw an excellent representation of a house and later displayed much native shrewdness in her answers explaining the meaning of proverbs. It could not be said, therefore, that perseveration in her case was simply a fragment of general clouding of consciousness for if time were allowed to elapse between stimuli she displayed no evidence of it. Neither could the perseveration be explained by "inattention" nor by impairment of immediate memory.

A case described by Adams and Hurwitz (1963) illustrates perseveration of a complex skilled action in which the required task was repeated over and over again with increasing speed, in what was described as "the sorcerer's apprentice syndrome." This was an elderly man who had recovered from a cerebral vascular episode. His movements showed no apraxia. In drawing a clock he made a series of concentric pencil strokes with gathering speed. When given a brush he began to use it on his clothes with increasing speed and vigour until stopped. Given a match box he proceeded to strike each one skilfully (blowing each out in turn) until the box was empty.

In man all forms of perseveration are said to dominate the clinical picture when there is involvement of the frontal lobes, and monkeys after frontal lobe ablations were found by Jacobsen (1939) particularly to show perseveration. In our series the brain lesions were probably more generalised.

Symonds (1937) found perseveration of common occurrence after head injury but by definition he attributed this to impaired consciousness and not necessarily to focal lesions. However, the anatomical lesion accounting for perseveration need not concern us here. Goldstein (1936) postulates that in organic states abnormal central expansion of a stimulus occurs and that this lasts an abnormal period of time, being expressed at the level of mental function as perseveration. Kay (1959) discusses such theories of perseveration as retro-active and pro-active interferences and the continuous error repetition frequently found in the elderly. In an earlier contribution (Kay 1955) he suggests that the older person fails when he perseverates in making irrelevant transfers or does not try to transfer from relevant learnings. Lorge (1956) suggests that older subjects are penalized by speed on intelligence tests. The point to be emphasized is that any subject who perseverates will probably not do well in timed tests and conversely it may be that timed tests are more sensitive to organically determined perseveration than to senescence itself.

Synkinesia

Another feature of performance which has long been recognised as neurologically based is mirror and associated movements here grouped together as "synkinesia." Møgens Fog in a personal communication has described the natural evolution of this in children. With maturity it becomes less in evidence, disappearing in adolescence. In children with brain damage, however, it persists into adult life. Attention has not often been paid to synkinesia in old age, though one might expect from Jacksonian principles that in "dissolution" it would reappear. We have found synkinetic movements both in the normal and the affected limbs following stroke in old people and in whom the synkinesia hampered the performance of a task and particularly the speed with which that task was done.

Poverty of Movement

Another motor sign of brain damage frequently found is poverty of movement which is similar to that seen in Parkinson's disease. Although akinesia is the hallmark of that condition, "kinesia paradoxica" is not uncommon. Thus, some patients may do everything at a running trot although showing fixity of expression and rigidity of the limbs. Very often the immobility can be released by emotional factors and a remarkable speed of reaction can then occur. In institutions where patients with post-encephalitic Parkinsonism are cared for there is a wealth of stories concerning this. A typical one is as follows—two middle-aged patients were virtually immobile on account of the disease. Both were confined to wheel chairs and were unable to rise from a sitting position. Both had rather obsessional bowel habits. One day when they were being wheeled to the toilet only one happened to be vacant and they arrived on its threshold simultaneously. Before either of their attendants could give way they jumped up from their chairs and struck each other with rapid and accurate blows. Then both protagonists fell to the ground and reverted to their former immobility.

The inference, of course, is that any tests given to patients suffering from Parkinsonism or to old people in whom poverty of movement is pronounced, could have variable results, even at a verbal level, for rigidity of the muscles of vocalisation could change with emotional factors. The speed of reaction both for "motility" and for "central processes" would be affected.

Impairment of Memory

We have noticed that old people suffering from diffuse cerebral cortical atrophy and showing early signs of dementia can usually recall the names of things they see, hear or touch, whereas they may have the greatest difficulty in recalling them without such stimuli. Kahn and Thompson (1934) noticed this inability "to use memory as a tool" as they called it, as an early feature of primary dementia, and one of us (Allison 1962) has drawn attention to the fact that if such patients are prompted with related facts, they can often provide further details gratuitously, indicating that there is no actual memory loss, only an inability to use it.

Although associated with a mood of indifference, we do not believe that emotional factors are responsible for this phenomenon. Focal lesions in the neighborhood of the third ventricle and bilateral lesions of the temporal lobes are known to be associated particularly with disturbances of memory, but this "priming of the pump" phenomenon (Allison 1962) suggests that what is lacking is the appropriate stimulus to recall. When this can be supplied, memory is often surprisingly good. In a few patients who did "register," i.e. who were able to repeat the information immediately after it had been given to them, recall was in fact grossly impaired so that after a few seconds it had been forgotten.

Metabolic Disturbances

Critchley (1955) in his chapter on neurological changes in the aged speaks of the "mental viscosity" of some old people and suggests as one possible explanation that proprioceptive impulses are failing to attain awareness. It is to be expected that elderly people have partial deafness, defective vision and are subject to chronic aches and pains which, although not crippling or disabling, have the effect of distracting attention or of serving as justifiable excuses for narrowing the range of activity, both mental and physical. In addition, variation in psychological testing may arise from changes in the internal milieu, such as disturbances in water and electrolyte balance, or incipient liver failure. The performance on tests of patients with liver disease is worse in the evening than it is in the morning; worse on a high protein diet than it is on a low one. These aspects will now be described.

In 1954, we saw a patient (Wh.) one year after porta-caval anastomosis for cirrhosis of the liver, who was extremely sensitive to protein in his diet. When first seen he showed considerable intellectual deterioration only after having his Sunday dinner and in his abnormal behaviour constructional and dressing apraxias dominated.

A high protein diet will lead to deterioration in the E.E.G. in patients with liver disease and this effect is one of the additive tests whose value is discussed by Hurwitz and Allison (1955) and Laidlaw and Read (1963). For some years we have used this test for patients showing signs of dementia of undetermined aetiology and on two occasions it has led to the diagnosis of hepatic disease with encephalopathy in patients in whom there was no clear evidence of liver disease clinically.

> Mrs. E. G. aged sixty had been noticed to have increasing failure of memory over the preceding six months and to be more easily angered. When first seen, clinical examination revealed some tremulousness of the arms but no other abnormality. The usual liver function tests were quite normal. The E.E.G. became worse with high protein diet and she would then show constructional and dressing difficulties. Perseveration was also present but not to any great degree. With treatment by neomycin and a 20 gram. protein diet the E.E.G. and mental state returned to normality. In two years follow-up her tolerance for protein feeding has slowly decreased and anything more than 10 grams daily in the diet leads to intellectual changes. There is still no sign of portal hypertension; She has no liver palms or spider naevi but the bromsulphthalein retention is grossly abnormal indicating a spontaneous portal systemic shunt. She does not have Wilson's disease but is developing persistent extrapyramidal features, e.g., choreoathetotic movements similar to the patient (Wh.) mentioned above who had a porta-caval anastomosis operation and who came to autopsy seven years later (Gibson 1963).

Protein intoxication obviously affects the mental state very rapidly and there can be an equally rapid improvement when protein is withdrawn. Although this does not annul the value of any one psychological test as an index of intellectual deterioration, the interpretation of such tests can only be valid when related to the time of the last meal or even the state of the gut. Variations in the performance of a test in a single day may indeed sometimes be wide enough to suggest that the patient is suffering from hysteria.

Allison (1952) summarised the disturbances which may occur in old people following surgical operations. He was particularly interested in patients whose eyes were bandaged following cataract removal and who, being somewhat deaf and confined to bed, had considerable sensory deprivation. Delirious states were common, but he found that these were related to many other factors, the most important being the injudicious use of barbiturates or morphine, dehydration and electrolyte disturbances. The correction of these usually led to quite remarkable recovery in the mental state. The same author studied patients who had had severe anoxic insults, particularly from carbon monoxide poisoning or hypoglycaemia. In the recovery state, there was often constructional apraxia, difficulty in the correct directioning of arrows, and perseveration, all which symptoms tended to improve over the succeeding weeks or months. This improvement could be correlated with improvement in the extent of their general awareness. In such pathological states the ability to do more complex tasks correlated well with improvement in constructional apraxia, perseveration, improvement in the E.E.G. and the conscious level. However, no measured tests of changes in speed of reaction were made.

INFLUENCES RELATED TO AFFECTIVE DISTURBANCES

Some years ago we became interested in ways and means of confirming the presence of suspected dementia, being impressed by the work of Weinstein *et al.* (1953) on the use of intravenous amytal. Our own modification of their procedure was to investigate the effects of agents one might expect to find more naturally in everyday life, i.e., alcohol. We studied ten patients with presenile dementia of unknown aetiology and ten non-demented patients of the same age group, forty to sixty years, suffering from a variety of other complaints. We gave them 1 oz. absolute alcohol diluted in water by stomach tube and tested their ability to register and recall, to construct simple designs and their reasoning ability and capacity for abstract thinking. About thirty minutes later at a time when the E.E.G. was showing maximal changes the mental tests were repeated. The E.E.G. in all cases showed deterioration in a decrease of dominant frequency. However, performances in the presenile group remained either the same or was slightly improved while in the control group six out of ten showed a slight, though not very significant, worsening of performance which we interpreted as being due to their tendency to drowsiness. The improvement seen in some of the suspected dements could have been due to reduction in anxiety. This was borne out on another occasion when the opportunity was taken of testing the effects on an elderly patient with an old cerebral vascular lesion of large doses of bromide. Instead of causing further intellectual deterioration, performance actually improved and this was at a time when the blood bromide level was over 300 mgs. per cent.

Co-existing psychoneurosis may influence a state of mild intellectual impairment so that the patient appears to be grossly demented. These patients often perform badly on tests that require a quick response but improve after a few days in hospital as their anxiety diminishes.

It is also true that the clinical distinction between a severe depression and dementia in old persons can on occasion be very difficult, and tests involving speed of reaction are of no help in the differential diagnosis.

SUMMARY

It is accepted that slowness in the performance of psychological tests is a feature commonly associated with old age. But many contributory factors are involved. Some of these are more constant than others; some related more to the external environment; others more to the "milieu interieur." A further difficulty arises in that organic brain disease and affective disturbances or psychoneurosis often co-exist. Examples are given from clinical observations made on over 200 patients in later life, in the majority of whom the underlying pathological cause of deterioration was known. These illustrations would appear to justify the exercise of caution in the interpretation of timed tests and the need for correlation of the results with the patient's mental and physical state at the time. Attention is drawn particularly to the fact that many so-called normal old people have unsuspected brain disease and that in others the influence disturbing performance in tests may vary in its effects from day to day or even during the course of a single day, dependent on the patient's metabolic state.

REFERENCES

Adams, G. F. and Hurwitz, L. J.: (1963) Mental barriers to recovery from strokes. *Lancet, ii:*533-537.

Allison, R. S.: (1952) Psychiatric disorders in later life. *Brit. Med. J., ii:* 1286-1289.

Allison, R. S.: (1956) Discussion on clinical consequences of cerebral anoxia. *Proc. Roy. Soc. Med.,* 49:609-622.

Allison, R. S.: (1962) *The Senile Brain.* London, Edward Arnold Ltd.

Brain, Lord: (1961) *Speech Disorders.* London, Butterworths.

Chapman, L. F. and Wolff, H. G.: (1958) Disease of the Neopallium and impairment of the highest integrative functions. *Med. Clin. N. A.,* 677-689, Philadelphia & Sonson, W. B. Saunders & Co.

Critchley, M.: (1956) Neurological changes in the aged—in The neurologic and psychiatric aspects of the disorders of ageing. *Res. Publ. Ass. Res. Nerv. Ment. Dis.,* 35.

Gibson, J. B.: (1963) Encephalopathy after portacaval shunt. *Brit. Med. J.,* i:1652-1655.

Goldstein, K.: (1936) The modifications of behavior consequent to cerebral lesions. *Psychiat. Quart.,* 10:586-610.

Goldstein, K.: (1942) *After Effects of Brain Injuries in War.* London, Heinemann.

Hurwitz, L. J. and Allison, R. S.: (1955) Recurring mental confusion after portacaval anastomosis. *Brit. Med. J.,* i:387-389.

Kahn, E. and Thompson, L. J.: (1934) Concerning Pick's Disease. *Amer. J. Psychiat.,* 13:937-946.

Kay, H.: (1959) Theories of learning and ageing. In *Handbook of Ageing and the Individual,* J. E. Birren, ed., Chicago, University of Chicago Press.

Kay, H.: (1959) Some experiments on adult learning. In *Old Age in the Modern World,* Edinburgh, Livingstone, p. 259.

Jacobsen, C. F.: (1939) Effects of extirpations on higher brain processes. *Physiol. Rev.,* 19:303-322.

Laidlaw, J. and Read, A. E.: (1963) The E.E.G. in hepatic encephalopathy. *Clin. Sci.,* 24:109-120.

Lashley, K. S.: (1929) *Brain Mechanisms and Intelligence.* Chicago, University of Chicago Press.

Lorge, I.: (1956) Ageing and intelligence, In The neurological and psychiatric aspects of the disorders of ageing. *Res. Publ. Ass. Res. Nerv. Ment. Dis.,* 35.

Neisser (1894), quoted by Wilson, S. A. K.: (1908) A contribution to the study of apraxia. *Brain,* 31:164-216.

Rolleson, H.: (1932) *Medical Aspects of Old Age.* London, Macmillan.

Symonds, C. P.: (1937) Mental disorder following head injury. *Proc. Roy. Soc. Med.,* 30:1081-1094.

Weinstein, E. A., Kahn, R. L., Sugarman, L. A. and Linn, L. I.: (1953) Diagnostic use of amobarbital sodium in brain disease. *Amer. J. Psychiat.,* 109:889-894.

Yates, A. J.: (1960) Abnormalities of psychomotor functions. In *Handbook of Abnormal Psychology,* H. J. Eysenck, ed., New York, Basic Books.

25

PSYCHOMOTOR CHANGES WITH AGE, PSYCHOPATHOLOGY AND BRAIN DAMAGE

H. E. KING

INTRODUCTION

Tʜᴇ ᴘᴀᴛʜᴏʟᴏɢɪᴇꜱ of human behavior present essentially practical problems; problems of an urgency that demanded public action for their care, and a medical approach to treatment, long in advance of any scientific approach to their description or study. Under the pressure of practical need, and in the absence of either a systematic taxonomy of human behavior or adequate test methods that might serve as a basis for defining disordered states, what has grown up to fill the needs of most modern societies has been a system for identifying deviant behavior, and forming it into classes, that is based on mixed criteria of normality drawn in unequal proportions from legal, medical, moral, social and biologic sources. As the behavior of man touches each of these frames of reference, it is altogether reasonable that each should come to play a part in the practical definition of his states of faulty behavior. The mixed origins of the behavior pathologies urges caution upon all who would contrast pathologic behavior with that of the normal, however, and serve as a reminder that these groups are as often based on symptom as cause and were originally formulated to reflect man-in-society rather than an always understood defect in body structure or physiologic function. While errors of this kind are known to

476

occur, in certain instances, causal biologic defects remain as yet undiscovered for many of the obvious pathologies of behavior. These qualifying comments need not blind us to the value of the study of abnormal states, or what may be inferred about usual function from careful observation of a system in disorder— if such observation is approached in a spirit of guarded inquiry. An attention to what is not usual, and to the unexpected, has often proved to be productive of insight in the search for causal relationships, and so it may be for the study of human behavior as well. The more so, it might appear, since we cannot manipulate the body structure or the conditions of man's life at will simply to observe the contrast of changed conditions in an experimental way, and we find ourselves strongly dependent upon those variations that occur naturally to provide us with a glimpse of what may happen when ordinary function or the usual control of behavior is altered. Beginning from a clear position that the pathologic approach to human behavior holds both unique advantages and hazards, and with a continuing effort to keep these factors in sensible balance, what may be learned about psychomotor speed and adequacy from among the behavior disorders that may have special relevance to the study of age changes in the speed of behavior?

Until quite recently the only possible basis for grouping the disorders of behavior as a rough unity has been the disorganization of behavior itself; by definition, a faulty pattern of human adaptation to life in society. There have been no biologic measures or test techniques available that would consistently establish the presence of behavior disorder, nor gauge its severity, other than the behavior and mental content of the patient himself, his social history and his clinical record. For certain subclasses of disorder a cause is understood, or has been strongly inferred, from what has been learned about faulty brain structure and function; such as the presence of central nervous system tumor, trauma or vascular disease. For other disruptions the causal factors remain unknown, are called idiopathic or are imperfectly understood; as is true for many of the clinical classes of mental retardation and the major psychoses. To these general groupings we may add a third category, of more recent history and the greatest theoretical importance, comprised of those temporary derangements of organized behavior that result from man-made (and reversible) changes produced in the nervous system. These changes may be made directly to the CNS or may be brought about indirectly by modifying the physiological or psychological status of otherwise normal persons, or of patients with a pre-existing behavior disorder. The common denominator for all of these broad groupings has been, until now, adaptive behavior; judged clinically for its adequacy in a variety of everyday life situations. A clue has long been present, in the vast literature on disturbed behavior, that another more-or-less independent correlate of states of faulty human adaptation may be found by a careful observation of the psychomotor adequacy of patients suffering from what appear to be at first sight a broad variety of clinical conditions. The experimental and clinical evidence gathered from this point of view within the last decade or two combines to suggest that another rough but general unity may be described from among quite different pathologies of behavior by turning the attention of the observer to patterns of motility and to psychomotor performance obtained under special test conditions (Hunt and Cofer, 1944; Huston, Shakow and Riggs, 1937; King, 1954, 1961; Weaver, 1961; Wulfeck, 1941).

The utility of approaching the study of behavior disorder from the psychomotor point of view is a concept that has been long in maturing. Although the idea is not new, and would appear to be a reasonably self-evident one, it has been only within recent years that it has received widespread empirical support and experimental use. This may appear to be the more surprising in view of the absence of successful biologic assays for detecting the presence of the behavior disorders, but the psychomotor approach to disorganized states of adaptation has remained relatively dormant since at least the middle 1800's. Even today it receives little or no attention from the clinician, whose need for an independent measure of the presence or degree of behavior disorder would seem to be equally as great as for those concerned with problems of research. One can only speculate as to why this may be true. Despite the evidence of bizarre posturings, slowed or awkward body motions and discordant gestures that may be seen in many disorganized patients, it was not until advances had been made in the techniques of motion measurement and in the ways of making controlled psychological observations that this approach could be placed on a firm footing and its data sensibly related to other sources of information about the patient.

The maturing of other disciplines, outside the purely psychological but with a relevance to its problems, during the same era may also have played a part. The "telephone switchboard" theories of brain function held in the 1920's and '30's offered sterile ground for the generation or growth of ideas about central nervous system plasticity or self-modifying organismic function. So, too, the psychological theories of that day, under the influence of the psychometric movement and disconcerted by the low-order correlations found between the intelligence and motor measures, were probably equally inhospitable. Then, as now, one may also observe a noticeable reluctance on the part of many to consider *human* movement as anything other than an executive proceeding; something that is carried out "once the mind has decided upon a course of action," rather than as a dynamic of the contact of the individual with his environment and a part of both input and output in his adaptation to its continuous ebb and flow. Whatever may be the surmise, from looking backward, as to why a psychomotor approach to behavior disorder was slow in taking hold, it is of less importance than why it seems to be a fruitful concept and is finding an increasing experimental use today.

The newer techniques of neurophysiology and experimental anatomy, typified by the electroencephalogram, implanted electrodes for brain stimulation or recording in otherwise intact and responding animals, and the discovery of powerful central-acting biochemical substances have brought concurrent changes in concepts of brain function, its level of activation and the organization and plasticity of central nervous system function. A corresponding shift has also taken place in the psychological techniques and concerns of today, from those designed for the measurement of abilities or faculties to methods more capable of reflecting changes in process, typified by the development of tools

and concepts for the study of learning, drive and emotion, in-
formation-processing and the vigilance of the responder. These
changes in approach and method, and recent evidence for the
usefulness of relating scientific techniques drawn from more than
one discipline (e.g., in observing the effects of delivering electrical stimulation to the brain during learning) have brought a
new significance to the study of psychomotor activity in human
subjects and its possible relation to information derived from
other scientific disciplines and to the broader patterns of human
behavior.

As the psychomotor is but an aspect of the organism's response
capacity, it will inevitably be tied to other factors governing
response: the physiological condition of the subject, his psychological state and the quality of the test behavior under study.
One would expect, then, to obtain data of a mixed variance with
this approach, depending on the relative weight of the entry of
such factors into the experimental situation. The possible sources
of confusion and confounding become apparent and emphasize
the need for exercising care in the interpretation of all results before making any conclusion very general. But if man is organismic in response, and his behavior nearly always a complex blend
of varied contributing elements, then we must expect that psychomotor activity, if it reflects a vital aspect of that adaptation,
to be correspondingly complex. The value of the systematic
study of movement as an important quality of response is not
that it is simpler, but that it is detectable and can be measured
and may, therefore, be related to other forms of "public data"
available about the individual under study.

A term is needed, for which I have suggested *psychomotility*
(King, 1954, 1961), that will be appropriate for referring to this
general aspect of human activity and yet be broad enough to
include the study of many and varied types of human action. An
inclusive view is particularly needed to be able to review the
evidence available from the field of behavior disorder, for neither
the test approach nor the groups that have been observed have
been standard enough to impress order on what has been learned
thus far. Observations have been recorded among the pathologies
of behavior that vary from the speed of reaction and dextrousness through measures of muscular tension and tremor, motor

learning, grip and body sway, limb movement and work decrement and a variety of other possible dimensions of psychomotor performance. As measures of psychomotor function characteristically exhibit only low, positive inter-correlation among normal subjects, grouping such data together for purposes of discussion must not be taken to imply factor simplicity. It has been made quite clear (King, 1954, 1961; Yates, 1961) that different tests and experimental psychomotor approaches may tap different levels of subject response, and that future experimentation in the behavior disorders—if it is to be more effective than much of the work that has been done in the past—must clarify the dimension under observation and specify the procedures employed as well as strive for greater homogeneity in the groups of patients placed under scrutiny. The relative independence of such measures of somatic reactivity as heart rate, muscle tension, blood pressure, electrodermal level and respiration rate does not prevent their useful inclusion under the concept of autonomic responsiveness, however, which may better serve as a model for psychomotility than would a construct based on purely mental activities, such as intelligence. Proceeding from the position that movement is a basic life property which appears as an aspect of quite varied forms of organismic response (King, 1954, 1961), we may review and attempt to weigh what has been found when persons in a patent state of behavior disorganization come under scrutiny for their *psychomotility*, meaning by this term the adequacy of their psychomotor functioning in a variety of sample activities and experimental situations. A summary of what has been observed may be broken, for convenience in presentation, into the broad divisions of *Psychopathology*, where the biologic causes or substrates for the disorganization of behavior are still imperfectly known, and *Brain Damage and CNS Dysfunction*, where the causes of accompanying behavior disruptions are somewhat better understood.

PSYCHOPATHOLOGY

Psychoneurosis
Group Descriptive

Patients termed psychoneurotic are most often treated privately, or by an out-patient facility, and are rarely found in large enough concentration in hospitals to permit the descriptive study of sizable subject groups. The *fine* psychomotor movement patterns of a sample of twenty-three neurotic patients, drawn from an out-patient clinic source, have been observed by King (1954) and their performance compared with that of a normal group, matched for age and sex, on the same experimental series. (The term *fine* psychomotor movement patterns, as used here and to follow, is to distinguish between the *gross* coordinations of full-body action and the smaller coordinations typical of the manual skills, as many of the experimental findings related to these classes of response differ in important ways] (Seashore, 1951). The *fine* psychomotor movement patterns are those in which speed or accuracy, or both, are more important than strength (Seashore, 1951; Seashore, Buxton, and McCullum, 1940); and are usually accomplished by the small muscle groups of the extremities). A comparison of measures obtained from normal and neurotic groups on speed in simple auditory reaction-time, in tapping, in the dextrous placing and assembly of small metal bits and in disjunctive reaction-time revealed an average level and pattern of performance by the neurotic patients that was similar on the whole, to that achieved by the non-neurotic control subjects. The mean scores given in Table 1, which were obtained after a period of prolonged practice and familiarization with the test procedures, illustrate the general similarity in performance

TABLE 1

MEAN SCORES ON KEY TESTS OF THE EXPERIMENTAL
PSYCHOMOTOR BATTERY FOR THE NEUROTIC AND NORMAL
GROUPS, MATCHED FOR AGE AND SEX (AFTER KING, 1954)

Test		Neurotic (n =23)	Normal (n =99)
Reaction Time (Lift)	M	200	201
(ms.)	σ	31.1	27.0
Tapping Speed	M	20.7	23.7
(taps per 5 sec.)	σ	3.7	2.5
Assembly	M	41.7	44.0
(bits per min.)	σ	4.3	5.7
Disjunctive Reaction Time (Lift)	M	287	281
(ms.)	σ	57.2	51.1

by the two groups for key measures taken from this series. The practice curves (the acquisition and stabilization of response) for the groups were also compared, based on observations separately recorded prior to the measures shown in Table 1, and were also found to be strikingly similar for both types of subjects. As the same experimental test battery was also applied to patient groups with other forms of behavior disorder, where more positive differences in performance were observed, the speed values for the normal group cited in Table 1 may serve as a point of reference for later comparison.

An experimental variation of the preparatory interval used in tests of reaction-time has been reported by Hall and Stride (1954) for the comparative performance of normal and neurotic subject groups, carefully matched for age and sex, in which the signal to initiate a response was preceded either by no warning, or by warnings given at regular and irregular intervals prior to the signal to respond. No significant differences were observed in the speed of performance by the two groups under these conditions of differing cues to respond, apart from the finding of a somewhat more variable response by the patient group.

Samples of twenty-five neurotic patients and fifty normal subjects, well-matched for age and sex, have been compared by Wulfeck (1941a) in their performance on tests that he has described as being "motor tasks of intermediate levels of integration." These measures call for movements dependent upon simple, non-identical, sequential coordination requiring both a preparation to respond and sustained activity of short duration. A comparison was made in terms of both speed and error scores for performance on tests of: the estimation of known sizes, work-decrement on a pneumoergograph, pattern tracing, reaction-coordination (initiating and completing a coordinated series of movements to a stimulus) and the synchronizing of a motor response with regular and irregular rhythmic patterns presented by means of audible "clicks." The psychoneurotic subjects were found to perform at about the same level of competence as did normal individuals on the varied psychomotor tasks presented at this level of integrative complexity, exhibiting no clear or characteristic variation in the general level of speed demonstrated or in patterns of response adequacy. As Wulfeck also applied the same test battery to patients falling under other diagnostic groupings of behavior disorder, where unmistakable differences in performance were recorded, his finding of essentially normal performance speeds among neurotic subjects does not appear to reflect an insensitivity of the test methods themselves, and his data will be referred to again in the description of psychomotor performance at "intermediate levels of integration" by other diagnostic groups.

These examples of attempts to describe the group performance of normal and neurotic subjects, together with the results of other less systematic and less well-controlled observations, indicate that little obvious difference seems to obtain between the performance of neurotic and non-neurotic subjects when quantitative measures of the speed of response are based on simple tests of speed in *fine* psychomotor movement, or in the speed of execution of tasks demanding a moderate level of response integration, when made under ordinary test conditions.

Special Conditions

Several investigators have compared the motor responses of neurotic patients with those of normal subjects when both groups were observed while working under some form of experimental pressure, or mild stress. Under these circumstances a greater difference has usually been noted in the degree of motor control shown by the groups compared. McFarland and Barach (1937) reported a differential deterioration of motor control among neurotic subjects on tasks of choice reaction, mirror-drawing, body-balancing and arm-hand coordination under conditions of oxygen deprivation, when compared with performance on identical tasks and under identical deprivation by normal control subjects. Malmo, Shagass and Davis (1950) have turned attention to the degree of skeletal muscle control evident when both normal and neurotic test subjects were similarly exposed to a sudden, loud auditory stimulus. An analysis of electromyographic tracings taken of the forearm muscle tension under these circumstances indicated a similar immediate reaction (startle) for each group, but tracings of the normal subjects forearm EMG soon returned to the baseline level while those of the psychoneurotic group showed a continued augmentation of response and prolonged response throughout the period of stimulation (Figure 1).

Malmo and Shagass (1949) have also reported the motor response of patients with anxiety as a leading symptom, compared with non-anxious normal control subjects, when a pain stimulus (thermal) was applied to the skin. Records taken of striate muscle activity, in the form of finger movement and muscle potentials from the neck, served as an index of the degree to which the "emergency reaction" extended to the motor response system. They report that the less anxious subjects showed a better control of motor activity and a restriction to appropriate

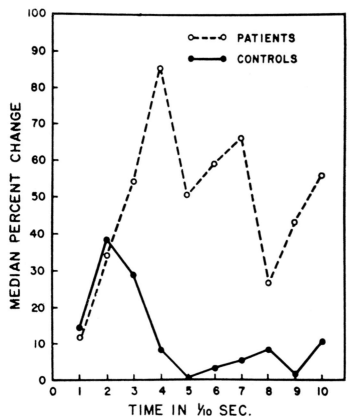

Figure 1. Per cent change in EMG response during first second of stimulation. Interval of measurement = 0.1 second. (After Malmo, Shagass and Davis, 1950.)

response, while the more anxious subjects revealed excessive preparatory activity during intervals between stimulation and a tendency to overreact when the stimulus was applied. Similar differences in the psychomotor response of neurotic and normal subjects have been reported when the stress is of a more psychological nature. Variants of the classical technique devised by Luria (1932) for the detection of deception, by observing the degree of disruption of voluntary muscle response, have been applied in a comparative way to neurotic and normal subjects during interviews probing the emotions (Barnacle, Ebaugh and Lemere, 1935), and while the subjects observed were making increasingly difficult, forced-speed perceptual choices (Malmo, Shagass, Belanger and Smith, 1951). These studies agree in their indication of notably less motor disorganization exhibited by normal subjects under stress than was exhibited by neurotic patients and in their endorsement of the value of the psychomotor approach when compared with measures obtained of concommitant reactivity in the autonomic nervous system.

It would appear from the general agreement of the data derived from studies of this kind that the application of some form of pressure, whether of a physiological or psychological nature, may serve to bring out differences in the psychomotor efficiency of neurotic subjects, compared with the non-neurotic, that may not be seen when testing under ordinary (non-stress) conditions. This finding lends weight to the value of employing special experimental conditions when examining the psychomotor adequacy of individuals with a behavior disorder.

Disorders Possibly Related to Psychoneurosis

Some of the milder disruptions of ordinary behavior that might have a neurotic basis, but which are not severe enough to be so diagnosed by symptom pattern, have been approached for study by one or another technique of psychomotor evaluation. What are called *Unstable Children* have been described by Yarmolenko (1935) as exhibiting defective hand movements in muscular work when compared with normal children, and by Chorus (1943a, 1943b) as showing a greater variability in tapping rates from trial to trial, throughout the course of a day and again when their performance is observed over a period of months. A number of writers (Arps, 1934; Cross, 1936; Kopp, 1943; Stern, 1939) have reported the finding of a more defective motor performance by *Speech Defectives* and *Stammerers* than is to be found among children without such disturbances. Using such varied techniques of observation as gymnastic tests, the Oseretsky Scale and the rate of muscle movement by jaws and hands in specific tests of motor skill, there is a consensus that an appreciable motor defect may be detected among those with a speech disorder. *Social Maladapts,* defined only as people in trouble with society via the law (e.g., adolescent delinquents and felons) have been found by Peters (1946) to perform less well than normal controls on mirror-tracing tasks when evaluated by independent scoring methods and by King (1961a) in performance on tests of fine psychomotor ability as reflected in tests of reaction time, tapping speed and finger dexterity.

The rather consistent finding of a degree of psychomotor defect among groups showing such tentatively defined disruptions of ordinary behavior, and without the need of any special experimental stress to bring it forward, suggests that the underlying problem may be more than something only "possibly related to psychoneurosis" and may be akin to what is seen in some of the borderline conditions of central nervous system dysfunction to be described below.

Schizophrenia
Group Descriptive
The availability of large populations of chronic schizophrenic patients, typically longterm residents in mental hospitals, has made possible many systematic studies from the psychomotor point of view. As the experimental investigation of psychomotor disruption among schizophrenic patients has formed the subject of Chapters XX and YY, a detailed description of the findings need not be duplicated here. In general, marked disruptions of psychomotor adequacy, usually expressed as losses in the speed of response, have been consistently reported (Hunt and Cofer, 1944; Huston, Shakow and Riggs, 1937; King, 1954a, 1961; Weaver, 1961; Wulfeck, 1941a) and a gradation of the psychomotor defect

has been found to parallel the severity of the disorder (Edwards, 1954; King, 1954a, 1961a; Weaver, 1961). The slowing of response is most notable among tests directed toward registry of the latency of initiating reactions to stimuli, but is also present in a wide variety of ongoing responses, such as in tapping speed, finger dextrousness, continuous problem solving and the synchronizing of a motor response with sequential sensory stimuli (King, 1949, 1954, 1961a, 1962c). As striking as the reduction observed in the average speed of response is the obvious and consistently reported expansion of variability, in reaction time test performance, both when a schizophrenic group is compared with normal performance (interindividual variation) and between the responses made by the same individual on different trials (intraindividual variation). That these changes are related, but may usefully represent different aspects of the psychomotor defect present has been shown (King, 1962b) and they may be conceived as representing different aspects of the overall vigor of response. The persistent and significant elevation of muscle tension response reflected in the electromyographic records taken under conditions of rest as well as stress (Reynolds, 1962; Whatmore and Ellis, 1959) suggests that this state of chronic, inner hyperactivity may partly underlie the speed deficiencies observable in overt psychomotor performance by means of a partial spasticity present in the skeletomotor system.

Special Conditions

As other chapters have been devoted specially to this topic, we need only emphasize here that although the defective psychomotor responsiveness typical of the schizophrenic patient can be influenced to a degree by changes in experimental conditions, (such as shifts in the stimulus modality or intensity or variations in the preparatory interval or motivating instructions) the factor of clinical status (the presence of schizophrenia) tends to dominate the variance in the data obtained. This is true to an extent that either obscures or obliterates the action of biologic variables, such as age and sex, as well. For the same reason, changes that come about with improvements or worsenings of the clinical condition bring the most decided shifts in the degree of psychomotor defect detectable.

Groups Possibly Related to Schizophrenia

A symptom-picture is often met that presents a first impression of being one of the psychoneuroses, but proves to be—after the evaluation of more detailed clinical data—an attenuated expression of schizophrenia. This syndrome, called *Pseudoneurotic Schizophrenia* (Hoch and Polatin, 1949), or *Schizophrenic Reaction, Chronic Undifferentiated Type,* includes the so-called "latent," "incipient," and "prepsychotic" reactions (Comm. Nomenclature and Statistics, Amer. Psychiat. Ass'n, 1952). The disorder has been little studied from an experimental point of view, despite its clinical and theoretical importance, possibly owing to the unavailability of patient groups for study. As is the case for

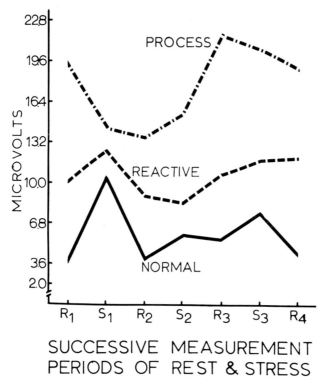

SUCCESSIVE MEASUREMENT
PERIODS OF REST & STRESS

Figure 2. Mean muscle tension response levels for normal, reactive schizophrenic and process schizophrenic groups over the course of a one-hour experiment. S_1 is a thirty second period of exercise, S_2 a cold pressor test and S_3 a failure and criticism stressor; R_1-R_4 are interpolated rest periods (after Reynolds, 1962).

the neurotic patients whom they resemble, they are rarely to be found concentrated in hospitals. The psychomotor performance of two samples of pseudoneurotic schizophrenics, derived from out-patient clinic sources, has been reported (King, 1949a, 1961a) and compared with corresponding values obtained from samples of chronic schizophrenic patients and from normal subjects. Tests of reaction time, tapping speed, finger dexterity and disjunctive reaction time were made, following prolonged practice and familiarization with the tasks to be performed (*see,* pp. xxx-xxx, 000-00o, Table 1 and Figure 3). The pattern of psychomotor scores obtained from the pseudoneurotic schizophrenic group reflected, in a lesser degree, most of the same alterations that had been evident in greater magnitude in the performance of chronic schizophrenic patients on the identical test series; i.e., a significantly less rapid level of response and an expanding of interindividual variability in reaction-time performance with accompanying significant reductions in mean score on the tapping test and on measures of finger dexterity. The milder, but consistent, defects appearing in the fine psychomotor abilities of this group would seem to be congruent with its clinical description as a form of incompletely penetrated schizophrenic disorder, differentiable from the psychoneurotic disturbances, though resembling them.

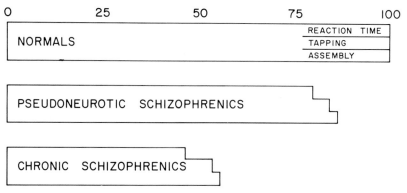

Figure 3. Mean performance of schizophrenic subgroups on tests of fine psychomotor ability expressed as a per cent of performance by normal subjects matched for age and sex. N = 700.

The presence of mental illness in children may often be recognized and take a definite form, including what have been called the *Childhood Schizophrenias.* Because the form of the disorder is necessarily different in the very young, the group is often described as a condition allied to the schizophrenias in which the diagnosis rests on somewhat different criteria than when made for an adult. A number of studies that have been made of such psychotic children agree in pointing to marked defects that are discernible in the motor area, along with other signs of maladaptation that may be present, and suggest that the evidence for such disruption points to a direct relationship between the level of motility functioning and the severity of difficulty in overall psychological adjustment (Berkowitz, 1961; Rotham, 1961). Investigation of the oculomotor and postural patterns existing among schizophrenic children have also revealed the presence of deviant postural and vestibular reactions in many, when compared with similar functions among the non-schizophrenic disorders and normal children (Pollack and Krieger, 1958). These authors concluded, on the basis of such signs of malfunction as involuntary head-turning during optokinetic stimulation and an inability to dissociate head and eye movement, that the routine neurologic examination is frequently inadequate to demonstrate dysfunction in children diagnosed as schizophrenic and have called for a more detailed study of neurophysiologic function among schizophrenic, brain-damaged and normal children alike.

The consistency of a conclusion of a partial defect that may be demonstrated in the motor responsiveness from these quite varied approaches to some of the conditions allied to schizophrenia may not be unexpected, in view of the marked defects that have been found to characterize the chronic, core condition. The methods are disparate, however, and the populations that have been observed quite small; further experimental study would be welcome.

Manic-Depressive Psychosis

There are fewer systematic studies of psychomotor function among manic-depressive patients than have been made of schizophrenics, owing, presumably, to the lower incidence of the disorder and to the development of effective therapies which have reduced both the need for hospitalization and shortened the length of hospital stay when it is required. The most inclusive of the investigations available is that of Wulfeck (1941a) who has reported the results on seven psychomotor tests, sampling performance at intermediate levels of integrative ability. The identical series was applied to groups of normal, neurotic, schizophrenic and manic-depressive subjects (*see,* pp. xxx-000, xxx-000) and was intended to provide a contrast, by the observation of these sequential coordinations and linked patterns of movement, with the studies of simpler and more unitary kinds of activity represented by reaction-time, tapping speed and the like. Summing the overall results of this varied battery, it was found that the manic-depressive group as a whole did not perform very differently from the normal control subjects, although they did exhibit an occasional reliably retarded performance score. When the group was broken into the manic and depressive subgroups, however, more definite patterns of difference in performance emerged. The records of the *manic* patients (n = 8) were much like those of the normal subjects, with more errors shown in performance (e.g., star-tracing), but with no important reduction in speed. The performance of the *depressives* was more often retarded, at times reliably so, but also exhibited some inexplicable

TABLE 2

MEAN REACTION-TIME (IN MILLISECONDS) FOR A NORMAL
CONTROL GROUP AND FOR A DEPRESSIVE GROUP LESS THAN
FORTY YEARS OF AGE (<40) AND A DEPRESSIVE GROUP MORE
THAN FORTY YEARS OF AGE (40 +) (AFTER HALL AND STRIDE, 1954)

Category	Sex	No. of Cases	Simple (No Warning: Approx. 5 sec.s)		Warning (10 sec.s Delay)		Warning (Varied Delay; 1-15 sec.s)	
			M	σ	M	σ	M	σ
Normals	M	10	174	54.8	177	57.2	193	23.1
	F	10	185	30.8	194	31.5	227	43.6
Depressives <40	M	10	227	79.4	177	39.0	223	41.2
	F	10	227	69.8	223	86.8	226	86.7
Depressives 40 +	M	10	314	179.4	304	207.7	308	184.1
	F	10	283	166.9	336	178.4	362	200.3

reversals such as giving a performance superior to that of the normal group on the Miles test of Reaction-Coordination. They were found, on the whole, to be more variable in response than the control subjects, but less variable than chronic schizophrenes. Shakow and Huston (1938), in a study of a very small group of mixed manic-depressive patients (n = 13), reported a significant reduction in tapping speed for their group, while Hall and Stride (1954) found a significant increase in reaction-time among depressives, over age forty. This investigation is notable for its careful attention to the age factor, and the mean figures for differing age groups shown in Table 2 indicate the direction of their findings. Depressives below age forty were found to be significantly quicker than those above forty and these younger depressives did not differ reliably from the normal control subjects in their reaction time, whereas the older depressives differed markedly from the normals in reaction latencies. The authors concluded that the relation between the clinical condition and psychomotor response was probably considerably more complex than is often assumed. Several studies have agreed in finding significant elevation of indices of muscle tension among manic depressive patients, such as EMG tracings (Whatmore and Ellis, 1959), finger tremor (Edwards, 1957) and the pneumodeike (Wulfeck, 1941b). The depressive group studied by Whatmore and Ellis (1959) was divided into subgroups of those showing obvious clinical signs of retardation and those not so described. Although the measures of residual activity recorded by electromyogram were significantly above that of control subjects for both groups, the level of the clinically retarded group was observed to be much higher (Figure 4). These investigators term the condition "hyperponesis" and also note that the rate of residual muscle activity goes up with age among their normal control subjects, as shown in Table 3.

The fragmentary investigations available on manic-depressive psychosis appear to indicate little disturbance in the execution of simple and moderately complex acts by the group as a whole, tending toward defective performance as the patients are selected for depression, greater chronological age, or both. The defects, when they appear, are not as severe as those which typify chronic

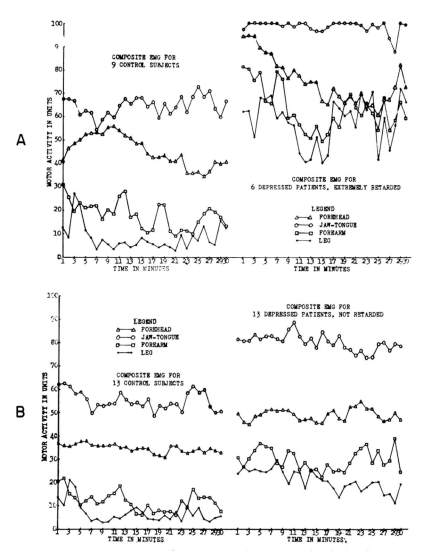

Figure 4. Composite group-electromyographic tension levels for depressive patients with clinical signs of motor retardation (A) and those without (B). (After Whatmore and Ellis, 1959.)

schizophrenia, but are of a more intermediate degree with regard to both the average of response and its consistency. The consensus of a finding of increased muscle tension, obtained by several different methods among manic-depressive patients and among normals of greater age, is most interesting and, as muscle tension has also been reported to be significantly elevated among the schizoprenias, this suggests one possible explanation for a variety of the changes in the speed of psychomotor behavior that have been reported in aging and in psychopathology.

Senile Psychosis

Almost nothing has been reported of a systematic nature about the psychomotor aspects of this common-enough disorder despite its many clinical signs of weakened motor function and its obvious linkage to the brain-damaged groups. It is mentioned here because of the interest it bears for those concerned with the disabilities of aging and for the reflection that it casts on the practical quality of problems of behavior disorder mentioned at the outset of this chapter. Here that may be seen in the form of an available but unstudied group, even by those with only theoretical interests, presumably because little can be done to aid those so afflicted and their problem is brief and self-limiting when compared with those posed by the other psychoses.

BRAIN-DAMAGE AND CNS DYSFUNCTION

Functional

Although this term has come to have a usage that lends a meaning of "alleged brain-damage" where proof is lacking but

TABLE 3
GRAND MEANS FOR ALL UNITS OF ELECTROMYOGRAPHIC ACTIVITY
(RECORDED FROM: FOREHEAD, JAW, FOREARM AND LEG) MEASURI D
OVER A 30 MINUTE PERIOD FOR NORMAL SUBJECTS OF DIFFERENT AGES
(WHATMORE AND ELLIS, 1959)

Median Age	Grand Mean
33	19.9
52	27.4
66	34.7

damage is assumed to exist, it is employed here in the more general sense to denote a change in the usual activity of the central nervous system produced by a temporary shift in its balance, but without affecting structure irreversibly. Changes of this kind may be brought about *directly*, by methods that alter brain function without intermediary, such as electric excitation, or *indirectly* by influencing the whole organism and therefore affecting the nervous system through an intermediary, such as the circulatory system.

Indirect Changes

This chapter cannot review in detail the large literature available on the psychomotor alterations produced by sleep loss, extremes of temperature, starvation, fluctuations of body temperature, fatigue states, oxygen deprivation and the like (Tufts, 1951, 1952; King, 1954a, 1961; Brozek and Taylor, 1954; Teichner, 1954), but it is appropriate to emphasize here that whereas changes of these variables may affect the reaction process at several levels of control, it is the central action of each that is held to be the most important. Recent studies of the effect of physiological shifts on dependent psychomotor variables indicate, for example, significant losses in reaction-time to accompany acute sleep-loss (Williams, Lubin and Goodnow, 1959), in pursuit-rotor performance, mirror-drawing and rail-walking after sensory deprivation (Vernon, McGill, Gulick and Candland, 1959), reaction-time after exposure to cold (Teichner, 1958) and on the Complex Behavior Simulator after periods of sleep of varying duration (Langdon and Hartman, 1961). Phasic shifts in ordinary physiologic state, such as periods of "autonomic emission" (Lacey and Lacey, 1958), phases of the alpha rhythm of the brain (Lansing, Schwartz and Lindsley, 1959) and with periods of the cardiac cycle (Birren, Cardon and Phillips, 1963) have been reported to have measurable effects on the speed of initiating a response to a stimulus, as measured by the reaction-time method. Psychological pressures have, similarly, been shown to influence psychomotor response, for example in measures made of contact-time and lift-time for pencilled drawings made of dots and triangles under conditions of inversion of the visual field (Rhule and Smith, 1959), on tapping efficiency under conditions of delayed auditory feed-back (Chase, Harvey, Standfast, Rapin and Sutton, 1959) and on motor learning (Baratt, 1959; Smith, 1958) with manipulated levels of subject anxiety.

It may be concluded from this broad array of materials that appropriately selected and administered psychomotor test methods sensitively reflect man-made alterations of the functional balance of the central nervous system, usually by a defective performance of actions that are carried out at a higher level of competence under the more optimal conditions of no-change in the physiological or psychological environment. The most common denominator of the changes so produced appears to be in the speed of action, but this may be expressed variously, either directly as in the speed of initiating a response to a momentary stimulus or less obviously where speed combines with another aspect of the test situation, e.g., in the handling of spatial relationships.

Direct Changes

Influencing the action of brain structures and connections directly, and reversibly, by electrical means provides the most pertinent experimental situation for the study of momentary change in brain function, but has only rarely been accomplished on human subjects in a context permitting the simultaneous measurement of psychomotor performance. In the few instances where an intervention of this direct kind has been reported (King, Young, Corrigan and Bersadsky, 1954; King, 1954a, 1961a, 1961b) the subjects observed have uniformly been patients suffering from disease or trauma, such as intractable pain from cancer; from neurological defects, such as Parkinsonism; or from a mental disorder, such as schizophrenia, in which an alteration of the central nervous system is undertaken as a therapeutic measure. All such patients are unusual subjects, and the interpretation of momentary changes in their behavior may be confounded by their original condition.

Measures of several forms of reaction time, of tapping speed and of varied forms of finger dexterity have been reported for two small groups of patients receiving prolonged series of electric excitation of the septal brain (King, Young, Corrigan and Bersadsky, 1954; King, 1961b). Activation of this brain region is held to produce changes in the affective sphere and to be related to the level of organism arousal and awareness (Heath, 1954, 1955). The psychomotor measures were recorded before a brain stimulation series was begun, and again at intervals of one, four and eight months during a treatment program of three stimulation periods per week (30 minutes, each period) extending over the next year. Stimulating currents, varying between 1 and 13 m.a., were delivered by way of bipolar electrodes implanted in the *septum* and took the form of rectangular pulse durations at a frequency repetition rate of 100/sec. Despite the appearance of marked alteration in the electrographic tracings recorded from the region stimulated, from surrounding structures and from the cerebral cortex, no change in the level of psychomotor performance consequent upon stimulation could be detected, apart from those changes that reflected an alteration in psychotic state where one had pre-existed. Perhaps no change outlasting the current flow of actual stimulation would be expected. For this reason, experimental observations were also made of the influence of limbic system excitation upon *on-going* psychomotor activity (King, 1961b). Figure 5 presents an example, in graphic form, of the effects of septal-region stimulation on a stereotyped movement pattern, the speed of tapping, in progress at the instant stimulation was applied. The patient, a non-retarded schizophrenic, was well-practiced at the task and had reached a stable level of response, here reflected in the base-line stability of the pre-stimulation period. The application of a 3 m.a. current to the septal electrodes, without the knowledge of the subject or any change in his instructions, produced a significant increase in tapping rate which disappeared immediately after the stimulating current was discontinued. This effect was obtained repeatedly and could be found among other, non-schizophrenic, patients who were similarly tested. In contrast, no change in on-going tapping speed was found to accompany stimulation of the *hippocampus,* whereas excitation of the nucleus of the *caudate* raised the mean rate of response only slightly, but noticeably increased the intra-individual variability observed (King, 1961b). These data are too fragmentary to be weighted properly for their significance just yet. It should be noted, however, from what has been observed thus far, that the excitation of a part of the human brain undertaken to heighten the general level of organism arousal (the *septum*) was reflected in an increased rate of on-going psychomotor activity, made the more striking by its appearance in mid-performance.

Related techniques for the local microinjection of chemicals directly into brain structures have been developed (Heath and Founds, 1960; Heath and de Balbian Verster, 1961) and the measurement of their effects upon on-going psychomotor behavior has been undertaken, but is not yet available for summary. As many

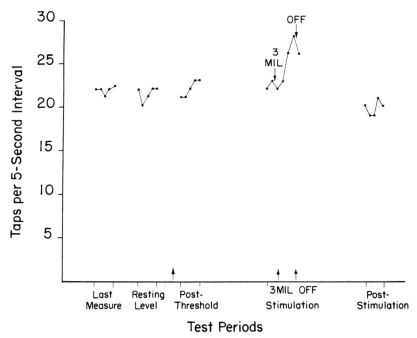

Figure 5. Tapping speed during subcortical electrical stimulation of electrodes implanted in the septal area. Each point represents the mean of five trials. *Last Measure* refers to values obtained on the day preceding; *Resting Level* to performance in the stimulation chamber prior to stimulation and *Post-Threshold* to another resting level determined after physiological procedures were completed for determining stimulation strength to be used, but also prior to stimulation (after King, 1961b).

drugs transported by the bloodstream are known to be central in their site of action, these too may be considered to be directly producing changes in brain function, or they may be subsumed under the more general heading of changes of an indirect physiological nature. However they may be classified, we cannot review the vast literature existing on the effects of drug action on psychomotor activity here (Tufts, 1952; Eysenck and Trouton, 1961; Ross and Cole, 1960), especially in view of the special problems that bear upon their interpretation, such as dosage, time-course, placebo-effect, tolerance and the well-known differences of individual reactivity. We may note in passing, however, that psychomotor techniques have for long been employed to reflect the temporary changes in central nervous system function so produced and that when they have been appropriately selected and controlled they have proved to be one of the more effective indicators of altered organismic state. It is notable that the changes so registered in psychomotor behavior are most often in the direction of a slowed, or faulty, performance and that the introduction of stimulants (for other body systems) does not appreciably improve psychomotor speed or accuracy above the level of a rested, non-drug condition; given in strong doses they may, in fact, produce a slowing of motor speeds. We may infer from this that, in nature, the characteristic psychomotor speeds, observed under ordinary circumstances, are probably nearly optimal for the organism. The experimental study of so obvious a deranger of organized behavior as alcohol, to cite but a single and common example from this area, yields ample evidence for a corresponding deterioration to be found in the speed and/or accuracy of psychomotor response (Tufts, 1952; Jellinek and McFarland, 1940; Trouton and Eysenck, 1961).

Organic

The impact of permanent, irreversible change in brain tissue on psychomotor speed and adequacy may be inferred, within the limits of the test data available, from performance by patients of two kinds: a) those undergoing brain-surgical procedures, and b) those with a structural defect of the CNS that is the result of trauma or of disease process.

Brain-Surgical

The experimental and clinical investigations growing up in the wake of the development of a psychosurgical treatment for mental disorder have provided a great deal of important information on motor function that is probably too narrow in scope for its relevant inclusion here, e.g., on the direct action of muscle groups, alterations of patterns of reflexes, body torsions, gait etc. (Mettler, 1949, 1952; Freeman and Watts, 1950; Lewis, Landis and King, 1956). They also report, at the opposing extreme, many findings based on psychometric evaluations that include an effector component, or are called perceptuo-motor, e.g., maze-test performance, letter-cancellation tasks or continuous problem-solving (with hand response), which are probably too broad for relevant inclusion, in view of the entry of cognitive and other elements in their execution (Porteus and Peters, 1947; Halstead, 1947; King, 1949; Sheer and Shuttleworth, 1952; Sheer, 1956; Petrie, 1952; Tow, 1955). Only a relatively few of the experiments published have been concerned with psychomotor activity as the term has been used thus far in this chapter.

Tests of reaction time to visual and auditory stimuli, tapping speed and of finger dexterity for right and left hands, singly and when used together, have been applied to groups of psychosurgical patients before surgery and again at intervals of ten days and two months postoperatively (King and Clausen, 1952, 1956; King, 1950, 1954b). Psychotic and pseudoneurotic schizophrenic patients receiving Prefrontal Venous Ligation (bilateral occlusion of all cortico-dural veins visible between a point 2 cm caudal to the tip of the frontal pole and a point 2 cm caudal to the coronal suture), Superior Topectomy (bilateral excision of Brodman's cortical area 9, sometimes 10, 8 and 32) and Orbital Topectomy (bilateral excision of Brodman's areas 11, sometimes 47, 10 and Walker's 13) all exhibited significantly decreased (slowed) psychomotor performance when measured ten days after operation, but re-tests made two months after surgery showed that preoperative levels of ability were nearly exactly regained on all tests. The operative subgroups were affected differently, with the Superior Topectomy cases showing the greatest temporary reduction in speed of performance, Prefrontal

Venous Ligation cases showing less and the Orbital Topectomy patients reflecting the least interference in these forms of psychomotor performance. As the patients from both chronic and pseudoneurotic schizophrenic diagnostic groups exhibited similar amounts of speed reduction, and as concomitant losses were not observed on sensory tests applied at the same time, it was concluded that removal of, or interference with, the function of the orbitofrontal cortex temporarily impaired the motor integrative system at the higher levels, the impairment being greater when the damage was on the superior surface of the brain. The same psychomotor tests, applied to a very limited number of patients receiving thermocoagulation of the Brodman frontal cortical areas 9 and 10 and Transorbital Lobotomy revealed no reductions in psychomotor speed. The lobotomy (leucotomy) subjects examined by Petrie and LeBeau (1956) improved their performance speed on tests of manual dexterity and track-tracing when measured some time after the operative procedure, presumably a reflection of the improved status of their behavior disorder, while those examined by Tow (1955) showed no significant change in track-tracing time.

A comparison of speed in an oscillatory finger movement, the maximum rate of down-stroke by the dominant index-finger, has been offered by Halstead (1947), who compared patients under-

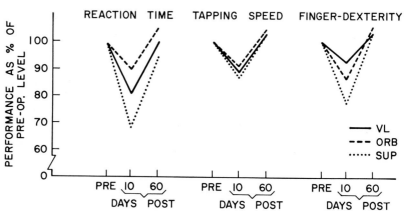

Figure 6. Temporary reductions in speed of fine psychomotor movement consequent upon Venous Ligation (VL), Orbital Topectomy (Orb) and Superior Topectomy (Sup) surgical procedures.

going Cerebral Lobectomy procedures, for the removal of lesions or the control of tumor growth, with similar data gathered by the same test measure from normal control subjects. When measures were made postoperatively, the lobectomy groups observed were significantly reduced in speed on this simple, oscillatory perform- ance compared with normal control subjects. The frontal lobec- tomy subjects exhibited the greatest degree of impairment, more than was shown by the non-frontal cases of parietal, temporal, occipital and cerebellar resection.

A single, but theoretically important, set of experimental ob-

TABLE 4

PERFORMANCE BY NORMAL AND LOBECTOMIZED SUBJECTS
ON FINGER-OSCILLATION TEST (AFTER HALSTEAD, 1947)

Group		*n*	*Average*	*Significance of Difference*		
Control	(X_1)	30	54.92	X_1, X_2	X_1, X_3	X_2, X_3
				t = 7.14	t = 2.74	t = 1.80
				p < .001	p < .006	p < .054
Frontal Lobectomy	(X_2)	27	43.90			
Non-Frontal Lobectomy	(X_3)	20	48.40			

TABLE 5

RESPONSE TIME (HUNDREDTHS OF A SECOND) IN DIFFERENT PSYCHOLOGICAL
REACTIONS BEFORE AND AFTER SURGICAL SECTION OF THE COMMISSURAL
PATHWAYS (AFTER SMITH, 1947a)

Psychological Reactions	*Pre-Op.* M	σ	*Post-Op.* M	σ	*Md*	*t*	*Level of Confidence*	*Diff.* %
N = 6								
Simple reaction time	.18	.042	.29	.078	.11	4.58	.01	+61
Visual discrimination reaction time	.38	.074	.44	.062	.06	1.85	*	+16
Visual discrimination reaction time (uncrossed)	.37	.076	.43	.066	.06	1.88	*	+16
Visual discrimination reaction time (crossed)	.39	.076	.45	.067	.06	2.17	*	+15

*Indicates a value below an acceptable level of confidence.

servations is also available on the effects of interrupting the fibers of the *corpus callosum* in human subjects on simple reaction-time, and crossed and uncrossed visual reaction time. Smith (1947a, 1947b) has reported measures made upon six subjects before, and again after, section of this massive bundle of intercortical fibers for the control of *grand mal* convulsions. In a test of the hypothesis that interhemisphere connections represent a significant

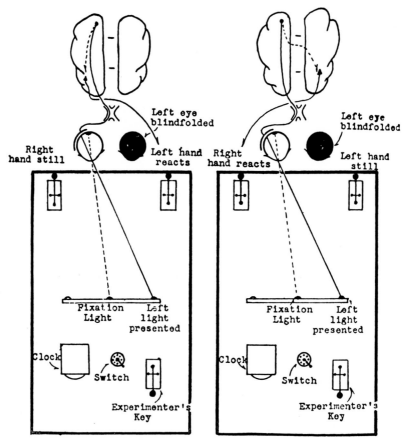

Figure 7. The difference between two types of crossed and uncrossed visual reactions (after Smith, 1947b). *Uncrossed Reaction:* Involving the left stimulus light, right temporal retina, right visual cortex, right motor cortex, and left hand. *Crossed Reaction:* Involving the left stimulus light, right temporal retina, right visual cortex, left motor cortex, and right hand.

part of the neural associative system, and that sensori-motor functions involving crossed relations between the hemispheres should be more affected by their interruption than those involving only unilateral connections within the nervous system, these psychomotor measures (along with others for verbal-association times) were subjected to pre- and post-comparison. Figure 7 presents, in diagrammatic form, the types of crossed and uncrossed reactions that were tested. Although occasional discrepancies were observed on crossed sensori-motor reactions (Smith, 1947b), it was concluded that, on the whole, these reactions were not significantly altered by section of the commissural neurones. In marked contrast to this somewhat surprising result, in view of long-cherished theory, the data secured on simple reaction-times show a significant and consistent increase in the latency of response. Smith concluded that "this radical increase in response time for simple reactions appears to be the only psychological function disturbed significantly by surgical section of the cerebral commissures among many different perceptual, motor, intellectual and sidedness activities which have been studied" (Smith, 1947b, p. 375).

These sparse experimental approaches to the evaluation of psychomotor adequacy before and after brain-damage of surgical origin have been described in detail for their rarity and for the unique opportunity they offer to observe the consequences of deliberate modification of human brain structure. They are in agreement in reflecting either a temporary or a permanent decrease in the speed of simple psychomotor responding by patients suffering surgical damage to the brain, without totally disrupting the capacity to make such responses.

Trauma and Disease

Those patients called *Brain-Damaged* or *Brain-Injured,* in the neurological sense, do not form a homogeneous class, as the term includes not only the entire brain in all its varied functions, but also a great variety in the kinds of disrupting pathology that may be present. There is probably even less reason, therefore, to expect that patients bearing such assorted afflictions will fall into any facile psychological unity or to vary together in any given way from normal psychological function. There is a certain medical utility served in placing together those patients suffering from different kinds of structural brain-damage, be it caused by tumor, vascular accident, head-injury, atrophy, abscess or degenerative disease, for although each type of lesion may vary with the individual sustaining it, as well as the variation that exists between the kinds of disorder, the group taken as a whole bears more than a passing similarity in syndrome as opposed to, say, spinal cord disorders. The patients so grouped have formed the subject of much psychological investigation designed to observe the consequent changes in mental ability or functioning. Some of the advantages and drawbacks of experimental work of this kind have been reviewed by Meyer (1957, 1961) and others (Yates, 1954; Klebanoff, Singer and Wilensky, 1954; King, 1962a; Fitzhugh and Fitzhugh, 1961). Psychomotor evaluations have been less frequent than assays of cognitive or perceptual change, but a number of investigators have reported quantitative findings on motor speed or adequacy among brain-damaged subjects in recent years.

Simple and choice reaction time latencies (to light stimuli) were recorded by Blackburn and Benton (1955) for a brain-injured group bearing unequivocal diagnoses of supra-tentorial disease and compared with identical measures derived from a control group of neurological patients exhibiting no evidence of cerebral disease or trauma. Significant differences were found for performance by the brain-damaged group in both the simple and choice reaction-time situations, a retardation of about 46 per cent and 24 per cent, respectively. The responses made by the brain-injured were more variable for both types of task, significantly so for the choice reaction. The choice reaction was found to be "*not a more discriminative index than simple reaction-time. Indeed, where differences in discriminative efficiency are found, they appear to favor the simple function*" (Blackburn and Benton, 1955, p. 335). The same investigators (Benton and Blackburn, 1957), employing similar patient and control groups, found no differences between groups in the practice effects shown in either simple or choice reaction time over a series of thirty trials. Benton and Joynt (1959), comparing the reaction time performance of brain-damaged patients with the lesion restricted to either the right or to the left cerebral hemisphere with the latencies observed for matched control subjects, found the performance of the brain-damaged patients to be significantly slower for the ipsilateral hand as well as for the hand contralateral to the side of the lesion. Those with a right hemispheric involvement were significantly quicker in right hand response than with the left; a similar trend for the patients with left hemispheric lesions did not achieve statistical significance. They concluded that the reaction-time findings indicate that "Focal lesions have both a general bilateral and a specific unilateral effect on reaction-time in patients *without* clinically apparent motor defects." The influence of changes attempted in "motivating instructions" on reaction-time performance by brain-injured subjects has not been found to be impressive. Neither "standard," "relaxing," and "urging" instructions (Blackburn, 1958), nor "success" and "failure" instructions (Shankweiler, 1959) have significantly altered the discrimination in performance between groups of the brain-damaged and matched control subjects.

A form of the test of tapping-speed, the Halstead Finger-Oscillation Test (maximal speed in downstroke of counter, moved by the extended, dominant index-finger; 10 sec. interval), has been applied to the study of brain-injured patients and their performance compared with measures obtained from a matched control group composed of neurological patients without brain-injury or disease (Reitan, 1955; Ross and Reitan, 1955; Fitzhugh and Fitzhugh, 1961). A significantly lower level of average performance by the brain-damaged subjects has been consistently reported for this measure. A subgroup comparison of the tapping-speed performance by patients with *acute* lesions, versus those with *static* lesions, has shown both subgroups to be retarded with reference to control-group performance, but not to differ from each other (Fitzhugh and Fitzhugh, 1961). Another group of patients with a more diffuse kind of cerebral damage, *Multiple Sclerosis,* was found to fall significantly below the normal in finger-oscillation speed as well, and to show a degree of retardation intermediate between control performance and the losses in speed exhibited by patients with definite, focal organic damage (Ross and Reitan, 1955).

Two experimental studies made upon groups of patients with a specific form of central disorder may be cited, more to illustrate the potential usefulness of making psychomotor observations under special conditions than to report the status of these particular disorders. Eliasberg (1955) has reported on what may be learned by a systematic comparison of handwriting samples, collected from *angiospastic* patients* at different periods of this phasic disorder, emphasizing the value of psychomotor observation-over-time and pointing to the correlation of changes in this "biomotor" indicator with other periodic clinical signs. Patients with Parkinson's Disease have been compared in their performance on tasks measuring response speed of differing kinds: in jump-reaction time to an auditory signal, in traverse over the same path initiated by the patient (voluntary) and in traverse over the same path initiated by the patient and including a rudimentary manipulation (shift a pencil from one slot to another). Increasing degrees of retardation were demonstrable in the same patient depending upon the level of organization of the effector response (King, 1959).

The epileptic disorders, with their disruption of CNS function and obvious motor involvement, have been surprisingly little studied from the psychomotor point of view, as the term has been used in this chapter. The tempo of finger-tapping, and finger-tapping in synchrony with sound stimuli, have been employed to observe the influence of subclinical seizures upon ongoing motor behavior (Yeager and Guerrant, 1957) and the time-to-respond to sound and light stimuli has been reported for stimuli delivered between periods of seizure activity (Schwab, 1947). The effects obtained seem to reflect chiefly periods of "blocking" or "clouding" of the consciousness, with an all-or-none type of effect on psychomotor response, i.e., response either being usual between seizures or ceasing completely during periods of seizure activity, as recorded by the electroencephalogram. An investigation of

---

* One is Franklin D. Roosevelt.

psychomotor speed in simple activity by a patient group defined by the presence of temporal lobe electrical "spiking" on E.E.G. examination has reported a finding of definitely retarded psychomotor performance on tests of reaction time, disjunctive reaction time, tapping speed and finger dexterity by this group of patients that had never received any form of psychiatric treatment.

A subgroup analysis revealed an interesting pattern of psychomotor deficit: those patients with no epileptic seizures showed little departure from normal (control) performance, those with *Grand Mal* seizure patterns exhibited an obvious retardation, those with *Simple Psychomotor Seizures* showed still greater slowing and those with *Complex Psychomotor Seizures* exhibited the greatest degree of retardation in performance on this battery of tests of speed in fine psychomotor response (Ervin, Epstein and King, 1955). The psychiatric investigation of these patients, who had no previous official record of behavior disorder, found them to be "no less impaired than the other twenty-two patients with a complaint of psychiatric disorder" (Ervin, Epstein and King, 1955, p. 9). The data drawn from these patients and from others showing the same focal, electrical sign in E.E.G. tracings have been combined with findings made upon other groups of patients with positive indications of neurologic trauma and disease to determine whether or not any systematic relation existed between the degree of disorder to organized behavior, as measured by a systematic behavior rating, and performance on a test of speed in responding that had been applied to all (King, 1961c, 1962a). Figure 8 shows that a near-linear relationship between behavior adequacy and jump reaction-time was found to exist for a wide variety of neurological and brain-injured patients when considered as an overall assembly of individuals with one or another form of organic disorder.

Temporary changes in brain function, brought about by chemical or electrical means, appear to produce temporary but detectable changes in psychomotor speed and adequacy, while the more permanent changes in function that result from structural alteration by either surgical procedure or disease process seem to decrease speed in psychomotor performance in a general and more permanent way, not always predicted by the side or site of the lesion. The extent of the loss produced by stressful changes in brain function of a reversible nature would appear to approximate those observed among the milder disorders of psychopathology, and to be as great for patients sustaining more permanent and irreversible changes of structure as those observed in the serious disorganizations of behavior found in chronic schizophrenia.

SUMMARY AND IMPLICATIONS FOR THE STUDY OF AGING

The indications of a general speed-change in behavior appear to be found, then, well-distributed among the kinds and grades of faulty adaptation that we identify as the behavior disorders, whether these disorganizations of the usual life-pattern are thought to arise from interpersonal factors, or to be traceable to known faults in biologic structure and function. Psychomotor tests have been observed to reflect a reduction in the speed of performance among most of the diagnostic groupings of psychopathology and brain damage that have been studied and to covary with the degree of clinical severity. There are substantial indica-

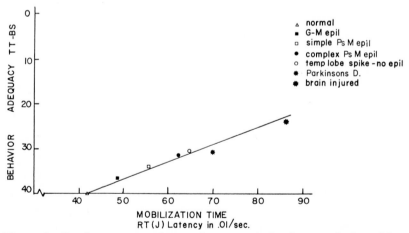

Figure 8. Psychomotor speed as a function of the degree of clinical behavior disorder. The ratings shown on the ordinate (Tulane Test-Behavior Scale) indicate the impairment of organized behavior; ranging between 0 and 40 with low numerical scores reflecting markedly disturbed behavior. Reaction-time (jump) scores, on the abscissa, are latency measures and high numerical values reflect markedly slowed response (after King, 1962.)

tions that the adequacy of psychomotor control may be affected
by experimental modification of the physiological or psychological
condition of the responding subject, and that temporary changes
induced in brain function bring with them temporary alterations
in psychomotor speed and control, while more permanent changes
to brain structure, and function, appear to result in general and
lasting defects in the speed of maximum performance. That the
existing data are still fragmentary and, all-too-often, subject to
influences falling outside exact experimental control must be
acknowledged, as is true in much of medical research. There is a
consistency, however, and a pattern of regularity among the data
that have been reported by a variety of investigators, working
with diverse psychomotor techniques and often with quite different patient groups, that is most unusual in this field of study
which for so long has failed to demonstrate rough unity in any
way, other than by the broad disruptions of ordinary behavior
that define it.

The need for a formal review of the chain of empirical evidence
that has been presented to illustrate the paralleling observed
between measures of psychomotor adequacy and the presence or
severity of a behavior disorder is perhaps less pressing than for
an interpretation of what the history of these investigations, and
their findings, would seem to imply for the future study of age-
changes in the speed of behavior. By history is meant simply the
lessons of experience, for not the least value of a review of the
psychomotor investigative work among the behavior disorders is
to make it possible to specify more exactly the conditions needed
for improved inquiry, whether future research be conducted
among these or other clinical populations, including the aged.
Finally, we may consider some of the speculations or hypotheses
that have been derived to account for the systematic losses observed in psychomotor speed among the psychopathological and
the brain-damaged that may help to explain the reduced speed in
psychomotor performance found to be characteristic of the aged
as well, or at the least to suggest or to support certain experimental approaches to the problem. To state what has been found
to be useful from this overview of psychomotor study among the
behavior disorders in a more positive form, and as the experience

gained might be applied to the strengthening of future research
with clinical samples, at least four aspects may be commented
upon briefly. They are factors related to the groups under study,
the test methods that are employed, the conditions of study and
some observations on the consistency of performance.

The homogeneity of patients falling within a given clinical
category selected as the subject of psychomotor investigation will
inevitably contain imperfections arising from variance in the
medical and human elements of the subjects comprising the
group. Beyond this basic limitation, however, it is clear that the
greater the effort that is made to establish experimental criteria
by which a cohesive group may be formed, or to delimit with
care the existence of identifiable subgroups within the whole, the
more power will be lent to generalizations that may be made
about the primary characteristic for which the group has been
isolated, the diagnosis. That age and sex will have some bearing
on psychomotor performance and will require control is obvious,
and is usually observed. Other possible criteria that may prove
to be equally relevant, but which are less immediately obvious,
are to be found among such physiological factors as the metabolic
rate, the amount of daily locomotor activity, body temperature,
the residual level of muscular tension or the vigor of orienting
responses in a rested condition, any or all of which may exert
some influence upon observed levels of psychomotor responsiveness. Clinical descriptions of subgroup criteria, such as whether
the patient is working or inactive, regular in sleep-pattern or
irregular, showing clinical signs of motor retardation and the like,
may also prove to be important characteristics either for establishing groups composed of similar members, or may permit the
making of analytic contrasts between subgroups present within
the diagnostic category as a whole.

In a similar way, a definite gain in potential can be obtained by
increasing the number and kind of psychomotor tests applied to
identical persons, once a statement about changes in the speed
of performance by the group can be made on the basis of prior
study. Within reasonably definable limits, falling above the
mechanical level of motor control as the term is used by the
neurologist (twitches; torsions) and below the level of motor acts

strongly mixed with cognitive control as often used by the clinical psychologist (digit-symbol substitution; design-copying), there are any number of measurable levels of psychomotor activity, here grouped under the term psychomotility. Although speed in execution may be something of a common denominator to them all, the correlations among them are far from unity. The use of a series of measures, to reflect the speed of initiating action, speed in repetitive and oscillatory movement, actions demanding speed alone contrasted with those requiring speed and control or the observation of speed in motor learning may serve as examples of how the scope of observation may be widened to augment the store of information on any given clinical population. The factor purity (Seashore, Buxton and McCullom, 1940; Fleishman, 1953, 1958; Fleishman and Hempel, 1956; Guilford, 1958; Brozek, 1961; Brozek and Taylor, 1954) of the tests comprising a battery of this kind can often best be determined in advance, or at least begun, with less-critical subjects from the normal population to lend appropriate weighting to the spectrum of findings that may obtain from applications later made to the rarer clinical material available for study.

The value of observing psychomotor performance under specially devised experimental conditions that has emerged from the study of psychopathological or brain-damaged subjects would also seem to offer an appropriate generalization for methods to be applied to the study of the aged or other clinical groupings. The manipulation of mild stress-conditions of either a psychological or physiological kind, or the use of what are called "activating" and "relaxing" drugs will serve as examples of contrasting experimental conditions that may bring forward different levels of response adequacy within a clinical grouping that can be observed when testing under the more usual, optimal laboratory conditions. Both the degree of resistance to, as well as accentuation by, manipulated conditions of the kind may be expected to broaden our perspective of the degree of psychomotor control possible among the disordered.

Finally, of the suggestions that may be offered to strengthen future research among clinical groups based upon a reflection on efforts that have been made in the past, we may note that many of the results of studies made among the pathologies of behavior underscore the value of observing the relative consistency shown in performance by the individual, as well as by the group. The dramatic expansion of interindividual variability in reaction-time among chronic schizophrenic patients, for example, has its counterpart in the very considerable increase in intraindividual variability in response by any given member from that group. Inter-series variation, especially as this may covary with a changed condition, such as the time-of-day or with mood swing, can be seen to be clearly reflected in the psychomotor scores achieved by certain kinds of neurological patient, such as in Parkinson's Disease. Repeated measurements over time may provide not only a way to record variations of this kind, but may help to emphasize the underlying need for reliability in the test-instruments used and may therefore improve the quality of the psychomotor approach selected and employed. Factor-purity alone does not account for all of the differences in observation that have been reported in the past; these have often seemed to rest in the procedures of different investigations and the degree to which stabilization in response was achieved.

If a simple and summary truism were to be sought to include the insights gained from the experimental study of clinical groupings of the past, it would be the reminder of the essential meaning of each of the terms, experimental and clinical. An attention to the systematic structuring of clinical samples, test methods or conditions of observation will undeniably enhance what may be generalized from the performance of any diagnostic group. At the same time, an attention to the human factors that may contribute to performance on a given task, because of the way in which they affect the organism as a whole, may encourage the investigator to broaden his approach to background information that may causally relate to his findings on any particular indicator of speed in behavior.

Turning, now, to an inspection of the more specific findings from psychomotor experimentation among the behavior disorders, we may begin with an attempt to place in rough perspective the degree of retardation observed when speed in performance is compared with what has been reported to be characteristic of the aging process. The estimate will vary with the function sampled, of course, with the disorder and the conditions of test; what is desired here is simply an approximation of the relative defects in speed of behavior by the aged and the disorganized. The speed-reductions of subjects sixty years of age and above, when compared with the peak-year performance of groups nearer twenty, appear to be moderate—somewhere near 20 per cent, and are approximately equivalent to the losses shown among the milder behavior disorders, such as neurotics under stress, the socially-maladapt and in Pseudoneurotic Schizophrenia; they are something less than half the magnitude of the retardation that has been usually reported to characterize the more severe behavior disorganizations of chronic schizophrenia and the brain injured. Where an identical test battery has been applied to both young (20-30 years) and older (60-70) subjects and to a variety of the behavior disorders, an opportunity is afforded to inspect both the amount of loss and its pattern among psychomotor tasks of differing kinds with speed in execution as a common indicator. The literature on aging suggests (Birren and Botwinick, 1955: Singleton, 1954; Clement, 1960; Clark and King, 1960; Simon, 1960; Welford, 1951, 1961) that the reactions of the aged are least affected on simpler tasks and may increase more noticeably where response selection, shifting response or the exercise of monitoring control over continuous movement become a factor in the actions required. Effects of this kind may be seen to occur in the normal control group observed by King (1954a, pp. 49, 52), where jump reaction-time scores, which include a traverse of space, are proportionately more slowed among older subjects than the latency of simple lift reaction-time; where the addition of an element of choice in response is reflected in a greater slowing of disjunctive response among the aged than is speed in simple reaction-time (lift or jump) and in the relatively greater reductions in the speed of performance on the more complex dexterity tests than on the simple. The more severe retardations of chronic schizophrenia reflect a rather different pattern of loss on the identical test battery. The simplest responses, both lift and jump reaction-time, show the greatest impairment and are of about equal magnitude (in per cent of normal performance). The addition of an element of choice was not reflected in a proportional increase in the speed of discriminative reaction time, either of simple lift response or where combined with the traverse of space, while losses in dexterity were found to be the least of all, but did reflect a greater loss on the more complex tasks than on the simple. In brief, the speed losses of the advanced age group would appear to be roughly comparable to what has been found to be characteristic of the milder behavior disorders, to be noticeably less than those recorded among the more severe disorganizations of behavior and to exhibit a different pattern of loss when an identical test battery was applied to both types of subject.

The data drawn from experimental studies of psychopathological and brain-damaged human subjects have indicated that a general relationship appears to exist between what might be called the integrity of the total organism and its adequacy or effectiveness in psychomotor response. Measures of some of the simplest human psychomotor functions have been found to reflect, in miniature, those physiological and psychological states of the organism which are less than optimal. Being rooted directly in physiological mechanisms, yet demanding continuous psychological control, they have been seen to parallel with considerable accuracy and in convenient form the effectiveness of the total organism in its give-and-take with the environment that we call organized behavior. Among the milder states of faulty adaptation, such as the neuroses, little evidence of disturbance can be found, at the simpler levels of psychomotor functioning, until some form of stress is applied that may bring forward an over-reactivity or faulty channeling of control. Patients in a depressed or manic state show rather more of an error in responsiveness, expressed as a slowing combined with a greater variation in response, but the extent of these defects is somewhat less than might be anticipated on the basis of gross observations of their excited or withdrawn general behavior.

A greater degree of pychomotor retardation has been shown to occur among older depressives than for the younger, indicating a possible interaction of age and clinical state. Schizophrenia, with its profound disruptions of the degree of contact between the individual and his environment, is reflected in the marked disruptions visible in the speed and variation of psychomotor response, exhibiting a degree of retardation that has been found to parallel the clinical severity of the disorder, among subgroups, and which may be modified by changes in the clinical state to reflect either improvements or worsenings. The minor and reversible physiological changes produced by experimental means, or by nature, that are strong enough to affect organized behavior, such as conditions of oxygen-deprivation or extreme sleep-loss, have been shown often to be reflected in a systematic way in the adequacy of simple psychomotor functioning. Changes to brain structure and function that are of a more serious variety, produced either by surgical means or the processes of disease and trauma, usually bring profound changes in the adequacy of general behavior patterning by the individual that find a counterpart in the serious retardations that have been measured in their speed in psychomotor performance. The reductions in speed appear to be the consequent of damage in a general sense, rather than being specifically localized or confined to one side of the brain or body, although the observed differences do appear to be dependent in some degree on the severity of the injury.

These changes in the speed of psychomotor responsivity that make their appearance coincident with alterations of the state of general behavior adequacy of the individual appear to extend across test measures that exhibit only a moderate degree of correlation when they are applied to a normal population, which would imply the action of some very general factor in producing the changes observed rather than the action of a specific mechanism. Either a relatively unitary general factor is being influenced which underlies them all, or there must be a rather large aggregate of specific mechanisms. There is a suggestion, from the available data on residual muscle tension among the normal aged, schizophrenic, depressive and brain-damaged patients, that a state of mild and sustained partial spasticity of the skeleto-muscular system may be the inward representation of the reduced effectiveness that has been observed in instructed movement, a suggestion that does not serve to explain the basic cause, but which would appear to offer a promising lead for future correlative study.

It is possible to conceive of the organism as a whole-system, one normally "tuned" to a state of reasonably optimal adaptibility to its environment, a state that rests upon the entirety of biologic structure, growth and balance in its physiological and psychological state. Any change of the factors that may affect the balance of this total state, then, such as damage to its communication system, the presence of prolonged emotional states or momentary physiological variation with an indirect influence on the function of the nervous system that is strong enough to produce clinically detectable changes in organized and adaptive behavior may then be seen to affect the psychomotor adequacy of the individual— not so much as the result of any given submechanism, but as an aspect of the integrity of the whole and as an important component in its continuing contact with the environment. It is the very plasticity of this integrated system that makes it possible for it to adapt to the myriad and changing demands made upon it, permitting learning and constant adjustment to the ebb and flow of external circumstances, which may account for its reduction by fractions of its performance in sub-optimal states rather than by the step-wise dislocations that a pathology of more specific mechanisms would imply. For these reasons it would appear that beyond the obvious features of the mechanics of responding members, vigor in movement may reflect the most general aspects of the organization of living things, always and only much affected by what affects the organism as a whole. We may register, somewhat imperfectly, the changes wrought by strong fear, severe oxygen lack, damage to the integrating system and the like, by measures made of the resiliency of the psychomotor system and even succeed in reflecting some of the lesser states of imbalance of organism integrity where they are strong enough to produce a degree of visible change in the overall adaptiveness of everyday behavior.

It would be presumptuous to offer as an ultimate biological basis for the speed changes that may be observed among the aged any explanation that has been derived solely from experience gained among the psychopathologies and the brain-damaged, for despite the greater degrees of psychomotor retardation to be found among patients with these afflictions we are only beginning to recognize the organization of the phenomena from fragmentary and imperfect data and are far from understanding their meaning or cause. On the basis of what evidence is at hand, however, it seems not unreasonable to regard responsive movement as a vital aspect of the contact of the organism with its environment, reflecting in its vigor the quality of integration in its total response. From this point of view, the independent measurement methods that would be the most likely to covary with the changes observed in the speed of instructed response are to be sought among those measures shaped to reflect the total-organism quality of arousal, activation, vigilance or other names that may be given to the state of optimal functioning of the individual as a unit (Malmo, 1959).

REFERENCES

Arps, W.: (1934) Über die motorische Leistungsfähigkeit bei Grundschulkindern der Spracheil-, Volks- und Hilfsschule. *Hamburg, Lehrztg., 13:*597-599.

Baratt, E.: (1959) Anxiety and impulsiveness related to psychomotor efficiency. *Percept. Mot. Skills, 9:*191-198.

Barnacle, C. H., Ebaugh, F. G. and Lemere, F.: (1935) Association-motor investigation of the psychoneuroses. *Amer. J. Psychiat., 91:* 925-937.

Benton, A. L. and Blackburn, H. L.: (1957) Practice effects in reaction-time tasks in brain-injured patients. *J. Abnorm. Soc. Psychol., 54:* 109-113.

Benton, A. L. and Joynt, R.: (1959) Reaction time in unilateral cerebral disease. *Confin. Neurol., 19:*247-256.

Berkowitz, P.: (1961) Some psychophysical aspects of mental illness in children. *Genet. Psychol. Monogr., 63:*103-148.

Birren, J. and Botwinick, J.: (1955) Speed of response as a function of perceptual difficulty and age. *J. Geront., 10:*433-436.

Birren, J., Cardon, P. and Phillips, S.: (1963) Reaction time as a function of the cardiac cycle in young adults. *Science, 140:*195-196.

Blackburn, H. L.: (1958) Effects of motivating instructions on reaction time in cerebral disease. *J. Abnorm. Soc. Psychol., 56:*359-366.

Blackburn, H. L. and Benton, A. L.: (1955) Simple and choice reaction-time in cerebral disease. *Confin. Neurol., 15:*327-338.

Brožek, J.: (1961) Significance and limitations of laboratory studies on fitness. In Specter, H., Brožek, J. and Peterson, M., eds.: *Performance Capacity*, Chicago, USA Quartermaster Food and Container Institute.

Brožek, J. and Taylor, H. L.: (1954) Tests of motor functions in investigations on fitness. *Amer. J. Psychol.*, *67*:590-611.

Chase, R., Harvey, S., Standfast, S., Rapin, I. and Sutton, S.: (1959) Comparison of the effects of delayed auditory feedback on speech and key tapping. *Science*, *129*:903-904.

Chorus, A. M. J.: (1934a) Le rhythme personnel (das persönlische Tempo) et le rythme de travail des enfants instables. *Z. Kinderpsychiat.*, *10*:2-8.

Chorus, A. M. J.: (1943b) Le rythme personnel (das persönlische Tempo) et le rythme de travail des enfants instables. *Z. Kinderpsychiat.*, *10*:40-51.

Clark, J. and King, G.: (1960) Perceptual and motor speed in an extended age group: a factor analysis. *Percept. Mot. Skills*, *11*:99-102.

Clement, F.: (1960) Un test d'apprentissage, psycho-moteur influence de l'âge et de divers facteurs sur ses résultats. *Gerontologia*, *4*:120-139.

Committee on Nomenclature and Statistics of the American Psychiatric Association: (1952) *Mental Disorders: Diagnostic and Statistical Manual*. Washington, D. C., APA Mental Hospital Service.

Cross, H. M.: (1936) The motor capacities of stutterers. *Arch. Speech*, *1*:112-132.

Edwards, A. S.: (1954) The relation of involuntary movement to certain psychomotor activities. *J. Gen. Psychol.*, *50*:111-127.

Eliasberg, W.: (1955) Angiospastic states and Parkinson disease. *Amer. J. Psychiat.*, *111*:841-844.

Ervin, F., Epstein, A. and King, H. E.: (1955) Behavior of epileptic and non-epileptic patients with "temporal spikes." *AMA Arch. Neurol. Psychiat.*, *74*:488-497.

Eysenck, H. J. and Trouton, D.: (1961) The effects of drugs on behavior. In Eysenck, H. J., ed.: *Handbook of Abnormal Psychology*, New York, Basic Books, Chapter 17.

Fitzhugh, K., Fitzhugh, L. and Reitan, R.: (1961) Psychological deficits in relation to acuteness of brain dysfunction. *J. Consult. Psychol.*, *25*: 61-66.

Fleishman, E.: (1953) Testing for psychomotor abilities by means of apparatus tests. *Psychol. Bull.*, *50*:241-262.

Fleishman, E.: (1958) Dimensional analysis of movement reactions. *J. Exp. Psychol.*, *55*:438-453.

Fleishman, E. and Hempel, W.: (1956) Factorial analysis of complex psychomotor performance and related skills. *J. Appl. Psychol.*, *40*: 96-104.

Freeman, W. and Watts, J.: (1950) *Psychosurgery*. 2nd ed., Springfield, Thomas.

Guilford, J. P.: (1958) A system of the psychomotor abilities. *Amer. J. Psychol.*, *71*:164-174.

Hall, K. R. L. and Stride, E.: (1954) Some factors affecting reaction times to auditory stimuli in mental patients. *J. Ment. Sci., 100*:462-477.

Halstead, W. C.: (1947) *Brain and Intelligence.* Chicago, University of Chicago Press.

Heath, R. G.: (1954) *Studies in Schizophrenia.* Cambridge, Harvard University Press.

Heath, R. G.: (1955) Correlations between levels of psychological awareness and physiological activity in the central nervous system. *Psychosom. Med., 17*:383-395.

Heath, R. G. and deBalbian Verster, F.: (1961) Effects of chemical stimulation to discrete brain areas. *Amer. J. Psychiat., 117*:980-990.

Heath, R. G. and Founds, W.: (1960) A perfusion cannula for intercerebral microinjections. *Electroenceph. Clin. Neurophysiol., 12*: 930-932.

Hoch, P. and Polatin, P.: (1949) Pseudoneurotic forms of schizophrenia. *Psychiat. Quart., 23*:248-276.

Hunt, J. McV. and Cofer, C.: (1944) Psychological deficit. In *Personality and the Behavior Disorders,* New York, Ronald, Chapt. 32.

Huston, P., Shakow, D. and Riggs, L.: (1937) Studies of motor function in schizophrenia: II Reaction time. *J. Gen. Psychol., 16*:39-82.

Jellinek, E. M. and McFarland, R. A.: (1940) Analysis of psychological experiments on the effects of alcohol. *Quart. J. Stud. Alcohol, 1*: 272-371.

King, H. E.: (1949) Intellectual function. In Mettler, F. A., ed.: *Selective Partial Ablation of the Frontal Cortex,* New York, Hoeber, Chap. 14.

King, H. E.: (1950) Psychomotor aspects of the orbitofrontal cortex. *Fed. Proc., 9*:70.

King, H. E.: (1954a) *Psychomotor Aspects of Mental Disease.* Cambridge, Harvard University Press.

King, H. E.: (1954b) Sensorimotor function of the orbitofrontal cortex. *Bull. Tulane Med. Fac., 14*:5-10.

King, H. E.: (1959) Defective psychomotor movement in Parkinson's disease: exploratory observations. *Percept. Mot. Skills, 9*:326.

King, H. E.: (1961a) Some explorations in psychomotility. *Psychiat. Res. Reports Amer. Psychiat. Ass. 14*:62-86.

King, H. E.: (1961b) Psychological effects of excitation in the limbic system. In Sheer, D., ed.: *Electrical Stimulation of the Brain,* Austin, University of Texas Press, Chapter 33.

King, H. E.: (1961c) Non-specific indicators of CNS damage. *Fed. Proc., 20*:329.

King, H. E.: (1962a) Psychomotor indications of behavior disorder arising from neurologic trauma and disease. *Psychiat. Comm., 5*:31-35.

King, H. E.: (1962b) Reaction-time as a function of stimulus intensity among normal and psychotic subjects. *J. Psychol.*, 54:299-307.

King, H. E.: (1962c) Anticipatory behavior: Temporal matching by normal and psychotic subjects. *J. Psychol.*, 53:425-440.

King, H. E. and Clausen, J.: (1952) Psychophysiology. In Mettler, F. A., ed.: *Psychosurgical Problems*, Philadelphia, Blakiston, Chap. 13.

King, H. E. and Clausen, J.: (1956) Psychophysiology. In Lewis, N., Landis, C. and King, H. E., eds.: *Studies in Topectomy*, New York, Grune, Chapt. 9.

King, H. E., Young, K. M., Corrigan, R.and Bersadsky, L.: (1954) Psychological observations before and after stimulation. In Heath, R. G., ed.: *Studies in Schizophrenia*, Cambridge, Harvard University Press, Chapter 16.

Klebanoff, S., Singer, J. and Wilensky, H.: (1954) Psychological consequences of brain lesions and ablations. *Psychol. Bull.*, 51:1-41.

Kopp, H.: (1943) The relationship of stuttering to motor disturbances. *Nerv. Child*, 2:107-116.

Lacey, J. and Lacey, B.: (1958) The relationship of resting autonomic activity to motor impulsivity. *Res. Publ. Assn. Nerv. Ment. Dis.*, 36: 144-209.

Langdon, D. and Hartman, B.: (1961) Performance upon sudden awakening. *USAF Sch. Aerospace Med. Rep.*, No. 62-17.

Lansing, R., Schwartz, E. and Lindsley, D.: (1959) Reaction time and EEG activation under alerted and nonalerted conditions. *J. Exp. Psychol.*, 58:1-7.

Lewis, N. D. C., Landis, C. and King, H. E., eds.: (1956) *Studies In Topectomy*. New York, Grune.

Luria, A. R.: (1932) *The Nature of Human Conflicts*, W. H. Gantt, Trans. New York, Liveright.

McFarland, R. A. and Barach, A. L.: (1937) The response of psychoneurotics to variations in oxygen tension. *Amer. J. Psychiat.*, 93: 1315-1341.

Malmo, R. B.: (1959) Activation: a neuropsychological dimension. *Psychol. Rev.*, 66:367-386.

Malmo, R. B. and Shagass, C.: (1949) Physiologic studies of reaction to stress in anxiety and early schizophrenia. *Psychosom. Med.*, 11:9-24.

Malmo, R. B., Shagass, C. and Davis, J. F.: (1950) A method for the investigation of somatic response mechanisms in psychoneurosis. *Science*, 112:325-329.

Malmo, R. B., Shagass, C., Belanger, D. J. and Smith, A. A.: (1951) Motor control in psychiatric patients under experimental stress. *J. Abnorm. Soc. Psychol.*, 46:539-547.

Mettler, F. A., ed.: (1949) *Selective Partial Ablation of the Frontal Cortex.* New York, Hoeber.

Mettler, F. A., ed.: (1952) *Psychosurgical Problems.* Philadelphia, Blakiston.

Meyer, V.: (1957) Critique of psychological approaches to brain damage. *J. Ment. Sci., 103:*80-109.

Meyer, V.: (1961) Psychological effects of brain damage. In Eysenck, H. J., ed.: *Handbook of Abnormal Psychology,* New York, Basic Books, Chapter 14.

Peters, H. N.: (1946) The mirror tracing test as a measure of social maladaptation. *J. Abnorm. Soc. Psychol., 41:*437-448.

Petrie, A.: (1952) *Personality and the Frontal Lobes.* New York, Blakiston.

Pollack, M. and Krieger, H.: (1958) Oculomotor and postural patterns in schizophrenic children. *AMA Arch. Neurol. Psychiat., 79:*720-726.

Porteus, S. D. and Peters, H.: (1947) Maze test validation and psychosurgery. *Genet. Psychol. Monogr., 36:*3-86.

Reitan, R. M.: (1955) Investigation of the validity of Halstead's measures of biological intelligence. *AMA Arch. Neurol. Psychiat., 73:* 28-35.

Reynolds, D. J.: (1962) An investigation of the somatic response system in chronic schizophrenia. Unpublished dissertation, University of Pittsburgh.

Rhule, W. and Smith, K.: (1959) Effects of inversion of the visual field on human motions. *J. Exp. Psychol., 57:*338-343.

Ross, S. and Cole, J. O.: (1960) Psychopharmacology. *Ann. Rev. Psychol., 11:*415-438.

Ross, A. T. and Reitan, R. M.: (1955) Intellectual and affective functions in multiple sclerosis. *AMA Arch. Neurol. Psychiat., 73:*663-677.

Rothman, E. P.: (1961) Some aspects of the relationship between perception and motility in children. *Genet. Psychol. Monogr., 63:*67-102.

Schwab, R.: (1947) Reaction time in petit mal epilepsy. *ARNMD Proc., 26:*339-341.

Seashore, R. H.: (1951) Work and motor performance. In Stevens, S. S., ed.: *Handbook of Experimental Psychology,* New York, Wiley, Chapter 36.

Seashore, R. H., Buxton, C. E. and McCullom, I. N.: (1940) Multiple factorial analysis of fine motor skills. *Amer. J. Psychol., 53:*251-259.

Shakow, D. and Huston, P. E.: (1936) Studies of motor function in schizophrenia: I. Speed of tapping. *J. Gen. Psychol., 15:*63-103.

Shankweiler, D.: (1959) Effects of success and failure instructions on reaction time in patients with brain damage. *J. Comp. Physiol. Psychol., 52:*546-549.

Sheer, D. E.: (1956) Psychometric studies. In Lewis, N., Landis, C. and King, H. E., eds.: *Studies in Topectomy,* New York, Grune, Chapt. 6.

Sheer, D. E. and Shuttleworth, M.: (1952) Psychometric studies. In Mettler, F. A., ed.: *Psychosurgical Problems,* Philadelphia, Blakiston, Chapt. 9.

Simon, J.: (1960) Changes with age in the speed of performance on a dial setting task. *Ergonomics,* 3:169-174.

Singleton, W.: (1954) The change of movement timing with age. *Brit. J. Psychol.,* 45:166-172.

Smith, K.: (1947a) The functions of the intercortical neurones in sensorimotor coordination and thinking in man. *Science,* 105:234-235.

Smith, K.: (1947b) Bilateral integrative action of the cerebral cortex in man in verbal association and sensorimotor coordination. *J. Exp. Psychol.,* 37:367-376.

Smith, P.: (1958) Emotional variables and human motion. *Percept. Mot. Skills,* 8:195-198.

Stern, E.: (1939) Sprache, Sprachstörungen, Intelligenz und Motorik. *Pract. Oto-Rhinolaryng.,* 2:212-231.

Teichner, W. H.: (1954) Recent studies of simple reaction time. *Psychol. Bull.,* 51:128-149.

Teichner, W. H.: (1958) Reaction time in the cold. *J. Appl. Psychol.,* 42:54-59.

Tow, P.: (1955) *Personality Changes Following Frontal Leucotomy.* London, Oxford University Press.

Tufts College Institute of Applied Experimental Psychology: (1951) *Handbook of Human Engineering Data,* Part VI. Port Washington, New York, Special Devices Center, Office of Naval Research.

Tufts College Institute of Applied Experimental Psychology: (1952) *Handbook of Human Engineering Data,* Part VII. Port Washington, New York, U. S. Naval Training Service Center.

Vernon, J., McGill, T., Gulick, W. and Candland, D.: (1959) Effect of sensory deprivation on some perceptual and motor skills. *Percept. Mot. Skills,* 9:91-97.

Weaver, L.: (1961) Psychomotor performance of clinically differentiated schizophrenics. *Percept. Mot. Skills,* 12:27-33.

Welford, A. T.: (1951) *Skill and Age. An Experimental Approach.* London, Oxford University Press.

Welford, A. T.: (1961) Psychomotor performance. In Birren, J. E., ed.: *Handbook of Aging and the Individual,* Chicago: Univ. Chicago Press, Chapter 17.

Whatmore, G. and Ellis, R.: (1958) Some motor aspects of schizophrenia: an EMG study. *Amer. J. Psychiat.,* 114:882-889.

Whatmore, G. and Ellis, R.: (1959) Some neurophysiologic aspects of depressed states: An electromyographic study. *AMA Arch. Gen. Psychiat.*, 1:70-80.

Williams, H., Lubin, A. and Goodnow, J.: (1959) Impaired performance with acute sleep loss. *Psychol. Monogr.*, 73:14:1-26.

Wulfeck, W.: (1941a) Motor function in the mentally disordered: I. A comparative investigation of motor function in psychotics, psychoneurotics and normals. *Psychol. Rec.*, 4:271-323.

Wulfeck, W.: (1941b) Motor function in the mentally disordered: II. The relation of muscle tension to the performance of motor tasks. *Psychol. Rec.*, 4:326-348.

Yarmalenko, A. V.: The exactness of hand movements in psychoneurotic children. *Nov. Psikhonevrol. Det. Vozr.*, 129-138; *Psychol. Abstr.*, 10:1782.

Yates, A.: (1954) The validity of some psychological tests of brain damage. *Psychol. Bull.*, 51:359-379.

Yates, A.: (1961) Abnormalities of psychomotor function. In Eysenck, H. J., ed.: *Handbook of Abnormal Psychology*, New York, Basic Books, Chapt. 2.

Yeager, C. and Guerrant, J.: (1957) Subclinical epileptic seizures: Impairment of motor performance and derivative difficulties. *Calif. Med.*, 86:242-247.

26

INITIATION OF RESPONSE, AND REACTION TIME IN AGING, AND WITH BRAIN DAMAGE[1]

George A. Talland

I_F ONE thinks of the human organism as engaged in the formulation and execution of plans, the initiation of movements becomes a very complex process, with a history often hard to unravel. My topic is limited to the initiation of responses that are not much more intricate than those typical of reaction time experiments. The acts under consideration are selected in advance, and are initiated in response to predictable events; the association between them is largely arbitrary.

How far the paradigm of these experiments can be generalized outside the psychology laboratory is a debatable issue. Closely similar situations undoubtedly arise in common life, perhaps when one is driving, possibly also when walking, along the road. Even at this stage of automation, industry may still provide comparable examples but, I believe, the purest illustration will be found in the world of sports and entertainment.

Speed of response, like other biological capacities, rises from birth up to a certain age, and then declines. Our concern here is with the declining branch of the curve which, though indicative of an irreversible trend, does not drop at a continuous rate. Indeed its pace may be faster first, then slower, then faster again.

---

[1] Report of research supported in part by grant M-4889 from the USPHS.

The peak is somewhere in that narrow range of years that also mark the culmination of other biologically determined abilities. In the absence of reliable experimental data, it would be quite safe to survey the ages of the short distance champions on the track, in the pool, or field. Allowing a margin of three to five years for the perfection of special skills, the estimate would be accurate enough. With more complex techniques the age may go up, but I doubt if in recent years any one of the major singles tennis championships has been won by a man past his thirties. Yet, tennis is a game that depends on shrewd tactics, judgment, and special skills perfected through persistent drill and varied experience, as much as on speed.

The applause, that welcomed the sexagenarian Borotra to Wimbledon, was accorded him for gallantry in contesting the championship against a younger generation, not in anticipation or acknowledgment of his victory. No audience would have applauded the octogenarian Beecham or Backhaus merely for trying to conduct a concert or give a recital. Where middle aged athletes can no longer compete with their younger rivals, many musicians are able to keep their place in the front rank well into old age, and some may not even reach it before. Moreover, they are also just as likely to excel in a fast as in a slow movement.

While it is difficult to reduce a scherzo and a game of tennis to a common temporal metric, the music does not seem to offer either the easier pace or necessarily the more regular rhythm. How does it happen that professional skill can bridge the gap between speed and age in one instance, but cannot in the other? Some of the distinctive features appear quite unpromising, such as the auditory feedback in music, the visual and proprioceptive feedback in tennis, or even the necessity to adapt one's entire posture to each returning ball. More relevant seems to be the fact that music follows a detailed program; each bar, each note can be anticipated, and if all goes well the event confirms the expectancy. In tennis, the goal is to confound the opponent's prediction, to face him suddenly with the unexpected. As we grow older, we may indeed need more time to respond to the unforeseen with finger or wrist, arm or leg, but it is the response to the isolated event, coping with uncertainty, rather than acting unprepared

that becomes harder with age. Abrupt reversal or the modula-
tion of movement, the coding and transmission of the signals to
the effector apparatus, the development and maintenance of states
of optimal readiness, all of which are executed over a microscopic
time scale, though still within that temporal range, may take
longer with increasing age.

Rather than speculate how any one of these processes enter into
a game of tennis, I shall turn from the court and concert hall to
the experimental laboratory. There our interest in the effects of
age on reaction time is not so much to explain the feats in performance or the course of careers in sports and arts, as to investigate certain functional changes and their relationships in the
organism. Though simple reaction time, as its name implies, is an
elementary example of controlled behavior, it involves both
exteroceptor and effector operations, and their efficient co-ordination. It tests the organism's capacity in the speedy execution of an
act; more complex tests of reaction time probe still other capacities in handling and transmitting information. Aging is only one
of several conditions that impair these capacities; to the extent
that different types of biological change impair one of these capacities more than the others, inferences can be made to the
mechanisms or functions involved.

BIOLOGICAL CHANGE AND REACTION TIME

The adverse effect of age on speed of response is one of the
least disputed propositions in psychology. No matter how the
task is defined, latency tends to increase with age. The same
effect on reaction time has been attributed, and with comparable
unanimity, to schizophrenia (Benton *et al.*, 1959; Huston *et al.*,
1937; King, 1954; Sutton *et al.*, 1959; Tizard and Venables, 1956;
Wells and Kelley, 1922). It has also been repeatedly advanced
as a characteristic of that somewhat arbitrarily assembled class of
patients labelled as brain damaged (Benton, 1958; Blackburn and
Benton, 1955; Costa, 1962). I also noticed that a group of
men and women treated in our out-patients clinic by psychother-
apy for problems of alcoholism, who function quite well at home
and at work, and who kindly gave me their time as control subjects in a project, tended to respond rather more slowly to visual

signals than their age peers without similar problems. Recently I followed up that observation in two studies specificially designed for the purpose (Talland, 1963b). A second sample drawn from the same population of patients performed with reliably longer latencies in various tests of finger reaction than the control group composed of men and women matched for age. Another group of chronic alcoholic men, incarcerated for drunkenness, also had significantly longer reaction times than an age-matched control group imprisoned at the same institution for offenses of a different kind.

My reason for mentioning the alcoholic patients is not that they offer me a clue to the causes of slower responses in any one of these groups. On the contrary; while I have little doubt that the longer delay of older persons or of schizophrenic patients is a direct consequence of biological changes with age or with mental illness, one manifestation of a generally lowered level of organismic function, I am not even certain that a propensity to excessive consumption of alcohol is a cause rather than an effect of psychomotor retardation. Let me stress that in none of these studies was alcohol an active physiological agent; the patients as well as the prisoners were quite sober at the time of testing. On the other hand, alcohol in doses of one or two ounces had no significant effect on the reaction times of alcoholic or non-alcoholic men; and an experimental group, recruited from chronic alcoholic men, continued to speed up their responses on repeated tests during two weeks in which they drank a daily ration of thirty ounces of eighty-six proof whisky.

It would be a somewhat contrived and probably also fruitless effort to try to arrive at a common denominator or mechanism in old age, schizophrenia, and chronic alcoholism. The processes of the organism involved even in tests of simple reaction time are sufficiently complex to be susceptible to several diverse influences, and probably at several different stages in the chain of events from readiness for the signal to execution of the movement. For aging, experimental studies (Birren, 1956; Weiss, in press; Welford 1962a) have conclusively demonstrated that the initiation of movements is retarded more by the advancing years than their execution, i.e. that neither defects in the receptor nor in the effector mechanisms are the principal source of longer latencies. More-over, the magnitude of age changes in reaction time are of an order far in excess of the time impulses travel along the peripheral nerves. Birren and Botwinick (1955a) have also experimentally demonstrated that the effect of age on speed of response is un-related to distance between effector organ and brain. A colleague of mine recently tried to push this technique to its limit, by direct stimulation of the sensory nucleus in the thalamus through an implanted electrode. The manual responses he elicited in this fashion were no faster than to visual signals.

For some time now there has been general consensus about tracing the effects of aging on speed of response to changes in the central processes in the brain. It is quite probable that the similar deficit observed in schizophrenic patients and in alcohol addicts also stems from some impairment of cerebral function. But as we know nothing definite about the brain pathology of schizophrenia or alcoholism, and since normal aging is character-ized by a diffuse loss of brain cells, our gain in localizing the organic counterpart of the behavioral deficit has not been very substantial.

Perhaps, this is not quite a fair verdict. The brain has been considered heuristically as an undifferentiated organ; in the pres-ent context as well as in others. If reports about reliably longer reaction times in mixed samples of brain damaged patients were conclusive, the explanatory connection between loss of brain cells and slowing reaction times with age would indeed be strong, though also in need of refinement beyond gross neuropathological diagnosis. For a link between the latter and behavioral observa-tions, Welford (1962a) has proposed two complementary hypoth-eses, and these would lose none of their appeal though the neural damage were to be limited to certain functional systems of the brain.

There are, however, reasons for seeking other explanations of age effects on speed of response than a diffuse loss of brain cells. Indeed, it is doubtful if there is a human function that is almost equally vulnerable to damage in any part of the brain. Quite considerable cerebral lesions have been found *post mortem* in adults who had given no sign of impaired behavior. The experimental evidence is inevitably limited to patients whose cerebral damage is associated with some disturbance in behavior or pain or other medical condition. I also have experimental data of my own that force me to question a direct causal relationship between brain damage and loss of speed.

My acquaintance with brain damaged patients is based primarily on two neurological diseases: the Korsakoff or amnesic syndrome and Parkinsonism. There is little doubt that both these diseases are characteristized by lesions in the brain, and that the lesions are not typically in the neocortex. I mention this because most of the brain damaged patients discussed in the literature are grouped for damage in one or another neocortical region. The results with the Korsakoff patients were somewhat inconclusive (Talland, 1960). Their reaction time to visual signals following visual warning was longer than that of the control group; their reaction times to visual signals without previous warning in simple or disjunctive tests were not significantly longer. The results are inconclusive also because the control group itself was recruited from a population that seems to be abnormally slow in this type of test—it consisted of the alcoholic patients mentioned earlier. The mean age of the Korsakoff patients was fifty-three years (SD 9.0), and the control group was matched in this respect. Three years later age-matched samples of the two populations were retested; their mean ages, however, were higher by more than three years, and their reaction times had increased quite considerably. Still they did not differ significantly in simple reaction, or in disjunctive tests with two visual or two auditory signals. Significant differences were found only when the choice had to be made between two or four signals that cut across the sense modalities, the neurological patients being the slower.

Though inconclusive, these results are of interest because in some other tests of sensori-motor skills the same two groups did differ significantly, and because chronic Korsakoff patients are as notorious for their passivity, their lack of initiative as for their amnesic disturbance. Parkinsonian patients are most severely handicapped in motor functions, by rigidity, tremor, weakness, or a combination of these symptoms. We (Talland, 1963a) compared a group of ambulatory parkinsonian patients with an age-matched sample of healthy men and women on several tests of reaction time. There were no significant differences between the two groups; only that third of the patient sample was reliably slower which was also rated as severely incapacitated on clinical criteria. Let me add that those who were rated mildly or moderately disabled still needed medical help and, in most instances, depended on drug treatment. They were also significantly slower than the control group in a continuous motor task: operating a manual tally counter. This finding is in agreement with King's (1959) conclusion from an experiment, that in Parkinson's disease "the time taken to initiate a response is virtually normal," an observation that may not be difficult to accept, according to one's theoretical formulation of the derangement in Parkinson's disease. If this is attributed primarily to a deficiency in monitoring proprioceptive signals, then an adequate response to an isolated external signal should be within the capacity of the parkinsonian patient. What concerns us here, however, is only that patients with a brain lesion of clinical severity, and also afflicted with a motor disorder, can attain their age norms in reaction time.

An interesting problem in the relationship of cerebral dysfunction and reaction time arises when schizophrenic patients develop parkinsonian signs as a result of drug therapy. Though, by the evidence available, the structural properties of the brain may be as unaffected in schizophrenia as they are by tranquilizers, both of these conditions are probably characterized by derangements in brain function and, in some sense, these are antagonistic. Since schizophrenia has been shown to retard reaction time and parkinsonism to exert no significant effect on this capacity, one would expect that tranquilized psychotic patients show little change in latencies or, commensurately with their general improvement, these would be shortened. Brooks and Weaver (1961) indeed found that, in their patients, reaction time as well as hand steadiness was "sensitive to the change in psychiatric status, but did not reflect the effects of muscular dysfunction."

Since I have already extended my terms of reference from structural brain damage to cerebral dysfunction, let me add a few words about centrally acting drugs. Reaction time seems to be unaffected by quite a variety of these. We have tested its susceptibility to fairly large doses of barbiturates and methamphetamine in student volunteers, each subject serving as his control under the three medications, and found that barbiturates slowed down reaction time, as compared with placebo. Kornetsky (1958) failed to demonstrate any reliable effect of these two pharmacological agents on reaction time, and the balance of the evidence (Weiss and Laties, 1962) of the effect of caffeine is equally negative. Only when offsetting the influence of fatigue, do the amphetamines speed up response.

REACTION TIME AND THE NORMAL AGING PROCESS

In three experiments comparing the performance of old and young men, and in two instances of a middle aged group as well, we confirmed the findings of others that the time to respond increases with age. This is the rule, whether the task be simple or disjunctive, whether the response cue follow a warning signal or arrive without preparation. The rate, however, at which this age effect progresses is not uniform.

Figure 1 illustrates the regression of reaction time on age, with data collected from several groups of subjects without known neuro- or psychopathology, under identical experimental instructions. While the prolongation of simple reaction times without forewarning progresses at a steady rate from the twenties to the eighties, responses to signals following a warning increase quite rapidly in the early stages of adulthood, and at a slow rate during the life span that is of primary interest in aging studies. Disjunctive response in a two-choice test with light signals displays the reverse trend: slow initial growth, accelerating in the fifties, and becoming steep in the seventies.

The fourth curve plotted on the graph represents the reciprocal values of mean brain weight in the successive decades (based on data given by Braunmühl). A curve plotting loss of weight from the peak level would be quite similar. The reason for looking at the changes in brain weight is that this seems to provide as informative a measure of the progressive loss of live brain cells as any data available, although it certainly reflects other biological changes also. If we are prepared, tentatively, to accept this

fourth curve as an index of the decay of neurons in the brain, a
remarkable parallel emerges from the graph. Disjunctive reaction
time increases over the life span at about the same rate as nerve
cells drop out. The explanation advanced for the progressively
longer responses may be valid to this extent, but would not be applicable to simple reaction times. Their progressive increase may
be more directly related to alterations in the vascular system and
its impact on neural arousal, or to neurochemical changes, or to
the gradual extension of synaptic delays. Although, as I wish to
stress once more, these speculations on the theme of Figure 1 are
quite tentative, they are plausible. While simple reaction time

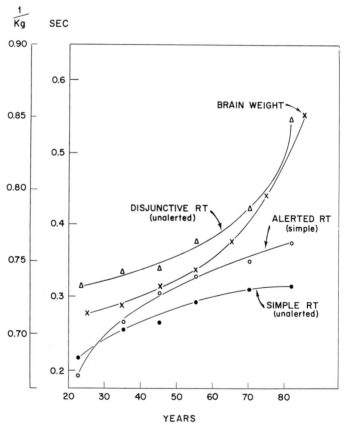

Figure 1. Age changes in reaction time and brain weight.

tests the mechanisms involved in arousal, readiness, and the transmission of messages along an undivided course, choice reaction
depends on discrimination, decision, and switching of pathways.
The latter operations are traditionally ranked among the "higher"
mental processes, and may indeed be more dependent on neocortical systems and on their anatomic integrity.

While we are still surveying the general effects of advancing
age on reaction times, let me consider one more set of observations that may be relevant to Birren's (Birren *et al.*, 1963; Birren
and Spieth, 1962) and Callaway's (in press) recent experiments
investigating the relationship of response latencies to the cardiac
cycle. Several previous reports (Goldfarb, 1941; Obrist, 1953;
Pierson and Montoye, 1958) included the observation, and all
our studies have confirmed it, that both inter-individual and intra-
individual variability as well as the mean length of responses increase with age. The most likely source of this age change is a
more frequent incidence of longer than the modal reaction times.
These may correspond to blocks, somewhat enigmatic physiological events, observed by Bills (1941) and which, in Broadbent's
(1958) communication system model of the brain, represent an
impediment in focusing the single channel to the object of attention.

Fortunately I need not speculate about the possible effects of
age on this hypothetical mechanism. Our analysis of simple reaction times, under varying instructions and in two independent
experiments, has shown that blocks occur no more frequently in
old age (the 8th and 9th decades) than in young adulthood
(the 20's). Counting the frequency of reaction times two SD's
above the mean score, they occurred once, twice or not at all in
any one subject's twenty trials; the two age groups averaged
between .81 and 1.23 (4 to 6 per cent), the one having the higher
mean as often as the other. Evidently, the incidence of unusually
fast reaction times must also contribute to the higher variances
of older subjects.

The rise of between-subject variability with age is very marked,
and also quite reliable. In three different studies, we examined
the unalerted simple reaction times which, in both old and young

age groups, varied to a significantly larger extent between than within the eighteen or twenty subjects, and also differed significantly between the two groups. Nevertheless, 22, 20 and 26 per cent of the old men's scores were below the group mean of the young subjects. One or two of the older men also had individual mean reaction times shorter than the young group, but a third of them did not score below that level once in 20 or 40 trials. That the effects associated with age are not a simple chronological function hardly needs stressing. It is, nevertheless, worth mentioning that the very considerable between-subject variability we have observed was in a relatively homogeneous group of old men. Veterans of the Spanish-American War provided samples in all three of our experiments. Their age range was between seventy-seven and eighty-nine years, with means of eighty-one and eighty-two; and they had all been screened for incapacitating chronic diseases.

WARNING AND PREPARATION

Experiments in reaction time are of interest for the inferences they allow to a capacity to develop and maintain states of readiness and, more widely still, to attention. Typically, these experiments consist of strings or blocks of trials, with a fixed preparatory period between warning and response signals. In addition, they may also include series in which this interval is systematically varied from trial to trial. In most of our studies we followed a somewhat different design. Simple reaction time was tested by manual response to a series of signals that were given without forewarning, each following the subject's last response at intervals arbitrarily varied between one and three seconds. They corresponded most closely to reaction times with variable foreperiods, but for the difference that each foreperiod began with the previous response. Our "alerted" simple reaction time corresponds to the fixed foreperiod paradigm, except that in several of our experiments we followed a traffic light model: sequences of red-yellow-green lights, in which the first two served as preparatory signals, each flashing on for about one second. An outline of our three experimental schedules is presented in Table 1.

Since in simple reaction time we had no program for, nor records of inter-trial intervals, I also assumed that our subjects would accept their randomness with alike equanimity, and make no attempt at formulating expectancies about the onset of the next signal. This may have been a rash assumption, but probably it was not so wide of the mark. At any rate, we found that our young men and women, without known psychiatric or neurological disability, had significantly longer reaction times under these conditions than in the alerted trials of the traffic light design. Several other groups of subjects, on the contrary, responded more slowly

TABLE 1

EXPERIMENTS OF AGE CHANGES IN RT

Subjects	*N*	*Mean Age*	*SD*	*Tests*	*Signal*
Experiment I					
Spanish-American War Veterans	20	81	2.0	Simple unalerted	G
Elderly men and women	20	70	2.6	Simple alerted	R-Y-G
Young men and women	20	26	6.10	Disjunctive	G/R
Experiment II a: Simple RT					
Spanish-American War Veterans	18	81	3.2		
Middle aged men	18	48	8.7	See Table 4	
Students	18	23	2.1		
b: Disjunctive RT					
Veterans and Students	as under II a			Alerted	R-G/Bz-BZ
				Unalerted	G/BZ
Experiment III					
Spanish-American War Veterans	18	82	3.8	Simple unalerted	G BZ
Young men	18	29	4.6	Simple alerted	R-Y-G Y-G Y-BZ
				Disjunctive unalerted	G/R G/Bz BZ/Bz G/R/BZ/Bz

NOTE: G =green; R =red; BZ and Bz =buzzers; - =sequence, / =alternate. Experiments with Korsakoff and Parkinson's patients followed schedule of Experiment I.

to green lights following the warning signal than in the unalerted series. As listed in Table 2, they included the Korsakoff patients, a motley selection of psychiatric patients, two of the alcoholic groups; in fact, all our experimental or control samples with a mean age over forty years. I hardly need add that this reversal of the expected trend also held for our several samples of the elderly population, though there was enough variability among the members of these groups to render the difference statistically unreliable.

Botwinick, Brinley and Robbin (1959) observed a similar para-doxical effect of regular warning signals on older subjects, but only with preparatory intervals that were considerably longer than those we used. Huston *et al.* (1937) noted this reversal with schizophrenic patients even at relatively short preparatory period , and Costa (1962) found it applied to brain damaged patients, no matter what the length of the alerting interval.

The results of our first study with two older age groups were entirely contrary to my expectation. In attempting to account for them, my first thought was that possibly the time allowed for preparation by a rapid succession of the traffic light signals would not be optimal for older persons. With advancing years, more time may be necessary to prepare a response, or for wearing off an inhibitory response that had been aroused by the warning signal.

TABLE 2

MEAN SIMPLE RT WITH AND WITHOUT WARNING:
RESPONSE TO GREEN LIGHT; ALERTING SIGNAL A CONTINUOUS
SEQUENCE OF RED-AMBER-GREEN RED AND AMBER LIGHT EACH
DISPLAYED FOR APPROXIMATELY ¾ SEC.

	N	Mean Age	RT without Warning	RT with Warning	t Ratio
Young men and women	20	26	.25 sec.	.22 sec.	2.86 $p < .01$
Middle aged men and women	20	70	.31 sec.	.35 sec.	n.s.
Veterans	20	81	.33 sec.	.37 sec.	2.12 $p < .05$
Korsakoff's patients	15	53	.38 sec.	.49 sec.	3.43 $p < .005$
Parkinson's patients	25	57	.37 sec.	.37 sec.	n.s.
Alcoholic men and women	15	53	.37 sec.	.38 sec.	n.s.

Two other[*] hypotheses were suggested by a comparison of the experimental conditions of our alerted and unalerted tests. The latter presented the subject with a uniform series of green light signals, the other with sequences of three colored lights. Age may affect the speed of perceptual discrimination or the rate at which signals are received and coded, and a chain of signals would therefore produce a cumulative delay. Alternately, aging may reduce the storage capacity for several simultaneous signals; it becomes easier to attach the response to one signal only, rather than to several in varying relations. In other words, with progressing years it may be more efficient to treat all signals but one as noise.

A second experiment with the veterans helped to rule out some of these hypotheses, even though it may not have given very strong support for the remaining one. The experiment divided comfortably into two sections, and at present I shall confine myself to tests of simple reaction time. The experimental group consisted of eighteen men aged between seventy-five and eighty-eight years (mean 81, SD 3.21). They were all in reasonably good health, all lived at home, and came to our laboratory without escort. The control group was made up of 18 college students in their twenties. A sample of 18 men drawn from an intermediate age group, forty-four to fifty-eight years (mean 48, SD 12.7) was tested under all conditions but one; these men had been recruited through an employment agency.

The experimental design is set out in Table 3. There was one test corresponding to our "unalerted" model, presenting green light signals. Alerting in this experiment was done by a single signal which, in all instances but one, terminated sometime before the onset of the cue for response. Four different signals were available: two buzzers and two lights, red and green. These

---

[*] Still another explanation was suggested by the findings of some experiments, using autonomic indices, which showed that older persons took longer to reach a given level of arousal but then maintained it with far less fluctuation than was observed in younger subjects. By analogy, older men should be slower or less efficient than the young in getting ready for each discrete response signal in a reaction time experiment. By the same token, they should also show less variability in their latencies. In fact, however, the variability of reaction time increases with age just as reliably as its length.

signals were combined in three ways to provide forewarning and response cue in one ipsimodal and two cross-modal pairs, as shown in the third line of Table 3. Three alerting intervals were tested with each signal pairing, one, two and one-half and four minutes measured from the onset of the warning signal which itself always lasted one half second. Further, in series D, there was one condition in which the two signals followed each other without a break, the red light showing through the entire alerting period of two and one-half seconds. Response signals terminated with the subject's pressing the button, and their exposure, i.e., reaction time, was measured in 1/100 seconds. Each signal combination occupied a continuous segment of the experimental schedule, in series A, B, and C, balanced in order across subjects. Within every series, two blocks of ten trials tested each alerting interval. The design was that of constant preparatory periods; uncertainty would enter only into the first and second trial of each block.

TABLE 3
EXPERIMENT II: SCHEDULE OF SIMPLE RT TESTS

Series RT	A Alerted Simple	B Alerted Simple	C Alerted Simple	D Unalerted and Alerted
Signals	R-G	R-B$_1$	B$_2$-G	G R-G
Block 1	1 sec. warning	4 sec. warning	2½ sec. warning	2½ sec. continuous alerting signal
Block 2	2½ sec. warning	1 sec. warning	4 sec. warning	no warning
Block 3	4 sec. warning	2½ sec. warning	1 sec. warning	(Disjunctive)
Block 4	2½ sec. warning	1 sec. warning	4 sec. warning	no warning
Block 5	4 sec. warning	2½ sec. warning	1 sec. warning	(Disjunctive)
Block 6	1 sec. warning	4 sec. warning	2½ sec. warning	2½ sec. continuous alerting signal

NOTE: G = green; R = red; Bz and BZ = buzzers.

Throughout the experiment, response to green light and buzzer was by pressing down a black button with the right hand; to red light it was with the left hand on a red button. The buttons formed part of a rather stiff microswitch, specially installed for our parkinsonian patients who were apt to lean so heavily on the keys of more delicate switches as to put them out of action half-way through the experiment. The pressure that had to be exerted in making contact with these sturdier switches undoubtedly lengthened simple reaction times, possibly by a constant within each age group as well as for each subject. Premature responses were not scored, and substitute trials were given for them within each block.

Mean reaction times are listed in Table 4, and let us have it on record that means, between-subject and within-subject variances were all significantly ($p < .01$) larger in the older than in the other two age groups. Mean reaction times in the middle aged men were significantly larger than in the students. There were no significant inter-group differences in premature responses, and at all three age levels inter-subject variability was significantly larger under all conditions than intra-subject variability. The differential effect of the several experimental conditions on reaction time can be calculated from the data given in Table 4; the same effects in proportionate terms are listed in Table 5. These

TABLE 4
EXPERIMENT II: MEAN SIMPLE RT IN SEC.

Warning Signal	Foreperiod	Response Signal	RT		
			Young	Middle-Aged	Old
None	None	G	.23	.29	.40
R ½ sec.	1 sec.	G	.18	.31	.38
R ½ sec.	2½ sec.	G	.19	.32	.40
R ½ sec.	4 sec.	G	.21	.34	.39
Bz ½ sec.	1 sec.	G	.18	.31	.34
Bz ½ sec.	2½ sec.	G	.19	.33	.36
Bz ½ sec.	4 sec.	G	.20	.33	.36
R ½ sec.	1 sec.	BZ	.16	.32	.37
R ½ sec.	2½ sec.	BZ	.18	.34	.36
R ½ sec.	4 sec.	BZ	.18	.34	.40
R ½ sec.	2½ sec.	G	.20	——	.39

NOTE: G = green; R = red; Bz and BZ = buzzers.

TABLE 5
EXPERIMENT II: SIMPLE RT MEAN RATIO SCORES

| Warning Signal | Divisor | | Dividend | | | Young | Middle Aged | Old |
	Alerting Interval	Response Signal	Warning Signal	Alerting Interval	Response Signal			
R ½ sec.	1 sec.	G	none	none	G	.80	.98	.97
R ½ sec.	1 sec.	G	R ½ sec.	4 sec.	G	.91	.94	1.00
Bz ½ sec.	1 sec.	G	BZ ½ sec.	4 sec.	G	.91	.96	.95
R ½ sec.	1 sec.	BZ	R ½ sec.	4 sec.	BZ	.91	.98	.96
R 2½ sec.	2½ sec.	G	R ½ sec.	2½ sec.	G	.98	—	.97
Bz ½ sec.	1 sec.	G	R ½ sec.	1 sec.	G	.98	.99	.89
Bz ½ sec.	2½ sec.	G	R ½ sec.	2½ sec.	G	1.02	1.02	.90
Bz ½ sec.	4 sec.	G	R ½ sec.	4 sec.	G	.97	.99	.93
R ½ sec.	1 sec.	BZ	R ½ sec.	1 sec.	G	.88	1.00	.99
R ½ sec.	2½ sec.	BZ	R ½ sec.	2½ sec.	G	.90	.98	.90
R ½ sec.	4 sec.	BZ	R ½ sec.	4 sec.	G	.88	.95	1.01

NOTE: G = green; R = red; Bz and BZ = buzzers.

include, in the order of tabulation, the presence, the length, and the modal relationship of the warning signals, and the duration of the alerting interval. Analysis of variance was calculated separately for the age groups. If an *F* ratio was significant for the oldest, and pointed in the same direction as in the other groups, differential and ratio measures of this effect were calculated for each subject. Between group differences were then tested for significance on these derived scores.

All regular alerting intervals helped to speed up the students' reaction times, and this effect was statistically significant. With the middle aged men, the difference occurred in the reverse direction. Judged by group means, the veterans tended to gain in speed with warning signals, but in no instance was the difference statistically significant. Thus, the finding of our previous study was reproduced to the extent that with advancing age regular forewarning had no reliable effect on reaction time. It is also evident that this effect cannot be restored merely by lengthening the preparatory period. On the contrary, reaction times tend to become longer with increasing delay between warning and response signal. Young and old do not differ in this respect. Loss in speed that follows the extension of the alerting period beyond one second was significant at all ages, though only the youngest men were still further slowed down by increasing the preparatory period from two and one-half to four seconds. It is quite improbable that alerting intervals longer than four seconds should reverse this trend at any age. At the other end, regular preparatory intervals shorter than one second may indeed be optimal for young subjects, but not for older persons (Botwinick and Brinley, 1962).

Lengthening the warning signal from one half to two and one-half seconds clearly offered no advantage to old or young men, and the two age groups did not differ in this respect, even though the group means shifted in opposite directions. The majority of the members of either age sample did better with the shorter alerting signal. It is therefore unlikely that the cessation with age of a facilitating effect of regular warning signals is due to an increased inhibitory response, unless such an inhibition occurs at the onset and is unaffected by the continued presence of the signal.

MODALITY OF SIGNAL

The modal combination of the two signals proved to be a significant source of variation in reaction time for the oldest and youngest men but not for the middle aged. In general, cross-modal alerting was the most favorable, but the students responded fastest when the buzzer came in the second position, the old men when it served as a warning. In neither group did the other cross-modal combination result in significantly shorter latencies than the ipsimodal pair of signals. The findings are not incompatible with the hypothesis that older persons may have greater difficulty than the young in distinguishing more than one "signal" from "noise." The buzzer produced a fairly penetrating sound that could not be missed, even though the subject may have been set for one signal only, the visual cue, for response. But before embarking on a tenuous speculation, I ought to remind myself that even this optimal warning failed to reduce reliably the latencies of the veterans, and that the effect of the buzzer on their reaction time raises some further questions.

It has been well established (Teichner, 1954; Woodworth and Schlosberg, 1954) that normally reaction time is shorter to auditory than to visual signals. We have found this to be the rule with a standard warning in a group of men aged twenty-five to thirty-four years (mean 29), but not reliably so when the design provided for no alerting signals. Our veterans, however, were significantly slower in responding to the buzzer, with or without preparation. The data shown in Table 6 were derived from our third experiment with the Spanish-American War veterans. Once again reaction time to alerted signals was longer than to unalerted, but the differences were not signficant.

Venables and O'Connor (1959) observed the same paradoxical

TABLE 6
EXPERIMENT III: MEAN SIMPLE RT IN SECONDS

| | Alerted | | Unalerted | |
	Light (Y-G)	Buzzer (Y-Bz)	Light (G)	Buzzer
Veterans	.39	.41	.37	.39
Young men	.19	.18	.22	.20

difference in schizophrenic patients, and drew the conclusion that reaction time is shorter to auditory than to visual signals when it is fast, but when it is slow the difference occurs in the opposite direction. Our data support this argument, and so does the work of Sutton and his associates (1959) with schizophrenic patients. Benton *et al.* (1959), however, with the same schedule of mixed visual and auditory signals as Sutton, failed to extend the rule to several groups of brain damaged patients. All these experiments were without warning signals; Sutton's and Benton's furthermore, were concerned with the effect of random change between two visual and two auditory cues in continuous series.

Botwinick and Brinley (1962), using regularly and irregularly varying preparatory intervals, obtained faster responses to sound than to visual signals from their old and young men alike. The evidence supporting Venables and O'Connor's proposition is by no means solid but, if the arousal effect of auditory signals should be slower than of the visual for certain special classes of persons, their alerting service may indeed be superior. By the same token, for the general population visual warning signals should be more effective.

UNCERTAINTY

The preceding comparison of various alerting signals and periods with each other, and with response signals without previous warning, was concerned with one aspect of uncertainty—uncertainty about the onset or the cue for response on reaction times at different age levels (*cf.* Karlin, 1959). There is considerable evidence that older persons, or those whose reaction time is unusually long, gain little from regular alerting signals. Botwinick and Brinley (1962), who equated regularity with the predictable change concluded that with advancing age more time is needed, not to organize a rapid response, but to correct errors in anticipating the moment of response. Their conclusion was based on the finding that, with a descending series of foreperiods, old and young men did not differ in reaction time even when the alerting interval was as short as one-half second.

The explanation advanced by Botwinick and Brinley seems convincing in that it agrees with observations made on older persons outside the laboratory. It does not, however, account for the failure of regular alerting intervals to speed up the responses of older persons. It also rests on a vulnerable assumption that subjects can reliably estimate the forthcoming preparatory interval, regardless of their age. The experimental evidence available does not support this assumption. Feifel (1957) reported that his older subjects tended to make significantly larger errors by underestimation when asked to mark intervals varying between thirty and 300 seconds by the production method. We arrived at the same conclusion in an experiment that called for the reproduction of intervals of two and twenty seconds. The veterans, almost without exception, underestimated both time spans on repeated trials, and differed significantly from a control group of students in the magnitude of these errors. It seems possible that Botwinick and Brinley's older subjects achieved their fast responses in descending series by attempting to reproduce the last interval and underestimating its length.

This reasoning is not advanced as a criticism of Botwinick and Brinley's conclusion, for I also believe that older persons, and most patients with cerebral disorders, have unusual difficulties in correcting inappropriate expectancies. There remains, though, the possibility that in tests of reaction time these classes of subjects may not develop sets to the same extent as do control subjects representing a younger and neurologically intact population. In our second experiment the alerting interval changed from each block of ten trials to the next. Consequently, some disconfirmation of expectancy was likely in the first trial of a block, and did in fact appear in exceptionally long reaction times, but old and young and middle aged men did not differ in this effect. More to the point still is an experiment with the traffic light signals that started off with a series of complete red-yellow-green light sequences, but subsequently intermixed among these several irregular signal sequences: red followed immediately by green, or yellow and green without a preceding red light. Responses to these irregular sequences were slower at all age levels, but the youngest and oldest men did not differ in this respect, and neither did our two samples of brain damaged patients from their control groups. Since we hypothesize that these subjects would have been more delayed by the adjustment from an incorrect estimate, it seems probable that they were less apt to make such estimates or to rely on them. The suggestion that older persons, Korsakoff patients and, perhaps, all classes of subjects with abnormally slow responses, are also less dependent on set in tests of reaction time will be considered again under disjunctive tasks.

DISJUNCTIVE REACTION

The conditions and manner in which choice and decision affect reaction times have been systematically investigated, and have been analyzed in terms of the information handling capacities of the aging brain, most notably here in Cambridge (Birren and Botwinick, 1955b; Crossman and Szafran, 1956; Singleton, 1955; Welford, 1958, 1961). The delay in response with additional alternatives increases with age; so does the delay caused by the complexity of the response pattern or of its correspondence with the signal display. A summary of the experiments investigating these variables is not within the compass of the present report. My discussion of disjunctive reaction time will be confined to some of our own experiments, all of which set tasks at a low level of complexity.

In our first study (Talland and Cairnie, 1961) of age and reaction time, it appeared that the additional retarding effect of a two-choice instruction set in at some stage in the seventies. Our sample of men and women between sixty-five and seventy-five years did not show it; the Spanish-American War veterans did, significantly differing from the former as well as from the youngest subjects, alike in a proportionate and differential measure of this effect. The Korsakoff, parkinsonian and alcoholic samples we tested were not slowed down by two-choice disjunctive tests more than their control groups. Benton *et al.* (1959) remarked that schizophrenic and brain damaged patients showed more marked retardation in simple than in choice reaction times.

Here we seemed to have hit on an important difference between very old persons and others with slow reaction times, but our subsequent findings considerably weakened its reliability. Our second experiment tested disjunctive reaction to a light or sound in veterans and students, both without alerting and with ipsimodal warning signals. The foreperiods were the same as in simple reaction: one, two and one-half, and four seconds, and so was the effect of forewarning; it helped the young men to reduce latencies but not the old. Since, however, the veterans tended to speed up their disjunctive responses with longer alerting intervals, positive warning effects may still be confirmed for them with preparatory periods over four seconds. As in simple reaction, the young men were faster with auditory, the old men with visual signals. Disjunctive reaction times were uniformly slower than simple reaction times but, in this experiment, the two age groups did not differ in this respect, either in absolute or in relative terms. It is quite probable that any age difference in the retarding effect of choice instruction was masked by the longer time needed to activate the stiff microswitches. The delay in the effector operation would coincide with the extra time required by the older men to process the information and make a choice.

Our third study with the veterans re-established the interaction effect of age and disjunctive instruction on reaction time, at least when this was measured in differences. Tested by the proportionate increment in each subject's response time, the veterans did not lose significantly more speed in a two-choice test. Here may be another example of Birren's (1956) observation about certain increments in task difficulty that show in the aged an absolutely, though not relatively, larger increase in response time, an effect that Welford (1962b) associates with situations in which data must be gathered rapidly. In this study there were three different tests of two-choice reaction, each presenting either signal twenty times in a randomized order. The mean scores of the eighteen veterans and of eighteen men aged twenty-nine to thirty-seven

TABLE 7
EXPERIMENT III: MEAN DISJUNCTIVE RT IN SECONDS (NO WARNING)

			Two Choice				Four Choice			
	Green/Red		Green/ Buzzer		Buzzer/ Buzzer		Green/Red/Buzzer₁/Buzzer₂			
Veterans	.54	.55	.53	.59	.67	.69	.81	.82	.98	1.01
Young men	.33	.32	.34	.36	.39	.38	.44	.46	.51	.48

years are listed in Table 7. Both groups reacted faster to visual than to auditory signals but, while in the younger age range this difference was unreliable, being reversed in almost half the subjects, it held for all but one of the veterans. Even though the choice in response was limited to two keys in both types of tasks, four signals very markedly slowed down reaction times as compared with two, cross-modal or ipsimodal. This effect was more pronounced in the older age group, very significantly larger in differential increment but less so ($p < .05$) in proportionate measures.

In the recent literature of reaction time experiments, set has been considered in terms of anticipating the arrival of the signal, of maintaining a state of readiness. Another aspect of set would be manifested in the preferential expectancy of one type of signal against others, in shorter reaction times with one response mechanism as compared with the alternative. One observable outcome of such a bias would be the incidence of errors on one side but not the other, in response to one or several signals at the exclusion of the preferred one. Relatively few errors by incorrect response occurred in our experiments with disjunctive reaction time. They tended to be concentrated in a few individuals, and did not differ systematically with age. Another measure of the same preferential tendency is a consistent margin between reaction times to one and the other signal in disjunctive tests. My interest in this index of set stems from a different type of experiment.

We investigated proficiency in developing, maintaining, and switching sets in a perceptual task (Talland, 1959; Talland and Miller, 1959). Lists of words were presented at the subject's threshold of auditory intelligibility, and his task was to recognize each. The operation of set was inferred from performance above the chance level, the influence of an inappropriate set from performance below it. In one of the tests two concurrent sets were established explicitly by instruction. The subject was advised that he would hear names of birds and parts of the body. The list of thirty-six words presented to him did indeed include twelve items from each category but also twelve additional words selected from as many different classes. Unless a subject were biased one way or the other, he would correctly reproduce eight to ten items from either category, and some two to four of the mixed words. Our Korsakoff patients differed from this norm, in that they could function efficiently with only one set, but could not alternate between the two. This is evident from their scores in Table 8 which lists mean performance according to any one subject's major and minor set, irrespective of the class he may have preferred. Our older men and women also fell short of the norm established by a younger age group, but not because they could not maintain a double set. They were indeed facilitated by the two simultaneous expectancies but functioned at an all round lower level of efficiency, and the oldest age group displayed the same decrement even more markedly.

Looking at our disjunctive reaction time scores, however, an entirely different picture emerges. It appears from Table 9 that the Korsakoff patients showed the least tendency to prefer one signal or one side over the other, and significantly differed in this

TABLE 8

AUDITORY PERCEPTION: PERFORMANCE WITH MAJOR AND MINOR SET AND AGAINST SET: MEAN CORRECT OUT OF A TOTAL TWELVE

	N	Mean Age	Major Set	Minor Set	No Set
Young men and women	27	26	8.2	7.1	5.5
Old men and women	10	70	6.6	5.2	2.9
Veterans	20	81	5.7	4.5	1.8
Middle aged men and women	18	46	9.8	8.4	2.4
Korsakoff patients	21	54	7.5	4.2	2.5

TABLE 9

MEAN DIFFERENCE IN RT TO MAJOR AND MINOR SET (IN SEC.)

	N	Mean Age	Visual (G/R)	Auditory (Bz/BZ)	Mixed (G/BZ)
Veterans	18	82	.63	.89	.94
Middle aged men	16	58	.50	.51	.53
Young men	18	32	.36	.53	.49
Korsakoff patients	15	61	.13	.10	.12

respect from healthy men and women at their age. In the normal population the trend was a progressive bias in favor of one signal or hand with advancing years, though this age difference failed to reach statistical significance. It should not be too difficult to reconcile the seemingly contrary results of the perceptual and motor experiments with double sets. In the former the Korsakoff patients operated with a single set when they should have switched between two; in the latter they maintained a general expectancy for signals but no specific expectancy for one type of signal. In the normal course of aging, the propensity to adopt specific expectancies in choice situations is likely to increase, or at any rate, is not relinquished, but if the prediction is unconfirmed its correction takes more time. The absence of significant aging effect in this aspect of set could be attributed to the divergent rate of these two age changes, though of course it cannot be regarded as evidence in support of the argument.

TALLY COUNTING

Reaction time experiments study the speed of response to discrete events, any one of which is theoretically unrelated to those that preceded it or are still to come. The effect of age on skill that involves the successive initiation of movements has been very extensively investigated here by the Nuffield Unit (Welford, 1958) in a variety of serial reaction and tracking experiments. These studies have reaffirmed the conclusion of simple reaction time experiments, namely, that the retardation of motor skills with age is not caused by delays in the execution of movements, but in their initiation and subsequent control. They also pointed out other difficulties that arise with advancing years, more especially in matching the perceptual feedback with the action plan, in arriving at decisions while engaged in a response, and in integrating sequences of movements into rhythmic patterns.

Another experiment of continuous performance we have used in our aging study is tallying with a manual counter, similar to the tapping test. The subject holds the counter in the hollow of his dominant hand and presses its key with the thumb, a spring resets it, and he presses it down again, rhythmically as fast as he can keep it up for five minutes. The score is read every thirty seconds. As can be seen from Figure 2, this is a task that can be performed at a remarkably steady rate in old age as well as in youth. Brain damage, such as is associated with Korsakoff's disease, impairs neither the mean rate nor steadiness of this performance (Talland, 1960). Normal aging affects the rate but not its stability (Talland, 1962) Parkinson's disease tends to damage both (Talland, 1963a). Barbiturates slow down, methamphetamine speeds up performance, at any rate in young men. The finding that is relevant to my topic, however, does not stand out clearly in the graph, i.e., the rate of initial response.

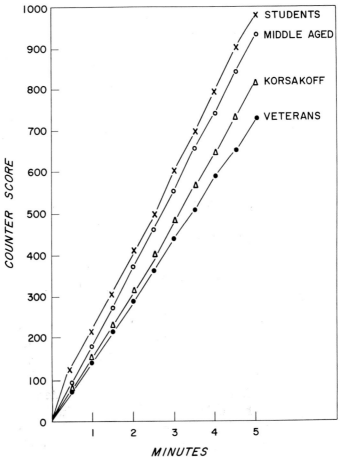

Figure 2. Rate of working tally counter.

If we calculate the difference between scores of the first and second minute periods, we find that the group mean is 8 for the veterans and 28 for the students, or a drop of 5 per cent against 15 per cent. This difference is significant, as is that between the first and third periods. Here is another example, in a repetitive motor performance, of the slower initial response in old age than in youth. Reaction time and tallying are two independent skills; their correlation is low and insignificant at all ages, and so is in early adulthood the correlation between reaction time and initial drop in tallying rate. In old age, however, these two measures of initiating movement are quite highly correlated ($r = .56$, $p <$ .01). This suggests that the age change may not be limited to performance that depends on a sustained readiness for isolated events.

INITIATION OF VERBAL RESPONSE

In conclusion, a few words about the speed of verbal response. Wits, notorious for their biting tongue or quick repartee in political debate or drawing room conversation, are not reputed to lose the vigor of their thrust with age. The experimental laboratory is an inpropitious setting for the exercise of this verbal art but even there it makes an occasional appearance, as often with old subjects as with young.

In formal tests, however, the speed of verbal response declines with age. Table 10 lists the mean word association time of fourteen men in each of three age groups, one about thirty years, another in the fifties, and the third Spanish-American War Veterans. Four lists of ten items were presented for word association. List A consisted of words that have no logical opposites; lists B and C of nouns, verbs and adjectives that do; list D was made up of the

TABLE 10
MEAN WORD ASSOCIATION TIME IN SECONDS

	Mean Age	N	List A	List B	List C	List D
Veterans	81	14	3.2	3.3	3.4	3.1
Middle aged men	52	14	2.5	2.5	2.3	2.0
Young men	31	14	2.3	2.5	1.8	1.7

opposites of list B, alternating with it in order across subjects. The instruction preceding lists A and B called for the fastest response with any word that happened to come to mind first; the instruction for lists C and D was to name the opposite of each word.

Latencies tended to increase with age, but significantly only past the fifties and with the instruction to name opposites. The reason for this was that the youngest men responded significantly

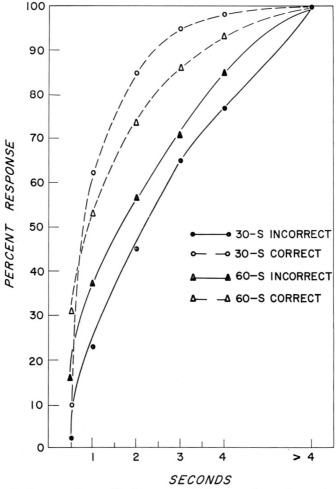

Figure 3. Latency in recall of consonant trigrams after substracting serial threes for 3, 9 and 18 sec.

faster with a definite than with an open instruction, and the same trend was evident also in middle age, though not statistically reliable. Familiarity with the words or their opposites in itself showed no significant effect on speed of response. Korsakoff patients also reacted significantly faster (Talland, 1960) with a definite set than under a loose instruction, and thus resembled the younger and differed from the older men. This difference between healthy old persons and a group of brain damaged patients is of interest in its own right, and also as a reminder that set refers to a class of dispositional states rather than to a unitary variable.

Apparently, when we know the answer, we are all likely to be quickest in saying that which is expected, but as we grow older we are not much slower in saying whatever answer comes to mind. This conclusion hardly agrees with the many observation about caution increasing apace with the years, but it is supported by some incidental results of another experiment. These emerged from an investigation of very short-term memory function by the Petersons' (1959) technique. Trigrams of consonants with low association value are presented and immediately followed by a three digit number. The subject's task is, varying with the instruction, to repeat the number or not repeat it, but in either case immediately to begin subtracting serial threes from it. In this arithmetic exercise he is stopped after intervals of three, nine or eighteen seconds, and asked to reproduce without delay the three letters in the original sequence. The delay of this response is often infinitesimal, but more often it spreads into several seconds. Figures 3 and 4 offer a representative sample of latencies in the responses of eighteen men in the thirties and twelve men in the sixties. The two groups differ only a little in their tendencies to delay correct answers; the older men are more apt to speak within half a second, but in the next half second the younger men are ahead. When the right answer is not available, however, the young men are more likely to wait and search for it. The subject is often unaware of the inadequacy of his response but quite frequently he knows that he has forgotten it. Only 3 per cent of the unmistakably incorrect or incomplete responses were given with a latency of one second or less by the younger subjects, as compared with 26 per cent by the older. Perhaps, with the years, one no longer entertains vain hopes about recovering that which is irrevocably lost; at any rate, verbal responses can be as instantaneous as they were in young adulthood, whether they make sense or nonsense, whether they are right or wrong.

CONCLUSION

An abundance of data may be worth less than even an indifferent theory but, at least, it can guard from premature theorizing. In recent years, a great deal of information has been accumulated about the effects of the normal aging process on speed of per-

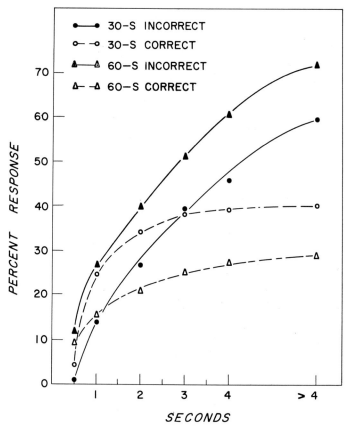

Figure 4. Latency in recall of consonant trigrams after subtracting serial threes for 3, 9 and 18 sec.: Cumulative Frequencies converted into Percentages of combined Total of successful and unsuccessful Trials.

formance, and about the ranges within which such effects vary. Much less is known about the changes the brain undergoes in the course of adult life, and less still about the neural changes that may be relevant to the behavioral manifestations of aging. We have reason to believe that gerontological research will help to bridge the present gap between neurological and psychological observations and conceptual systems.

Certain facts about the influence of advancing years upon the speed of initiating responses are inescapable. Reaction time increases with age. Similar changes can be observed in younger persons as a result of cerebral damage, and can also be induced by drugs. The evidence is convincing that the biological changes that are manifested in longer reaction times occur in the brain. We hardly need being told at this time to study central neural processes in our search for the mechanisms that account for changes in performance with age. There is certainly hope that neurophysiology and other medico-biological sciences may offer useful guides for theory and observation to the behavioral student in gerontology. It seems to me, though, that at present systematic investigations of changes in performance are most likely to reveal the complex and conditional hierarchical structure of organismic function that undergoes changes with age. Even within such a limited sample of behavior changes as occur in the initiation of responses, there is a rich mine open to the psychologist who will explore co-variations, speculate about the mechanisms affected, formulate hypotheses and test them, with or without reference to changes in structure and physiologic function of the organism.

From the evidence available, it seems premature at present to trace to changes in one single mechanism or system the various instances in which the initiation of responses is slowed down by age. It is probable that age affects the capacity for speedy reaction, raising the level of the fastest response available to a person. Age certainly reduces the probability of his fastest response being available to him. Aging also diminishes a person's gain from forewarning of the ensuing response signal, and increases his delay in certain choice situations. These four kinds of change with age in reaction time all occur without demanding complex or serial responses, and each is theoretically independent of the others. In fact, they do tend to occur in conjunction, though one or more of them have been observed, without being accompanied by the others, in certain atypical situations, such as arise in psychiatric or neurological disease and with some centrally acting drugs.

Age changes in the initiation of responses can be traced to perceptual and central processing operations, but can also be found in action programs that do not involve discriminations, decisions, or the monitoring of discrete events, i.e., in continuous repetitive motor performance. Age may not affect the speed of verbal responses. This could be explained by the fact that latencies of verbal responses are of a different order than motor reaction times. By inference from experimental observations, it is unlikely that the longer preparation available for a verbal response offers a comparative advantage to older persons, though common sense would favor this argument. It is also possible that much of the deficit observed in older persons in reaction time experiments is an artifact of the unaccustomed test. Older people are at a disadvantage when faced with unfamiliar tasks. This handicap may affect their motivation but, apart from motivation, they are also slower in bringing to bear their experience and skill in a novel situation. Any contribution from this source to their slower reaction times must, however, be partial, since observations in industry show a decline with age in the speed of over-practiced skills.

I am still puzzled by the contrast of the athlete who, at thirty, is too old for the championship and the maestro who, at eighty, can treat us to a memorable performance on the concert stage. The virtuoso needs all the speed of youth, has to sustain a constant state of readiness, respond instantly to cues, and make rapid decisions as he performs; he must evaluate with minute precision the sensory feedback of his own output, and shapes his actions into rhythmic wholes. All these powers remain at his command when, off the platform, he is not visibly different from other old men. Are our aged masters freaks of nature, paragons of self-discipline, or do they but demonstrate the inadequacy of our present notions about the effects of age on human capacities?

REFERENCES

Benton, A. L.: (1958) Le temps de reaction chez les malades presentant des lesions cerebrales. *Rev. Psychol. Appl.*, 8:103-119.

Benton, A. L., Jentsch, R. C. and Wahler, H. J.: (1959) Simple and choice reaction times in schizophrenia. *Arch. Neurol. Psychiat.*, 81:373-376.

Benton, A. L., Sutton, S., Kennedy, J. A. and Brokaw, J. R.: (1962) The crossmodal retardation in reaction time of patients with cerebral disease. *J. Nerv. Ment. Dis.*, 135:413-418.

Bills, A. G.: (1931) Blocking: a new principle in mental fatigue. *Amer. J. Psychol.*, 43:230-245.

Birren, J. E.: (1956) The significance of age changes in speed of perception and psychomotor skills. In Anderson, John E., ed.: *Psychological Aspects of Aging*, Washington, D. C., Amer. Psychol. Assoc.

Birren, J. E.: (1959) Sensation, perception and modification of behavior in relation to the process of aging. In Birren, J. E., Imus, H. A. and Windle, W. F., eds.: *The Process of Aging in the Nervous System*, Springfield, Thomas.

Birren, J. E. and Botwinick, J.: (1955a) Age differences in finger, jaw, and foot reaction time to auditory stimuli. *J. Geront.*, 10:429-432.

Birren, J. E. and Botwinick, J.: (1955b) Speed of response as a function of perceptual difficulty and age. *J. Geront.*, 10:433-436.

Birren, J. E., Cardon, P. V. and Phillips, S. L.: (1963) Reaction time as a function of the cardiac cycle in young adults. *Science, 140*:195-196.

Birren, J. E. and Spieth, W.: (1962) Age, response speed, and cardiovascular functions. *J. Geront.*, 17:390-391.

Blackburn, H. L. and Benton, A. L.: (1955) Simple and choice reaction time in cerebral disease. *Confin. Neurol.*, 15:327-338.

Botwinick, J., Brinley, J. F. and Birren, J. E.: Set in relation to age. *J. Geront.*, 12:300-305.

Botwinick, J. and Brinley, J. F.: (1962) Aspects of RT set during brief intervals in relation to age and sex. *J. Geront.*, 17:295-301.

Botwinick, J., Brinley, J. F. and Robbin, J. S.: (1959) Maintaining set in relation to motivation and age. *Amer. J. Psychol.*, 72:585-588.

Braunmühl, A. von (1957) Alterserkrangungen des Zäntralnervensystems. In O. Lubarsch, F. Henke, and R. Rossle, eds.: *Handbuch der Spziellen Pathologischen Anatomie und Histologie*, 13:I:337-539, Berlin, Springer. (Ref. to p. 346, based on measurements by Rössle and Roulet).

Broadbent, D. E.: (1958) *Perception and Communication.* London, Pergamon Press.

Brooks, G. W. and Weaver, L.: (1961) Some relations between psychiatric and psychomotor behavior changes associated with tranquilizing medications. *Compr. Psychiat.*, 2:203-210.

Callaway, E.: (in press) Interaction between the visual evoked response and two spontaneous biological rhythms: the EEG alpha cycle and the cardiac arousal cycle. *Proc. N. Y. Acad. Sci.*

Costa, L. D.: (1962) Visual reaction time of patients with cerebral disease as a function of length and constancy of preparatory interval. *Percept. Mot. Skills, 14:*391-397.

Crossman, E. R. R. W. and Szafran, J.: (1956) Changes with age in the speed of information-intake and discrimination. *Experienta, Supplementum IV.*

Feifel, H.: (1957) Judgment of time in younger and older persons. *J. Geront., 12:*71-74.

Goldfarb, W.: (1941) *An investigation of reaction time in older adults and its relationship to certain observed mental test patterns. Teachers College Contributions to Education,* No. 831, New York, Columbia Univ.

Huston, P. E., Shakow, D. and Riggs, L. E.: (1937) Studies of motor function in schizophrenia: II. Reaction time. *J. Gen. Psychol., 16:*39-82.

Karlin, L.: (1959) Reaction time as a function of foreperiod duration and variability. *J. Exp. Psychol., 58:*185-191.

King, H. E.: (1954) *Psychomotor Aspects of Mental Disease.* Cambridge, Mass., Harvard University Press.

King, H. E.: (1959) Defective psychomotor movement in Parkinson's Disease: exploratory observations. *Percept. Mot. Skills, 9:*326.

Kornetsky, C.: (1958) Effects of meprobamate, phenobarbital and dextroamphetamine. *J. Pharmacol. Exp. Ther., 123:*216-219.

Leonard, J. A.: (1959) Tactual choice reactions. *Quart. J. Exp. Psychol., 11:*76-83.

Obrist, W. D.: (1953) Simple auditory reaction time in aged adults. *J. Psychol., 35:*259-266.

Peterson, L. R. and Peterson, M. J.: (1959) Short term retention of individual verbal items. *J. Exp. Psychol., 58:*193-198.

Pierson, W. R. and Montoye, H. J.: (1958) Movement time, reaction time, and age. *J. Geront., 13:*418-421.

Singleton, W. T.: (1954 & 1955) Age and performance timing on simple skills, in Old Age in the Modern World. *Proc. Intern. Assoc. Geront., 3rd Congr.,* 221-231, London, 1954, London, England, E. & S. Livingstone, 1955, 656 pp.

Sutton, S., Hakerem, G., Portnoy, M. and Zubin, J.: (Oct. 1959) The effect of shift of sensory modality on serial reaction time: a comparison of schizophrrenics and normals. *Amer. J. Psychol.*

Talland, G. A.: (1959) Facilitation of accurate perception by anticipatory sets: the progressive effects of aging. *Gerontologia, 3:*339-350.

Talland, G. A.: (1960) Psychological studies of Korsakoff's Psychosis: V. Spontaneity and activity rate. *J. Nerv. Ment. Dis., 130:*16-25.

Talland, G. A.: (1962) The effect of age on speed of simple manual skill. *J. Genet. Psychol., 100:*69-76.

Talland, G. A.: (1963a) Manual skill in Parkinson's Disease. *Geriatrics, 18:* 613-20.

Talland, G. A.: (1963b) Alcoholism and reaction time. *Quart. J. Stud. Alcoh.* 24:610-621.

Talland, G. A. and Cairnie, J.: (1961) Aging effects on simple, disjunctive, and alerted finger reaction time. *J. Geront., 16:*370-374.

Talland, G. A. and Miller, A.: (1959) Perceptual sets in Korsakoff's Psychosis. *J. Abnorm. Soc. Psychol.,* 58:234-240.

Teichner, W. H.: (1954) Recent studies of simple reaction time. *Psychol. Bull., 51:*128-149.

Tizard, J. and Venables, P. H.: (1956) Reaction time responses by schizophrenics, mental defectives, and normal adults. *Amer. J. Psychiat., 112:* 803-807.

Venables, P. H. and O'Connor, N.: (1959) Reaction times to auditory and visual stimulation in schizophrenic and normal subjects. *Quart. J. Exp. Psychol., 11:*175-179.

Weis, A. D.: The focus of reaction time change with set, motivation, and age. To be published.

Weiss, B. and Laties, V. G.: (1962) Enhancement of human performance by caffeine and the amphetamines. *Pharmacol. Rev., 14:*1.

Welford, A. T.: (1958) *Aging and Human Skill.* London: Oxford Univ. Press.

Welford, A. T.: (1959) Psychomotor performance. In Birren, J. E., ed.: *Handbook of Aging and the Individual,* Chicago, Univ. Chicago Press.

Welford, A. T.: (1961) Age changes in the times taken by choice, discrimination and the control of movement. *Gerontologia, 5:*129-145.

Welford, A. T.: (1962a) On changes of performance with age. *Lancet,* 335-339.

Welford, A. T.: (1962b) Changes in the speed of performance with age their industrial significance. *Erogonomics, 5:139-145.*

Wells, F. L. and Kelley, C. M.: (1922) The simple reaction time in psychosis. *Amer. J. Psychiat.,* 2:53-59.

Woodworth, R. S. and Schlesberg, H.: (1954) *Experimental Psychology.* New York, Holt.

27

EFFECT OF SEQUENCE ON REACTION
TIME IN SCHIZOPHRENIA[1]

SAMUEL SUTTON AND JOSEPH ZUBIN

W HEN ALL uncertainty regarding identity of stimulus, time of its presentation and choice of response are eliminated in a reaction time experiment, continued practice will reduce response latency to a minimum and whatever variability remains can probably be attributed to fluctuations in the state of the organism. As the sources of uncertainty are reintroduced, systematic variability in reaction time will reappear. "Complications" involving increase in uncertainty were introduced in the classical experiments (Donders, Wundt, Cattel, to cite only a few) to measure the duration of "mental" processes and in more recent experiments (see reviews by Welford, 1960, Garner, 1962) to cast light on information processing in man. In almost all such experiments, variation in the stimulus was associated with variation in the required response; in other words, the subject had to make a choice. However, there is a variant of the simple reaction experiment, in which the stimulus is varied but not the response. The subject has no choice but to make the same response what-

[1] This work was supported in part under United States Public Health Service grants MH-0776 and M1541 from the National Institute of Mental Health. We are indebted to Dr. Nathan Beckenstein, Director of Brooklyn State Hospital, and his staff for the generous provision of facilities and access to patients for conducting these experiments. We also wish to express our gratitude to Dr. Gad Hakerem and Dr. Muriel Hammer for their assistance with many aspects of this work; to Dr. Maurice Portnoy, Miss Julie Beasley, Mr. Howard Pollio, and Miss Kwan Wong for the testing of subjects; to Miss Joyce Kerr, Mrs. Margery Braren, Miss Verna Schmauder, Mrs. Rhoda Mead and Mr. Joseph Fleiss for assistance in the analysis of data; to Mr. Robert Laupheimer, Mr. Raymond Simon, Mr. Harry Adler and Mr. Jerome Meyer for their assistance with instrumentation.

ever the stimulus and whenever it occurs. Wundt, writing in 1893 in his *Grundzüge der physiologischen Psychologie*, gives some examples of the effects of varying the stimulus in this type of experiment:

"If, for example, I introduced in a series of sound trials strong and weak stimuli at random, so that the subject could never expect a particular sound strength, the reaction time was lengthened, while at the same time the average variation increased. . . . The reaction time becomes more significant if one unexpectedly inserts into a series of trials using strong stimuli one weak one, or one strong one into a series of weak ones. In this way one sometimes can see the reaction time for a stimulus near the threshold rise to .4 or .5 seconds. . . . The reason for the difference can lie only in the fact that where there is no preparatory concentration of the attention, the apperception- and will-times are greater. . . . The reaction time is lengthened more when the stimulus is completely unknown than when only the intensity of it is unknown. . . . One can produce this deliberately if in a long series of trials occurring at regular intervals the stimulus is suddenly presented at a shorter interval. . . . Slighter but still very noticeable is the retardation (in quickness of response) if one arranges the experiment to have the observer in ignorance as to whether light, sound, or touch impressions (stimuli) will be forthcoming, so that the attention cannot be turned to a particular sense organ. Immediately one notes a peculiar unrest because the strain of attention (die Aufmerksamkeit begleitende Spannungsgefühl) continuously vacillates among the several senses."[2]

The "complications" of the simple reaction time experiment described by Wundt only serve to point up some of the complexities than can be introduced by varying the parameters of the reaction time experiment. Aside from the question of whether one or more responses are used, i.e., simple vs. choice reaction time, two major sources of variation in reaction time experiments referred to by Wundt are the number of stimuli and the time of occurrence of the stimulus (foreperiod duration). The stimuli may or may not be ranged on some linear dimension such as in-

---

[2] Our own free translation, pp. 352f.

tensity, duration, or wavelength. If they are on one dimension, a further source of variation lies in the number of values chosen, their range, type of step interval (arithmetic, logarithmic, or some irregular function), and so on. Foreperiod duration may also be subject to similar manipulations. Many of these sources of variation have been studied and are known to affect reaction time.

Orthogonal to the above sources of variation are manipulations of sequence of stimulus presentation. Except for some limiting cases, such as the impossibility of manipulating stimulus sequence when only one stimulus is used, stimulus or foreperiod sequence may be manipulated independently of the other sources of variation discussed so far.

The number and relative frequency of stimuli or foreperiod durations, and the degree of randomness in the sequence, interact to produce various degrees of uncertainty in the program. The effects of some of these on reaction time have been studied intensively (see reviews by Welford, 1960; Garner, 1962). Information theory has provided a mathematical model for obtaining numerical values for this kind of uncertainty.

It should be pointed out here, that the term "uncertainty" refers to the objectively controlled variation of the stimulus pattern and not to subjective uncertainty in the subject. It might be better to introduce a separate term such as "incertitude" to refer to the subjective state which can be observed only indirectly. This incertitude is contributed to both by the experimenter's manipulations of the program of stimuli and of the number of responses allowed and also by factors within the subject related to his ability to predict what the stimuli will be, when they will occur, their magnitude, and so on. This incertitude therefore controls the state of readiness of the subject both with respect to preparation of the proper response in choice reaction time and the attainment of optimal speed in simple reaction time. The latter has certain advantages for the study of the subject's state of readiness since questions of adequacy of learning and of response conflict are minimized.

Of the many classes of experiments made possible by the Cartesian product of the parameters which have been mentioned, only a few are considered in this paper; namely, the effect of stimulus sequence in reaction time experiments which include uncertainty in time of presentation or in type of stimulus. Almost all of these experiments can be classified as simple reaction experiments. However, a few choice reaction experiments which dealt with sequential effects are also described. In general all of the experiments dealt with can be subsumed under some loosely defined concept relating to readiness of the subject to respond to which the terms "set" or "expectancy" would seem to be relevant.

Apparently, human beings, unlike dice, are influenced by their previous experience and develop certain "expectancies," either consciously or unconsciously. These expectancies may be in the nature of facilitatory or inhibitory pathways established by previous experience. Thus they can include both sensory-physiological effects which depend on the degree of similarity of successive stimuli and conceptual factors involving stored memories of previous patterns of stimulation.

TIME UNCERTAINTY

In these experiments, the experimenter generally varies the time between the presentation of a ready signal and the occurrence of the stimulus. For a given block of trials the foreperiod may be either constant or varied. Even if varied, the amount of uncertainty in the sequence of foreperiods may be anywhere on a continuum from a simply patterned order to complete randomness.

The experimenter may also introduce variation with respect to number of different foreperiod durations and their relative frequency in a given block of trials and in the size of steps between foreperiod durations, or he may introduce variation with respect to the range of time which may be spanned in a given block of foreperiod durations. Similar manipulations can be applied to a series of trials, that is, blocks of trials in which the foreperiod is constant or varied may be interdigitated with each other in an ordered, quasi-random, or random manner.

There are, therefore, several sources of effects on reaction time when the parameters of the foreperiod are varied. While only three of these, the number of foreperiods, their relative frequency, and the degree of randomness in foreperiod sequence have been used to derive direct measures of uncertainty, others may contribute to the subject's incertitude. These are the effect of the particular sequence, for example a predictably ascending or descending series of foreperiods both of which result in zero uncertainty;[3] the effect of the step intervals between foreperiods and the range of foreperiods; and the direct effect of foreperiod duration. The way in which the last of these may contribute to the subject's incertitude and affect his reaction time is suggested by the following quotation from Woodrow's 1914 monograph:

> "If the subject could estimate the 20 second interval with the same absolute accuracy as the 2 second interval; however weak, wandering or fluctuating his attention, there is no reason why he cannot be just as attentive at the end of 20 seconds as at the end of 2 seconds. He would not need to maintain good attention during the whole interval, but only to be ready at the end of it . . . since the increase in reaction time is perfectly smooth, gradual and regular from 2 seconds up to 24 seconds, it is plain that the accuracy of the estimation of intervals decreases gradually and regularly from 2 seconds up to 24 seconds."

Woodrow is suggesting, therefore, that the effect of foreperiod duration on reaction time can be attributed to time incertitude, i.e., his ability to estimate different durations with equal accuracy. Klemmer (1956, 1957) has recently shown that reaction time is a joint function of two factors: one is the time uncertainty introduced by the experimenter through manipulation of the foreperiod variability and the other is the subject's imperfect time-keeping ability.

FOREPERIOD STUDIES IN SCHIZOPHRENIA

The earliest study of the effect of foreperiod on reaction time in schizophrenia was made by Huston, Shakow and Riggs in 1937, and this work was extended by Rodnick and Shakow in 1940. The basic method is to use a given set of foreperiods which are pre-

---

[3] Information theory deals with whether successive events are the same or different, while of interest here are the effects on reaction time due to the specific nature of the difference as can be seen in the results of Zahn, Rosenthal and Shakow, (1961) described below.

sented in both a regular and an irregular procedure. In the regular procedure the foreperiod is kept constant within a block of trials but is varied from block to block while in the irregular procedure the same set of six foreperiod durations are presented in a quasi-random sequence.[4] Chronic schizophrenic patients, of course, have slower reaction times than normals on both procedures (see chapter by Dr. King in this volume) but the basic finding relates to the relative performance on the two procedures in each group (Fig. 1). Normals generally give faster reaction times on the regular procedure than on the irregular procedure at all fore-periods but the longest. The patients give faster reaction times

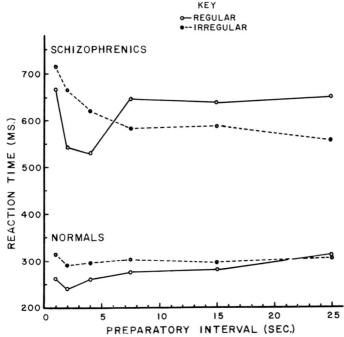

Figure 1. Mean reaction time of twenty-five schizophrenic and ten normal subjects at the various preparatory intervals of the regular and irregular warning procedures (from Rodnick and Shakow, 1940).

---

[4] There are usually two constraints on randomness introduced. The first is that all foreperiods occur an equal number of times and the second is that every foreperiod precedes every other foreperiod an equal number of times.

on the regular procedure than on the irregular procedure only for the shortest foreperiods. The patient curves for the two procedures can be seen to cross over so that above a foreperiod length of about six seconds reaction time for the regular procedure is slower than for the irregular procedure. These findings were interpreted by Shakow and his collaborators as the "inability of the patients to maintain a major set," (Rosenthal, Lawlor, Zahn and Shakow, 1960, p. 26) or more specifically that although the patients are able to obtain a comparatively high preparatory set during the shorter foreperiods of the regular as compared to the irregular procedure, they have greater difficulty than do normals in maintaining the advantage. As a result, "they fall back upon a lower level of preparation at longer foreperiods" (Rodnick and Shakow, 1940, p. 223). Or still another statement that is made is that schizophrenics are unable to benefit from regularity at the longer foreperiods.

In order to consider the question of the degree of confirmation of these findings by subsequent studies, it is necessary to distinguish a "weak" and a "strong" form of the hypothesis. In the "weak" form, it may be stated that while normals react more rapidly on the regular than on the irregular procedure at almost all foreperiods used, patients have faster reaction times on the regular procedure only at the shortest foreperiods. In the "strong" form, one may add that at the longer foreperiods patients actually perform better on the irregular procedure than on the regular procedure. This is the "crossover" phenomenon. The weak form of the hypothesis has been confirmed in several studies from different laboratories (Huston, Shakow and Riggs, 1937; Rodnick and Shakow, 1940; Huston and Singer, 1945; Huston and Senf, 1952; Tizard and Venables, 1956; Rosenthal, Lawlor, Zahn and Shakow, 1960; Zahn, Shakow and Rosenthal, 1961). However while the crossover is statistically significant in only one study, this phenomenon may be observed in several other studies by visual inspection of the curves.

There have also been several studies which reported negative or equivocal findings (Knehr, 1954; Rosenbaum, MacKavey and Grissel, 1957; Jentsch, 1958; and Funke, 1961). However, in all of these studies the experimental conditions were so altered that it was not possible to consider these findings as directly bearing on the Worcester hypothesis. The most significant deviation in these studies has been the attempt to test the hypothesis with a smaller number of foreperiod durations. Knehr, for example, assumed that the findings could be checked by using only two foreperiods, one on either side of the alleged crossover point. However, he did not seem to realize that by such sampling he substantially reduced the degree of time uncertainty and the subject's incertitude by decreasing both the range and variability of foreperiods.

Two recent studies from Shakow's laboratory have attempted a further elucidation of the way in which foreperiods affect the reaction time of schizophrenics and normals. In one study (Zahn, Rosenthal, and Shakow, 1961) which completely eliminated not only intra-block time uncertainty but inter-block time uncertainty, that is, blocks of trials with fixed foreperiods are presented either in ascending or in descending order of foreperiod duration, the schizophrenic patients gave disproportionately longer reaction times (as compared to normals) toward the end of the series of blocks. In a still more recent study (Zahn, Rosenthal and Shakow, 1963), it was found that in the irregular procedure schizophrenic patients gave disproportionately longer reaction times at the shorter preparatory intervals—essentially the same finding reported by Botwinick, Brinley, and Birren (1957) for older normal subjects. Zahn *et al.* (1963) were able to show that this disproportionate impairment was due to the fact that patients were more influenced than normals by the relative duration of the foreperiod in the immediately preceding trial—that is, whether it was longer or shorter.

In still another study, Zahn, Shakow and Rosenthal (1961) were able to show that the disproportionate impairment of the schizophrenic patients at the longer foreperiods was not due to the slow tempo of events when foreperiods are long. They controlled the tempo of events by varying the length of the intertrial interval.

These recent studies clarify and extend the original findings. The crossover is not only contributed to by failure of the patients to benefit from the regular procedure at the longer foreperiods but also by their disproportionate impairment at the shorter intervals in the irregular procedure. Furthermore, the patients are not only disproportionately affected by the immediately preceding trial but also disproportionately affected by the sequence of blocks in the regular procedure. In other words, the schizophrenic patients are disproportionately sensitive both to influences which are contiguous in time and to influences which are removed in time.

In the 1940 study, Rodnick and Shakow computed an empirically derived index which discriminated chronic schizophrenics and normals without overlap. However, the index is heavily weighted by the overall difference in speed between patients and normals which by itself discriminated most of the patients from the normals. The Tizard and Venables (1956) study gave similar results. Rosenthal, Lawlor, Zahn and Shakow (1960) reported a correlation of .92 between the set index and an independent judgment of mental health although, again, most of the correlation is accounted for by the overall difference in speed of reaction between patients and normals. While no attempt has been made in these studies to covary out the speed factor in comparing patients and normals on the "set" data (the differences in pattern of responsiveness as a function of mode of foreperiod presentation), some attempt to control for this factor was made in three of the studies. Tizard and Venables (1956) found the same pattern of performance in patients with faster reaction times and Zahn, Rosenthal and Shakow (1961) obtained the same results when they limited their comparisons to patients and normals matched on reaction time level. Huston, Shakow and Riggs (1937) found that the differences between patients and normals held up even when limited to the patients considered to be the most cooperative.

It is not clear whether the schizophrenic pattern of performance also holds for acute or early schizophrenics, or whether it is limited to chronic schizophrenics. The samples in which positive results were obtained can generally be described as chronic. Huston and Senf (1952) found that only the chronic schizophrenics were unable to benefit from the regular mode of presentation at the longer foreperiods, whereas acute schizophrenics, manic depressives, and neurotics gave normal patterns of performance. Interestingly enough, drug therapy which resulted in temporary reduction of psychotic symptoms resulted in a normal pattern of response in the chronic schizophrenics even though the drugs resulted in an increase in the overall level of reaction time (Huston and Singer, 1945; Huston and Senf, 1952). Huston and Senf (1952), however, reported no correlation between their set index (computed differently from Rodnick and Shakow's) and duration of illness.

Knehr's negative findings may also in part have been due to the fact that his patient samples were not chronic schizophrenics. Knehr suggested on the basis of his findings that positive results might be due to the use of "deteriorated" patient samples with low I.Q.'s. This contention was effectively refuted by Tizard and Venables who found a normal pattern of responsiveness in a sample of mental defectives.

Stimulus Uncertainty Studies in Schizophrenia

Mowrer in the 1940's (Mowrer, 1941; Mowrer, Rayman, and Bliss, 1940) used several stimuli but only one response in conducting a series of reaction time experiments in normals. These experiments were performed in the context of a controversy on whether "set" was centrally or peripherally determined. In one experiment, series of reactions to sound alternated with series of reactions to light, but the point in the sequence at which the stimulus would shift was unknown to the subject. Mowrer found a substantial lengthening of reaction time at the point of shift into a new series. A repetition of the same experiment using two different colors of light did not, however, result in a lengthening of the reaction time to the "unexpected" stimulus. He repeated his experiments using different permutations of auditory, visual, and vibratory stimuli. In a paper from our laboratory published in 1961 (Sutton, Hakerem, Zubin, and Portnoy) we pointed out that in Mowrer's data, reaction time is lengthened in all the experiments in which the "unexpected" stimulus is in a different sensory modality, but not lengthened when the "unexpected" stimulus is in the same sensory modality. However, this finding is not consistent with the statements by Wundt quoted above and with the results of experiments described by Ach in his *Analyse des Willens* (1935). Ach, using a choice reaction time situation, reported large increases in reaction time for a single red light stimulus which was presented in a long series of reactions to green light stimuli.

The resolution of the conflict between these disparate findings is inherent in the results of the experiments to be presented below. The findings which resolve these contradictions may be anticipated now. First, the absolute increase in reaction time due to stimulus sequence is greater in the choice reaction time situation than in the simple reaction time situation (see Experiment B below). Secondly, the retardation due to sequence of different stimuli in the same modality is generally smaller in magnitude than that due to sequence of stimuli in different modalities (see Experiment C below). Thirdly, quite large effects may be obtained when the shift in stimulus has a low probability of occurrence (see experiment by Hannes below).

The pioneering study on the effects of stimulus sequence on reaction time in schizophrenia is again the work of Huston, Shakow and Riggs in 1937. They used the classical *c* reaction; subjects were instructed to respond to yellow light but not to red lights. In a given "trial," there might be a single yellow light (Y), or a variable number of red lights followed by a yellow light (e.g., rY, rrY, or rrrY). For one group of schizophrenic patients, those classified as least cooperative, there was a greater increase than for normals in reaction time for trials with yellow light which were preceded by trials which included both red and yellow lights (e.g., rrY or rrrY).

In an experiment published in 1961 (Sutton *et al.*) we reported that chronic schizophrenic patients showed a greater retardation in simple reaction time than did normals when the stimulus in the preceding trial was in a different sensory modality. The data from that study are summarized in Figure 2. In this experiment, the subject was instructed to make, as rapidly as possible, the identical finger-lift response, whichever of four stimuli (red light, green light, high tone, and low tone) was presented. The stimuli were presented in a quasi-random order. In the figure, the data are classified on the basis of the relationship of the stimulus in a given trial to the stimulus in the preceding trial. Roman numeral

I refers to all reaction times to stimuli which had an identical stimulus in the previous trial, e.g., a reaction to a red light which was preceded by a reaction to a red light, or a reaction to a high tone which was preceded by a reaction to a high tone, etc. Roman numeral II refers to all reaction times to stimuli which had a non-identical stimulus in the same modality in the previous trial, e.g., a reaction to a low tone which was preceded by a reaction to a high tone, etc. Roman numeral III refers to all reaction times to stimuli which had a stimulus in a different modality in the previous trial, e.g., a reaction to a green light which was preceded by a reaction to a low tone, etc. It should be clear,

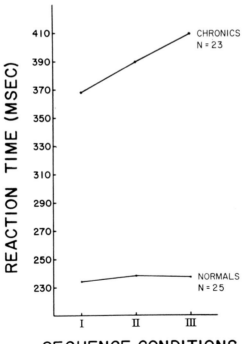

Figure 2. Mean simple reaction time as a function of type of stimulus sequence for chronic schizophrenic patients and normals.

therefore, that each of the three categories of response includes reactions to all four stimuli used in the study; the categories differ only in their relation to the stimuli of the immediately preceding trial. A non-parametric analysis of the data showed that the ipsimodal retardation—the increase of reaction time for category II over category I—did not discriminate patients and normals while the crossmodal retardation—the increase of reaction time for category III over category II—did discriminate patients and normals (for details see Sutton *et al.*, 1961).

The number of trials used in this experiment did not permit a more detailed analysis of the effects obtained. In experiment A below, the number of trials was substantially increased. The schizophrenic sample consisted of new hospital admissions classified by two psychiatrists as either process or reactive schizophrenics.[5]

EXPERIMENT A

Subjects

The patients were thirty-one male new hospital admissions who had not received any drugs or somatic treatment within a minimum of one week prior to testing. The patients were classified as either process or reactive schizophrenics on the basis of the Phillips Scale. The average age of the eighteen process patients was twenty-eight years (range, 19-42) and of the thirteen reactive, patients, twenty-nine years (range, 19-39). The thirty-two male normals consisted primarily of college students with an average age of twenty-five years (range, 19-44).

Procedure

The four stimuli were a 1000 cps tone, a 312 cps tone, a red light, and a green light. The stimuli were at a "comfortable" intensity level, the stimuli in the same modality were set at the same arbitrary intensity level. The visual stimuli were presented by having a small transclucent screen directly in front of the subject which turned either red or green. The sound stimuli were

---

[5] We are indebted to Dr. Robert Cancro of the New York State Medical School and to Dr. A. Arthur Sugerman of the Bureau of Research in Neurology and Psychiatry, Princeton, New Jersey for making the patients available and for the diagnostic aspects of this study.

emitted from a small loud-speaker mounted above the translucent screen. The subject was seated in front of the apparatus and was made familiar with his task and with the four stimuli. He was instructed to lift his forefinger from a plate as rapidly as possible whenever any one of the four stimuli was presented. The lifting of the finger terminated the stimulus and the subject returned his finger to the plate and waited for the next stimulus. Reaction time was measured from the onset of the stimulus to the lifting of the finger. No ready signal was given; the termination of each stimulus served as the signal that the next trial had begun. The time intervals between trials were random values between one and three seconds controlled by an electronic programming device.[6]

There were four runs of 132 trials each (see Table 1). The

TABLE 1

STIMULUS SEQUENCE AND DATA CLASSIFICATION IN "RANDOM" PROGRAM
(EXPERIMENTS A AND B)

Sequence of Simuli: GLHHGGRHRLL. . . .etc. 132 Trials

R = Red Light	H = High Tone
G = Green Light	L = Low Tone

Data Classification:

REACTIONS TO LIGHT

IPSIMODAL

I = IDENTICAL	II = NON-IDENTICAL	III = CROSSMODAL
rR — 8 Trials	rG — 8 Trials	hR — 8 Trials
gG — 8 Trials	gR — 8 Trials	lR — 8 Trials
		hG — 8 Trials
16 Trials	16 Trials	lG — 8 Trials
		32 Trials

REACTIONS TO SOUND

IPSIMODAL

I = IDENTICAL	II = NON-IDENTICAL	III = CROSSMODAL
hH — 8 Trials	lH — 8 Trials	rH — 8 Trials
lL — 8 Trials	hL — 8 Trials	gH — 8 Trials
		rL — 8 Trials
16 Trials	16 Trials	gL — 8 Trials
		32 Trials

[6] Time uncertainty is introduced only in order to decrease the anticipatory reactions which result when foreperiod is fixed. The foreperiods are completely random in relation to the stimulus sequence effects which are under study.

stimuli were presented in a quasi-random order with the major constraint on randomness consisting of the fact that there were an equal number of sequences of all permutations of the four stimuli taken two at a time.

Short rests of about one half minute were given after each group of thirty-three trials. Five to ten minute rests were given between runs.

Analysis of Data

For each subject, six median scores were obtained, three for reactions to sound stimuli (I, II, III) and three for reactions to light stimuli (I, II, III). Groups were compared by analysis of covariance with category I trials used as the baseline measure of overall level. The II-I analysis, therefore, gives the comparison between groups on the ipsimodal retardation and the III-I analysis gives the comparison between groups on the crossmodal retardation.

Results

The means and standard deviations are presented in Table 2 and correlations between experimental conditions are presented

TABLE 2

GROUP MEANS AND STANDARD DEVIATIONS FOR PATIENTS AND NORMALS
(EXPERIMENT A)

		Normals	Process	Reactive	Combined Patients
	N	32	18	13	31
Sound I	$\overline{X}$	188	225	207	216
	SD	24	47	35	44
II	$\overline{X}$	193	252	221	236
	SD	25	69	39	60
III	$\overline{X}$	193	256	224	240
	SD	28	72	46	64
Light I	$\overline{X}$	251	298	276	287
	SD	23	37	36	38
II	$\overline{X}$	259	305	279	292
	SD	20	40	29	38
III	$\overline{X}$	267	316	295	306
	SD	25	42	38	42

TABLE 3

CORRELATIONS ACROSS EXPERIMENTAL CONDITIONS FOR PATIENTS AND
NORMALS (EXPERIMENT A)

	Normals	Patients
Sound		
II - I	.98	.96
III - I	.95	.94
III - II	.96	.98
Light		
II - I	.97	.96
III - I	.89	.94
III - II	.93	.92

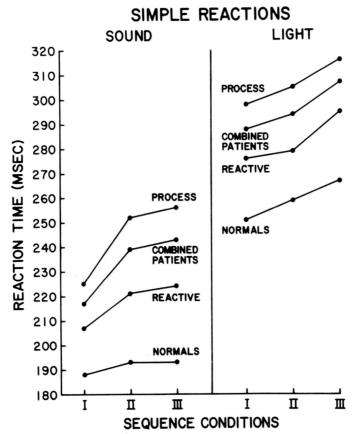

Figure 3. Mean simple reaction time to sound and light stimuli as a function
of type of stimulus sequence for schizophrenic patients and normals (Experiment A).

in Table 3. The high correlations between experimental conditions suggest the need for covariance analyses in order to compare groups on the effect of shifting to a new type of stimulus.

The means are plotted in Figure 3. Reactions to sound are presented on the left hand side of the figure and reactions to light are presented on the right hand side of the figure. For both sound and light, the process patients have the longest reactions, the normals the shortest reactions, and the reactive patients are intermediate.

The major hypotheses under test involve the increases in reaction time which result from the fact that the stimulus in the previous trial is different but in the same modality (category II) or is in a different modality (category III). These are examined by use of covariance analyses in which groups are compared on category II holding constant performance on category I, the ipsimodal retardation; and on category III holding constant performance on category I, the crossmodal retardation. A third possible analysis involves comparing groups on category III holding constant performance on category II. This analysis in effect deals with the increase in reaction time as a function of shifting modality which is over and above that achieved by introducing a shift within the same modality. The covariances are presented in Table 4. None of the covariances comparing process and reactive

TABLE 4

COVARIANCE ANALYSES COMPARING PATIENTS AND NORMALS (EXPERIMENT A)

Reactions to Sound	df	II-I		III-I		III-II	
		SSy'	MS	SSy'	MS	SSy'	MS
Patients vs. Normals	1	1,015	1,015	1,536	1,536	71	71
Within	60	11,489	191	19,713	329	12,050	201
Total	61	12,504		21,249		12,121	
		F = 5.3*		F = 4.7*		F = NS	
Reactions to Light Patients vs. Normals	1	5	5	82	82	207	207
Within	60	5,292	88	10,825	180	12,476	208
Total	61	5,297		10,907		12,683	
		F = NS		F = NS		F = NS	

*Significant at .05 level of confidence.

patients achieve statistical significance, and therefore, the combined results for both groups are presented. It will be noted that there are no significant differences between patients and normals on reactions to light. On reactions to sound, both the crossmodal retardation (III-I) and the ipsimodal retardation (II-I) discriminate patients and normals, while the alternative analysis for crossmodal retardation (III-II) does not discriminate patients and normals. In summary, for reactions to sound, when performance on identical sequences are held constant, patients have a greater increase in reaction time due either to shifting sensory modality or to shifting to a different stimulus in the same modality.

EXPERIMENT B

In order to study the effect of stimulus uncertainty in an uncontaminated way, we have purposely eliminated any response uncertainty. It is nevertheless of some interest to consider whether the disproportionate increase in schizophrenic reaction time as a function of stimulus sequence would also occur when response uncertainty was present; in other words in a choice reaction situation. In the present experiment, therefore, the sequence of trials is identical with Experiment A. However, the subject was trained to move his finger from the plate and to press one of four keys which had been preassigned to the four stimuli. In this experiment the inter-trial interval is necessarily longer (6 to 9 seconds). The four runs which took a longer period of time were done on two successive days, two runs for each day of testing. The patient sample consisted of chronic schizophrenic patients with a minimum of two years of continuous hospitalization prior to testing. Both males and females were tested. The mean age of the thirteen male patients was thirty-one years (range 23-40) and of the fourteen female patients was thirty-four years (range 26-39). The mean age of the ten male normals was thirty years (range 23-38) and of the ten female normals was thirty-three years (range 24-40). The normal sample was drawn from hospital attendant and research staff. About half of both samples had participated in previous studies using similar reaction time programs.

Results

The group means and standard deviations are presented in Table 5 and the correlations between experimental conditions are presented in Table 6. The group means are also plotted in Figure 4. Comparison with Figure 3 (in which only male subjects were used) shows the much higher reaction times obtained in a four-

TABLE 5

GROUP MEANS AND STANDARD DEVIATIONS FOR PATIENTS AND NORMALS
(EXPERIMENT B)

		Males		Females	
		Normals	Patients	Normals	Patients
Sound					
I	$\overline{X}$	661	1007	768	1045
	SD	66	249	88	236
II	$\overline{X}$	706	1072	785	1189
	SD	74	286	53	342
III	$\overline{X}$	733	1172	908	1292
	SD	74	273	170	375
Light					
I	$\overline{X}$	668	975	743	909
	SD	55	188	90	133
II	$\overline{X}$	680	986	750	925
	SD	53	198	74	140
III	$\overline{X}$	694	1054	785	975
	SD	65	266	91	167

TABLE 6

CORRELATIONS ACROSS EXPERIMENTAL CONDITIONS SEPARATELY BY SEX FOR
PATIENTS AND NORMALS (EXPERIMENT B)

	Males		Females	
	Normals	Patients	Normals	Patients
Sound				
II - I	.92	.98	.21	.92
III - I	.94	.95	.39	.91
III - II	.93	.98	.84	.94
Light				
II - I	.95	.98	.997	.98
III - I	.86	.95	.96	.93
III - II	.90	.94	.97	.95

choice reaction time situation. However, the trends are similar in that reaction time for crossmodal sequences (III) is longest and identical sequences (I) shortest, with the reaction times to ipsimodal non-identical sequences (II) falling in between.

Analyses of covariance are again used to compare groups on the effect of stimulus sequence. These are presented in Table 7 for the males and Table 8 for the females. None of the covariances for the females are statistically significant. For the males as in Experiment A, none of the covariances for reactions to light are statistically significant. For reactions to sound, both estimates of crossmodal retardation (III-I, III-II) discriminate patients and

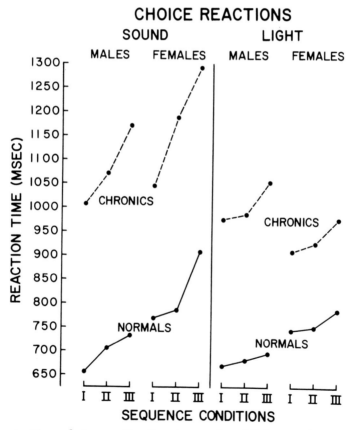

Figure 4. Mean choice reaction time to sound and light stimuli as a function of type of stimulus sequence for male and female chronic schizophrenic patients and male and female normals. (Experiment B).

TABLE 7

COVARIANCE ANALYSES COMPARING MALE PATIENTS AND MALE NORMALS
(EXPERIMENT B)

Reactions to Sound	df	II-I		III-I		III-II	
		SSy'	MS	SSy'	MS	SSy'	MS
Patients vs.							
Normals	1	1,755	1,755	19,763	19,763	32,980	32,980
Within	20	43,856	2,193	99,632	4,982	49,040	2,452
Total	21	45,611		119,395		80,020	
		F = NS		F = 4.0*		F = 13.5**	
Reactions to Light							
Patients vs.							
Normals	1	222	222	5,936	5,936	1,566	1,566
Within	20	23,444	1,172	101,975	5,099	115,083	5,754
Total	21	23,666		107,911		116,649	
		F = NS		F = NS		F = NS	

*Significant at .05 level of confidence.
**Significant at .01 level of confidence.

TABLE 8

COVARIANCE ANALYSES COMPARING FEMALE PATIENTS AND FEMALE NORMALS
(EXPERIMENT B)

Reactions to Sound	df	II-I		III-I		III-II	
		SSy'	MS	SSy'	MS	SSy'	MS
Patients vs.							
Normals	1	15,037	15,037	34	34	7,835	7,835
Within	21	372,750	17,750	594,676	28,318	371,644	17,697
Total	22	387,787		594,710		379,479	
		F = NS		F = NS		F = NS	
Reactions to Light							
Patients vs.							
Normals	1	626	626	49	49	524	524
Within	21	13,075	623	64,784	3,085	44,190	2,104
Total	22	13,701		64,833		44,714	
		F = NS		F = NS		F = NS	

normals. However, the ipsimodal retardation (II-I) does not discriminate patients and normals.

EXPERIMENT C

In studying the effect of sequence on reaction time, only the relationship with the stimulus of the immediately preceding trial has been considered. Yet there are probably cumulative sequential effects. If, for example, one assumed that some kind of sensory facilitation is involved in the reduction of reaction time as one repeats identical stimuli, one might also expect a greater retardation if one shifts modality after two identical stimuli than if one shifts modality after one stimulus. The present experiment was designed to test this hypothesis in a comparison of patients and normals. Specifically, they were compared only on reactions to low tone stimuli when these low tone stimuli had been preceded by either one, two, three, or four red light stimuli (III) or by one, two, three, or four high tones (II). The design of such a program is shown in Table 9. Four such runs were obtained for each subject. This program, as well as the other programs, proceeds without interruption except for short rests, and the subject, as in Experiment A, is required to react to all stimuli by simply lifting the finger. In other words, there is no response uncertainty. All other aspects of the experimental procedure were identical with Experiment A.

TABLE 9

STIMULUS SEQUENCE AND DATA CLASSIFICATION FOR "CUMULATIVE" PROGRAM (EXPERIMENT C)

Sequence of Stimuli: RLHHLRRRRLRRLHL....etc. 140 Trials

r = Red Light	h = High Tone
	L = Low Tone

Data Classification for Analysis of Low Tones:

II = IPSIMODAL	III = CROSSMODAL
hL—5 Trials	rL—5 Trials
hhL—5 Trials	rrL—5 Trials
hhhL—5 Trials	rrrL—5 Trials
hhhhL—5 Trials	rrrrL—5 Trials
20 Trials	20 Trials

The patients were twenty-one male schizophrenic subjects with mean age of twenty-nine years (range 18-40) and twenty-three female schizophrenic subjects with a mean age of twenty-eight years (range 18-38). All patients were new hospital admissions who had received no drugs or somatic treatment during the week of testing. The fifty-one normal subjects came from a wide range of occupations. The mean age of the twenty-seven male normals was twenty-nine years (range 18-56) and the twenty-four female normals was twenty-five years (range 16-40).

Results

The means and standard deviations are given in Table 10. The means for the males are plotted in Figure 5 and for the females in

TABLE 10

REACTION TIME TO LOW TONES AS A FUNCTION OF THE NUMBER OF PRECEDING HIGH TONES OR RED LIGHTS FOR PATIENTS AND NORMALS SEPARATELY BY SEX (EXPERIMENT C)

| | | *Males* | | *Females* | |
		Normals	*Patients*	*Normals*	*Patients*
	N	27	21	24	23
ONE PRECEDING					
II (h)	$\overline{\text{X}}$	190	207	199	278
	SD	26	29	38	92
III (r)	$\overline{\text{X}}$	200	235	216	284
	SD	25	49	49	86
TWO PRECEDING					
II (h)	$\overline{\text{X}}$	192	209	203	264
	SD	23	23	40	77
III (r)	$\overline{\text{X}}$	200	227	215	287
	SD	28	36	54	98
THREE PRECEDING					
II (h)	$\overline{\text{X}}$	192	212	206	280
	SD	25	28	51	90
III (r)	$\overline{\text{X}}$	203	236	211	283
	SD	31	55	54	87
FOUR PRECEDING					
II (h)	$\overline{\text{X}}$	197	208	206	277
	SD	26	26	55	89
III (r)	$\overline{\text{X}}$	205	235	219	314
	SD	25	46	72	120

Figure 6. Correlations between experimental conditions are shown in Table 11. For all groups, reaction time is longer on the crossmodal reactions to low tone stimuli (III) than on the ipsimodal reactions to low tone stimuli (II) whether there were one, two, three or four stimuli preceding the shift.

Covariance analyses were performed comparing patients and normals on category III (holding constant performance on cate-

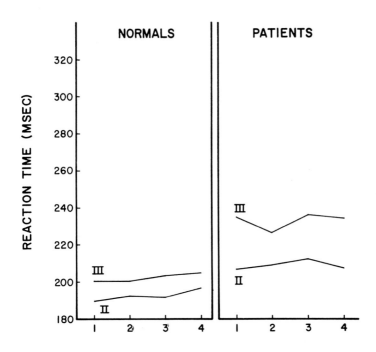

Figure 5. Mean simple reaction time to low tone stimuli as a function of the number of preceding red light or high tone stimuli for male normals and male acute schizophrenic patients.

gory II) for each of the conditions of the number of stimuli preceding the shift. These are presented in Table 12. As in Experiment B, none of the covariances are significant for the females.
Perhaps this is due to the consistently higher standard deviations
in the females of each group (Table 10). For the males, there is a
disproportionate increase in reaction time for the patients on the
crossmodal condition after the condition of one stimulus preced-

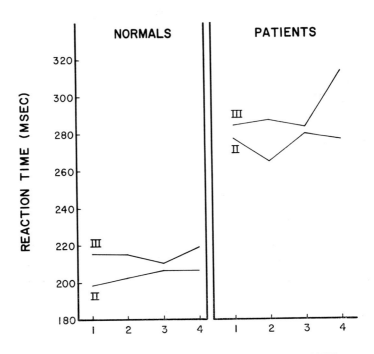

PROGRAM F – MEANS OF MEDIANS

REACTIONS TO LOW TONE

FEMALES

Figure 6. Mean simple reaction time to low tone stimuli as a function of the
number of preceding red light or high tone stimuli for female normals and
female acute schizophrenic patients.

ing the shift and of four stimuli preceding, but not for the intermediate sequence conditions.

The fact that the effect which discriminates male patients and male normals does not build up as one increases the repetitions before shifting would seem to militate against a sensory explanation in accounting for the phenomena. Rather, the patients behave as if a shift after one or after four stimuli is more unexpected than after two or three stimuli. In other words, these data suggest some kind of conceptual (though not necessarily conscious) differences between patients and normals are responsible for the discrimination.

However, there is another aspect of these data which argues the reverse of the above. Examination of the curves for the normals in Figures 5 and 6 show that they may be considered as sloping slightly upward, in other words reaction time is increasing slightly as the number of stimuli preceding the shift increases. This would be consistent with a sensory build-up of effect with repetition and inconsistent with a more conceptual explanation based on the degree of uncertainty. Reference to Table 9 makes it clear that after the subject has received one red light stimulus or one high tone stimulus, his subsequent stimulus may be either a low tone, or there may be one, two or three repetitions (of red or high) before a low tone appears. On the other hand, once the

TABLE 11

CORRELATIONS BETWEEN CROSSMODAL AND IPSIMODAL REACTIONS AS A
FUNCTION OF THE NUMBER OF PRECEDING STIMULI FOR PATIENTS AND
NORMALS SEPARATELY BY SEX (EXPERIMENT C)

| | *Males* | | *Females* | |
	Normals	*Patients*	*Normals*	*Patients*
ONE PRECEDING				
III - II	.82	.88	.85	.89
TWO PRECEDING				
III - II	.72	.65	.86	.86
THREE PRECEDING				
III - II	.63	.84	.98	.92
FOUR PRECEDING				
III - II	.64	.82	.98	.71

TABLE 12

COVARIANCE ANALYSES COMPARING PATIENTS AND NORMALS SEPARATELY BY SEX ON THE CROSSMODAL RETARDATIONS (III-II) AS A FUNCTION OF THE NUMBER OF PRECEDING STIMULI (EXPERIMENT C)

	df	One Preceding		Two Preceding		Three Preceding		Four Preceding	
		SSy'	MS	SSy'	MS	SSy'	MS	SSy'	MS
Males									
Patients vs. Normals	1	2,740	2,740	1,901	1,901	1,045	1,045	4,334	4,334
Within	45	19,878	442	25,850	574	41,276	917	29,884	664
Total	46	22,618		27,750		42,322		34,218	
		F = 6.2*		F = NS		F = NS		F = 6.5*	
Females									
Patients vs. Normals	1	2	2	61	61	159	159	3,576	3,576
Within	44	52,766	1,199	77,333	1,758	32,715	743	175,278	3,984
Total	45	52,768		77,394		32,874		178,854	
		F = NS		F = NS		F = NS		F = NS	

*Significant at .05 level of confidence.

subject has received four stimuli in sequence (red or high) it is absolutely certain that the next stimulus will be a low tone. In other words, as one moves along the abscissa the subject's uncertainty is decreasing and presumably his reaction time should decrease, yet in fact, if there can be said to be any trend, reaction time is increasing.

In Figures 7 and 8 are plotted the mean reaction time to red lights and high tones using only the data obtained from sequences

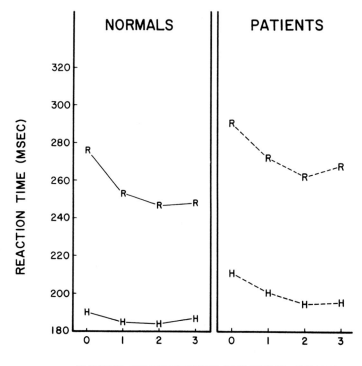

PROGRAM F - MEANS OF MEDIANS

MALES

NUMBER OF PRECEDING IDENTICAL STIMULI

Figure 7. Mean simple reaction time to sequential red light and high tone stimuli for male normals and male acute schizophrenic patients.

of four. For all groups, reaction time decreases as a function of the number of repetitions but this decrease appears to be greater for the patients. The patients starting out at a higher level of reaction time (poorer performance) seems to be benefiting more from repetition than are the normals. A test of the significance of the slope differences yields the finding that only the comparison of the curves for the male patients and the male normals for high

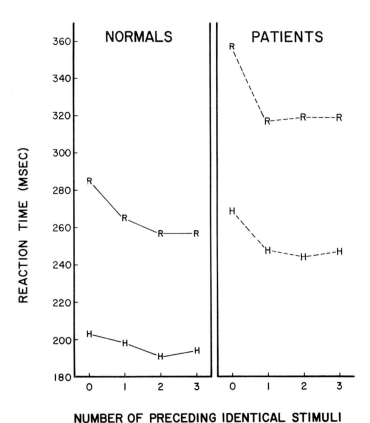

PROGRAM F – MEANS OF MEDIANS

FEMALES

Figure 8. Mean simple reaction time to sequential red light and high tone stimuli for female normals and female acute schizophrenic patients.

tone stimuli give a significant F ratio (first order interaction in the analysis of variance).

DISCUSSION

Summarizing the stimulus uncertainty work, it may be said that there is a consistent tendency across several studies for schizophrenic males to be disproportionately impaired on reactions to sound stimuli if the stimulus in the previous trial is a light. This impairment is over and above the differences in overall level of response between the two groups. Comparable analyses for reactions to light do not yield differences between patients and normals. None of the covariance analyses for the females yield significant differences between patients and normals. Neither of these negative findings can be explained on the basis of the present data.

For both patients and normals there is a general trend for reaction times to identical sequences to be shortest, for reaction times to non-identical sequences to be longer, and for reaction times to crossmodal sequences to be longest. The present data do not make clear whether this involves a primarily sensory or a primarily conceptual phenomenon, or that these hypotheses need to be in conflict. Nor is the source of the disproportionate crossmodal lengthening of reaction time to sound stimuli in the male patients apparent. There is some suggestion from Experiment C that it may be a primarily conceptual phenomenon.

The question of the source of these effects has been explored in some recent work by Mr. Martin Hannes of our laboratory. In the work presented thus far in this paper the sequential probabilities of stimuli are equated within any single run. In the "random" program every permutation of four stimuli taken two at a time occurs an equal number of times within a run. With this kind of program we have found that for normals the crossmodal retardation decreases and finally becomes zero over days of repeated testing with the same program. Similarly, in the "cumulative" program, all sequences used occurred an equal number of times within a run. It is possible, however, to manipulate the sequential probability of ipsimodal and crossmodal sequences so that these probabilities are not equal. This is done in the following way. Only two stimuli are used, one sound and one light. These are presented in pairs one second apart and with instructions to the subject to react to each. The pairs are separated from each other by intervals of fifteen seconds. In one program, three types of pairs are used: Sound-sound (SS), light-sound (LS), and light-light (LL). These pairs do not occur equally often in any

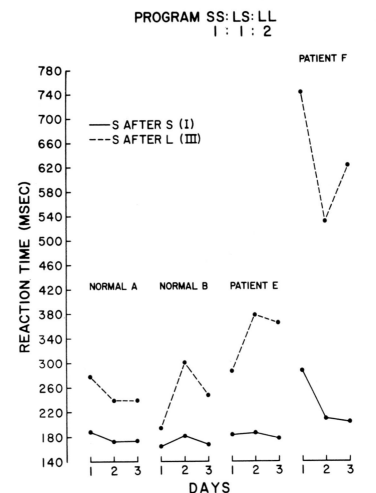

Figure 9. Median simple reaction time to sound stimuli for two normals and two schizophrenic patients as a function of successive days of testing on a program with low probability of crossmodal sequence.

given run but rather in the following ratios: SS = ¼, LS = ¼ and LL = 2/4. In such a program, once a subject has received a sound as the first member of the pair, there is complete certainty that the second member of the pair will be a sound, i.e., P(S/S) = 1. However, if the first member of the pair is a light, the second member of the pair will twice as often be a light as a sound P(L/S) = ⅓ and P(L/L) = ⅔. Therefore, this program decreases the probability of crossmodal sequence (LS) and increases the probability of ipsimodal sequence (LL). As in previous work, reaction to sound which was preceded by sound (sS, which is equivalent to category I above) is compared with reaction to sound which was preceded by light (lS, which is equivalent to Category III above).

In Figure 9 are plotted the results of pilot work with two normals and two patients on this kind of program. On the abscissa are successive days of testing and the crossmodal retardation is shown as the difference between the two curves. Note that the normals begin with a smaller crossmodal retardation than the patients and that for no individual is there a tendency for the crossmodal retardation to decrease continuously with successive days of testing. This is quite different from performance with the "random" program in which there is a decrease in retardation over successive days of testing which in normals finally reaches zero.

In Figure 10 we have a program in which the probability of ipsimodal sequence is decreased and the probability of crossmodal sequence is increased. After a light has occurred as the first member of a pair, there is complete certainty that the second member of the pair will be a sound. On the other hand, when a sound has occurred as the first member of a pair, the second member of the pair will twice as often be a light as it will be a sound. Again, the comparison is between reactions to sound preceded by sound (I) and sound preceded by light (III). With this program, as with the last, the patients begin with a larger crossmodal retardation than the normals, but the retardation decreases over successive days of testing—*more rapidly* for the patients than for the normals. This work indicates that the degree of crossmodal retardation can be readily manipulated by altering the probability of crossmodal and ipsimodal sequences and that both normals and patients are sensitive to the manipulation of conditional probabilities in the program.

In interpreting both the time uncertainty studies and the stimulus uncertainty studies, one must make some assumptions about the state of readiness of the subject. In the one, the subject is unaware of the exact moment in time when the stimulus to react is to occur. It is reasonable to assume that some aspect of readiness of the subject is fluctuating from moment to moment, either as measured by the levels of muscular tension or as measured by phase of the cortical alpha wave.[7] For the stimulus uncertainty experiments, there must be some comparable process,

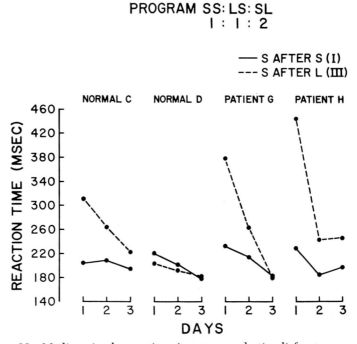

Figure 10. Median simple reaction time to sound stimuli for two normals and two schizophrenic patients as a function of successive days of testing on a program with low probability of ipsimodal sequence.

---

[7] For research in this area, see chapter by Dr. Callaway in this volume.

although how one prepares to observe with the eye rather than with the ear, or vice versa, is less apparent. In this connection, one might speculate on the possible role of descending inhibitory pathways which are present in most if not all sensory modalities.

Both groups of studies are consistent with the notion that the state of readiness fluctuates and that shorter reaction time may be taken as evidence that the stimulus occurred at a point in time corresponding to maximal readiness, or that the stimulus is one for which maximal readiness has been made. When the stimuli do not fall in with these "expectancies," there is retardation or lengthening of reaction time. Furthermore, in both groups of studies it has been shown that the state of readiness is influenced by the character of the preceding trial, viz., whether the fore-period is longer or shorter in the preceding trial and whether the stimuli are in the same or in a different sensory modality. Similarly in both groups of studies, reaction time is affected not only by the character of the immediately preceding trial, but by trends of the whole series of trials. In other words, the effects are both contiguous and remote in time.

With respect to the differences between schizophrenic patients and normals it may be suggested that both groups of studies strongly suggest that the state of readiness of the patient is disproportionately affected by events which are recent in time. In other words the patient is "over-prepared" by his last trial and reaction time is lengthened when this preparation is inaccurate. In the random program, since all sequences are equally probable best performance would occur if the subject assumed (correctly) that the next stimulus may be any of the four used. Therefore preparation for any one type of stimulus is maladaptive. It is also clear in the foreperiod experiments and suggested in the recent work on the modality experiments that long range influences operating over the whole series of trials act to "over-influence" and "over-prepare" the schizophrenic subject. These inferences are therefore in contrast to suggestions that have sometimes been made that the schizophrenic patient is more influenced by events which are contiguous in time than by events which are remote in time.

REFERENCES

Ach, N.: (1935): *Analyse des Willens.* Berlin, Urban und Schwarzenberg.

Botwinick, J., Brinley, J. F. and Birren, J. E.: (1957) Set in relation to age. *J. Geront., 12:*300-305.

Funke, A. S.: (1961) Patterns of reaction time and movement time among young and elderly normal subjects and young chronic schizophrenic patients. Unpublished doctoral dissertation, Pennsylvania State University.

Garner, W. R.: (1962) *Uncertainty and Structure as Psychological Concepts.* New York, John Wiley and Sons, Inc.

Huston, P. E. and Senf, Rita: (1952) Psychopathology of schizophrenia and depression. I. Effect of amytal and amphetamine sulphate on level and maintenance of attention. *Amer. J. Psychiat., 109:*131-138.

Huston, P. E., and Singer, M.: (1945) Effect of sodium amytal and amphetamine sulfate on mental set in schizophrenia. *Arch. Neurol. Psychiat., 53:*365-369.

Huston, P. E., Shakow, D. and Riggs, L. A.: (1937) Studies of motor function in schizophrenia: II. Reaction time. *J. Gen. Psychol., 16:*39-82.

Jentsch, R. C.: (1958) Reaction time in schizophrenia as a function of method of presentation and length of preparatory interval. *J. Personality, 26:*545-555.

Klemmer, E. T.: (1956) Time uncertainty in simple reaction time. *J. Exp. Psychol., 51:*179-184.

Klemmer, E. T.: (1957) Simple reaction time as a function of time uncertainty. *J. Exp. Psychol., 54:*195-200.

Knehr, C. A.: (1954) Schizophrenic reaction time responses to variable preparatory intervals. *Amer. J. Psychiat., 110:*585-588.

Mowrer, O. H.: (1941) Preparatory set (expectancy)—Further evidence of its 'central' locus. *J. Exp. Psychol., 28:*116-133.

Mowrer, O. H., Rayman, N. N. and Bliss, E. L.: (1940) Preparatory set (expectancy)—An experimental demonstration of its 'central' locus. *J. Exp. Psychol., 26:*357-372.

Rodnick, E. H. and Shakow, D.: (1940) Set in the schizophrenic as measured by composite reaction time index. *Amer. J. Psychiat., 97:*214-225.

Rosenbaum, G., MacKavey, W. R. and Grisell, J. L.: (1957) Effects of biological and social motivation on schizophrenic reaction time. *J. Abnorm. Soc. Psychol., 54:*364-368.

Rosenthal, D., Lawlor, W. G., Zahn, T. P. and Shakow, D.: (1960) The relationship of some aspects of mental set to degree of schizophrenic disorganization. *J. Personality, 28:*26-38.

Sutton, S., Hakerem, G., Zubin, J. and Portnoy, M.: (1961) The effect of shift of sensory modality on serial reaction time: a comparison of schizophrenics and normals. *Amer. J. Psychol., 74:*224-232.

Tizard, J. and Venables, P. H.: (1956) Reaction time responses by schizophrenics, mental defectives, and normal adults. *Amer. J. Psychiat., 112:* 803-807.

Welford, A. T.: (1960) The measurement of sensory-motor performance: survey and reappraisal of twelve years' progress. *Ergonomics,* 3:189-230.

Woodrow, H.: (1914) The measurement of attention. *Psychol. Monogr., 17:* 5: No. 76.

Woodworth, R. S. and Schlosberg, H.: (1954) *Experimental Psychology.* Rev. ed., New York, Holt.

Wundt, W.: (1893) *Grundzüge der physiologischen Psychologies.* 4th ed., Leipzig, Wilhelm Engelmann.

Zahn, T. P., Rosenthal, D. and Shakow, D.: (1961) Reaction time in schizophrenic and normal subjects in relation to the sequence of series of regular preparatory intervals. *J. Abnorm. Soc. Psychol.,* 63:161-168.

Zahn, T. P., Rosenthal, D. and Shakow, D.: (1963) Effects of irregular preparatory intervals on reaction time in schizophrenia. *J. Abnorm. Soc. Psychol.,* 67:44-52.

Zahn, T. P., Shakow, D. and Rosenthal, D.: (1961) Reaction time in schizophrenic and normal subjects as a function of preparatory and intertrial intervals. *J. Nerv. Ment. Dis.,* 133:283-287.

28

SLOWNESS IN SCHIZOPHRENIA*

P. H. VENABLES

THE SPEED of the behaviour of most although not all schizophrenics shows considerable retardation. Experimental studies give the impression that patients may exhibit gross degrees of slowness, upon which are superimposed other minor forms of speed loss which are often exaggerated reactions to the stimulus conditions prevailing. By changing, for instance, the intensity, modality or temporal uncertainty of the stimulus, the schizophrenics' response may be speeded up. However, even with optimal stimulus conditions there is often a residual gross slowness that does not seem to be amenable to modification.

The first part of this paper is concerned with a brief description of some experiments which have been carried out to assess the effects of variation in stimulus parameters in bringing about changes in response speed. Under this heading, we may divide stimuli into those to which response is made, these we may call "cue stimuli," and those which are additional to the cue stimuli. One class of the latter group we may conveniently call background stimuli as they provide the "ground" against which the cue stimuli are the "figure." They may be thought of as having effects by central mediation and provide results forming part of the general body of findings concerned with inter-sensory inter-

* This paper is a review of some of the work carried out in the Medical Research Council's Unit at the Institute of Psychiatry, London, and does not aim to be a general review of the problem of slowness in schizophrenia.

598

action. The second class of additional stimuli are warning stimuli which serve to modify the state of time uncertainty in which the cue stimulus is presented. This class will not be dealt with as it is covered by Dr. Sutton's contribution.

In a rather different category are those studies in which the immediately absent sub-set of a larger group of cue stimuli modify the response to the present cue stimulus. These are experiments concerned with expectancy and uncertainty in the information theory sense. Two experiments concerned with uncertainty arising from degrees of choice are described. Experiments dealing with uncertainty generated by changes in the sequence of stimuli are dealt with by Dr. Sutton.

In the final part of the paper experiments are described which tentatively present findings which suggest the existence of quantal degrees of gross slowness upon which the earlier described minor slowing is superimposed.

Experiments dealing with the effect of intensity, modality and complexity of cue stimuli will first be considered.

Pavlov claimed that dogs with "weak, inhibitory nervous systems" tend to respond to conditioned stimuli in a manner which is qualitatively different from that of healthy animals. Among the pathological phenomena which these dogs exhibit are "paradoxical" effects in which weak stimuli lead to larger conditioned responses than strong stimuli; and also "ultra paradoxical effects" in which excitatory stimuli are converted into inhibitory ones and inhibitory stimuli into excitatory ones. Pavlov claimed that schizophrenic withdrawal and negativism are examples of such phenomena. Such evidence as there is to support Pavlov's claims is either clinical or is based on analogy with studies on animals. No experimental studies with human subjects appear to have been carried out. If paradoxical phenomena do occur in schizophrenics it would seem that they should be demonstrable in a reaction time study using different intensities of stimulation where increase in stimulus intensity should result in an increase in RT. In normal subjects increase in stimulus intensity should result in a decrease in RT to an asymptotic value. In a pilot study (Venables and Tizard, 1956a) using four lights of different intensities twenty-one out of twenty-four schizophrenics showed paradoxically slower RTs to the brighter lights than to lights of moderate intensity in contrast to normals, who showed no increase in RT with increase in light intensity. A second, better controlled, study (Venables and Tizard, 1956b) was carried out, where alteration of light intensity was made by the use of neutral density filters placed in front of the light source. Thus differences in colour or in speed of illumination at different intensities were avoided. Eight intensities were used covering a 2 log unit range from 16 to 1500ft candles. Twenty responses were made by each subject to each of the eight intensities presented in balanced order. Twenty-four chronic schizophrenics were tested. It was found that, on the first occasion of testing, twenty-two out of the twenty-four showed an increase in RT from the moderate intensities of 135 and 275 foot candles to the high intensities of 800 and 1500ft candles. This paradoxical effect was however only shown on the first occasion of testing and did not appear on a second occasion twenty-four hours later when a uniformly slow RT, (slower than that to the medium intensities on the first occasion) was given to all intensities. A further group of less severely ill short stay schizophrenics showed no paradoxical effect on either occasion, as was the case with a normal group of subjects.

The regression slope of increase in RT from the moderate to the high intensities was calculated for each subject and related to his general speed of reaction for which the RT to the lowest stimulus intensity was used as an index. It was found that there was on this basis a correlation of 0.74 ($p < .001$) between the extent of the paradoxical effect and the general speed of the subject. Thus the slower, and therefore probably the more disturbed the patient, the greater the extent of the decrease in speed with increase in intensity. This type of phenomenon is shown in an extreme form by those patients who were too ill to co-operate. These patients appeared to be unable to release the response key while an intense stimulus was present and were only able to make a response when the stimulus was switched off. This apparently could be considered an example of the ultraparadoxical effect.

So far we have been dealing only with stimuli in the visual modality. Further experiments were carried out to see whether paradoxical phenomena were present with auditory stimuli (Venables and Tizard, 1958). Preliminary experimentation seemed to show that no paradoxically long RTs were made to stimuli in this modality. In order to make sure that patients who were being tested were those in which these phenomena were present in the visual modality, stimuli were presented in both modalities. One group was tested first on four visual and then on four auditory intensities, a second group was tested first on auditory and then on visual stimuli. The results are shown in Table 1.

Here it will be seen that the group tested first with the visual stimuli showed paradoxical effects in that modality. Thirteen out of the sixteen patients gave this pattern of response times. No paradoxical increase in RT was shown in the auditory modality or in the visual modality on the second occasion.

It might be argued that the patients who showed no paradoxical effects when tested first in the auditory modality could not be checked by the nature of their responses to the visual modality. However, as their mean RTs are slower than those of the other group the likelihood of them showing the effect is high.

Two further attempts to achieve paradoxical effects in the auditory modality were made using white noise and a pure tone of 200cps at intensities up to a maximum of 115db. No evidence for this phenomenon was given.

These experiments show that there is a pathological effect due to intensity of stimuli in the visual modality but this only occurs on the first occasion of testing, that is when the stimuli are

TABLE 1

REACTION TIMES (SECS.) TO AUDITORY AND VISUAL STIMULI OF FOUR INTENSITIES

| | Visual Stimuli | | | | |
	16ft C	135ft C	600ft C	1500ft C	N
Group 1 (visual-auditory)	.74	.67	.69	.74	16
Group 2 (auditory-visual)	.77	.71	.69	.68	16
	Auditory Stimuli (1000cps)				
	30db	50db	70db	90db	N
Group 1 (visual-auditory)	.97	.90	.78	.71	16
Group 2 (auditory-visual)	1.17	1.05	.97	.75	16

novel. Further experimentation is obviously required here to assess what factors would be required to maintain the novelty of the situation, and in addition what length of time between presentations of the stimuli would have to elapse before intense visual stimulation would again provoke paradoxically lengthened reaction times.

In addition to the differences between modalities which have arisen in their differential ability to produce the pathological phenomena described, examination of Table 1 reveals a further peculiarity. Here it will be seen that practically without exception responses to visual stimuli are shorter than those to auditory stimuli. This is a reversal of the findings of fourteen studies of normal subjects reported by Teichner (1954), which show auditory RTs to be shorter than visual. A further experiment was therefore carried out to examine this finding (Venables and O'Connor, 1959). RTs to a visual stimulus with an intensity of 320 ft L and an auditory stimulus of 500cps with an intensity of 60db were compared. The intensity of the visual stimulus was chosen to be the highest which would not produce paradoxically lengthened RTs in schizophrenics. Two forms of response were used, the normal manual one and the verbal one of saying the nonsense syllable BIP which operated a voice key.

It was found that in normal subjects auditory RTs were faster than those to the visual stimulus. In all schizophrenics except those classified as intact coherent paranoids the RT to the auditory stimulus was longer than that to the visual stimulus. The results which were shown to be significant by analysis of variance are given in Table 2.

TABLE 2

REACTION TIMES (SECS.) IN FOUR EXPERIMENTAL CONDITIONS.

	Stimulus Responses	Auditory		Visual		N
		Manual	Verbal	Manual	Verbal	
	Normal	.27	.37	.32	.41	20
Subjects	Paranoid schizophrenic	.41	.50	.41	.53	12
	Non-paranoid schizophrenic	.64	.76	.62	.69	36

Closer examination of the data showed that the differences in RT in the two modalities between normals and schizophrenics were more reasonably attributed to the level of general speed of response. For instance in the case of three normal subjcts with auditory manual RTs greater than .40sec the visual RT was shorter than the auditory, conversely of the sixteen schizophrenics who had auditory manual RTs shorter than 0.39sec, 12 had larger visual RTs than auditory. There is thus suggestive evidence that the pattern of relationship between auditory and visual responses is not confined to subjects diagnosed as schizophrenic but may be a function of general level of response speed. This suggestion is supported by data on older subjects presented by Dr Talland in his paper. It should be noted that in the present experiment speed of response was correlated with age only to the extent of $+.001$ in the schizophrenic group, this is not surprising in view of the greater influence on response speed of the mental condition of the patients. In the normal group the correlation of RT with age was $+.22$(NS). However, as the maximum age of subjects in both groups was fifty-six years no marked slowing with age would be expected. In neither the schizophrenic nor the normal data was there any evidence which suggested that the size of difference between manual and verbal response could be related to any category of subject. A mean value for the difference between these two modes of response was 0.1sec on the total of sixty-eight subjects.

As an extension of this experiment (O'Connor and Venables, 1960), speed of verbal response was examined when the stimulus was a 500cps tone or was a word of approximately the same duration, 200msec, and of the same intensity, namely 60db. It was found that if the patients were divided on the basis of a rating scale score into those who exhibited marked withdrawal and those who did not, there was no difference in RT to the two forms of stimulus in the non-withdrawn subjects. RT = 0.64sec in each case. However, in the withdrawn patients the RT to the tonal signal was 0.78sec and that to the verbal signal 0.93sec, a difference significant at the $p<.01$ level. The withdrawal scale used with the patients was strictly inappropriate as a means of classifying normal subjects insofar as it is based on rating of ward behaviour. However, the attempt to measure withdrawal in normal subjects who in this instance were hospital artisan staff was nevertheless made on the basis of ratings by their supervisor on a modified version of the scale. The twenty normal subjects tested were divided on the basis of this scale into non-withdrawn and withdrawn groups. In the non-withdrawn group the verbal signal gave a faster response (.25sec) than the tonal signal (.33 sec), and in the withdrawn group the reverse was the case, tonal .40sec, verbal .43sec. An interaction term in an analysis of variance showed these results were significant ($p < .05$). It thus appears again that the differences due to type of stimulus may not be confined to schizophrenics but may rather be due to the general level of response speed on which these effects are superimposed.

A further parameter of the stimulus situation which might be thought to be conducive to excessive slowness in schizophrenics is that of complexity. Hunt and Cofer (1944) summarize work on this subject and say that "as the complexity of performance increases so the slowness of schizophrenics becomes progressively more marked." None of the studies which these authors review cover a large range of task complexity and no distinction is drawn between task complexity due for instance to number of available stimuli or to difficulty of discrimination between stimuli. A study (Venables, 1958) was carried out to test the effect of complexity of the former kind in which responses could be made to sets of from one to eight equiprobable alternative stimuli. The study followed the experiment of Hyman (1953) who confirmed the earlier findings of Hick (1952) the reaction time is a linear function of the log of the number of equiprobable alternatives (log n). A paraphrase of Hunt and Cofer's summary might be taken to imply (a) that the slope of the linear function relating RT to log n would be steeper in schizophrenics, or (b) that RT might be related to a positively accelerated function of log n. Two schizophrenic groups having different degrees of severity of illness and a normal group were tested. The display used eight stimulus lights which in contrast to Hyman's experiment had the numbers 1 to 8 painted on them; the subjects had to respond by saying the number on the light which was lit. Response speed was measured using a voice key. Eight conditions, each using a different number of equiprobable alternative light stimuli were presented according to the rows of Latin Squares to each subject. Plotting the data showed a linear relation of RT with log n for all groups. None of the data from any schizophrenic or normal subject gave evidence for a curvilinear relation between RT and log n, furthermore an analysis of variance which showed highly significant differences between groups and between degrees of choice did not show a significant interaction between these two main factors. The data are perhaps best summarized by presenting the values of *a* and *b* in the linear regression line RT = a + b log n for each group.

It is seen from Table 3 that the suggestion of a difference between schizophrenics and normals in the slope of the regression line relating RT and stimulus complexity is not upheld. The difference between the groups is shown only in their overall response speed.

In a review by Welford (1961) the suggestion was made that in tasks where the exposure of the signal for a choice or a discriminatory response is short, the difference in performance due to age is seen in the value *a* in the formula above. On the other hand when the exposure time is relatively long there is a change with age in the constant *b* reflecting the slope of the regression line. It is suggested that with long exposures the opportunity is given for the subject to continue inspecting the stimulus material until he has gathered sufficient information to be confident in the performance of his response. The difference in slope with age is thought to arise because the older subject needs more time to be confident about the more complex stimuli. The parallel suggestion that the more severely ill schizophrenic needs relatively more

TABLE 3

VALUES OF MEAN LINEAR REGRESSION CONSTANTS FOR TWO SCHIZOPHRENIC AND ONE NORMAL GROUP FOR ONE TO EIGHT CHOICE RT TASKS

	a	*b*
Normals	0.41	0.094
Moderately ill schizophrenics	0.62	0.094
Severely ill schizophrenics	0.74	0.109

time to be certain about an eight choice than a single choice reaction does not seem to be applicable. In the experiment described the stimulus remained "on" until the subject responded and thus was similar to the long exposure situation described above, but as already shown the difference between the groups was not shown in the value of slope b but rather in the intercept value a. It thus seems unlikely that an explanation in terms of a need for greater certainty before responding is true of the schizophrenic. The overall difference is response speed shown by the schizophrenic as compared with the normal groups may be more efficiently explained in terms of motor slowness. In this experiment where there was a relatively similar response to any stimulus, response complexity was minimized; however, data are available from an unpublished card sorting study which show the effect of an increase in response complexity. The experiment was essentially a repetition of that of Crossman (1953) involving the sorting of ordinary playing cards. Complexities of sorting ranged from a simple Red/Black two choice division to a twenty-six choice sort. Seven degrees of sorting complexity were involved and were presented in the order of rows of Latin squares to seven normal subjects and seven withdrawn and seven non-withdrawn chronic schizophrenics. The two patient groups did not differ significantly in either the slope or intercept of the regression line relating complexity and sorting time. The slope for the two patient groups combined (0.59secs/bit) did however differ significantly from that of the normals (0.25secs/bit), while the intercept values did not differ significantly. It would thus appear that in this type of experiment where complexity of response is introducted there is a tendency for the schizophrenic to be relatively impaired in more complex performances.

The point at which stimulus conditions must obviously be considered as having effect upon central state is where the important experimental variable is not the cue stimulus but the amount and type of background stimulation present in the context of which cue stimuli are presented.

Two studies were carried out (Tizard and Venables, 1957) which examined the effect of background stimulation on RT. In the first the effect of noise on visual RT was studied. Fifty RTs were made to a visual stimulus, 70db white noise was sounded in an experimental session during the presentation of stimuli 21 to 30. In a control session fifty visual RTs were made in quiet conditions throughout. The overall effect of the noise upon the total group of schizophrenics tested was nil. However, when the patients were divided into those who were withdrawn and those who were not it was found that the withdrawn patients tended to be faster when the noise was present. There was no evidence of any effect of noise on the RT of normal subjects.

A similar experiment was carried out in which auditory RTs were measured in two levels of background illumination. It was found that withdrawn patients tended to be faster in the condition of bright than in dim background illumination, while there was a tendency for non-withdrawn subjects to be faster under the dim conditions. That differential effect of background stimulation upon two subgroups of schizophrenics was not confined to speed of voluntary response was shown when a similar pattern of results was obtained with latency of skin potential response as the dependent variable (Venables, 1960a). In this experiment the effect of modality of stimulus was again evident; it was found that visual background stimuli had most effect upon the response speed of all schizophrenics except that of the non-withdrawn, coherent paranoids, in whom the auditory modality had the greatest effectiveness.

An attempt was made to provide an explanation for these results by the use of the inverted U shaped relationship between performance and level of activation or arousal (e.g., Hebb, 1955; Malmo, 1959). This model states, in effect, that performance is best at moderate states of arousal, and either too much or too little arousal leads to deterioration in efficiency. The hypothesis suggested to account for the results with schizophrenics was that withdrawn subjects were under-aroused and additional stimulation by increasing arousal would raise performance to a more nearly optimal level. On the other hand if non-withdrawn subjects were already in a hyperoptimal arousal state increased arousal would only worsen performance. To describe in detail at this juncture the experiments attempting to measure arousal or activation would make too great a diversion from the subject at hand. It is sufficient to say therefore that a measure of temporal resolution, the threshold of fusion of paired light flashes, was considered to be a suitable index of cortical excitability. Level of skin potential was used as a measure of autonomic or possibly sub-cortical activity. It was found that in schizophrenics these two measures of activity were related such that high autonomic activity shown by high skin potential was related to high cortical activity shown by a low two flash fusion threshold. On the other hand, this relationship was reversed in normal subjects, leading to the conclusion that earlier suggestions of interpretation in terms of a single factor of arousal were ruled out of court (Venables, 1963).

Although an inverted U shaped relationship between arousal or activation level and performance has tended to become generally accepted, not many attempts have been made to confirm it. Perhaps the most direct experiment was that of Freeman (1940) who reported an inverted U shaped relationship between skin conductance and simple RT. Attempts, however, to repeat Freeman's experiments have not met with success (e.g., Schlosberg and Kling, 1959).

One possible explanation for this difficulty is found in a set of recent experiments (Venables, 1964) in which an attempt was made to relate simple visual reaction time to the subject's threshold of fusion of paired flashes as a measure of his cortical arousal level. In an initial study a group of fifty-six chronic schizophrenics were tested and it was found on first inspection that no readily apparent relationship existed between the two variables. However, on the basis of some suggestions that had arisen in the consideration of earlier data an attempt was made to arbitrarily fit to the data a series of equally spaced Us rather than a single U as had been expected. Using Vs rather than Us in order to avoid the complication of curve fitting a significant fit to the data was achieved 86 per cent of the data being encompassed by the pattern. As this was very much of a "Procrustean bed" technique the experiment was repeated with fresh schizophrenic subjects. With this new data a significantly good fit was obtained to exactly the same pattern of relationships between two flash threshold and reaction time as had been arbitrarily fitted in the first experiment. Data from a group of normals did not significantly fit the pattern although those with the highest RTs did show a tendency to fall into line. As an additional check a transformation of the pattern was calculated by the use of an earlier derived regression line relating two flash threshold and skin potential (Venables, 1963). The data from the second experiment in which skin potential had been taken as an additional arousal measure to two flash threshold was used to examine whether an adequate fit to the transformed pattern could be achieved. Again a significant fit was achieved for the schizophrenic but not for the normal data. These results which appear at first glance to be rather surprising, have at least the merit of suggesting why it has been found difficult to repeat the original Freeman (1940) results.

The simulation of these results by means of an *ad hoc* pseudo-physiological model could be attempted. However, the likelihood that a model artificially constructed to encompass the results would have any physiological relevance seems doubtful.

Explanations of the single inverted U shaped function relating performance and activation level have been attempted by various writers, for example Hebb (1955), Malmo (1959), Welford (1962). The improvement in performance with increasing activation level up to an optimum point is explained in various related ways. Hebb talks of enhanced synaptic transmission; Welford, an increase in system sensitivity and responsiveness and Malmo, the facilitation of the circulation of neural impulses in closed chains. To achieve the magnitude of changes in RT found in the present experiments it seems unlikely that changes in synaptic delay or even in the number of parallel neurones firing can be responsible. Rather it is necessary to invoke varying numbers of successive delays caused by the series accumulation of circulation times of reverberatory circuits. Improved performance due to facilitation from the activation system could thus be expected to result from the elimination of delays formerly resulting from successive reverberations required to temporally summate impulses in order to overcome high synaptic thresholds.

The worsening of performance due to supra-optimal arousal levels has also various explanations. Hebb has suggested, the facilitation of irrelevant responses; Malmo, the growth of high synaptic thresholds in circulatory chains due to excessive bombardment and Welford, the random firing of neurones leading to noise in the system and a decrease in channel capacity.

Although differently expressed it is possible that the apparent contrast between these suggestions arises because they are on different levels of explanation.

Behavioural evidence of temporal periodicity in performance is consonant with the idea of quantal delays caused by the time of reverberation of cortico-thalamic circuits cf. Chang (1950), see also the chapter by Obrist in this Volume. Augenstine (1958) states "analysis of response times indicated that the performance of (these) simple tasks is undoubtedly quantized in units of 100msecs." Venables (1960b) provided evidence of a multimodal distribution of simple RTs given by schizophrenic subjects. Variogram analysis (Jowett, 1955) showed that the modal peaks tended to be spaced 100msec apart. Reaction times up to about 0.8sec tended to fall in the quantized pattern. In normal subjects the evidence was not so clear as speed of response was faster than that of schizophrenics; however, if early unpractised RTs are included in the analysed data some evidence of multimodality is apparent. Further evidence of periodicity in motor performance is given by the work of Crossman and Goodeve (1963), who suggest a sampling proportional feedback model for the control of hand movement in which the period of the sample over which integration takes place is 1/10th sec.

From these experiments it is not a very remote step to suggest how multiple U or V shaped patterns could be produced. The momentary sensitivity of motor neurones may demand for firing at any one time the summation of one more or one less impulse than previously. The reaction time at any one activation level may therefore rise or fall by the reverberation time of neuronal chain. Changes in RT on the same V could be brought about by changes in the numbers of reverberations in a single chain, while changes in RT from V to V could involve different numbers of reverberatory elements.

It is suggested that the relative independence of activation level of normal RTs is evidence of the optimal operation of the system without circulatory delays. It is only when the system is other than optimally sensitive that the relevance of the arousal system in the determination of the operation of delay circuits becomes manifest.

The extent to which gross slowness is determined is surprising. It must be borne in mind however that the present evidence is only directly applicable to manual performance. There are suggestions that for other motor performances such as movement of the eyes, periodicities of the order 20-40msec may be found (Latour and Bouman, 1961).

Clearly a considerable quantity of work must be completed before the suggestions put forward here may be considered to be confirmed. However, it is hoped that the proposal of two types of slowness; gross, due possibly to the state of the effector system and minor, due possibly to the conditions of transmission at the input or to the extent of central analysis required, may provide a stimulus to look at data from these points of view.

REFERENCES

Augenstine, L. G.: (1958) Human performance in information transmission. Report R75, Part 4, Control Systems Laboratory, Univ. Illinois.

Chang, H. T.: (1950) The repetitive discharges of cortico-thalamic reverberating circuit. *J. Neurophysiol.*, 13:235-57.

Crossman, E. R. F. W.: (1958) Entropy and choice time, the effect of frequency in balance on choice responses. *Quart. J. Exp. Psychol.*, 5:41-51.

Crossman, E. R. F. W. & Goodeve, P. J.: (1963) Feedback control of hand movement and Fitt's Law. Paper presented to meeting of the Experimental Psychology Society, Oxford.

Freeman, G. L.: (1940) The relationship between performance level and bodily activity level. *J. Exp. Psychol.*, 26:602-608.

Hebb, D. O.: (1955) Drives and the C.N.S. (conceptual nervous system). *Psychol. Rev.*, 62:243-254.

Hick, W. E.: (1952) On the rate of gain of information. *Quart. J. Exp. Psychol.*, 4:11-26.

Hunt, J. McV. & Cofer, C. N.: (1944) Psychological defect in J. McV. Hunt, ed.: *Personality and the Behaviour Disorders*, N.Y., Ronald Press.

Hyman, R.: (1953) Stimulus information as a determinant of reaction time. *J. Exp. Psychol.*, 45:188-196.

Latour, P. L. & Bouman, M. A.: (1961) A non-analog time component in visual pursuit movements. In Rosenblith, W. A., ed.:*Sensory Communication*, N.Y. M.I.T. Press & John Wiley.

Malmo, R. B.: (1959) Activation: a neuropsychological dimension. *Psychol. Rev.*, 66:367-386.

O'Connor, N. & Venables, P. H.: (1960) The response of chronic schizophrenics to verbal signals. *Acta Psychol.*, 17:3, 218-225.

Schlosberg, H. & Kling, J. W.: (1959) The relationship between "tension" and efficiency. *Percept. Mot. Skills*, 9:395-397.

Teichner, W. H.: (1954) Recent studies of simple reaction time. *Psychol. Bull.*, 51:128-148.

Tizard, J. & Venables, P. H.: (1957) The influence of extraneous stimulation on the reaction time of schizophrenics. *Brit. J. Psychol.*, 48:4:299-305.

Venables, P. H.: (1958) Stimulus complexity as a determinant of the reaction time of schizophrenics. *Canad. J. Psychol.*, 12:3:187-190.

Venables, P. H.: (1960a) The effect of auditory and visual stimulation on the skin potential response of schizophrenics. *Brain*, 83:1:77-92.

Venables, P. H.: (1960b) Periodicity in reaction time. *Brit. J. Psychol.*, 51:1:37-43.

Venables, P. H.: (1963) The relationship between level of skin potential and fusion of paired light flashes in schizophrenic and normal subjects. *J. Psychiat. Rec.* 1:279-287.

Venables, P. H.: (1964) Performance and level of activation in schizophrenics and normals. *Brit. J. Psychol.* 55:207-218.

Venables, P. H. & O'Connor, N.: (1959) Reaction times to auditory and visual stimulation in schizophrenic and normal subjects. *Quart. J. Psychol.*, XI:3:175-179.

Venables, P. H. & Tizard, J.: (1956a) The effect of stimulus light intensity on reaction time of schizophrenics. *Brit. J. Psychol.*, 47:144-145.

Venables, P. H. & Tizard, J.: (1956b) Paradoxical effects in the reaction time of schizophrenics. *J. abnorm. soc. Psychol.*, 53:2:220-224.

Venables, P. H. & Tizard, J.: (1958) The effect of auditory stimulus intensity on the reaction time of schizophrenics. *J. Ment. Sci.*, 104:437:1160-1164.

Welford, A. T.: (1961) Age changes in the time taken by choice discrimination and the control of movements. *Gerontologia*, 5:129-145.

Welford, A. T.: (1962) Arousal, channel capacity and decision. *Nature*, 194:365-366.

APPENDIX

THE STANFORD UNIVERSITY STUDIES
OF LATER MATURITY

Walter R. Miles

IT IS an honor to be asked to discuss this assigned topic before such a distinguished group of Gerontologists. My own interest in planning such studies as were undertaken at Stanford University was stimulated by labor troubles in San Francisco in the early stages of an economic depression in 1927. The newspapers of that city reported that workers of forty years age and over were having great difficulty in finding employement especially when they were dropped from one job and tried to find another. At this time I had been a member of the Psychology Faculty of Stanford University for five years. Dr. Lewis M. Terman's well integrated and famous program for studying the development of gifted children had been in progress for some time. He had been quite successful in securing financial support which helped make it an attractive field for graduate students. In the Psychology Laboratory, where I was in charge, most of our studies had been in visual perception and I was looking for an alternate program that could interest other graduate students and might afford them some fellowship support.

Professor Terman had become interested in the public discussion about the older worker and we were in agreement that Stanford University might be able to make a contribution through a suitably designed research program, providing we could secure the wherewithal. Two others of our colleagues in the department were interested, Professors E. K. Strong who was teaching in

613

the Business School and had developed a widely used vocational aptitude test, and Calvin P. Stone whose field was comparative psychology and was interested in the aging of lower animals. A departmental committee was appointed: Strong, Stone and Miles, the latter was chairman. We called it: Committee on Later Maturity Studies. We worked at this assignment endeavoring to develop interest and suggestions. The existence of our committee became known and there was some notice in the newspapers of our proposed intentions at Stanford. This rather put us "on the spot."

With considerable assistance from Professor Terman, who was more experienced in these matters than the rest of us, we formulated a rather extensive proposal which was submitted in March of 1927 to Mr. Frederick P. Keppel, President of the Carnegie Corporation of New York. Mr. Keppel replied courteously and promptly on March 28, 1927 stating that the Board would meet on April 20 and that he could see me at his office in New York on the 21st. With high expectations I met that appointment, and learned that no grant was forthcoming. However, Mr. Keppel said that the Board and he might have some continued interest in our proposal. I returned to the Pacific Coast by train, as I had come, and had several days to meditate the situation. A research program on Later Maturity continued to seem desirable. Our committee remained in full agreement that we should keep trying. At this time our thinking was that a measurement program for older people could be carried on at the Stanford Laboratory, and I continued to work on some simplified apparatus that might be useful in this connection.

In the summer of 1928, we had opportunity for conference with Professor Robert S. Woodworth of Columbia University who was at that time visiting in California. He had been Chairman of the Division of Psychology and Anthropology in the National Research Council, 1924-25, and now in 1928 was on the Social Science Research Council. He was later that summer to be chairman of an SSRC Conference at Hanover, New Hampshire, and he suggested we send a request to be considered by that conference. In this request we again outlined the project and this time respectfully asked for the modest sum of $2,500 to be matched with $2,500 from our own Thomas Welton Stanford

Funds. We felt that a beginning could be made with this amount of support for one year and we hoped to start testing operations about October 3, 1928. Our program and request were considered at some length by the Hanover Conference. A special SSRC committee was appointed to take it under advisement. After some months the chairman of that committee wrote us a lengthy report that the total project was premature and ill advised, as the science of psychology was not far enough advanced to make it a profitable undertaking. There were not enough standardized techniques and comparative data available.

The personnel of our Stanford Later Maturity Committee was undergoing the process of aging, and moreover we seemed to be in a rut. However, we revised and considerably amplified our prospectus, and communicated again with President Keppel of the Carnegie Corporation, informing him that an SSRC special committee had turned us down very flatly. We asked him if he would be willing to look again at our proposition. He signified his willingness and it was sent to him. Perhaps he was somewhat stimulated by the negative reaction of the Social Science Research Council, and the Division of Anthropology and Psychology of the National Research Council, anyway on October 15, 1928 he wrote asking "Would a grant of $10,000 to Stanford at this time and for a more narrow purpose be a help or hindrance?" To this we replied in some detail assuring him the $10,000 would be a great help. Under date of November 24, 1928, Mr. Keppel's letter to President Wilbur of Stanford University stated "Resolved that from the balance available for appropriation, the sum of $10,000 ($10,000) be and hereby is appropriated to Stanford University in support of a study of psychology of later maturity." The first two thousand dollars of this grant became available to us the middle of January 1929.

If I have presumed on your patience by reciting these details my motive has been to fortify your courage to fight with persistence for the needed financing of research in Gerontology.

RECRUITMENT OF PEOPLE AS EXPERIMENTAL SUBJECTS

It took us some months of vigorous skirmishing to discover a method suitable and comfortable for employing older people in psychological measurements. A number of unemployed individuals in San Francisco volunteered by mail to be subjects but it was impractical to arrange for their transportation and working hours with us. We tried employing a well-trained and highly qualified woman to solicit subjects from house-to-house explaining our community interest and objectives, but this proved ineffective. The people approached could not be readily convinced and motivated for a cooperative study, and begged to be excused. We tried enlisting the interest of local high school students to themselves serve as subjects and also to persuade their parents and grandparents to come at appointed times. It was to be a paying proposition for the students but this did not prove at all popular. Finally "we struck oil" to use a success phrase. We found that by enlisting the cooperation of existing clubs, societies and other social clusters, we could secure an effective approach that would result in supplying us with numerous subjects. We rewarded the organization not the individual. The loyalty the individual felt for the group to which he belonged directly or indirectly supplied the interest and motivation that was necessary for his cooperation. One appointment for a two hour period became, in the mind of the subject, a part of his club activity and was something to be enjoyed. This natural psychological set-up offered a far reaching possibility. By watching the subject input in terms of educational level and general economic status we could intensify our stimulation of some groups and hold back others. In this way we had some control of our sampling.

THE TESTING LOCALE

We had found very early in our Stanford effort that we could not do this work of testing inexperienced subjects, profitably and conveniently for all, in the psychological laboratory in the presence of our busy university students. Especially the older individuals were made somewhat self-conscious by the presence of these young people. Consequently we rented a cottage in a quiet residential section of Palo Alto and fitted it up for our special purposes. We aimed at achieving a home-like atmosphere and employed a capable receptionist to greet the subjects as they came. We treated them as guests, they signed our Guest Book. A good bit of attention first and last was given to introductions.

On arrival the receptionist greeted the "visitor" as a "representative" of such and such club or group. The word "representative" was usually taken in a personally favorable and complimentary sense. The receptionist looked over the information form which the visitor had been requested to fill out at home and to bring to the Annex. Any ommissions were now completed before introducing the visitor to the first examiner. The two-hour period of service at the Annex was divided into four half-hour sections each in a different room and with a different examiner. After completing the work in one room that examiner introduced the subject to the next one. When this circuit was finished the receptionist congratulated the visitor on his or her work. Each person on leaving was told that his club would receive a report of his service and the appropriate monetary contribution would be made to that club in his name. Offers to serve again were frequent.

Serious testing began in our Annex at 603 Middlefield Road, Palo Alto on March 21, 1930 and continued until August 28, 1930 by which time we had examined 728 people. Usually we took three people successively in the morning and three in the afternoon six days a week. Our testing in a similar Annex in Redwood City, California began on July 7, 1930 and here we tested 143 individuals. Maintaining rather tight schedules in adjoining communities helped to keep the recruiters active with public interest and esteem at a favorable level.

THE PROBLEM OF A SUITABLE TEST BATTERY

There were some psychological traditions of value for guidance. Francis Galton in 1882 envisaged possibilities from measuring humans and his plan took form as a laboratory in the South Kensington Museum, London which continued until about 1895. Here by paying a small fee, visitors could have certain tests made on them. In addition to some physical measurements, they were tested for keenness of eyesight and hearing, for color sense, highest audible tone, for reaction time and errors in dividing lines and angles. Professor Joseph Jastrow at the World Columbian Exposition, Chicago 1893 operated a psychological laboratory in which several tests of strictly psychological character were administered to visitors who would volunteer to take them. These examples had stimulated thoughtful planning by Professor J. McKeen Cattell. At the Philadelphia meeting of the American Psychological Association, December 1895, a committee consisting of Professors Cattell, Baldwin, Jastrow, Sanford and Witmer was appointed to consider the feasibility of cooperation among the various psychological laboratories in the collection of mental and physical statistics. Cattell had in fact at an earlier date collected physical and mental measurement results on students at Cambridge University and later at the University of Pennsylvania and at Bryn Mawr College. He had published some of his results in 1890 and had continued this type of program on the students at Columbia University in 1894-5 and in 1895-6. Cattell requested the freshmen of the School of Art and of the School of Mines to come by appointment. About one half of them came. These took the tests and agreed to be tested at the end of the Sophomore and Senior years. His object was to have a series of tests that could be completed in forty minutes to one hour, as he says "varying within these limits according to the skill of the recorder, the intelligence of the student and the degree to which the apparatus is in order." Catell's inventory of tests aside from some anthropometric measurements included strength of hand, keenness of sight, reaction time, perception of weight, sensitiveness to pain, perception of time, accuracy of movement, memory and visual images. A considerably crop of studies concerning ability and aging began to appear in the mid 1920s. Examples are Hollingworth's, Mental Growth and Decline; Thorndike's, Adult Learning; Jones, Conrad and Horn, Observation and recall as a function of age; Ruger and Stoeasiger, on the growth curves of certain characters in man (males); to mention a few. From this hasty review it is evident that at Stanford we had some earlier psychological traditions to consider in our efforts to construct a trellis of likelihood for evidences of ability in later maturity.

THE STANFORD LATER MATURITY PROGRAM OF 1930

At the time of recruitment our subjects were given an information blank to be filled out at home and taken with them when they came to their appointment at the annex. This form entitled "Stanford Maturity Study" was well-itemized. It requested information about the subject, who had volunteered to take the test, his siblings, parents and his children and grandchildren, if any. The individual was asked to rate himself in this family constellation. He rated himself on his various capacities, physical and psychological, as of now in comparison with his memory of how he was five years earlier. He was encouraged to do this in a conscientious manner. There were general fields and sub-items, The final sub-item was, "compared with myself five years ago my general happiness is: much more, more, same, about the same, a little less, less, much less."

The first half hour with each visitor was devoted to introducing him or her to the process of being tested, following directions and performing simple acts, some of them to be repeated several times. The first item was visual acuity tested at sixteen feet, eight feet and at near. If the visitor wore spectables he used them in these tests. He was briefly examined for eye dominance, color blindness and handedness. His manual quickness was demonstrated in a ten-second test repeated a few times. This was followed by an exhibition of dexterity in opening a sealed envelope with a letter opener. Seated comfortably in front of a simplified reaction apparatus he demonstrated how promptly he could execute reactions with his forefinger, either by lifting the finger at a signal or by pressing at a signal and also how quickly he could lift his foot to release pressure on a key following a buzz auditory signal. He exhibited his dexterity in hand and arm coordination. Starting on a buzz signal he reached a few inches, grasped an object, put it in a new position and returning his hand shut off the buzz signal. This series of reaction and coordination tests was accomplished from the same seated position and with one rugged and simplified piece of equipment. From these simple tests, which of themselves were of measurement value, the examiner gained a direct impression of the subject's ability to perform and his cooperativeness. On this basis the subject could be passed on to one or another of our subsequent testing programs.

We administered an intelligence test which had been developed by Dr. Otis, who gave us permission to reprint it in large type without his name. The caption read "Good Judgment Question Series." We used two variations of MacQuarie Mechanical Aptitude Tests. He had developed his battery as a graduate student in our Laboratory. One of these was for "visual pursuit" and the other was "letter placement." We used tests from the Johnson-Paschal Code Test series. Also we included some parts of the Stanford Motility Test Battery developed by Dr. Robert H. Seashore, and we employed a self-administering exposure apparatus developed by Dr. Bronson Price for measuring promptness and range of perception capacity. Doctor Floyd L. Ruch's doctoral thesis resulted from his work with these subjects at the 1930 annex in Palo Alto. The title was "The Differentiative Effects of Age on Human Learning" (*J. Gen. Psychol.*, 11:261-286, 1934.

Our original $10,000 grant from the Carnegie Corporation supported some graduate students who worked at the annex and two others who worked with especially selected subjects whom *they* recruited. One of these was Dr. Albert Walton who prepared his Doctor's dissertation on "Old and Young Male Athletes Compared in Simple Motor Skill and Learing Ability." (Unpublished.) He used young athletes at Stanford University compared with older athletes at the Athletic Club in San Francisco and he made a particularly interesting study of trap shooting scores of younger and older men when engaged in a national contest. There was a post-doctoral study by Doctor Keith Sward. It was a very clever investigation and was published under the title "Age and Mental Ability in Superior Men" (*Amer. Jour. of Psychol.*, 85:443-478, 1945.) This was a study of forty-five university professors aged sixty to eighty compared with a group of forty-five younger academic men twenty-five to thirty-five. Each older man was matched for academic field with a younger man. The examinations were individual in the subject's own home or study and they were untimed. Eight validated tests were employed. The techniques and results for this notable piece of research cannot be gone into on this occasion.

Other research studies carried out by our cooperating graduate students who had fellowships during one or both years include the following unpublished documents:

Roger G. Barker: "Age and Fatiguability for Light Muscular Work," Ph.D. thesis, 1932 data.

Paul Buttenwiesser: "Age and Skill in Expert Chess Players," Ph.D. thesis (research on official records of individuals), completed 1935.

Charles J. Marsh: "Reaction Time of Persons Over Fifty Years of Age," M.A. thesis 1930 data, also "Performance Test Abilities of Adults," Ph.D. thesis, 1932 data.

Bronson Price: "Perceptual Ability of Persons Over Fifty Years of Age," M.A. thesis 1930 data, also "Age and Ability to Grasp Spoken Directions," Ph.D. thesis, 1932 data.

There was a second grant, $12,000, from the Carnegie Corporation of New York. The data gathering for this investigation was carried out in a laboratory temporarily set up at 510 Waverley Street, Palo Alto. Subjects were recruited in the same manner from Churches and clubs as in the earlier study. Testing was in progress intensively from April 11 to June 11, 1932. During this period 1,240 adults (605 women and 635 men) age range twenty-five to ninety were examined.

In responding to the invitation to present this background, I have believed that arrangements and methods for conducting gerontological research would be of more interest than data heaped up in profiles with etas and Pearson product moments tagging along at numerous points.

APPORTIONMENT OF RESEARCH BUDGETS

Research costs in this decade seem much greater than in the 1930s. However, the proportionate costs for different parts of the Stanford program may be of sufficient interest to include them in this review. We naturally endeavored to use our Carnegie Corporation of New York grants in as productive and economical a manner as we could devise. From the $10,000. available to us for the program of 1930 we set aside $850. for use by Professor E. K. Strong, Jr. This sum enabled him to work up his large collection of data for publication in book form under the title, *Change of Interests with Age*.

Provision of the temporary laboratory "Annex" in Palo Alto for eight months, and the one in Redwood City for a much shorter period involved rents, upkeep, insurance, fuel, water and electricity and also the purchase of some furniture. These necessary items took almost ten per cent, i.e., $990. For testing apparatus, purchased and constructed and the printing of test materials, blanks and forms and some micellaneous supplies our total outlay was $840. Thus for about 18 per cent of our grant we were able to cover the material parts of what we might call a specialized research facility or vehicle, but it needed a good driver.

In round numbers 66 per cent of our grant was paid to or for people who took part in this research effort. No part of a professor's salary came from these funds. Our "Annex" required a competent matron to be in charge. She must arrange the appointment schedule, keep in contact with the recruiters, greet the "guests," introduce them and see that their departures were such as to retain friendly interest. We were fortunate in this appointment at a nine per cent cost.

For the services of 870 age-specified guest subjects who each cooperated in two-hour individual examinations we paid the recruiting agencies $1400; on the general average this was $1.60 per person. Perhaps we should be criticized for this seemingly very low pay rate, a sliding scale was actually used. But the stipend was not all, these various organizations were competing and the individuals were enjoying a novel experience. They rightly believed they were rendering a public service by helping to advance our understanding of human life and behavior.

The objective of providing financial support of fellowships for graduate students which was mentioned earlier was realized by devoting 30 per cent of our grant in this direction. Four graduate fellowships at $750. each for one academic year bolstered the prestige of psychology at Stanford.

Other students in our department served by the hour in some of our testing and examining, in scoring records, working up the data in tabular form and in statistical calculations. Much was accomplished in this way at a cost of $1,000. For clerical help, postage and communications expenses we paid out $200.

When we were so fortunate as to receive $12,000. from the Carnegie Corporation of New York as a second grant for the continuation of the Later Maturity Research at Stanford with confidence we divided this into four equal sub-budgets of $3,000. each. The first was to provide four $750. graduate fellowships for nine months. Each recipient was to give half time to the Later Maturity Program. The second sub-budget was to pay the salaries of matrons in charge of a relocated laboratory "annex" and of the complicated appointment schedules and pay for the services of several university students as laboratory assistants at the "annex." A third portion was to meet payments to the recruiting organizations that supplied our subjects, and also the cottage rental and associated expenses. The last sub-budget was for paying university student assistants to work on our data, for secretarial help and expected publication expenses.

The Carnegie Corporation's grants to Stanford for this field of study were generous ones for the time. Our efforts to put them to good use might be characterized as vigorous. In getting this project underway we were greatly aided by our departmental chairman, Professor Lewis M. Terman, and by the other committee members Professor Edward K. Strong and Professor Calvin P. Stone. In the conduct of the study we had the devoted service of our "Annex" Matrons, contributions and faithful assistance from fellowship appointees and from the other Stanford students. Dr. Catharine Cox Miles cooperated in many phases of the study, especially in selecting and adapting the intelligence tests and their administration and in writing up these and other results for publication.

CRITIQUE OF THE STANFORD PLAN

What has been said here about the budgeting, arrangements and conduct of the Stanford studies is not proposed as a model to be followed by a majority of the investigations in this big field. In our apparatus and tests we strove for obvious simplicity. Our aim was to make the test tasks inviting and not mysterious. To relieve feelings of doubt and awkwardness we complimented and encouraged the subjects. This may be unnecessary or not suitable for some groups of subjects. We found an "Annex" away from the University essential but other groups of subjects or circumstances may not require this arrangement. We tested both males and females so that our data are rather rich in terms of sex differences. This complication is not essential in all aging research.

Our statistical work-up was in line with the time. Fortunately we had the advice of Professor Truman L. Kelley and the assistance of some of his trained students, and now there have been advances in this field.

Our total intake of data might now give a better impression and be more useful had it been presented in one or two sizable volumes. This was at first our plan. After our 1930 campaign it seemed desirable to get out some papers promptly to support our continuing effort to find more research money. There was also, let us be truthful, the small matter of priority. These publication efforts brought pressing invitations to attend conferences on aging and to prepare chapters for inclusion in books treating the topic of aging from the social, biological and medical viewpoints. A second season of data gathering, that of 1932, unfortunately was coincident with my transfer to another academic post. The accumulated data were carefully guarded and transported but in competition with new duties less time could be devoted to them. The writing of chapters and the editing of dissertations made some progress but not enough to clear the decks for publication before we were caught in the civilian turmoil of preparations and then engagement in a long period of international conflict. Some of our cooperating graduate students have suffered losses by this unfortunate complex of intervening events. For this I have deep and unquieted regrets. The data in their bound theses in the Stanford Library still have historical and probably to some extent practical values.

In conclusion I believe we all agree on the importance of advancing in every way possible man's understanding of himself and his relations to living in the universe. The title that Sherrington adopted for his small great book; *Man On His Nature* spells out an enduring program for us and those who will succeed us.

INDEX